List of the Elements with Their Atomic Symbols and Atomic Weights

Name	Symbol	Atomic Number	Atomic Weight	Name	Symbol	Atomic Number	Atomic Weight
Actinium	Ac	89	227.028	Mendelevium	Md	101	(258)
Aluminum	Al	13	26.9815	Mercury	Hg	80	200.59
Americium	Am	95	(243)	Molybdenum	Mo	42	95.94
Antimony	Sb	51	121.76	Neodymium	Nd	60	144.24
Argon	Ar	18	39.948	Neon	Ne	10	20.1797
Arsenic	As	33	74.9216	Neptunium	Np	93	237.048
Astatine	At	85	(210)	Nickel	Ni	28	58.693
Barium	Ba	56	137.327	Niobium	Nb	41	92.9064
Berkelium	Bk	97	(247)	Nitrogen	N	7	14.0067
Beryllium	Be	4	9.01218	Nobelium	No	102	(259)
Bismuth	Bi	83	208.980	Osmium	Os	76	190.23
Bohrium	Bh	107	(264)	Oxygen	O	8	15.9994
Boron	B	5	10.811	Palladium	Pd	46	106.42
Bromine	Br	35	79.904	Phosphorus	P	15	30.9738
Cadmium	Cd	48	112.411	Platinum	Pt	78	195.08
Calcium	Ca	20	40.078	Plutonium	Pu	94	(244)
Californium	Cf	98	(251)	Polonium	Po	84	(209)
Carbon	C	6	12.011	Potassium	K	19	39.0983
Cerium	Ce	58	140.115	Praseodymium	Pr	59	140.908
Cesium	Cs	55	132.905	Promethium	Pm	61	(145)
Chlorine	Cl	17	35.4527	Protactinium	Pa	91	231.036
Chromium	Cr	24	51.9961	Radium	Ra	88	226.025
Cobalt	Co	27	58.9332	Radon	Rn	86	(222)
Copper	Cu	29	63.546	Rhenium	Re	75	186.207
Curium	Cm	96	(247)	Rhodium	Rh	45	102.906
Darmstadtium	Ds	110	(271)	Roentgenium	Rg	111	(272)
Dubnium	Db	105	(262)	Rubidium	Rb	37	85.4678
Dysprosium	Dy	66	162.50	Ruthenium	Ru	44	101.07
Einsteinium	Es	99	(252)	Rutherfordium	Rf	104	(261)
Erbium	Er	68	167.26	Samarium	Sm	62	150.36
Europium	Eu	63	151.965	Scandium	Sc	21	44.9559
Fermium	Fm	100	(257)	Seaborgium	Sg	106	(266)
Fluorine	F	9	18.9984	Selenium	Se	34	78.96
Francium	Fr	87	(223)	Silicon	Si	14	28.0855
Gadolinium	Gd	64	157.25	Silver	Ag	47	107.868
Gallium	Ga	31	69.723	Sodium	Na	11	22.9898
Germanium	Ge	32	72.61	Strontium	Sr	38	87.62
Gold	Au	79	196.967	Sulfur	S	16	32.066
Hafnium	Hf	72	178.49	Tantalum	Ta	73	180.948
Hassium	Hs	108	(269)	Technetium	Tc	43	(98)
Helium	He	2	4.00260	Tellurium	Te	52	127.60
Holmium	Ho	67	164.930	Terbium	Tb	65	158.925
Hydrogen	H	1	1.00794	Thallium	Tl	81	204.383
Indium	In	49	114.818	Thorium	Th	90	232.038
Iodine	I	53	126.904	Thulium	Tm	69	168.934
Iridium	Ir	77	192.22	Tin	Sn	50	118.710
Iron	Fe	26	55.847	Titanium	Ti	22	47.88
Krypton	Kr	36	83.80	Tungsten	W	74	183.84
Lanthanum	La	57	138.906	Uranium	U	92	238.029
Lawrencium	Lr	103	(260)	Vanadium	V	23	50.9415
Lead	Pb	82	207.2	Xenon	Xe	54	131.29
Lithium	Li	3	6.941	Ytterbium	Yb	70	173.04
Lutetium	Lu	71	174.967	Yttrium	Y	39	88.9059
Magnesium	Mg	12	24.3050	Zinc	Zn	30	65.39
Manganese	Mn	25	54.9381	Zirconium	Zr	40	91.224
Meitnerium	Mt	109	(268)				

Fundamentals of General, Organic, and Biological Chemistry
Volume 1

John McMurry
Mary Castellion
David S. Ballantine
Carl A. Hoeger
Virginia E. Peterson

A Custom Edition for Washington State University

Taken from:
Fundamentals of General, Organic, and Biological Chemistry, Sixth Edition
by John McMurry, Mary Castellion, David S. Ballantine, Carl A. Hoeger, and
Virginia E. Peterson

Custom Publishing

New York Boston San Francisco
London Toronto Sydney Tokyo Singapore Madrid
Mexico City Munich Paris Cape Town Hong Kong Montreal

Cover Art: Courtesy of PhotoDisc/Getty Images.

Taken from:

Fundamentals of General, Organic, and Biological Chemistry, Sixth Edition
by John McMurry, Mary Castellion, David S. Ballantine, Carl A. Hoeger, and Virginia E. Peterson
Copyright © 2010, 2007, 2003, 1999, 1996, 1992 by Pearson Education, Inc.
Published by Prentice Hall
Upper Saddle River, New Jersey 07458

This special edition published in cooperation with Pearson Custom Publishing.

Printed in the United States of America

10 9 8 7 6 5 4 3 2 1

2009180336

JG

Pearson
Custom Publishing
is a division of

www.pearsonhighered.com

ISBN 10: 0-558-38779-9
ISBN 13: 978-0-558-38779-2

About the Authors

John McMurry, educated at Harvard and Columbia, has taught approximately 17,000 students in general and organic chemistry over a 30-year period. A Professor of Chemistry at Cornell University since 1980, Dr. McMurry previously spent 13 years on the faculty at the University of California at Santa Cruz. He has received numerous awards, including the Alfred P. Sloan Fellowship (1969–71), the National Institute of Health Career Development Award (1975–80), the Alexander von Humboldt Senior Scientist Award (1986–87), and the Max Planck Research Award (1991).

David S. Ballantine received his B.S. in Chemistry in 1977 from the College of William and Mary in Williamsburg, VA, and his Ph.D. in Chemistry in 1983 from the University of Maryland at College Park. After several years as a researcher at the Naval Research Labs in Washington, DC, he joined the faculty in the Department of Chemistry and Biochemistry of Northern Illinois University, where he has been a professor for the past twenty years. He was awarded the Excellence in Undergraduate Teaching Award in 1998 and was recently named the departmental Director of Undergraduate Studies. In addition, he is the faculty advisor to the NIU Chemistry Club, an American Chemical Society Student Affiliate program.

Carl A. Hoeger received his B.S. in Chemistry from San Diego State University and his Ph.D. in Organic Chemistry from the University of Wisconsin, Madison in 1983. After a postdoctoral stint at the University of California, Riverside, he joined the Peptide Biology Laboratory at the Salk Institute in 1985 where he ran the NIH Peptide Facility while doing basic research in the development of peptide agonists and antagonists. During this time he also taught general, organic, and biochemistry at San Diego City College, Palomar College, and Miramar College. He joined the teaching faculty at University of Califiornia, San Diego in 1998. Dr. Hoeger has been teaching chemistry to undergraduates for over 20 years, where he continues to explore the use of technology in the classroom. In 2004 he won the Paul and Barbara Saltman Distinguished Teaching Award from UCSD. He is currently the General Chemistry coordinator at UCSD, where he is also responsible for the training and guidance of over 100 teaching assistants in the Chemistry and Biochemistry departments.

Virginia E. Peterson received her B.S. in Chemistry in 1967 from the University of Washington in Seattle, and her Ph.D. in Biochemistry in 1980 from the University of Maryland at College Park. Between her undergraduate and graduate years she worked in lipid, diabetes, and heart disease research at Stanford University. Following her Ph.D. she took a position in the Biochemistry Department at the University of Missouri in Columbia and is now an Associate Professor. Currently she is the Director of Undergraduate Advising for the department and teaches both senior capstone classes and biochemistry classes for nonscience majors. Awards include both the college level and the university-wide Excellence in Teaching Award and, in 2006, the University's Outstanding Advisor Award and the State of Missouri Outstanding University Advisor Award. Dr. Peterson believes in public service and in 2003 received the Silver Beaver Award for service from the Boy Scouts of America.

Brief Contents

Contents

Applications

Preface

This textbook is primarily designed to provide students in the allied health sciences with an appropriate background in chemistry and biochemistry. But it also provides a general context for many of the chemical concepts so that students in other disciplines will gain a better appreciation of the importance of chemistry in everyday life. The coverage in this sixth edition includes sufficient breadth and depth to ensure adequate context and to provide students with opportunities to expand their knowledge.

To teach chemistry all the way from "What is an atom?" to "How do we get energy from glucose?" is a challenge. Throughout our general chemistry and organic chemistry coverage, the focus is on concepts fundamental to the chemistry of living things and everyday life. In our biochemistry coverage we strive to meet the further challenge of providing a context for the application of those concepts in biological systems. Our goal is to provide enough detail for thorough understanding while avoiding so much detail that students are overwhelmed. Many practical and relevant examples are included to illustrate the concepts and enhance student learning.

The material covered is ample for a two-term introduction to general, organic, and biological chemistry. While the general and early organic chapters contain concepts that are fundamental to understanding the material in biochemistry, the later chapters can be covered individually and in an order that can be adjusted to meet the needs of the students and the duration of the course.

The writing style is clear and concise and punctuated with practical and familiar examples from students' personal experience. Art work, diagrams, and molecular models are used extensively to provide graphical illustration of concepts to enhance student understanding. Since the true test of knowledge is the ability to apply that knowledge appropriately, we include numerous worked examples that incorporate consistent problem-solving strategies.

Regardless of their career paths, all students will be citizens in an increasingly technological society. When they recognize the principles of chemistry at work not just in their careers but in their daily lives, they are prepared to make informed decisions on scientific issues based on a firm understanding of the underlying concepts.

Organization

GENERAL CHEMISTRY: CHAPTERS 1–11   The introduction to elements, atoms, the periodic table, and the quantitative nature of chemistry (Chapters 1–3) is followed by chapters that individually highlight the nature of ionic and molecular compounds (Chapters 4 and 5). The next two chapters discuss chemical reactions and their stoichiometry, energies, rates, and equilibria (Chapters 6 and 7). Topics relevant to the chemistry of life follow: Gases, Liquids, and Solids (Chapter 8); Solutions (Chapter 9); and Acids and Bases (Chapter 10). Nuclear Chemistry (Chapter 11) closes the general chemistry sequence.

ORGANIC CHEMISTRY: CHAPTERS 12–17   These chapters concisely focus on what students must know in order to understand biochemistry. The introduction to hydrocarbons (Chapters 12 and 13) includes the basics of nomenclature, which is thereafter kept to a minimum. Discussion of functional groups with single bonds to oxygen, sulfur, or a halogen (Chapter 14) is followed by a short chapter on amines, which are so important to the chemistry of living things and drugs (Chapter 15). After introducing aldehydes and ketones (Chapter 16), the chemistry of carboxylic acids and their derivatives (including amides) is covered (Chapter 17), with a focus on similarities among the derivatives.

BIOLOGICAL CHEMISTRY: CHAPTERS 18–29   Rather than proceed through the complexities of protein, carbohydrate, lipid, and nucleic acid structure before getting to the roles of these compounds in the body, structure and function are integrated in this text. Protein structure (Chapter 18) is followed by enzyme and coenzyme chemistry (Chapter 19). After that we cover the function of hormones and neurotransmitters, and the action of drugs (Chapter 20). With enzymes introduced, the central pathways and themes of biochemical energy production can be described (Chapter 21). If the time you have available to cover biochemistry is limited, stop with Chapter 21 and your students will have an excellent preparation in the essentials of metabolism. The following chapters cover carbohydrate chemistry (Chapters 22 and 23), then lipid chemistry (Chapters 24 and 25). Next we discuss nucleic acids and protein synthesis (Chapter 26) and genomics (Chapter 27). The last two chapters cover protein and amino acid metabolism (Chapter 28) and provide an overview of the chemistry of body fluids (Chapter 29).

Changes to This Edition

COVERAGE OF GENERAL CHEMISTRY

Once again, there is a major emphasis in this edition on problem-solving strategies. This is reflected in expanded solutions in the Worked Example problems and the addition of more Key Concept Problems that focus on conceptual understanding. The most significant change in the Worked Example problems is the addition of a Ballpark Estimate at the beginning of many problems. The Ballpark Estimate provides an opportunity for students to evaluate the relationships involved in the problem and allows them to use an intuitive approach to arrive at a first approximation of the final answer. The ability to think through a problem before attempting a mathematical solution is a skill that will be particularly useful on exams, or when solving "real world" problems.

Other specific changes to chapters are provided below:

Chapter 1

- The Scientific Method is introduced in the text and reinforced in Applications presented in the chapter.

Chapter 3

- Discussion of the critical experiments of Thomson, Millikan, and Rutherford are included in the Application "Are Atoms Real" to provide historical perspective on the development of our understanding of atomic structure.
- Electron dot structures are introduced in Chapter 3 to emphasize the importance of the valence shell electronic configurations with respect to chemical behavior of the elements.

Chapter 4

- Electron dot structures are used to reinforce the role of valence shell electronic configurations in explaining periodic behavior and the formation of ions.

Chapter 5

- The two methods for drawing Lewis dot structures (the "general" method and the streamlined method for molecules containing C, N, O, X, and H) are discussed back-to-back to highlight the underlying principle of the octet rule common to both methods.

Chapter 6

- The concept of limiting reagents is incorporated in Section 6.7 in the discussion of reaction stoichiometry and percent yields.

Chapter 7

- The discussion of free energy and entropy in Section 7.4 has been revised to help students develop a more intuitive understanding of the role of entropy in spontaneous processes.

- Section 7.8 includes more discussion of how the equilibrium constant is calculated and what it tells us about the extent of reaction.

Chapter 8

- Sections 8.3–8.10 include more emphasis on use of the kinetic molecular theory to understand the behavior of gases described by the gas laws.

- Section 8.15 includes more discussion on the energetics of phase changes to help students understand the difference between heat transfer associated with a temperature change and heat transfer associated with the phase change of a substance.

Chapter 9

- Discussion of equivalents in Section 9.10 has been revised to emphasize the relationship between ionic charge and equivalents of ionic compounds.

- Discussion of osmotic pressure (Section 9.12) now includes the osmotic pressure equation and emphasizes the similarity with the ideal gas law.

Chapter 10

- Both the algebraic and logarithmic forms of K_w are presented in Section 10.8 to give students another approach to solving pH problems.

- The discussion of buffer systems now introduces the Henderson-Hasselbalch equation. This relationship makes it easier to identify the factors that affect the pH of a buffer system and is particularly useful in biochemical applications in later chapters.

- Discussion of common acid-base reactions has been moved back in the chapter to provide a more logical segue into titrations in Section 10.15.

Chapter 11

- Treatment of half-life in Section 11.5 now includes a generic equation to allow students to determine the fraction of isotope remaining after an integral or non-integral number of half-lives, which is more consistent with "real world" applications.

- The Applications in this chapter have been expanded to include discussion of new technologies such as Boron Neutron-Capture Therapy (BNCT), or to clear up misconceptions about current methods such as MRI.

COVERAGE OF ORGANIC CHEMISTRY

A major emphasis in this edition was placed on making the fundamental reactions organic molecules undergo much clearer to the reader, with particular vision toward those reactions encountered again in biochemical transformations. Also new to this edition is the expanded use and evaluation of line-angle structure for organic molecules, which are so important when discussing biomolecules. Most of the Applications have been updated to reflect current understanding and research.

Other specific changes to chapters are provided below:

Chapter 12

- This chapter has been significantly rewritten to provide the student with a stronger foundation for the organic chemistry chapters that follow.

- A clearer description of what a functional group is, as well as a more systematic approach to drawing alkane isomers have been made.

- The topic of how to draw and interpret line structures for organic molecules has been added, along with worked examples of such.
- The discussion of conformations has been expanded.

Chapter 13

- A more general discussion of cis and trans isomers has been added.
- The discussion of organic reaction types, particularly rearrangement reactions, have been simplified.

Chapter 14

- The topic of oxidation in organic molecules has been clarified.

Chapter 15

- The role of NO in human biology has been updated to reflect current research.

Chapter 16

- A more detailed discussion of what is meant by toxic or poisonous has been added.

Chapter 17

- A discussion of ibuprofen has been added.

COVERAGE OF BIOLOGICAL CHEMISTRY

New topics, such as the use of anabolic steroids in sports, have been added to many of these chapters to highlight the relevance of biochemistry in modern society. In this text, nutrition is not treated as a separate subject but is integrated with the discussion of each type of biomolecule.

Chapter 18

- The discussion of sickle cell anemia has been expanded and the role of an amino acid substitution on hemoglobin structure clarified.
- The Application *Prions—Proteins That Cause Disease* has been updated to reflect current research.

Chapter 19

- Incorporated the information about lead poisoning into the discussion of enzyme inhibition.

Chapter 20

- The discussion of anabolic steroids has been updated.
- The discussion of drugs and their interaction with the neurotransmitter acetylcholine has been expanded.

Chapter 21

- The discussion of ATP energy production has been revised.

Chapter 22

- An explanation of the chair conformation of glucose has been included to enhance understanding of the shape of cyclic sugars.
- The Application *Chirality and Drugs* has been updated.
- The Application *Cell Surface Carbohydrates and Blood Type* has been revised.

Chapter 23

- The explanation of substrate level phosphorylation has been expanded for clarity.
- The emerging medical condition referred to as Metabolic Syndrome has been added to the text discussion of diabetes.
- The Application *Diagnosis and Monitoring of Diabetes* has been updated to include metabolic syndrome.
- Section 23.11 now contains an expanded discussion of gluconeogenesis.
- The discussion of polysaccharides has been updated.

Chapter 24

- The description of the cell membrane has been expanded.
- A discussion of some inhibitors of Cox 1 and Cox 2 enzymes, important in inflammation, has been added.

Chapter 25

- The discussion of triacylglycerol synthesis has been expanded.
- The discussion of ketone body formation has been expanded.
- A thorough explanation of the biosynthesis of fatty acids has been added.

Chapter 26

- The Application *Viruses and AIDS* has been updated.
- Information about the 1918 influenza pandemic was included in the Application *"Bird Flu": The Next Epidemic?*

Chapter 27

- A discussion of the problems associated with using recombinant DNA for commercial protein manufacture has been added.
- In Section 27.5, new bioethical issues are pointed out to reflect modern concerns.
- The discussion of recombinant DNA and polymerase chain reactions has been moved to this chapter from Chapter 26.

Focus on Learning

WORKED EXAMPLES   Most Worked Examples, both quantitative and not quantitative, include an Analysis section that precedes the Solution. The Analysis lays out the approach to solving a problem of the given type. When appropriate, a "Ballpark Estimate" gives students an overview of the relationships needed to solve the problem, and provides an intuitive approach to arrive at a rough estimate of the answer. The Solution presents the worked-out example using the strategy laid out in the Analysis and, in many cases, includes expanded discussion to enhance student understanding. The use of the two-column format introduced in the fifth edition for quantitative problems has been applied to more Worked Examples throughout the text. Following the Solution there is a Ballpark Check that compares the calculated answer to the Ballpark Estimate, when appropriate, and verifies that the answer makes chemical and physical sense.

KEY CONCEPT PROBLEMS are integrated throughout the chapters to focus attention on the use of essential concepts, as do the ***Understanding Key Concepts*** problems at the end of each chapter. Understanding Key Concepts problems are designed to test students' mastery of the core principles developed in the chapter. Students thus have an opportunity to ask "Did I get it?" before they proceed. Most of these Key Concept Problems use graphics or molecular-level art to illustrate the core principles and will be particularly useful to visual learners.

PROBLEMS The problems within the chapters, for which brief answers are given in an appendix, cover every skill and topic to be understood. One or more problems, many of which are *new* to this edition, follow each Worked Example and others stand alone at the ends of sections.

MORE COLOR-KEYED, LABELED EQUATIONS It is entirely too easy to skip looking at a chemical equation while reading. We have extensively used color to call attention to the aspects of chemical equations and structures under discussion, a continuing feature of this book that has been judged very helpful.

MOLECULAR MODELS Additional computer-generated molecular models have been introduced, including the use of *electrostatic-potential maps for molecular models*.

KEY WORDS Every key term is boldfaced on its first use, fully defined in the margin adjacent to that use, and listed at the end of the chapter. These are the terms students must understand to get on with the subject at hand. Definitions of all Key Words are collected in the Glossary.

END-OF-CHAPTER SUMMARIES Here, the answers to the questions posed at the beginning of the chapter provide a summary of what is covered in that chapter. Where appropriate, the types of chemical reactions in a chapter are also summarized.

Focus on Relevancy

Chemistry is often considered to be a difficult and tedious subject. But when students make a connection between a concept in class and an application in their daily lives the chemistry comes alive, and they get excited about the subject. The applications in this book strive to capture student interest and emphasize the relevance of the scientific concepts. The use of relevant applications makes the concepts more accessible and increases understanding.

- **Applications** are both integrated into the discussions in the text and set off from the text in Application boxes. Each boxed application provides sufficient information for reasonable understanding and, in many cases, extends the concepts discussed in the text in new ways. The boxes end with a cross-reference to end-of-chapter problems that can be assigned by the instructor. Some well-received Applications from previous editions that have been retained include *Breathing and Oxygen Transport, Buffers in the Body, Prions, Protein Analysis by Electrophoresis, The Biochemistry of Running,* and *DNA Fingerprinting.*

- **New Applications in this edition** include *Aspirin—A Case Study, Temperature-Sensitive Materials, Anemia—A Limiting Reagent Problem, GERD: Too Much Acid or Not Enough,* and *It's a Ribozyme!*

FOCUS ON MAKING CONNECTIONS AMONG GENERAL, ORGANIC, AND BIOLOGICAL CHEMISTRY This can be a difficult course to teach. Much of what students are interested in lies in the last part of the course, but the material they need to understand the biochemistry is found in the first two-thirds. It is easy to lose sight of the connections among general, organic, and biological chemistry so we use a feature, **Concepts to Review**, to call attention to these connections. From Chapter 4 on, the Concepts to Review section at the beginning of the chapter lists topics covered in earlier chapters that form the basis for what is discussed in the current chapter.

We have also retained the successful concept link icons and Looking Ahead notes.

- **Concept link icons** ⬤▭⬤ are used extensively to indicate places where previously covered material is relevant to the discussion at hand. These links provide for cross-references and also serve to highlight important chemical themes as they are revisited.

- **Looking Ahead notes** call attention to connections between just-covered material and discussions in forthcoming chapters. These notes are designed to illustrate to the students why what they are learning will be useful in what lies ahead.

Making It Easier to Teach: Supplements for Instructors

MasteringChemistry™ **(www.masteringchemistry.com)** MasteringChemistry is the first adaptive-learning online homework system. It provides selected end-of-chapter problems from the text, as well as hundreds of tutorials with automatic grading, immediate answer-specific feedback, and simpler questions on request. Based on extensive research of precise concepts students struggle with, MasteringChemistry uniquely responds to your immediate needs, thereby optimizing your study time.

Instructor Resource Manual (0-32-161241-8) Features lecture outlines with presentation suggestions, teaching tips, suggested in-class demonstrations, and topics for classroom discussion.

Test Item File (0-32-161514-X) Updated to reflect the revisions in this text and contains questions in a bank of more than 2,000 multiple-choice questions.

Transparency Pack (0-32-161513-1) More than 225 full-color transparencies chosen from the text put principles into visual perspective and save you time while you are preparing for your lectures.

Instructor Resource Center on CD/DVD (0-32-161242-6) This CD/DVD provides an intergrated collection of resources designed to help you make efficient and effective use of your time. This CD/DVD features most art from the text, including figures and tables in PDF format for high-resolution printing, as well as four pre-built PowerPoint™ presentations. The first presentation contains the images/figures/tables embedded within the PowerPoint slides, while the second includes a complete modifiable lecture outline. The final two presentations contain worked "in chapter" sample exercises and questions to be used with Classroom Response Systems. This CD/DVD also contains movies and animations, as well as the TestGen version of the Test Item File, which allows you to create and tailor exams to your needs.

BlackBoard® and WebCT®—Practice and assessment materials are available upon request in these course management platforms.

Making It Easier to Learn: Supplements for Students

Study Guide and Full Solutions Manual (0-32-161238-8) and **Study Guide and Selected Solutions Manual (0-32-161239-6),** both by Susan McMurry. The selected version provides solutions only to those problems that have a short answer in the text's Selected Answer Appendix (problems numbered in blue in the text). Both versions explain in detail how the answers to the in-text and end-of-chapter problems are obtained. They also contain chapter summaries, study hints, and self-tests for each chapter.

For the Laboratory

Exploring Chemistry: Laboratory Experiments in General, Organic and Biological Chemistry, 2nd Edition (0-13-047714-1) by Julie R. Peller of Indiana University. Written specifically to accompany Fundamentals of General, Organic and Biological Chemistry, this manual contains 34 fresh and accessible experiments specifically for GOB students.

Catalyst: The Prentice Hall Custom Laboratory Program for Chemistry. This program allows you to custom-build a chemistry lab manual that matches your content needs and course organization. You can either write your own labs using the Lab Authoring Kit tool, or select from the hundreds of labs available at www. prenhall.com/catalyst. This program also allows you to add your own course notes, syllabi, or other materials.

Acknowledgments

From conception to completion, the development of a modern textbook requires both a focused attention on the goals and the coordinated efforts of a diverse team. We have been most fortunate to have had the services of many talented and dedicated individuals whose efforts have contributed greatly to the overall quality of this text.

First and foremost, we are grateful to Kent Porter Hamann who, as senior editor of this text through many past revisions, provided exemplary leadership and encouragement to the team in the early stages of this project. Very special appreciation goes to Ray Mullaney, editor in chief of book development, who mentored the new team members and managed to coordinate the many and varied details. Irene Nunes, our developmental editor, worked closely with the authors to ensure accuracy and consistency. We also are grateful for the services of Wendy Perez, project manager; Laurie Varites, assistant editor; Lia Tarabokjia, and Jill Traut and Robert Walters, production project managers. Finally, special thanks also to Susan McMurry and Margaret Trombley, whose efforts on the Solutions Manuals and MasteringChemistry tutorial software, respectively, have added value to the overall package.

Finally, many instructors and students who have used the fifth edition have provided valuable insights and feedback and improved the accuracy of the current edition. We gratefully acknowledge the following reviewers for their contributions to the sixth edition:

Sheikh Ahmed, *West Virginia University*
Stanley Bajue, *CUNY-Medgar Evers College*
Daniel Bender, *Sacramento City College*
Dianne A. Bennett, *Sacramento City College*
Alfredo Castro, *Felician College*
Gezahegn Chaka, *Louisiana State University, Alexandria*
Michael Columbia, *Indiana University-Purdue University, Fort Wayne*
Rajeev B. Dabke, *Columbus State University*
Danae R. Quirk-Dorr, *Minnesota State University, Mankato*
Pamela S. Doyle, *Essex County College*
Marie E. Dunstan, *York College of Pennsylvania*

Karen L. Ericson, *Indiana University-Purdue University, Fort Wayne*
Charles P. Gibson, *University of Wisconsin, Oshkosh*
Clifford Gottlieb, *Shasta College*
Mildred V. Hall, *Clark State Community College*
Meg Hausman, *University of Southern Maine*
Ronald Hirko, *South Dakota State University*
L. Jaye Hopkins, *Spokane Community College*
Margaret Isbell, *Sacramento City College*
James T. Johnson, *Sinclair Community College*
Margaret G. Kimble, *Indiana University-Purdue University Fort Wayne*

Grace Lasker, *Lake Washington Technical College*
Ashley Mahoney, *Bethel University*
Matthew G. Marmorino, *Indiana University, South Bend*
Diann Marten, *South Central College, Mankato*
Barbara D. Mowery, *York College of Pennsylvania*
Tracey Arnold Murray, *Capital University*
Andrew M. Napper, *Shawnee State University*
Lisa Nichols, *Butte Community College*
Glenn S. Nomura, *Georgia Perimeter College*

Douglas E. Raynie, *South Dakota State University*
Paul D. Root, *Henry Ford Community College*
Victor V. Ryzhov, *Northern Illinois University*
Karen Sanchez, *Florida Community College, Jacksonville-South*
Mir Shamsuddin, *Loyola University, Chicago*
Jeanne A. Stuckey, *University of Michigan*
John Sullivan, *Highland Community College*
Deborah E. Swain, *North Carolina Central University*
Susan T. Thomas, *University of Texas, San Antonio*
Yakov Woldman, *Valdosta State University*

The authors are committed to maintaining the highest quality and accuracy and look forward to comments from students and instructors regarding any aspect of this text and supporting materials. Questions or comments should be directed to the lead co-author.

David S. Ballantine
dballant@niu.edu

▲ **The reactants.** The flat dish contains pieces of nickel, an element that is a typical, lustrous metal. The bottle contains hydrochloric acid, a solution of the chemical compound hydrogen chloride in water. These reactants are about to be combined in the test tube.

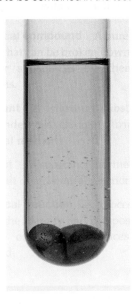

▲ **The reaction** As the chemical reaction occurs, the colorless solution turns green when water-insoluble nickel metal slowly changes into the water-soluble chemical compound nickel chloride. Gas bubbles of the element hydrogen are produced and rise slowly through the green solution.

▶ **The product** Hydrogen gas can be collected as it bubbles from the solution. Removal of water from the solution leaves behind the other product, a solid green chemical compound known as nickel chloride.

●▬ **KEY CONCEPT PROBLEM 1.6**

Identify the process illustrated in the figure below as a chemical change or a physical change. Explain.

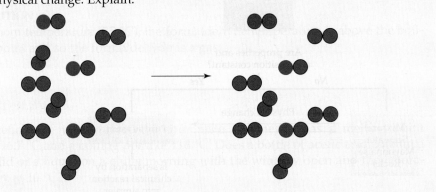

1.4 An Example of a Chemical Reaction

If we take a quick look at an example of a chemical reaction, we can reinforce some of the ideas discussed in the previous section. The element *nickel* is a hard, shiny metal, and the compound *hydrogen chloride* is a colorless gas that dissolves in water to give a solution called *hydrochloric acid*. When pieces of nickel are added to hydrochloric acid in a test tube, the nickel is slowly eaten away, the colorless solution turns green, and a gas bubbles out of the test tube. The change in color, the dissolving of the nickel, and the appearance of gas bubbles are indications that a chemical reaction is taking place.

Overall, the reaction of nickel with hydrochloric acid can be either written in words or represented in a shorthand notation using symbols, as shown below in brackets. We will explain the meaning of these symbols in the next section.

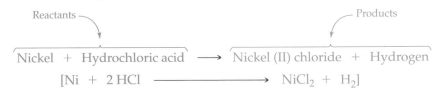

1.5 Chemical Elements and Symbols

As of the date this book was printed, 117 chemical elements had been identified. Some are certainly familiar to you—oxygen, helium, iron, aluminum, copper, and gold, for example—but many others are probably unfamiliar—rhenium, niobium, thulium, and promethium. Rather than write out the full names of elements, chemists use a shorthand notation in which elements are referred to by one- or two-letter symbols. The names and symbols of some common elements are listed in Table 1.2, and a complete alphabetical list is given inside the front cover of this book.

Note that all two-letter symbols have only their first letter capitalized, whereas the second letter is always lowercase. The symbols of most common elements are the first one or two letters of the elements' commonly used names, such as

APPLICATION ▶ Aspirin—A Case Study

Acetylsalicylic acid, more commonly known as aspirin, is perhaps the first true wonder drug. It is used as an analgesic to reduce fevers and to relieve headaches and body pains. It possesses anticoagulant properties, which in low doses can help prevent heart attacks and minimize the damage caused by strokes. But how was it discovered, and how does it work? The "discovery" of aspirin is a combination of serendipity and the scientific method.

The origins of aspirin can be traced back to the ancient Greek physician Hippocrates in 400 B.C., who prescribed the bark and leaves of the willow tree to relieve pain and fever. In 1828 scientists isolated from willow bark a bitter-tasting yellow extract, called salicin, that was identified as the active ingredient responsible for the observed medical effects. Salicin could be easily converted to salicylic acid (SA), which by the late 1800s was being mass-produced and marketed. SA had an unpleasant taste, however, and often caused stomach irritation and indigestion.

The discovery of acetylsalicylic acid (ASA) has often been attributed to Felix Hoffman, a chemist working for the Bayer pharmaceutical labs, but the first synthesis of ASA was reported by a French chemist, Charles Gerhardt, in 1853. Nevertheless, Hoffman obtained a patent for ASA in 1900, and Bayer marketed the new drug, now called aspirin, in water-soluble tablets.

How does aspirin work? In 1971 the British pharmacologist John Vane discovered that aspirin suppresses the body's production of prostaglandins (⬤▬⬤, Section 24.9), which are

▲ **Hippocrates.** The ancient Greek physician, prescribed a precursor of aspirin found in willowbark to relieve pain.

responsible for the pain and swelling that accompany inflammation. This discovery of this mechanism led to the development of new analgesic drugs.

Research continues to explore aspirin's potential for preventing colon cancer, cancer of the esophagus, and other diseases.

See Additional Problem 1.52 at the end of the chapter.

H (hydrogen) and Al (aluminum). Pay special attention, however, to the elements grouped in the last column to the right in Table 1.2. The symbols for these elements are derived from their original Latin names, such as Na for sodium, once known as *natrium*. The only way to learn these symbols is to memorize them; fortunately they are few in number.

Only 90 of the elements occur naturally; the remaining elements have been produced artificially by chemists and physicists. Each element has its own distinctive

TABLE 1.2 Names and Symbols for Some Common Elements

ELEMENTS WITH SYMBOLS BASED ON MODERN NAMES						ELEMENTS WITH SYMBOLS BASED ON LATIN NAMES	
Al	Aluminum	**Co**	Cobalt	**N**	Nitrogen	**Cu**	Copper (*cuprum*)
Ar	Argon	**F**	Fluorine	**O**	Oxygen	**Au**	Gold (*aurum*)
Ba	Barium	**He**	Helium	**P**	Phosphorus	**Fe**	Iron (*ferrum*)
Bi	Bismuth	**H**	Hydrogen	**Pt**	Platinum	**Pb**	Lead (*plumbum*)
B	Boron	**I**	Iodine	**Rn**	Radon	**Hg**	Mercury (*hydrargyrum*)
Br	Bromine	**Li**	Lithium	**Si**	Silicon	**K**	Potassium (*kalium*)
Ca	Calcium	**Mg**	Magnesium	**S**	Sulfur	**Ag**	Silver (*argentum*)
C	Carbon	**Mn**	Manganese	**Ti**	Titanium	**Na**	Sodium (*natrium*)
Cl	Chlorine	**Ni**	Nickel	**Zn**	Zinc	**Sn**	Tin (*stannum*)

PROBLEM 1.10

Look at the periodic table inside the front cover, locate the following elements and identify them as metals or nonmetals:

(a) Cr, chromium **(b)** K, potassium

(c) S, sulfur **(d)** Rn, radon

PROBLEM 1.11

The seven metalloids are boron (B), silicon (Si), germanium (Ge), arsenic (As), antimony (Sb), tellurium (Te), and astatine (At). Locate them in the periodic table, and tell where they appear with respect to metals and nonmetals.

APPLICATION ▶ Mercury and Mercury Poisoning

Mercury, the only metallic element that is liquid at room temperature, has fascinated people for millennia. Egyptian kings were buried in their pyramids along with containers of mercury, alchemists during the Middle Ages used mercury to dissolve gold, and Spanish galleons carried loads of mercury to the New World in the 1600s for use in gold and silver mining. Even its symbol, Hg, from the Latin *hydrargyrum,* meaning "liquid silver," hints at mercury's uniqueness.

Much of the recent interest in mercury has concerned its toxicity, but there are some surprises. For example, the mercury compound Hg_2Cl_2 (called *calomel*) is nontoxic and has a long history of medical use as a laxative, yet it is also used as a fungicide and rat poison. Dental amalgam, a solid alloy of approximately 50% elemental mercury, 35% silver, 13% tin, 1% copper, and trace amounts of zinc, has been used by dentists for many years to fill tooth cavities. Yet exposure to elemental mercury *vapor* for long periods leads to mood swings, headaches, tremors, and loss of hair and teeth. The widespread use of mercuric nitrate, a mercury compound to make the felt used in hats, exposed many hatters of the eighteenth and nineteenth centuries to toxic levels of mercury. The eccentric behavior displayed by hatters suffering from mercury poisoning led to the phrase "mad as a hatter"—the Mad Hatter from Lewis Carroll's *Alice in Wonderland* is a parody of this stereotype.

Why is mercury toxic in some forms but not in others? It turns out that the toxicity of mercury and its compounds is related to solubility. Only soluble mercury compounds are toxic, because they can be transported through the bloodstream to all parts of the body where they react with different enzymes and interfere with various biological processes. Elemental mercury and insoluble mercury compounds become toxic only when converted into soluble compounds, reactions that are extremely slow in the body. Calomel, for example, is an insoluble mercury compound that passes

▲ The Mad Hatter's erratic behavior was a parody of the symptoms commonly associated with mercury poisoning.

through the body long before it is converted into any soluble compounds. Mercury alloys were considered safe for dental use because mercury does not evaporate readily from the alloys and it neither reacts with nor dissolves in saliva. Mercury vapor, however, remains in the lungs when breathed, until it is slowly converted into soluble compounds.

Of particular concern with regard to mercury toxicity is the environmental danger posed by pollution from both natural and industrial sources. Microorganisms present in lakes and streams are able to convert many mercury-containing wastes into a soluble and highly toxic compound called *methylmercury*. Methylmercury is concentrated to high levels in fish, particularly in shark and swordfish, which are then hazardous when eaten. Although the commercial fishing catch is now monitored carefully, more than 50 deaths from eating contaminated fish were recorded in Minimata, Japan, during the 1950s before the cause of the problem was realized.

See Additional Problem 1.53 at the end of the chapter.

SUMMARY: REVISITING THE CHAPTER GOALS

1. **What is matter?** *Matter* is anything that has mass and occupies volume—that is, anything physically real. Matter can be classified by its physical state as *solid*, *liquid*, or *gas*. A solid has a definite volume and shape, a liquid has a definite volume but indefinite shape, and a gas has neither a definite volume nor shape.

2. **How is matter classified?** A substance can be characterized as being either *pure* or a *mixture*. A pure substance is uniform in its composition and properties, but a mixture can vary in both composition and properties, depending on how it was made. Every pure substance is either an *element* or a *chemical compound*. Elements are fundamental substances that cannot be chemically changed into anything simpler. A chemical compound, by contrast, can be broken down by chemical change into simpler substances.

3. **What kinds of properties does matter have?** A *property* is any characteristic that can be used to describe or identify something. A *physical property* can be seen or measured without changing the chemical identity of the substance, (that is, color, melting point). A *chemical property* can only be seen or measured when the substance undergoes a *chemical change*, such as a chemical reaction.

4. **How are chemical elements represented?** Elements are represented by one- or two-letter symbols, such as H for hydrogen, Ca for calcium, Al for aluminum, and so on. Most symbols are the first one or two letters of the element name, but some symbols are derived from Latin names—Na (sodium), for example. All the known elements are commonly organized into a form called the *periodic table*. Most elements are *metals*, 17 are *nonmetals*, and 7 are *metalloids*.

KEY WORDS

Change of state, *p. 5*

Chemical change, *p. 3*

Chemical compound, *p. 6*

Chemical formula, *p. 10*

Chemical reaction, *p. 6*

Chemistry, *p. 3*

Element, *p. 6*

Gas, *p. 5*

Liquid, *p. 5*

Matter, *p. 3*

Metal, *p. 11*

Metalloid, *p. 12*

Mixture, *p. 6*

Nonmetal, *p. 12*

Periodic table, *p. 11*

Physical change, *p. 3*

Pure substance, *p. 6*

Product, *p. 6*

Property, *p. 3*

Reactant, *p. 6*

Scientific Method, *p. 3*

Solid, *p. 5*

State of matter, *p. 5*

UNDERSTANDING KEY CONCEPTS

The problems in this section are intended as a bridge between the Chapter Summary and the Additional Problems that follow. Primarily visual in nature, they are designed to help you test your grasp of the chapter's most important principles before attempting to solve quantitative problems. Answers to all Key Concept problems are at the end of the book following the appendixes.

1.12 Six of the elements at the far right of the periodic table are gases at room temperature. Identify them using the periodic table inside the front cover of this book.

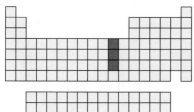

1.13 The so-called "coinage metals" are located near the middle of the periodic table. Identify them using the periodic table inside the front cover of this book.

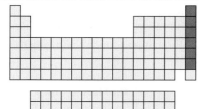

1.14 Identify the three elements indicated on the following periodic table and tell which is a metal, which is a nonmetal, and which is a metalloid.

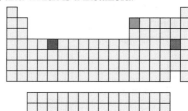

1.15 The radioactive element indicated on the following periodic table is used in smoke detectors. Identify it, and tell whether it is a metal, a nonmetal, or a metalloid.

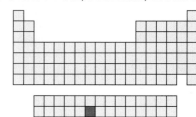

ADDITIONAL PROBLEMS

These exercises are divided into sections by topic. Each section begins with review and conceptual questions, followed by numerical problems of varying levels of difficulty. The problems are presented in pairs, with each even-numbered problem followed by an odd-numbered one requiring similar skills. The final section consists of unpaired General Questions and Problems that draw on various parts of the chapter and, in future chapters, may even require the use of concepts from previous chapters. Answers to all even-numbered problems are given at the end of the book following the appendixes.

CHEMISTRY AND THE PROPERTIES OF MATTER

1.16 What is chemistry?

1.17 Identify the following chemicals as natural or synthetic.

(a) The nylon used in stockings
(b) The substances that give roses their fragrance
(c) The yeast used in bread dough

1.18 Which of the following is a physical change and which is a chemical change?

(a) Boiling water
(b) Decomposing water by passing an electric current through it
(c) Dissolving sugar in water
(d) Exploding of potassium metal when placed in water
(e) Breaking of glass

1.19 Which of the following is a physical change and which is a chemical change?

(a) Steam condensing
(b) Milk souring
(c) Ignition of matches
(d) Breaking of a dinner plate
(e) Nickel sticking to a magnet
(f) Exploding of nitroglycerin

STATES AND CLASSIFICATION OF MATTER

1.20 Name and describe the three states of matter.

1.21 Name two changes of state, and describe what causes each to occur.

1.22 Sulfur dioxide is a compound produced when sulfur burns in air. It has a melting point of $-72.7\ °C$ and a boiling point of $-10\ °C$. In what state does it exist at room temperature ($25\ °C$)? (The symbol $°C$ means degrees Celsius.)

1.23 Menthol, a chemical compound obtained from peppermint or other mint oils, melts at $45\ °C$ and boils at $212\ °C$. In what state is it found at:

(a) Room temperature ($25\ °C$)? (b) $60\ °C$? (c) $260\ °C$?

1.24 Classify each of the following as a mixture or a pure substance:

(a) Pea soup   (b) Seawater
(c) The contents of a propane tank
(d) Urine   (e) Lead
(f) A multivitamin tablet

1.25 Classify each of the following as a mixture or a pure substance. If it is a pure substance, classify it as an element or a compound:

(a) Blood   (b) Silicon
(c) Dishwashing liquid   (d) Toothpaste
(e) Gold   (f) Gaseous ammonia

1.26 Classify each of the following as an element, a compound, or a mixture:

(a) Aluminum foil   (b) Table salt   (c) Water
(d) Air   (e) A banana   (f) Notebook paper

1.27 Which of these terms, (i) mixture, (ii) solid, (iii) liquid, (iv) gas, (v) chemical element, (vi) chemical compound, applies to the following substances at room temperature?

(a) Gasoline   (b) Iodine   (c) Water
(d) Air   (e) Sodium bicarbonate

1.28 Hydrogen peroxide, often used in solutions to cleanse cuts and scrapes, breaks down to yield water and oxygen:

$$\text{Hydrogen peroxide} \longrightarrow \text{Water} + \text{Oxygen}$$

(a) Identify the reactants and products.
(b) Which of the substances are chemical compounds, and which are elements?

1.29 When sodium metal is placed in water, the following change occurs:

$$\text{Sodium} + \text{Water} \longrightarrow \text{Hydrogen} + \text{Sodium hydroxide}$$

(a) Identify the reactants and products.
(b) Which of the substances are elements, and which are chemical compounds?

ELEMENTS AND THEIR SYMBOLS

1.30 How many elements are presently known? About how many occur naturally?

1.31 Where in the periodic table are the metallic elements found? The nonmetallic elements? The metalloid elements?

1.32 Describe the general properties of metals, nonmetals, and metalloids.

1.33 What is the most abundant element in the earth's crust? In the human body? List the name and symbol for each.

1.34 What are the symbols for the following elements?

(a) Gadolinium (used in color TV screens)
(b) Germanium (used in semiconductors)
(c) Technetium (used in biomedical imaging)
(d) Arsenic (used in pesticides)
(e) Cadmium (used in rechargeable batteries)

1.35 What are the symbols for the following elements?

(a) Tungsten   (b) Mercury   (c) Boron
(d) Gold   (e) Silicon   (f) Argon
(g) Silver   (h) Magnesium

1.36 Give the names corresponding to the following symbols:

(a) N   (b) K   (c) Cl
(d) Ca   (e) P   (f) Mn

1.37 Give the names corresponding to the following symbols:

(a) Te   (b) Re   (c) Be
(d) Cr   (e) Pu   (f) Mn

1.38 The symbol CO stands for carbon monoxide, a chemical compound, but the symbol Co stands for cobalt, an element. Explain how you can tell them apart.

1.39 Explain why the symbol for sulfur is S, but the symbol for sodium is Na.

1.40 What is wrong with the following statements? Correct them.

(a) The symbol for bromine is BR.
(b) The symbol for manganese is Mg.
(c) The symbol for carbon is Ca.
(d) The symbol for potassium is Po.

1.41 What is wrong with the following statements? Correct them.

(a) Carbon dioxide has the formula CO2.
(b) Carbon dioxide has the formula Co_2.
(c) Table salt, NaCl, is composed of nitrogen and chlorine.

1.42 What is wrong with the following statements? Correct them.

(a) "Fool's gold" is a mixture of iron and sulfur with the formula IrS_2.
(b) "Laughing gas" is a compound of nitrogen and oxygen with the formula NiO.

1.43 What is wrong with the following statements? Correct them.

(a) Soldering compound is an alloy of tin and lead with the formula TiPb.
(b) White gold is an alloy of gold and nickel with the formula GdNI.

1.44 Name the elements combined in the chemical compounds represented by the following formulas:

(a) $MgSO_4$ (b) $FeBr_2$ (c) CoP
(d) AsH_3 (e) $CaCr_2O_7$

1.45 How many atoms of what elements are represented by the following formulas?

(a) Propane (LP gas), C_3H_8
(b) Sulfuric acid, H_2SO_4
(c) Aspirin, $C_9H_8O_4$
(d) Rubbing alcohol, C_3H_8O

1.46 The amino acid glycine has the formula $C_2H_5NO_2$. What elements are present in glycine? What is the total number of atoms represented by the formula?

1.47 Benzyl salicylate, a chemical compound sometimes used as a sunscreen, has the formula $C_{14}H_{12}O_3$. What is the total number of atoms represented by the formula? How many are carbon?

1.48 What is the formula for ibuprofen: 13 carbons, 18 hydrogens, and 2 oxygens.

1.49 What is the formula for penicillin V: 16 carbons, 18 hydrogens, 2 nitrogens, 5 oxygens, and 1 sulfur.

1.50 Which of the following two elements is a metal, and which is a nonmetal?

(a) Osmium, a hard, shiny, very dense solid that conducts electricity
(b) Xenon, a colorless, odorless gas

1.51 Which of the following elements is likely to be a metal and which a metalloid?

(a) Tantalum, a hard, shiny solid that conducts electricity
(b) Germanium, a brittle, gray solid that conducts electricity poorly

Applications

1.52 The active ingredient in aspirin, acetylsalicylic acid (ASA), has the formula $C_9H_8O_4$ and melts at 140 °C.

Identify the elements and how many atoms of each are present in ASA. Is it a solid or a liquid at room temperature? [*Aspirin—A Case Study, p. 9*]

1.53 Why is Hg_2Cl_2 harmless when swallowed, yet elemental mercury is toxic when breathed? [*Mercury and Mercury Poisoning, p. 14*]

General Questions and Problems

1.54 Distinguish between the following:

(a) Physical changes and chemical changes
(b) Melting point and boiling point
(c) Elements, compounds, and mixtures
(d) Chemical symbols and chemical formulas
(e) Reactants and products
(f) Metals and nonmetals

1.55 Are the following statements true or false? If false, explain why.

(a) The combination of sodium and chlorine to produce sodium chloride is a chemical reaction.
(b) The addition of heat to solid sodium chloride until it melts is a chemical reaction.
(c) The formula for a chemical compound that contains lead and oxygen is LiO.
(d) By stirring together salt and pepper we can create a new chemical compound to be used for seasoning food.
(e) Heating sugar to make caramel is a physical change.

1.56 Which of the following are chemical compounds, and which are elements?

(a) H_2O_2 (b) Al   (c) CO
(d) N_2 (e) $NaHCO_3$

1.57 A white solid with a melting point of 730 °C is melted. When electricity is passed through the resultant liquid, a brown gas and a molten metal are produced. Neither the metal nor the gas can be broken down into anything simpler by chemical means. Classify each—the white solid, the molten metal, and the brown gas—as a mixture, a compound, or an element.

1.58 As a clear red liquid sits at room temperature, evaporation occurs until only a red solid remains. Was the original liquid an element, a compound, or a mixture?

1.59 Describe how you could physically separate a mixture of iron filings, table salt, and white sand.

1.60 Small amounts of the following elements in our diets are essential for good health. What is the chemical symbol for each?

(a) Iron   (b) Copper   (c) Cobalt
(d) Molybdenum   (e) Chromium   (f) Fluorine
(g) Sulfur

1.61 Obtain a bottle of multivitamins from your local drug store or pharmacy and identify as many of the essential elements from Table 1.4 as you can. How many of them are listed as elements, and how many are included as part of chemical compounds?

1.62 Consider the recently discovered or as yet undiscovered elements with atomic numbers 115, 117, and 119. Is element 115 likely to be a metal or a nonmetal? What about element 117? Element 119?

1.63 How high would the atomic number of a new element need to be to appear under uranium in the periodic table?

CHAPTER 2

Measurements in Chemistry

▲ The success of many endeavors, such as NASA's Deep Impact comet probe, depends on both the accuracy and the precision of measurements.

CONTENTS

CHAPTER GOALS

In this chapter we will deal with the following questions about measurement:

1. How are measurements made, and what units are used?

THE GOAL: Be able to name and use the metric and SI units of measure for mass, length, volume, and temperature.

2. How good are the reported measurements?

THE GOAL: Be able to interpret the number of significant figures in a measurement and round off numbers in calculations involving measurements.

3. How are large and small numbers best represented?

THE GOAL: Be able to interpret prefixes for units of measure and express numbers in scientific notation.

4. How can a quantity be converted from one unit of measure to another?

THE GOAL: Be able to convert quantities from one unit to another using conversion factors.

5. What techniques are used to solve problems?

THE GOAL: Be able to analyze a problem, use the factor-label method to solve the problem, and check the result to ensure that it makes sense chemically and physically.

6. What are temperature, specific heat, density, and specific gravity?

THE GOAL: Be able to define these quantities and use them in calculations.

How often do you make an observation or perform an action that involves measurement? Whenever you check the temperature outside, make a pitcher of lemonade, or add detergent to the laundry, you are making a measurement. Likewise, whenever you use chemical compounds—whether you are adding salt to your cooking, putting antifreeze in your car radiator, or choosing a dosage of medicine—quantities of substances must be measured. A mistake in measuring the quantities could ruin the dinner, damage the engine, or harm the patient.

2.1 Physical Quantities

Height, volume, temperature, and other physical properties that can be measured are called **physical quantities** and are described by both a number and a **unit** of defined size:

Number   Unit

61.2 kilograms

Physical quantity A physical property that can be measured.

Unit A defined quantity used as a standard of measurement.

The number alone is not much good without a unit. If you asked how much blood an accident victim had lost, the answer "three" would not tell you much. Three drops? Three milliliters? Three pints? Three liters? (By the way, an adult human has only 5–6 liters of blood.)

Any physical quantity can be measured in many different units. For example, a person's height might be measured in inches, feet, yards, centimeters, or many other units. To avoid confusion, scientists from around the world have agreed on a system of standard units, called by the French name *Système International d'Unites* (International System of Units), abbreviated *SI*. **SI units** for some common physical quantities are given in Table 2.1. Mass is measured in *kilograms* (kg), length is measured in *meters* (m), volume is measured in *cubic meters* (m^3), temperature is measured in *kelvins* (K), and time is measured in *seconds* (s, not sec).

SI units are closely related to the more familiar *metric units* used in all industrialized nations of the world except the United States. If you compare the SI and metric units shown in Table 2.1, you will find that the basic metric unit of mass is the *gram* (g) rather than the kilogram (1 g = 1/1000 kg), the metric unit of volume is the *liter* (L) rather than the cubic meter (1 L = 1/1000 m^3), and the metric unit of temperature is the *Celsius degree* (°C) rather than the kelvin. The meter is the unit of

SI units Units of measurement defined by the International System of Units.

(a) (b)

▶ **FIGURE 2.1** (a) The single-pan balance has a sliding counterweight that is adjusted until the weight of the object on the pan is just balanced. (b) A modern electronic balance.

▲ This pile of 400 pennies has a mass of about 1 kg.

comparing two weights. Figure 2.1 shows two types of balances used for measuring mass in the laboratory.

One kilogram, the SI unit for mass, is equal to 2.205 lb—too large a quantity for many purposes in chemistry and medicine. Thus, smaller units of mass such as the gram, milligram (mg), and microgram (μg), are more commonly used. Table 2.3 shows the relationships between metric and common units for mass.

TABLE 2.3 Units of Mass

UNIT	EQUIVALENT	UNIT	EQUIVALENT
1 kilogram (kg)	= 1000 grams = 2.205 pounds	1 ton	= 2000 pounds = 907.03 kilograms
1 gram (g)	= 0.001 kilogram = 1000 milligrams = 0.035 27 ounce	1 pound (lb)	= 16 ounces = 0.454 kilogram = 454 grams
1 milligram (mg)	= 0.001 gram = 1000 micrograms	1 ounce (oz)	= 0.028 35 kilogram = 28.35 grams
1 microgram (μg)	= 0.000 001 gram = 0.001 milligram		= 28,350 milligrams

2.3 Measuring Length and Volume

The meter is the standard measure of length, or distance, in both the SI and metric systems. One meter is 39.37 inches (about 10% longer than a yard), a length that is much too large for most measurements in chemistry and medicine. Other, more commonly used measures of length are the *centimeter* (cm; 1/100 m) and the *millimeter* (mm; 1/1000 m). One centimeter is a bit less than half an inch—0.3937 inch to be exact. A millimeter, in turn, is 0.03937 inch, or about the thickness of a dime. Table 2.4 lists the relationships of these units.

Volume is the amount of space occupied by an object. The SI unit for volume—the cubic meter, m^3—is so large that the liter (1 L = 0.001 m^3 = 1 dm^3) is much more commonly used in chemistry and medicine. One liter has the volume of a cube 10 cm (1 dm) on edge and is a bit larger than one U.S. quart. Each liter is further divided into 1000 *milliliters* (mL), with 1 mL being the size of a cube 1 cm on edge, or 1 cm^3. In fact, the milliliter is often called a *cubic centimeter* (cm^3, or cc) in medical work. Figure 2.2 shows the divisions of a cubic meter, and Table 2.5 shows the relationships among units of volume.

TABLE 2.4 Units of Length

UNIT	EQUIVALENT	UNIT	EQUIVALENT
1 kilometer (km)	= 1000 meters = 0.6214 mile	1 mile (mi)	= 1.609 kilometers = 1609 meters
1 meter (m)	= 100 centimeters = 1000 millimeters = 1.0936 yards = 39.37 inches	1 yard (yd)	= 0.9144 meter = 91.44 centimeters
		1 foot (ft)	= 0.3048 meter = 30.48 centimeters
1 centimeter (cm)	= 0.01 meter = 10 millimeters = 0.3937 inch	1 inch (in.)	= 2.54 centimeters = 25.4 millimeters
1 millimeter (mm)	= 0.001 meter = 0.1 centimeter		

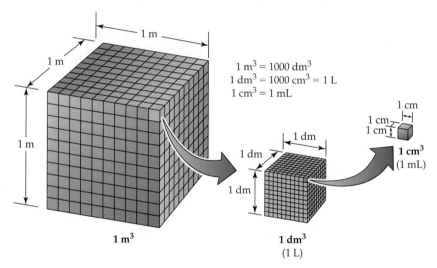

$$1 \text{ m}^3 = 1000 \text{ dm}^3$$
$$1 \text{ dm}^3 = 1000 \text{ cm}^3 = 1 \text{ L}$$
$$1 \text{ cm}^3 = 1 \text{ mL}$$

▲ **FIGURE 2.2**   A cubic meter is the volume of a cube 1 m on edge. Each cubic meter contains 1000 cubic decimeters (liters), and each cubic decimeter contains 1000 cubic centimeters (milliliters). Thus, there are 1000 mL in a liter and 1000 L in a cubic meter.

TABLE 2.5 Units of Volume

UNIT	EQUIVALENT
1 cubic meter (m³)	= 1000 liters = 264.2 gallons
1 liter (L)	= 0.001 cubic meter = 1000 milliliters = 1.057 quarts
1 deciliter (dL)	= 0.1 liter = 100 milliliters
1 milliliter (mL)	= 0.001 liter = 1000 microliters
1 microliter (μL)	= 0.001 milliliter
1 gallon (gal)	= 3.7854 liters
1 quart (qt)	= 0.9464 liter = 946.4 milliliters
1 fluid ounce (fl oz)	= 29.57 milliliters

2.4 Measurement and Significant Figures

How much does a tennis ball weigh? If you put a tennis ball on an ordinary bathroom scale, the scale would probably register 0 lb (or 0 kg if you have a metric scale). If you placed the same tennis ball on a common laboratory balance, however, you might get a reading of 54.07 g. Trying again by placing the ball on an expensive analytical balance like those found in clinical and research laboratories, you might find a weight of 54.071 38 g. Clearly, the precision of your answer depends on the equipment used for the measurement.

Every experimental measurement, no matter how precise, has a degree of uncertainty to it because there is always a limit to the number of digits that can be determined. An analytical balance, for example, might reach its limit in measuring mass to the fifth decimal place, and weighing the tennis ball several times might produce slightly different readings, such as 54.071 39 g, 54.071 38 g, and 54.071 37 g. Also, different people making the same measurement might come up with slightly different answers. How, for instance, would you record the volume of the liquid shown in Figure 2.3? It is clear that the volume of liquid lies between 17.0 and 18.0 mL, but the exact value of the last digit must be estimated.

To indicate the precision of a measurement, the value recorded should use all the digits known with certainty, plus one additional estimated digit that is usually considered uncertain by plus or minus 1 (written as ±1). The total number of digits used to express such a measurement is called the number of **significant figures**. Thus, the quantity 54.07 g has four significant figures (5, 4, 0, and 7), and the quantity 54.071 38 g has seven significant figures. *Remember*: All but one of the significant figures are known with certainty; the last significant figure is only an estimate accurate to ±1.

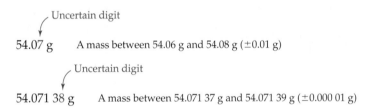

Deciding the number of significant figures in a given measurement is usually simple, but can be troublesome when zeros are involved. Depending on the circumstances, a zero might be significant or might be just a space-filler to locate the decimal point. For example, how many significant figures does each of the following measurements have?

94.072 g	Five significant figures (9, 4, 0, 7, 2)
0.0834 cm	Three significant figures (8, 3, 4)
0.029 07 mL	Four significant figures (2, 9, 0, 7)
138.200 m	Six significant figures (1, 3, 8, 2, 0, 0)
23,000 kg	*Anywhere* from two (2, 3) to five (2, 3, 0, 0, 0) significant figures

The following rules are helpful for determining the number of significant figures when zeros are present:

RULE 1. Zeros in the middle of a number are like any other digit; they are always significant. Thus, 94.072 g has five significant figures.

RULE 2. Zeros at the beginning of a number are not significant; they act only to locate the decimal point. Thus, 0.0834 cm has three significant figures, and 0.029 07 mL has four.

RULE 3. Zeros at the end of a number and *after* the decimal point are significant. It is assumed that these zeros would not be shown unless they were significant. Thus, 138.200 m has six significant figures. If the value were known to only four significant figures, we would write 138.2 m.

▲ The tennis ball weighs 54.07 g on this common laboratory balance, which is capable of determining mass to about 0.01 g.

Significant figures The number of meaningful digits used to express a value.

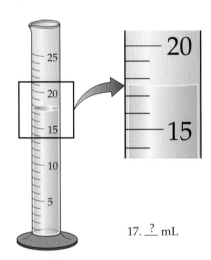

17. _?_ mL

▲ **FIGURE 2.3** What is the volume of liquid in this graduated cylinder?

RULE 4. Zeros at the end of a number and *before* an implied decimal point may or may not be significant. We cannot tell whether they are part of the measurement or whether they act only to locate the unwritten but implied decimal point. Thus, 23,000 kg may have two, three, four, or five significant figures. Adding a decimal point at the end would indicate that all five numbers are significant.

Often, however, a little common sense is useful. A temperature reading of 20 °C probably has two significant figures rather than one, because one significant figure would imply a temperature anywhere from 10 °C to 30 °C and would be of little use. Similarly, a volume given as 300 mL probably has three significant figures. On the other hand, a figure of 150,000,000 km for the distance between the earth and the sun has only two or three significant figures because the distance is variable. We will see a better way to deal with this problem in the next section.

One final point about significant figures: Some numbers, such as those obtained when counting objects and those that are part of a definition, are *exact* and effectively have an unlimited number of significant figures. Thus, a class might have *exactly* 32 students (not 31.9, 32.0, or 32.1), and 1 foot is defined to have *exactly* 12 inches.

▲ How many CDs are in this stack? (Answer: *exactly* 29.)

WORKED EXAMPLE 2.1 Significant Figures of Measurements

How many significant figures do the following measurements have?

    (a) 2730.78 m   **(b)** 0.0076 mL   **(c)** 3400 kg   **(d)** 3400.0 m^2

ANALYSIS All nonzero numbers are significant; the number of significant figures will then depend on the status of the zeros in each case. (Hint: which rule applies in each case?)

SOLUTION

  (a) Six (rule 1)   **(b)** Two (rule 2)
  (c) Two, three, or four (rule 4)   **(d)** Five (rule 3)

PROBLEM 2.4

How many significant figures do the following measurements have?

(a) 3.45 m   **(b)** 0.1400 kg
(c) 10.003 L   **(d)** 35 cents

◀◉ KEY CONCEPT PROBLEM 2.5

What is the temperature reading on the following Celsius thermometer? How many significant figures do you have in your answer?

APPLICATION ▶ Powers of 10

It is not easy to grasp the enormous differences in size represented by powers of 10 (scientific notation). A sodium atom has a diameter of 388 pm (3.88×10^{-10} m), a typical rhinovirus may have a diameter of 20 nm (2.0×10^{-8} m), and a single bacteria cell may be 3 μm long (3×10^{-6} m). Even though none of these objects can be seen with the naked eye, scientists know that the size of an atom relative to the size of a bacterium would be like comparing the size of a bowling ball with that of a baseball stadium. So how do scientists know the relative sizes of these items if we can not see them?

To study the miniature world of bacteria and viruses requires special tools. Optical light microscopes, for example, can magnify an object up to 1500 (1.5×10^3) times,

enabling us to study objects as small as 0.2 μm, such as bacteria. To study smaller objects, such as viruses, requires even higher magnification. Electron microscopy, which uses a beam of electrons instead of light, can achieve magnifications of 1×10^5 for scanning electron microscopy (SEM), and the ability to distinguish features on the order of 0.1 nm in length are possible with scanning tunneling microscopes (STM).

The change in magnification needed to distinguish features from 1 mm to 1 nm may not seem great, but it represents a million-fold (10^6) increase—enough to open a whole new world. Powers of 10 are powerful indeed.

See Additional Problems 2.78 and 2.79 at the end of the chapter.

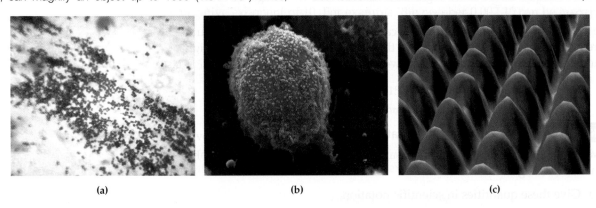

(a) (b) (c)

▲ (a) A light microscope image of bacteria; (b) a color-enhanced SEM image showing a T-lymphocyte white blood cell (in orange) with HIV particles (in blue) budding on the surface of the cell membrane; (c) an STM image of a "blue nickel" surface showing the orientation of individual metal atoms.

PROBLEM 2.6

Convert the following values to scientific notation:

(a) 0.058 g   (b) 46,792 m   (c) 0.006 072 cm   (d) 345.3 kg

PROBLEM 2.7

Convert the following values from scientific notation to standard notation:

(a) 4.885×10^4 mg   (b) 8.3×10^{-6} m   (c) 4.00×10^{-2} m

PROBLEM 2.8

Rewrite the following numbers in scientific notation as indicated:

(a) 630,000 with five significant figures

(b) 1300 with three significant figures

(c) 794,200,000,000 with four significant figures

PROBLEM 2.9

Ordinary table salt, or sodium chloride, is made up of small particles called *ions*, which we will discuss in Chapter 4. If the distance between a sodium ion and a chloride ion is 0.000 000 000 278 m, what is the distance in scientific notation? How many picometers is this?

2.6 Rounding Off Numbers

It often happens, particularly when doing arithmetic on a pocket calculator, that a quantity appears to have more significant figures than are really justified. For example, you might calculate the gas mileage of your car by finding that it takes 11.70 gallons of gasoline to drive 278 miles:

$$\text{Mileage} = \frac{\text{Miles}}{\text{Gallons}} = \frac{278 \text{ mi}}{11.70 \text{ gal}} = 23.760\ 684 \text{ mi/gal (mpg)}$$

Although the answer on a pocket calculator has eight digits, your measurement is really not as precise as it appears. In fact, as we will see below, your answer is good to only three significant figures and should be **rounded off** to 23.8 mi/gal.

How do you decide how many digits to keep? The full answer to this question is a bit complex and involves a mathematical treatment called *error analysis*, but for many purposes, a simplified procedure using just two rules is sufficient:

Rounding off A procedure used for deleting nonsignificant figures.

RULE 1. In carrying out a multiplication or division, the answer cannot have more significant figures than either of the original numbers. This is just a common-sense rule if you think about it. After all, if you do not know the number of miles you drove to better than three significant figures (278 could mean 277, 278, or 279), you certainly cannot calculate your mileage to more than the same number of significant figures.

Three significant figures

Three significant figures

$$\frac{278 \text{ mi}}{11.70 \text{ gal}} = 23.8 \text{ mi/gal}$$

Four significant figures

▲ Calculators often display more digits than are justified by the precision of the data.

RULE 2. In carrying out an addition or subtraction, the answer cannot have more digits after the decimal point than either of the original numbers. For example, if you have 3.18 L of water and you add 0.013 15 L more, you now have 3.19 L. Again, this rule is just common sense. If you do not know the volume you started with past the second decimal place (it could be 3.17, 3.18, or 3.19), you cannot know the total of the combined volumes past the same decimal place.

Volume of water at start ⟶ 3.18? ?? L ⟵ Two digits after decimal point
Volume of water added ⟶ + 0.013 15 L ⟵ Five digits after decimal point
Total volume of water ⟶ 3.19? ?? L ⟵ Two digits after decimal point

If a calculation has several steps, it is generally best to round off at the end after all the steps have been carried out, keeping the number of significant figures determined by the least precise number in your calculations. Once you decide how many digits to retain for your answer, the rules for rounding off numbers are straightforward:

RULE 1. If the first digit you remove is 4 or less, drop it and all following digits. Thus, 2.4271 becomes 2.4 when rounded off to two significant figures because the first of the dropped digits (a 2) is 4 or less.

RULE 2. If the first digit you remove is 5 or greater, round the number up by adding a 1 to the digit to the left of the one you drop. Thus, 4.5832 becomes 4.6 when rounded off to two significant figures because the first of the dropped digits (an 8) is 5 or greater.

WORKED EXAMPLE   2.5 Significant Figures and Calculations: Addition/Subtraction

Suppose that you weigh 124 lb before dinner. How much will you weigh after dinner if you eat 1.884 lb of food?

ANALYSIS When performing addition or subtraction, the number of significant figures you report in the final answer is determined by the number of digits in the least precise number in the calculation.

SOLUTION
Your after-dinner weight is found by adding your original weight to the weight of the food consumed:

$$
\begin{array}{r}
124 \quad \text{lb} \\
\underline{1.884 \text{ lb}} \\
125.884 \text{ lb} \quad \text{(Unrounded)}
\end{array}
$$

Because the value of your original weight has no significant figures after the decimal point, your after-dinner weight also must have no significant figures after the decimal point. Thus, 125.884 lb must be rounded off to 126 lb.

WORKED EXAMPLE   2.6 Significant Figures and Calculations: Multiplication/Division

To make currant jelly, 13.75 cups of sugar was added to 18 cups of currant juice. How much sugar was added per cup of juice?

ANALYSIS For calculations involving multiplication or division, the final answer cannot have more significant figures than either of the original numbers.

SOLUTION
The quantity of sugar must be divided by the quantity of juice:

$$
\frac{13.75 \text{ cups sugar}}{18 \text{ cups juice}} = 0.763\,888\,89\,\frac{\text{cup sugar}}{\text{cup juice}}\text{(Unrounded)}
$$

The number of significant figures in the answer is limited to two by the quantity 18 cups in the calculation and must be rounded to 0.76 cup of sugar per cup of juice.

PROBLEM 2.10

Round off the following quantities to the indicated number of significant figures:

(a) 2.304 g (three significant figures)
(b) 188.3784 mL (five significant figures)
(c) 0.008 87 L (one significant figure)
(d) 1.000 39 kg (four significant figures)

PROBLEM 2.11

Carry out the following calculations, rounding each result to the correct number of significant figures:

(a) 4.87 mL + 46.0 mL   (b) 3.4 × 0.023 g
(c) 19.333 m − 7.4 m   (d) 55 mg − 4.671 mg + 0.894 mg
(e) 62,911 ÷ 611

2.7 Problem Solving: Converting a Quantity from One Unit to Another

Many activities in the laboratory and in medicine—measuring, weighing, preparing solutions, and so forth—require converting a quantity from one unit to another. For example: "These pills contain 1.3 grains of aspirin, but I need 200 mg. Is one pill enough?" Converting between units is not mysterious; we all do it every day. If you run 9 laps around a 400 meter track, for instance, you have to convert between the distance unit "lap" and the distance unit "meter" to find that you have run 3600 m (9 laps times 400 m/lap). If you want to find how many miles that is, you have to convert again to find that 3600 m = 2.237 mi.

The simplest way to carry out calculations involving different units is to use the **factor-label method**. In this method, a quantity in one unit is converted into an equivalent quantity in a different unit by using a **conversion factor** that expresses the relationship between units:

$$\text{Starting quantity} \times \text{Conversion factor} = \text{Equivalent quantity}$$

As an example, we said in Section 2.3 that 1 km = 0.6214 mi. Writing this relationship as a fraction restates it in the form of a conversion factor, either kilometers per mile or miles per kilometer.

Since 1 km = 0.6214 mi, then:

Conversion factors between kilometers and miles
$$\frac{1 \text{ km}}{0.6214 \text{ mi}} = 1 \quad \text{or} \quad \frac{0.6214 \text{ mi}}{1 \text{ km}} = 1$$

Note that this and all other conversion factors are numerically equal to 1 because the value of the quantity above the division line (the numerator) is equal in value to the quantity below the division line (the denominator). Thus, multiplying by a conversion factor is equivalent to multiplying by 1 and so does not change the value of the quantity being multiplied:

These two quantities are the same.
$$\frac{1 \text{ km}}{0.6214 \text{ mi}} \quad \text{or} \quad \frac{0.6214 \text{ mi}}{1 \text{ km}}$$
These two quantities are the same.

The key to the factor-label method of problem solving is that units are treated like numbers and can thus be multiplied and divided (though not added or subtracted) just as numbers can. When solving a problem, the idea is to set up an equation so that all unwanted units cancel, leaving only the desired units. Usually, it is best to start by writing what you know and then manipulating that known quantity. For example, if you know there are 26.22 mi in a marathon and want to find how many kilometers that is, you could write the distance in miles and multiply by the conversion factor in kilometers per mile. The unit "mi" cancels because it appears both above and below the division line, leaving "km" as the only remaining unit.

$$26.22 \cancel{\text{ mi}} \times \frac{1 \text{ km}}{0.6214 \cancel{\text{ mi}}} = 42.20 \text{ km}$$

Starting quantity — Conversion factor — Equivalent quantity

The factor-label method gives the right answer only if the equation is set up so that the unwanted unit (or units) cancel. If the equation is set up in any other way, the units will not cancel and you will not get the right answer. Thus, if you selected the incorrect conversion factor (miles per kilometer) for the above problem,

▲ These runners have to convert from laps to meters to find out how far they have run.

Factor-label method A problem-solving procedure in which equations are set up so that unwanted units cancel and only the desired units remain.

Conversion factor An expression of the numerical relationship between two units.

you would end up with an incorrect answer expressed in meaningless units:

$$\text{Incorrect } 26.22 \text{ mi} \times \frac{0.6214 \text{ mi}}{1 \text{ km}} = 16.29 \frac{\text{mi}^2}{\text{km}} \text{ Incorrect}$$

WORKED EXAMPLE **2.7** Factor Labels: Unit Conversions

Write conversion factors for the following pairs of units (use Tables 2.3–2.5):

(a) Deciliters and milliliters

(b) Pounds and grams

ANALYSIS Start with the appropriate equivalency relationship and rearrange to form conversion factors.

SOLUTION

(a) Since 1 dL = 0.1 L and 1 mL = 0.001 L, then

$$1 \text{ dL} = (0.1 \text{ L}) \left(\frac{1 \text{ mL}}{0.001 \text{ L}} \right) = 100 \text{ mL}. \text{ The conversion factors are}$$

$$\frac{1 \text{ dL}}{100 \text{ mL}} \quad \text{and} \quad \frac{100 \text{ mL}}{1 \text{ dL}}$$

(b) $\dfrac{1 \text{ lb}}{454 \text{ g}}$ and $\dfrac{454 \text{ g}}{1 \text{ lb}}$

WORKED EXAMPLE **2.8** Factor Labels: Unit Conversions

(a) Convert 0.75 lb to grams.

(b) Convert 0.50 qt to deciliters.

ANALYSIS Start with conversion factors and set up equations so that units cancel appropriately.

SOLUTION

(a) Select the conversion factor from Worked Example 2.7(b) so that the "lb" units cancel and "g" remains:

$$0.75 \text{ lb} \times \frac{454 \text{ g}}{1 \text{ lb}} = 340 \text{ g}$$

(b) In this, as in many problems, it is convenient to use more than one conversion factor. As long as the unwanted units cancel correctly, two or more conversion factors can be strung together in the same calculation. In this case, we can convert first between quarts and milliliters, and then between milliliters and deciliters:

$$0.50 \text{ qt} \times \frac{946.4 \text{ mL}}{1 \text{ qt}} \times \frac{1 \text{ dL}}{100 \text{ mL}} = 4.7 \text{ dL}$$

PROBLEM 2.12

Write conversion factors for the following pairs of units:

(a) liters and milliliters   **(b)** grams and ounces

(c) liters and quarts

PROBLEM 2.13

Carry out the following conversions:

(a) 16.0 oz = ? g   (b) 2500 mL = ? L   (c) 99.0 L = ? qt

PROBLEM 2.14

Convert 0.840 qt to milliliters in a single calculation using more than one conversion factor.

PROBLEM 2.15

One international nautical mile is defined as exactly 6076.1155 ft, and a speed of 1 knot is defined as one international nautical mile per hour. What is the speed in meters per second of a boat traveling at a speed of 14.3 knots?

2.8 Problem Solving: Estimating Answers

The main drawback to using the factor-label method is that it is possible to get an answer without really understanding what you are doing. It is therefore best when solving a problem to first think through a rough estimate, or *ballpark estimate*, as a check on your work. If your ballpark estimate is not close to the final calculated solution, there is a misunderstanding somewhere and you should think the problem through again. If, for example, you came up with the answer 5.3 cm^3 when calculating the volume of a human cell, you should realize that such an answer could not possibly be right. Cells are too tiny to be distinguished with the naked eye, but a volume of 5.3 cm^3 is about the size of a walnut. The Worked Examples at the end of this section show how to estimate the answers to simple unit-conversion problems.

The factor-label method and the use of ballpark estimates are techniques that will help you solve problems of many kinds, not just unit conversions. Problems sometimes seem complicated, but you can usually sort out the complications by analyzing the problem properly:

STEP 1: Identify the information given, including units.

STEP 2: Identify the information needed in the answer, including units.

STEP 3: Find the relationship(s) between the known information and unknown answer, and plan a series of steps, including conversion factors, for getting from one to the other.

STEP 4: Solve the problem.

BALLPARK CHECK: Make a ballpark estimate at the beginning and check it against your final answer to be sure the value and the units of your calculated answer are reasonable.

Worked Examples 2.9, 2.10 and 2.11 illustrate how to use the analysis steps and ballpark checks as an aid in dosage calculations.

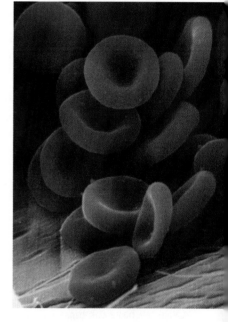

▲ What is the volume of a red blood cell?

WORKED EXAMPLE   **2.9** Factor Labels: Unit Conversions

A child is 21.5 in. long at birth. How long is this in centimeters?

ANALYSIS This problem calls for converting from inches to centimeters, so we will need to know how many cm are in an inch, and how to use this information as a conversion factor.

BALLPARK ESTIMATE It takes about 2.5 cm to make 1 in., and so it should take 2.5 times as many centimeters to make a distance equal to approximately 20 in., or about 20 in. × 2.5 = 50 cm.

SOLUTION

STEP 1: **Identify given information.**	Length = 21.5 in.
STEP 2: **Identify answer and units.**	Length = ?? cm
STEP 3: **Identify conversion factor.**	$1 \text{ in.} = 2.54 \text{ cm} \rightarrow \dfrac{2.54 \text{ cm}}{1 \text{ in.}}$
STEP 4: **Solve** Multiply the known length (in inches) by the conversion factor so that units cancel, providing the answer (in cm).	$21.5 \text{ in.} \times \dfrac{2.54 \text{ cm}}{1 \text{ in.}} = 54.6 \text{ cm (Rounded off from 54.61)}$

BALLPARK CHECK How does this value compare with the ballpark estimate we made at the beginning? Are the final units correct?

WORKED EXAMPLE 2.10 Factor Labels: Concentration to Mass

A patient requires injection of 0.012 g of a pain killer available as a 15 mg/mL solution. How many milliliters should be administered?

ANALYSIS Knowing the amount of pain killer in 1 mL allows us to use the concentration as a conversion factor to determine the volume of solution that would contain the desired amount.

BALLPARK ESTIMATE One milliliter contains 15 mg of the pain killer, or 0.015 g. Since only 0.012 g is needed, a little less than 1.0 mL should be administered.

▲ How many milliliters should be injected?

SOLUTION

STEP 1: **Identify known information.**	Dosage = 0.012 g Concentration = 15 mg/mL
STEP 2: **Identify answer and units.**	Volume to administer = ?? mL
STEP 3: **Identify conversion factors.** Two conversion factors are needed. First, g must be converted to mg. Once we have the mass in mg, then we can calculate mL using the conversion factor of mL/mg.	$1 \text{ mg} = .001 \text{ g} \Rightarrow \dfrac{1 \text{ mg}}{0.001 \text{ g}}$ $15 \text{ mg/mL} \Rightarrow \dfrac{1 \text{ mL}}{15 \text{ mg}}$
STEP 4: **Solve.** Starting from the desired dosage, we use the conversion factors to cancel units, obtaining the final answer in mL.	$(0.012 \text{ g})\left(\dfrac{1 \text{ mg}}{0.001 \text{ g}}\right)\left(\dfrac{1 \text{ mL}}{15 \text{ mg}}\right) = 0.80 \text{ mL}$

BALLPARK CHECK Consistent with our initial estimate of a little less than 1 mL.

WORKED EXAMPLE 2.11 Factor Labels: Multiple Conversion Calculations

Administration of digitalis to control atrial fibrillation in heart patients must be carefully regulated because even a modest overdose can be fatal. To take differences between patients into account, dosages are sometimes prescribed in micrograms per kilogram of body weight (μg/kg). Thus, two people may differ greatly in weight, but both will receive the proper dosage. At a dosage of 20 μg/kg body weight, how many milligrams of digitalis should a 160 lb patient receive?

ANALYSIS Knowing the patient's body weight (in kg) and the recommended dosage (in μg/kg), we can calculate the appropriate amount of digitalis.

BALLPARK ESTIMATE Since a kilogram is roughly equal to 2 lb, a 160 lb patient has a mass of about 80 kg. At a dosage of 20 μg/kg, an 80 kg patient should receive 80 × 20 μg, or about 1600 μg of digitalis, or 1.6 mg.

SOLUTION

STEP 1: Identify known information.

STEP 2: Identify answer and units.

STEP 3: Identify conversion factors. Two conversions are needed. First, convert the patient's weight in pounds to weight in kg. The correct dose can then be determined based on μg digitalis/kg of body weight. Finally the dosage in μg is converted to mg.

STEP 4: Solve. Use the known information and the conversion factors so that units cancel, obtaining the answer in mg.

Patient weight = 160 lb

Prescribed dosage = 20 μg digitalis/kg body weight

Delivered dosage = ?? mg digitalis

$$1 \text{ kg} = 2.205 \text{ lb} \rightarrow \frac{1 \text{ kg}}{2.205 \text{ lb}}$$

$$1 \text{ mg} = (0.001 \text{ g})\left(\frac{1 \mu g}{10^{-6} g}\right) = 1000 \ \mu g$$

$$160 \text{ lb} \times \frac{1 \text{ kg}}{2.205 \text{ lb}} \times \frac{20 \ \mu g \text{ digitalis}}{1 \text{ kg}} \times \frac{1 \text{ mg}}{1000 \ \mu g}$$

$$= 1.5 \text{ mg digitalis (Rounded off)}$$

BALLPARK CHECK Close to our estimate of 1.6 mg.

PROBLEM 2.16

(a) How many kilograms does a 7.5 lb infant weigh?

(b) How many milliliters are in a 4.0 fl oz bottle of cough medicine?

PROBLEM 2.17

Calculate the dosage in milligrams per kilogram body weight for a 135 lb adult who takes two aspirin tablets containing 0.324 g of aspirin each. Calculate the dosage for a 40 lb child who also takes two aspirin tablets.

2.9 Measuring Temperature   0 Kelvin = -273.15 °C
                              273.15 K = 0 °C

Temperature, the measure of how hot or cold an object is, is commonly reported either in Fahrenheit (°F) or Celsius (°C) units. The SI unit for reporting temperature, however, is the *kelvin* (K). (Note that we say only "kelvin," not "kelvin degree.")

The kelvin and the Celsius degree are the same size—both are 1/100 of the interval between the freezing point of water and the boiling point of water at atmospheric pressure. Thus, a change in temperature of 1 °C is equal to a change of 1 K. The only difference between the Kelvin and Celsius temperature scales is that they have different zero points. The Celsius scale assigns a value of 0 °C to the freezing point of water, but the Kelvin scale assigns a value of 0 K to the coldest possible temperature, sometimes called *absolute zero*, which is equal to −273.15 °C. Thus, 0 K = −273.15 °C, and +273.15 K = 0 °C. For example, a warm spring day with a temperature of 25 °C has a Kelvin temperature of 25 + 273.15 = 298 K (for most purposes, rounding off to 273 is sufficient):

$$\text{Temperature in K} = \text{Temperature in °C} + 273.15$$
$$\text{Temperature in °C} = \text{Temperature in K} - 273.15$$

For practical applications in medicine and clinical chemistry, the Fahrenheit and Celsius scales are used almost exclusively. The Fahrenheit scale defines the freezing point of water as 32 °F and the boiling point of water as 212 °F, whereas 0 °C and 100 °C are the freezing and boiling points of water on the Celsius scale. Thus, it takes 180 Fahrenheit degrees to cover the same range encompassed by only 100 Celsius degrees, and a Celsius degree is therefore exactly 180/100 = 9/5 = 1.8

Temperature The measure of how hot or cold an object is.

▲ Gold metal is a liquid at temperatures above 1064.4 °C?

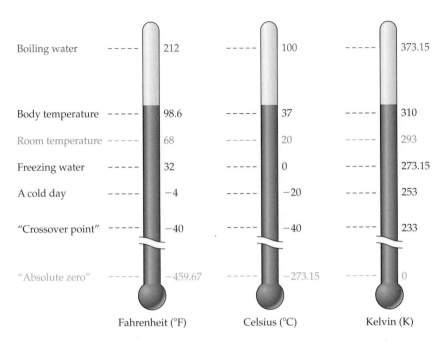

	Fahrenheit (°F)	Celsius (°C)	Kelvin (K)
Boiling water	212	100	373.15
Body temperature	98.6	37	310
Room temperature	68	20	293
Freezing water	32	0	273.15
A cold day	−4	−20	253
"Crossover point"	−40	−40	233
"Absolute zero"	−459.67	−273.15	0

▶ **FIGURE 2.4 A comparison of the Fahrenheit, Celsius, and Kelvin temperature scales.** One Fahrenheit degree is 5/9 the size of a kelvin or a Celsius degree.

times as large as a Fahrenheit degree. In other words, a change in temperature of 1.0 °C is equal to a change of 1.8 °F. Figure 2.4 gives a comparison of all three scales.

Converting between the Fahrenheit and Celsius scales is similar to converting between different units of length or volume, but is a bit more complex because two corrections need to be made—one to adjust for the difference in degree size and one to adjust for the different zero points. The size correction is made by using the relationship 1 °C = (9/5) °F and 1 °F = (5/9) °C. The zero-point correction is made by

APPLICATION ▶ Temperature–Sensitive Materials

Wouldn't it be nice to be able to tell if the baby's formula bottle is too hot? Or if the package of chicken you are buying for dinner has been stored appropriately? Temperature-sensitive materials are being used in these and other applications.

A class of materials called thermochromic materials change color as their temperature increases and they change from the liquid phase to a semicrystalline ordered state. These "liquid crystals" can be incorporated into plastics or paints, and can be used to monitor the temperature of the products or packages in which they are incorporated. For example, some meat packaging now includes a temperature strip that darkens when the meat is stored above a certain temperature, making the meat unsafe to eat. Hospitals and other medical facilities now routinely use temperature strips that, when placed under the tongue or applied to the forehead, change color to indicate the patient's body temperature. There are even clothes that change color based on the air temperature.

Can't decide what color bathing suit to wear to the beach? Pick one that will change color to fit your mood!

See Additional Problems 2.80 and 2.81 at the end of the chapter.

remembering that the freezing point is higher by 32 on the Fahrenheit scale than on the Celsius scale. Thus, if you want to convert from Celsius to Fahrenheit, you do a size adjustment (multiply °C by 9/5) and then a zero-point adjustment (add 32); if you want to convert from Fahrenheit to Celsius, you find out how many Fahrenheit degrees there are above freezing (by subtracting 32) and then do a size adjustment (multiply °C by 5/9). The following formulas show the conversion methods:

Celsius to Fahrenheit:

$$°F = \left(\frac{9\ °F}{5\ °C} \times °C \right) + 32\ °F$$

Fahrenheit to Celsius:

$$°C = \frac{5\ °C}{9\ °F} \times (°F - 32\ °F)$$

WORKED EXAMPLE **2.12** Temperature Conversions: Fahrenheit to Celsius

A body temperature above 107 °F can be fatal. What does 107 °F correspond to on the Celsius scale?

ANALYSIS Using the temperature (in °F) and the appropriate temperature conversion equation we can convert from the Fahrenheit scale to the Celsius scale.

BALLPARK ESTIMATE Note in Figure 2.4 that normal body temperature is 98.6 °F or 37 °C. A temperature of 107 °F is approximately 8 °F above normal; since 1 °C is nearly 2 °F, then 8 °F is about 4 °C. Thus, the 107 °F body temperature is 41 °C.

SOLUTION

STEP 1: Identify known information.

Temperature = 107 °F

STEP 2: Identify answer and units.

Temperature = ?? °C

STEP 3: Identify conversion factors.
We can convert from °F to °C using this equation.

$$°C = \frac{5\ °C}{9\ °F} \times (°F - 32\ °F)$$

STEP 4: Solve. Substitute the known temperature (in °F) into the equation.

$$°C = \frac{5\ °C}{9\ °F} \times (107\ °F - 32\ °F) = 42\ °C^*$$

BALLPARK CHECK Close to our estimate of 41 °C. (Rounded off from 41.666 667 °C)

*It is worth noting that the 5/9 conversion factor in the equation is an exact conversion, and so does not impact the number of significant figures in the final answer.

PROBLEM 2.18

The highest land temperature ever recorded was 136 °F in Al Aziziyah, Libya, on September 13, 1922. What is this temperature on the Celsius scale?

PROBLEM 2.19

The use of mercury thermometers is limited by the fact that mercury freezes at −38.9 °C. To what temperature does this correspond on the Fahrenheit scale? On the Kelvin scale?

2.10 Energy and Heat

All chemical reactions are accompanied by a change in **energy**, which is defined in scientific terms as *the capacity to do work or supply heat* (Figure 2.5). Detailed discussion of the various kinds of energy will be included in Chapter 7, but for now we will look at the various units used to describe energy, and the way heat energy can be gained or lost by matter.

Energy is measured in SI units by the unit *joule* (J; pronounced "jool"), but the metric unit *calorie* (cal) is still widely used in medicine. One calorie is the amount of heat necessary to raise the temperature of 1 g of water by 1 °C. A *kilocalorie* (kcal), often called a *large calorie (Cal)* or *food calorie* by nutritionists, equals 1000 cal:

$$1000 \text{ cal} = 1 \text{ kcal} \qquad 1000 \text{ J} = 1 \text{ kJ}$$
$$1 \text{ cal} = 4.184 \text{ J} \qquad 1 \text{ kcal} = 4.184 \text{ kJ}$$

Not all substances have their temperatures raised to the same extent when equal amounts of heat energy are added. One calorie raises the temperature of 1 g of water by 1 °C but raises the temperature of 1 g of iron by 10 °C. The amount of heat needed to raise the temperature of 1 g of a substance by 1 °C is called the **specific heat** of the substance. It is measured in units of cal/(g·°C).

$$\text{Specific heat} = \frac{\text{Calories}}{\text{Grams} \times °\text{C}}$$

Specific heats vary greatly from one substance to another, as shown in Table 2.6. The specific heat of water, 1.00 cal/(g·°C), is higher than that of most other substances, which means that a large transfer of heat is required to change the temperature of a given amount of water by a given number of degrees. One consequence is that the human body, which is about 60% water, is able to withstand changing outside conditions.

TABLE 2.6 Specific Heats of Some Common Substances

SUBSTANCE	SPECIFIC HEAT [cal/(g · °C)]
Ethanol	0.59
Gold	0.031
Iron	0.106
Mercury	0.033
Sodium	0.293
Water	1.00

Knowing the mass and specific heat of a substance makes it possible to calculate how much heat must be added or removed to accomplish a given temperature change, as shown in Worked Example 2.13.

$$\text{Heat (cal)} = \text{Mass } (\cancel{g}) \times \text{Temperature change } (\cancel{°C}) \times \text{Specific heat}\left(\frac{\text{cal}}{\cancel{g} \cdot \cancel{°C}}\right)$$

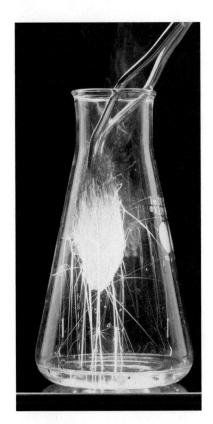

▲ FIGURE 2.5 The reaction of aluminum with bromine releases energy in the form of heat. When the reaction is complete, the products undergo no further change.

Energy The capacity to do work or supply heat.

Specific heat The amount of heat that will raise the temperature of 1 g of a substance by 1 °C.

WORKED EXAMPLE **2.13** Specific Heat: Mass, Temperature, and Energy

Taking a bath might use about 95 kg of water. How much energy (in calories) is needed to heat the water from a cold 15 °C to a warm 40 °C?

ANALYSIS From the amount of water being heated (95 kg) and the amount of the temperature change (40 °C − 15 °C = 25 °C), the total amount of energy needed can be calculated by using specific heat [1.00 cal/(g·°C)] as a conversion factor.

BALLPARK ESTIMATE The water is being heated 25 °C (from 15 °C to 40 °C), and it therefore takes 25 cal to heat each gram. The tub contains nearly 100,000 g (95 kg is 95,000 g), and so it takes about 25 × 100,000 cal, or 2,500,000 cal, to heat all the water in the tub.

SOLUTION

STEP 1: Identify known information.

Mass of water = 95 kg

Temperature change = 40 °C − 15 °C = 25 °C

STEP 2: Identify answer and units.

Heat = ?? cal

STEP 3: Identify conversion factors. The amount of energy (in cal) can be calculated using the specific heat of water (cal/g · °C), and will depend on both the mass of water (in g) to be heated and the total temperature change (in °C). In order for the units in specific heat to cancel correctly, the mass of water must first be converted from kg to g.

$$\text{Specific heat} = \frac{1.0 \text{ cal}}{g \cdot {}^{\circ}C}$$

$$1 \text{ kg} = 1000 \text{ g} \rightarrow \frac{1000 \text{ g}}{1 \text{ kg}}$$

STEP 4: Solve. Starting with the known information, use the conversion factors to cancel unwanted units.

$$95 \text{ kg} \times \frac{1000 \text{ g}}{\text{kg}} \times \frac{1.00 \text{ cal}}{g \cdot {}^{\circ}C} \times 25 \,{}^{\circ}C = 2,400,000 \text{ cal}$$

$$= 2.4 \times 10^6 \text{ cal}$$

BALLPARK CHECK Close to our estimate of 2.5 × 10⁶ cal.

PROBLEM 2.20

Assuming that Coca-Cola has the same specific heat as water, how much energy in calories is removed when 350 g of Coke (about the contents of one 12 oz can) is cooled from room temperature (25 °C) to refrigerator temperature (3 °C)?

PROBLEM 2.21

What is the specific heat of aluminum if it takes 161 cal to raise the temperature of a 75 g aluminum bar by 10.0 °C?

Density The physical property that relates the mass of an object to its volume; mass per unit volume.

2.11 Density

One further physical quantity that we will take up in this chapter is **density**, which relates the mass of an object to its volume. Density is usually expressed in units of grams per cubic centimeter (g/cm³) for solids and grams per milliliter (g/mL) for liquids. Thus, if we know the density of a substance, we know both the mass of a given volume and the volume of a given mass. The densities of some common materials are listed in Table 2.7.

$$\text{Density} = \frac{\text{Mass (g)}}{\text{Volume (mL or cm}^3\text{)}}$$

Most substances change their volume by expanding or contracting when heated or cooled, and densities are therefore temperature-dependent. For example, at 3.98 °C a 1 mL container holds exactly 1.0000 g of water (density = 1.0000 g/mL). As the temperature rises, however, the volume occupied by the water expands so that only 0.9584 g fits in the 1 mL container at 100 °C (density = 0.9584 g/mL). When reporting a density, the temperature must also be specified.

Although most substances contract when cooled and expand when heated, water behaves differently. Water contracts when cooled from 100 °C to 3.98 °C, but

▲ Which has the greater mass, the pillow or the brass cylinder? In fact, they have similar masses, but the brass cylinder has a higher *density* because of its smaller volume.

TABLE 2.7 Densities of Some Common Materials at 25 °C

SUBSTANCE	DENSITY*	SUBSTANCE	DENSITY*
Gases		Solids	
Helium	0.000 194	Ice (0 °C)	0.917
Air	0.001 185	Gold	19.3
Liquids		Human fat	0.94
Water (3.98 °C)	1.0000	Cork	0.22–0.26
Urine	1.003–1.030	Table sugar	1.59
Blood plasma	1.027	Balsa wood	0.12
		Earth	5.54

Densities are in g/cm³ for solids and g/mL for liquids and gases.

▲ Ice floats because its density is less than that of water.

below this temperature it begins to *expand* again. The density of liquid water is at its maximum of 1.0000 g/mL at 3.98 °C but decreases to 0.999 87 g/mL at 0 °C. When freezing occurs, the density drops still further to a value of 0.917 g/cm³ for ice at 0 °C. Since a less dense substance will float on top of a more dense fluid, ice and any other substance with a density less than that of water will float. Conversely, any substance with a density greater than that of water will sink.

Knowing the density of a liquid is useful because it is often easier to measure a liquid's volume rather than its mass. Suppose, for example, that you need 1.50 g of ethanol. Rather than use a dropper to weigh out exactly the right amount, it would be much easier to look up the density of ethanol (0.7893 g/mL at 20 °C) and measure the correct volume (1.90 mL) with a syringe or graduated cylinder. Thus, density acts as a conversion factor between mass (g) and volume (mL).

$$1.50 \text{ g ethanol} \times \frac{1 \text{ mL ethanol}}{0.7893 \text{ g ethanol}} = 1.90 \text{ mL ethanol}$$

WORKED EXAMPLE **2.14** Density: Mass-to-Volume Conversion.

What volume of isopropyl alcohol (rubbing alcohol) would you use if you needed 25.0 g? The density of isopropyl alcohol is 0.7855 g/mL at 20 °C.

ANALYSIS The known information is the mass of isopropyl alcohol needed (25.0 g). The density (0.7855 g/mL) acts as a conversion factor between mass and the unknown volume of isopropyl alcohol.

BALLPARK ESTIMATE Because 1 mL of isopropyl alcohol contains only 0.7885 g of the alcohol, obtaining 1 g of alcohol would require almost 20% more than 1 mL, or about 1.2 mL. Therefore, a volume of about 25 × 1.2 mL = 30 mL is needed to obtain 25 g of alcohol.

SOLUTION

STEP 1: **Identify known information.**

STEP 2: **Identify answer and units.**

STEP 3: **Identify conversion factors.** Starting with the mass of isopropyl alcohol (in g), the corresponding volume (in mL) can be calculated using density (g/mL) as the conversion factor.

STEP 4: **Solve.** Starting with the known information, set up the equation with conversion factors so that unwanted units cancel.

Mass of rubbing alcohol = 25.0 g
Density of rubbing alcohol = 0.7855 g/mL
Volume of rubbing alcohol = ?? mL

Density = g/mL → 1/density = mL/g

$$25.0 \text{ g alcohol} \times \frac{1 \text{ mL alcohol}}{0.7855 \text{ g alcohol}} = 31.8 \text{ mL alcohol}$$

BALLPARK CHECK Our estimate was 30 mL.

APPLICATION ▶ Obesity and Body Fat

According to the U.S. Center for Disease Control, the U.S. population is suffering from a fat epidemic. Over the last 25 years, the percentage of adults (20 years or older) identified as obese increased from 15% in the late 1970s to nearly 33% in 2004. Even children and adolescents are gaining too much weight: the number of overweight children in all age groups increased by nearly a factor of 3, with the biggest increase seen among teenagers (from 5% to 17.4%). How do we define obesity, however, and how is it measured?

Obesity is defined by reference to *body mass index* (BMI), which is equal to a person's mass in kilograms divided by the square of his or her height in meters. Alternatively, a person's weight in pounds divided by the square of her or his height in inches is multiplied by 703 to give the BMI. For instance, someone 5 ft 7 in. (67 inches; 1.70 m) tall weighing 147 lb (66.7 kg) has a BMI of 23:

$$\text{BMI} = \frac{\text{weight (kg)}}{[\text{height (m)}]^2}, \quad \text{or} \quad \frac{\text{weight (lb)}}{[\text{height (in.)}]^2} \times 703$$

A BMI of 25 or above is considered overweight, and a BMI of 30 or above is obese. By these standards, approximately 61% of the U.S. population is overweight.

Health professionals are concerned by the rapid rise in obesity in the United States because of the link between BMI and health problems. Many reports have documented the correlation between health and BMI, including a recent study on more than one million adults. The lowest death risk from any cause, including cancer and heart disease, is associated with a BMI between 22 and 24. Risk increases steadily as BMI increases, more than doubling for a BMI above 29.

Fat is not the enemy, however, because having some body fat is not just good, it is necessary! The layer of adipose tissue (body fat) lying just beneath our skin acts as a shock absorber and as a thermal insulator to maintain body temperature. It also serves as a long-term energy storehouse (see Section 25.6). A typical adult body contains about 50% muscles and other cellular material, 24% blood and other fluids, 7% bone, and 19% body fat. Overweight sedentary individuals

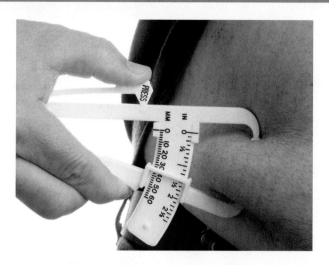

▲ A person's percentage body fat can be estimated by measuring the thickness of the fat layer under the skin.

have a higher fat percentage, whereas some world-class athletes have as little as 3% body fat. The problem occurs when the percentage of body fat is excessive.

An individual's percentage of body fat is most easily measured by the skinfold thickness method. The skin at several locations on the arm, shoulder, and waist is pinched, and the thickness of the fat layer beneath the skin is measured with calipers. Comparing the measured results to those in a standard table gives an estimation of percentage body fat.

As an alternative to skinfold measurement, a more accurate assessment of body fat can be made by underwater immersion. The person's underwater body weight is less than her weight on land because water gives the body buoyancy. The higher the percentage of body fat, the more buoyant the person and the greater the difference between land weight and underwater body weight. Checking the observed buoyancy on a standard table then gives an estimation of body fat.

See Additional Problems 2.82 and 2.83 at the end of the chapter.

Weight (lb)

	110	115	120	125	130	135	140	145	150	155	160	165	170	175	180	185	190	195	200
5'0"	21	22	23	24	25	26	27	28	29	30	31	32	33	34	35	36	37	38	39
5'2"	20	21	22	23	24	25	26	27	27	28	29	30	31	32	33	34	35	36	37
5'4"	19	20	21	21	22	23	24	25	26	27	27	28	29	30	31	32	33	33	34
5'6"	18	19	19	20	21	22	23	23	24	25	26	27	27	28	29	30	31	31	32
5'8"	17	17	18	19	20	21	21	22	23	24	24	25	26	27	27	28	29	30	30
5'10"	16	17	17	18	19	19	20	21	22	22	23	24	24	25	26	27	27	28	29
6'0"	15	16	16	17	18	18	19	20	20	21	22	22	23	24	24	25	26	26	27
6'2"	14	15	15	16	17	17	18	19	19	20	21	21	22	22	23	24	24	25	26
6'4"	13	14	15	15	16	16	17	18	18	19	19	20	21	21	22	23	23	24	24

Height

Body Mass Index (numbers in boxes)

PROBLEM 2.22

Which of the solids whose densities are given in Table 2.7 will float on water, and which will sink?

PROBLEM 2.23

Chloroform, once used as an anesthetic agent, has a density of 1.474 g/mL. What volume would you use if you needed 12.37 g?

PROBLEM 2.24

A glass stopper that has a mass of 16.8 g has a volume of 7.60 cm^3. What is the density of the glass?

2.12 Specific Gravity

Specific gravity The density of a substance divided by the density of water at the same temperature.

For many purposes, ranging from winemaking to medicine, it is more convenient to use *specific gravity* than density. The **specific gravity** (sp gr) of a substance (usually a liquid) is simply the density of the substance divided by the density of water at the same temperature. Because all units cancel, specific gravity is unitless:

$$\text{Specific gravity} = \frac{\text{Density of substance (g/mL)}}{\text{Density of water at the same temperature (g/mL)}}$$

At normal temperatures, the density of water is very close to 1 g/mL. Thus, the specific gravity of a substance is numerically equal to its density and is used in the same way.

The specific gravity of a liquid can be measured using an instrument called a *hydrometer*, which consists of a weighted bulb on the end of a calibrated glass tube, as shown in Figure 2.6. The depth to which the hydrometer sinks when placed in a fluid indicates the fluid's specific gravity: The lower the bulb sinks, the lower the specific gravity of the fluid.

Water that contains dissolved substances can have a specific gravity either higher or lower than 1.00. In winemaking, for instance, the amount of fermentation taking place is gauged by observing the change in specific gravity on going from grape juice, which contains 20% dissolved sugar and has a specific gravity of 1.082, to dry wine, which contains 12% alcohol and has a specific gravity of 0.984. (Pure alcohol has a specific gravity of 0.789.)

In medicine, a hydrometer called a *urinometer* is used to indicate the amount of solids dissolved in urine. Although the specific gravity of normal urine is about 1.003–1.030, conditions such as diabetes mellitus or a high fever cause an abnormally high urine specific gravity, indicating either excessive elimination of solids or decreased elimination of water. Abnormally low specific gravity is found in individuals using diuretics—drugs that increase water elimination.

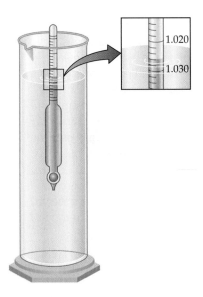

▲ **FIGURE 2.6 A hydrometer for measuring specific gravity.** The instrument has a weighted bulb at the end of a calibrated glass tube. The depth to which the hydrometer sinks in a liquid indicates the liquid's specific gravity.

PROBLEM 2.25

The sulfuric acid solution in an automobile battery typically has a specific gravity of about 1.27. Is battery acid more dense or less dense than pure water?

▲ The amount of fermentation that has taken place in the wine can be measured with a hydrometer.

SUMMARY: REVISITING THE CHAPTER GOALS

1. How are measurements made, and what units are used? A property that can be measured is called a *physical quantity* and is described by both a number and a label, or *unit*. The preferred units are either those of the International System of Units (*SI units*) or the *metric system*. Mass, the amount of matter an object contains, is measured in *kilograms* (kg) or *grams* (g). Length is measured in *meters* (m). Volume is measured in *cubic meters* (m³) in the SI system and in *liters* (L) or *milliliters* (mL) in the metric system. Temperature is measured in *kelvins* (K) in the SI system and in *degrees Celsius* (°C) in the metric system.

2. How good are the reported measurements? When measuring physical quantities or using them in calculations, it is important to indicate the exactness of the measurement by *rounding off* the final answer using the correct number of *significant figures*. All but one of the significant figures in a number is known with certainty; the final digit is estimated to ±1.

3. How are large and small numbers best represented? Measurements of small and large quantities are usually written in *scientific notation* as the product of a number between 1 and 10, times a power of 10. Numbers greater than 10 have a positive exponent, and numbers less than 1 have a negative exponent. For example, $3562 = 3.562 \times 10^3$, and $0.003\ 91 = 3.91 \times 10^{-3}$.

4. How can a quantity be converted from one unit of measure to another? A measurement in one unit can be converted to another unit by multiplying by a *conversion factor* that expresses the exact relationship between the units.

5. What techniques are used to solve problems? Problems are best solved by applying the *factor-label method*, in which units can be multiplied and divided just as numbers can. The idea is to set up an equation so that all unwanted units cancel, leaving only the desired units. Usually it is best to start by identifying the known and needed information, then

KEY WORDS

Conversion factor, *p. 31*

Density, *p. 39*

Energy, *p. 38*

Factor-label method, *p. 31*

Mass, *p. 21*

Physical quantity, *p. 19*

Rounding off, *p. 29*

Scientific notation, *p. 26*

SI units, *p. 19*

Significant figures, *p. 24*

Specific gravity, *p. 42*

Specific heat, *p. 38*

Temperature, *p. 35*

Unit, *p. 19*

Weight, *p. 21*

decide how to convert the known information to the answer, and finally check to make sure the answer is reasonable both chemically and physically.

6. **What are temperature, specific heat, density, and specific gravity?** *Temperature* is a measure of how hot or cold an object is. The *specific heat* of a substance is the amount of heat necessary to raise the temperature of 1 g of the substance by 1 °C. Water has an unusually high specific heat, which helps our bodies to maintain an even temperature. *Density*, the physical property that relates mass to volume, is expressed in units of grams per milliliter (g/mL) for a liquid or grams per cubic centimeter (g/cm^3) for a solid. The *specific gravity* of a liquid is the density of the liquid divided by the density of water at the same temperature. Because the density of water is approximately 1 g/mL, specific gravity and density have the same numerical value.

UNDERSTANDING KEY CONCEPTS

2.26 How many milliliters of water does the graduated cylinder in (a) contain, and how tall in centimeters is the paper clip in (b)? How many significant figures do you have in each answer?

(a)   (b)

2.27 Using a metric ruler, measure the following objects:
  (a) Length of your calculator
  (b) Width of a page in this text book
  (c) Height and diameter of a 12 ounce can

2.28 **(a)** What is the specific gravity of the following solution?
  (b) How many significant figures does your answer have?
  (c) Is the solution more dense or less dense than water?

2.29 Assume that you have two graduated cylinders, one with a capacity of 5 mL (a) and the other with a capacity of 50 mL (b). Draw a line in each showing how much liquid you would add if you needed to measure 2.64 mL of water. Which cylinder do you think is more precise? Explain.

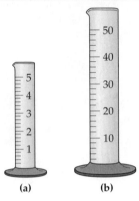

(a)   (b)

2.30 State the length of the pencil depicted in the accompanying figure in both inches and cm.

2.31 Assume that you are delivering a solution sample from a pipette. Figures (a) and (b) show the volume level before and after dispensing the sample, respectively. State the liquid level (in mL) before and after dispensing the sample, and calculate the volume of the sample.

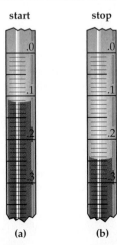

(a)   (b)

2.32 **(a)** Pour the contents of a 12 ounce can into a measuring cup. Record the volume in both fluid ounces and in cups. Which measurement is more precise?

(b) Pour the contents of a 12 ounce can into a 400 mL beaker. What is the volume in mL?

ADDITIONAL PROBLEMS

DEFINITIONS AND UNITS

2.34 What is the difference between a physical quantity and a number?

2.35 What is the difference between mass and weight?

2.36 What are the units used in the SI system to measure mass, volume, length, and temperature?

2.37 What are the units used in the metric system to measure mass, volume, length, and temperature?

2.38 What is the difference between a cubic decimeter (SI) and a liter (metric)?

2.39 What is the difference between a kelvin (SI) and a Celsius degree (metric)?

2.40 Give the full name of the following units:

(a) cL   **(b)** dm   **(c)** mm
(d) nL   **(e)** mg   **(f)** m^3
(g) cc

2.41 Write the symbol for the following units:

(a) nanogram   **(b)** centimeter   **(c)** microliter
(d) micrometer   **(e)** milligram

2.42 How many picograms are in 1 mg? In 35 ng?

2.43 How many microliters are in 1 L? In 20 mL?

SCIENTIFIC NOTATION AND SIGNIFICANT FIGURES

2.44 Express the following numbers in scientific notation:

(a) 9457   **(b)** 0.000 07
(c) 20,000,000,000 (four significant figures)
(d) 0.012 345   **(e)** 652.38

2.45 Convert the following numbers from scientific notation to standard notation:

(a) 5.28×10^3 **(b)** 8.205×10^{-2}
(c) 1.84×10^{-5} **(d)** 6.37×10^4

2.46 How many significant figures does each of the following numbers have?

(a) 237,401   **(b)** 0.300   **(c)** 3.01
(d) 244.4   **(e)** 50,000   **(f)** 660

2.47 How many significant figures are there in each of the following quantities?

(a) Distance from New York City to Wellington, New Zealand, 14,397 km

(b) Average body temperature of a crocodile, 25.6 °C

(c) Melting point of gold, 1064 °C

(d) Diameter of an influenza virus, 0.000 01 mm

(e) Radius of a phosphorus atom, 0.110 nm

2.48 The diameter of the earth at the equator is 7926.381 mi.

(a) Round off the earth's diameter to four significant figures, to two significant figures, and to six significant figures.

(b) Express the earth's diameter in scientific notation.

2.33 Assume that identical hydrometers are placed in ethanol (sp gr 0.7893) and in chloroform (sp gr 1.4832). In which liquid will the hydrometer float higher? Explain.

2.49 Round off each of the numbers in Problem 2.46 to two significant figures, and express them in scientific notation.

2.50 Carry out the following calculations, express each answer to the correct number of significant figures, and include units in the answers.

(a) 9.02 g + 3.1 g
(b) 88.80 cm + 7.391 cm
(c) 362 mL − 99.5 mL
(d) 12.4 mg + 6.378 mg + 2.089 mg

2.51 Carry out the following calculations, express the answers to the correct numbers of significant figures, and include units in the answers.

(a) $5,280 \dfrac{ft}{mi} \times 6.2$ mi

(b) 4.5 m × 3.25 m

(c) $2.50 \text{ g} \div 8.3 \dfrac{g}{cm^3}$

(d) 4.70 cm × 6.8 cm × 2.54 cm

UNIT CONVERSIONS AND PROBLEM SOLVING

2.52 Carry out the following conversions:

(a) 3.614 mg to centigrams
(b) 12.0 kL to megaliters
(c) 14.4 μm to millimeters
(d) 6.03×10^{-6} cg to nanograms
(e) 174.5 mL to deciliters
(f) 1.5×10^{-2} km to centimeters

2.53 Carry out the following conversions. Consult Tables 2.3–2.5 as needed.

(a) 56.4 mi to kilometers and to megameters
(b) 2.0 L to to quarts and to fluid ounces
(c) 7 ft 2.0 in. to centimeters and to meters
(d) 1.35 lb to kilograms and to decigrams

2.54 Express the following quantities in more convenient units by using SI unit prefixes:

(a) 9.78×10^4 g   **(b)** 1.33×10^{-4} L
(c) 0.000 000 000 46 g   **(d)** 2.99×10^8 cm

2.55 Which SI unit prefix corresponds to each of the following multipliers?

(a) 10^3 **(b)** 10^{-3}
(c) 10^6 **(d)** 10^{-6}

2.56 The speed limit in Canada is 100 km/h.

(a) How many miles per hour is this?
(b) How many feet per second?

2.57 The muzzle velocity of a projectile fired from a 9 mm handgun is 1200 ft/s.

(a) How many miles per hour is this?
(b) How many meters per second?

2.58 The diameter of a red blood cell is 6×10^{-6} m. How many red blood cells are needed to make a line 1 in. long?

2.59 The Sears Tower in Chicago has an approximate floor area of 418,000 m^2. How many square feet of floor is this?

2.60 A normal value for blood cholesterol is 200 mg/dL of blood. If a normal adult has a total blood volume of 5 L, how much total cholesterol is present?

2.61 One bottle of aspirin holds 50 tablets, each containing 250 mg of aspirin, and sells for $1.95. Another bottle holds 100 tablets, each containing 200 mg of aspirin, and sells for $3.75. For each bottle, calculate the value in milligrams of aspirin per dollar. Which bottle is the better bargain?

2.62 The white blood cell concentration in normal blood is approximately 12,000 cells/mm^3 of blood. How many white blood cells does a normal adult with 5 L of blood have? Express the answer in scientific notation.

2.63 The recommended daily dose of calcium for an 18-year-old male is 1200 mg. If 1.0 cup of whole milk contains 290 mg of calcium and milk is his only calcium source, how much milk should an 18-year-old male drink each day?

ENERGY, HEAT, AND TEMPERATURE

2.64 What is the normal temperature of the human body (98.6 °F) in degrees Celsius? In kelvins?

2.65 The boiling point of liquid nitrogen, used in the removal of warts and in other surgical applications, is −195.8 °C. What is this temperature in kelvins and in degrees Fahrenheit?

2.66 Diethyl ether, a substance once used as a general anesthetic, has a specific heat of 0.895 cal/(g · °C). How many calories and how many kilocalories of heat are needed to raise the temperature of 30.0 g of diethyl ether from 10.0 °C to 30.0 °C?

2.67 Copper has a specific heat of 0.092 cal/(g · °C). When 52.7 cal of heat is added to a piece of copper, the temperature increases from 22.4 °C to 38.6 °C. What is the mass of the piece of copper?

2.68 Calculate the specific heat of copper if it takes 23 cal to heat a 5.0 g sample from 25 °C to 75 °C.

2.69 The specific heat of fat is 0.45 cal/(g · °C), and the density of fat is 0.94 g/cm^3. How much energy (in calories) is needed to heat 10 cm^3 of fat from room temperature (25 °C) to its melting point (35 °C)?

2.70 A 150 g sample of mercury and a 150 g sample of iron are at an initial temperature of 25.0 °C. If 250 cal of heat is applied to each sample, what is the final temperature of each? (See Table 2.6.)

2.71 When 100 cal of heat is applied to a 125 g sample, the temperature increases by 28 °C. Calculate the specific heat of the sample and compare your answer to the values in Table 2.6. What is the identity of the sample?

DENSITY AND SPECIFIC GRAVITY

2.72 Aspirin has a density of 1.40 g/cm^3. What is the volume in cubic centimeters of a tablet weighing 250 mg?

2.73 Gaseous hydrogen has a density of 0.0899 g/L at 0 °C. How many liters would you need if you wanted 1.0078 g of hydrogen?

2.74 What is the density of lead (in g/cm^3) if a rectangular bar measuring 0.500 cm in height, 1.55 cm in width, and 25.00 cm in length has a mass of 220.9 g?

2.75 What is the density of lithium metal (in g/cm^3) if a cube measuring 0.82 cm $\times$ 1.45 cm $\times$ 1.25 cm has a mass of 0.794 g?

2.76 What is the density of isopropyl alcohol (rubbing alcohol) in grams per milliliter if a 5.000 mL sample has a mass of 3.928 g at room temperature? What is the specific gravity of isopropyl alcohol?

2.77 Ethylene glycol, commonly used as automobile antifreeze, has a specific gravity of 1.1088 at room temperature. What is the volume of 1.00 kg of ethylene glycol? What is the volume of 2.00 lb of ethylene glycol?

Applications

2.78 The typical rhinovirus has a diameter of 20 nm, or 2.0×10^{-8} m

(a) What is the length in centimeters?

(b) How many rhinoviruses would need to be laid end to end to make a chain 1 in. long?
   [*Powers of 10, p. 28*]

2.79 Blood cells have a mean cell volume of 90 fL, or 9.0×10^{-14} L

(a) Convert this volume to cubic centimeters.

(b) The formula for the volume of a sphere is $V = 4\pi r^2/3$. Assuming a spherical shape, calculate the mean diameter of a blood cell in centimeters.
   [*Powers of 10, p. 28*]

2.80 A thermochromic plastic chip included in a shipping container for beef undergoes an irreversible color change if the storage temperature exceeds 28 °F. What is this temperature on the Celsius and Kelvin scales?
   [*Temperature-Sensitive Materials, p. 36*]

2.81 A temperature-sensitive bath toy undergoes several color changes in the temperature range from 37 °C to 47 °C. What is the corresponding temperature range on the Fahrenheit scale?
   [*Temperature-Sensitive Materials, p. 36*]

2.82 Calculate the BMI for an individual who is:

(a) 5 ft 1 in. tall and weighs 155 lb

(b) 5 ft 11 in. tall and weigh 170 lb

(c) 6 ft 3 in. tall and weigh 195 lb

Which of these individuals is likely to have increased health risks?
   [*Obesity and Body Fat, p. 41*]

2.83 Liposuction is a technique for removing fat deposits from various areas of the body. How many liters of fat would have to be removed to result in a 5.0 lb weight loss? The density of human fat is 0.94 g/mL.
   [*Measuring Body Fat, p.41*]

General Questions and Problems

2.84 Refer to the pencil in Problem 2.30. Using the equivalent values in Table 2.4 as conversion factors, convert the length measured in inches to centimeters. Compare the calculated length in centimeters to the length in centimeters measured using the metric ruler. How do the two values compare? Explain any differences.

2.85 Gemstones are weighed in carats, where 1 carat = 200 mg exactly. What is the mass in grams of the Hope diamond, the world's largest blue diamond, at 44.4 carats?

2.86 If you were cooking in an oven calibrated in Celsius degrees, what temperature would you use if the recipe called for 350 °F?

2.87 What dosage in grams per kilogram of body weight does a 130 lb woman receive if she takes two 250 mg tablets of penicillin? How many 125 mg tablets should a 40 lb child take to receive the same dosage?

2.88 A clinical report gave the following data from a blood analysis: iron, 39 mg/dL; calcium, 8.3 mg/dL; cholesterol, 224 mg/dL. Express each of these quantities in grams per deciliter, writing the answers in scientific notation.

2.89 The density of air at room temperature is 1.3 g/L. What is the mass of the air **(a)** in grams and **(b)** in pounds in a room that is 4.0 m long, 3.0 m wide, and 2.5 m high?

2.90 Approximately 75 mL of blood is pumped by a normal human heart at each beat. Assuming an average pulse of 72 beats per minute, how many milliliters of blood are pumped in one day?

2.91 A doctor has ordered that a patient be given 15 g of glucose, which is available in a concentration of 50.00 g glucose/1000.0 mL of solution. What volume of solution should be given to the patient?

2.92 Reconsider the volume of the sample dispensed by pipette in Problem 2.31. Assuming that the solution in the pipette has a density of 0.963 g/mL, calculate the mass of solution dispensed in the problem to the correct number of significant figures.

2.93 Today thermometers containing mercury are used less frequently than in the past because of concerns regarding the toxicity of mercury and because of its relatively high melting point (−39 °C), which means that mercury thermometers cannot be used in very cold environments because the mercury is a solid under such conditions. Alcohol thermometers, however, can be used over a temperature range from −115 °C (the melting point of alcohol) to 78.5 °C (the boiling point of alcohol).

(a) What is the effective temperature range of the alcohol thermometer in °F?
(b) The densities of alcohol and mercury are 0.79 g/mL and 13.6 g/mL, respectively. If the volume of liquid in a typical laboratory thermometer is 1.0 mL, what mass of alcohol is contained in the thermometer? What mass of mercury?

2.94 In a typical person, the level of glucose (also known as blood sugar) is about 85 mg/100 mL of blood. If an average body contains about 11 pints of blood, how many grams and how many pounds of glucose are present in the blood?

2.95 A patient is receiving 3000 mL/day of a solution that contains 5 g of dextrose (glucose) per 100 mL of solution. If glucose provides 4 kcal/g of energy, how many kilocalories per day is the patient receiving from the glucose?

2.96 A rough guide to fluid requirements based on body weight is 100 mL/kg for the first 10 kg of body weight, 50 mL/kg for the next 10 kg, and 20 mL/kg for weight over 20 kg. What volume of fluid per day is needed by a 55 kg woman? Give the answer with two significant figures.

2.97 Chloral hydrate, a sedative and sleep-inducing drug, is available as a solution labeled 10.0 gr/fluidram. What volume in milliliters should be administered to a patient who is meant to receive 7.5 gr per dose? (1 gr = 64.8 mg; 1 fluidram = 3.72 mL)

2.98 When 1.0 tablespoon of butter is burned or used by our body, it releases 100 kcal (100 food calories) of energy. If we could use all the energy provided, how many tablespoons of butter would have to be burned to raise the temperature of 3.00 L of water from 18.0 °C to 90.0 °C?

2.99 An archeologist finds a 1.62 kg goblet that she believes to be made of pure gold. When 1350 cal of heat is added to the goblet, its temperature increases by 7.8 °C. Calculate the specific heat of the goblet. Is it made of gold? Explain.

2.100 In another test, the archeologist in Problem 2.99 determines that the volume of the goblet is 205 mL. Calculate the density of the goblet and compare it with the density of gold (19.3 g/mL), lead (11.4 g/mL), and iron (7.86 g/mL). What is the goblet probably made of?

2.101 The density of sulfuric acid, H_2SO_4, is 1.83 g/mL. What volume of sulfuric acid is needed to obtain 98.0 g of H_2SO_4?

2.102 Sulfuric acid (Problem 2.101) is produced in larger amounts than any other chemical: 2.01×10^{11} lb worldwide in 2004. What is the volume of this amount in liters?

2.103 The caliber of a gun is expressed by measuring the diameter of the gun barrel in hundredths of an inch. A "22" rifle, for example, has a barrel diameter of 0.22 in. What is the barrel diameter of a .22 rifle in millimeters?

2.104 Amounts of substances dissolved in solution are often expressed as mass per unit volume. For example, normal human blood has a cholesterol concentration of about 200 mg of cholesterol/100 mL of blood. Express this concentration in the following units:

(a) milligrams per liter **(b)** micrograms per liter
(c) grams per liter **(d)** nanograms per microliter

2.105 The element gallium (Ga) has the second largest liquid range of any element, melting at 29.8 °C and boiling at 2204 °C at atmospheric pressure.

(a) Is gallium a metal, a nonmetal, or a metalloid?
(b) What is the density of gallium in grams per cubic centimeter at 25 °C if a 1.00 in. cube has a mass of 0.2133 lb?

2.106 A sample of water at 293.2 K was heated for 8 min and 25 s, and the heating was carried out so that the temperature increased at a constant rate of 3.0 °F/min. What is the final temperature of the water in degrees Celsius?

2.107 At a certain point, the Celsius and Fahrenheit scales "cross," and at this point the numerical value of the Celsius temperature is the same as the numerical value of the Fahrenheit temperature. At what temperature does this crossover occur?

2.108 Imagine that you place a piece of cork measuring 1.30 cm × 5.50 cm × 3.00 cm in a pan of water and that on top of the cork you place a small cube of lead measuring 1.15 cm on each edge. The density of cork is 0.235 g/cm³, and the density of lead is 11.35 g/cm³. Will the combination of cork plus lead float or sink?

CHAPTER 3

Atoms and the Periodic Table

▲ The mineral formations of the Giant's Causeway in Northern Ireland are an example of periodicity—the presence of regularly repeating patterns—found throughout nature.

CONTENTS

CHAPTER GOALS

We will take up the following questions about atoms and atomic theory:

1. What is the modern theory of atomic structure?

THE GOAL: Be able to explain the major assumptions of atomic theory.

2. How do atoms of different elements differ?

THE GOAL: Be able to explain the composition of different atoms according to the number of protons, neutrons, and electrons they contain.

3. What are isotopes, and what is atomic weight?

THE GOAL: Be able to explain what isotopes are and how they affect an element's atomic weight.

4. How is the periodic table arranged?

THE GOAL: Be able to describe how elements are arranged in the periodic table, name the subdivisions of the periodic table, and relate the position of an element in the periodic table to its electronic structure.

5. How are electrons arranged in atoms?

THE GOAL: Be able to explain how electrons are distributed in shells and subshells around the nucleus of an atom, how valence electrons can be represented as electron-dot symbols, and how the electron configurations can help explain the chemical properties of the elements.

C hemistry must be studied on two levels. In the past two chapters we have dealt with chemistry on the large-scale, or *macroscopic*, level, looking at the properties and transformations of matter that we can see and measure. Now we are ready to look at the sub-microscopic, or atomic level, studying the behavior and properties of individual atoms. Although scientists have long been convinced of their existence, only within the past twenty years have powerful new instruments made it possible to see individual atoms themselves. In this chapter we will look at modern atomic theory and at how the structure of atoms influences macroscopic properties.

3.1 Atomic Theory

Take a piece of aluminum foil and cut it in two. Then take one of the pieces and cut *it* in two, and so on. Assuming that you have extremely small scissors and extraordinary dexterity, how long can you keep dividing the foil? Is there a limit, or is matter infinitely divisible into ever smaller and smaller pieces? Historically, this argument can be traced as far back as the ancient Greek philosophers. Aristotle believed that matter could be divided infinitely, while Democritus argued (correctly) that there is a limit. The smallest and simplest bit that aluminum (or any other element) can be divided into and still be identifiable as aluminum is called an **atom**, a word derived from the Greek *atomos*, meaning "indivisible."

Chemistry is founded on four fundamental assumptions about atoms and matter, which together make up modern **atomic theory**:

- All matter is composed of atoms.

- The atoms of a given element differ from the atoms of all other elements.

- Chemical compounds consist of atoms combined in specific ratios. That is, only whole atoms can combine—one A atom with one B atom, or one A atom with two B atoms, and so on. The enormous diversity in the substances we see around us is based on the vast number of ways that atoms can combine with one another.

- Chemical reactions change only the way that atoms are combined in compounds. The atoms themselves are unchanged.

Atoms are extremely small, ranging from about 7.4×10^{-11} m in diameter for a hydrogen atom to 5.24×10^{-10} m for a cesium atom. In mass, atoms vary from 1.67×10^{-24} g for hydrogen to 3.95×10^{-22} g for uranium, one of the heaviest naturally occurring atoms. It is difficult to appreciate just how small atoms are, although it might help if you realize that a fine pencil line is about 3 *million* atoms across, and that even the smallest speck of dust contains about 10^{16} atoms.

Atom The smallest and simplest particle of an element.

Atomic theory A set of assumptions proposed by the English scientist John Dalton to explain the chemical behavior of matter.

▲ How small can a piece of aluminum foil be cut?

▶ Atoms are so small that the radius of this circle is about three million atoms wide.

Subatomic particles Three kinds of fundamental particles from which atoms are made: protons, neutrons, and electrons.

Proton A positively charged subatomic particle.

Neutron An electrically neutral subatomic particle.

Electron A negatively charged subatomic particle.

Atoms are composed of tiny **subatomic particles** called *protons, neutrons,* and *electrons.* A **proton** has a mass of $1.672\ 622 \times 10^{-24}$ g and carries a positive (+) electrical charge; a **neutron** has a mass similar to that of a proton ($1.674\ 927 \times 10^{-24}$ g) but is electrically neutral; and an **electron** has a mass that is only 1/1836 that of a proton ($9.109\ 328 \times 10^{-28}$ g) and carries a negative (−) electrical charge. In fact, electrons are so much lighter than protons and neutrons that their mass is usually ignored. Table 3.1 compares the properties of the three fundamental subatomic particles.

TABLE 3.1 A Comparison of Subatomic Particles

NAME	SYMBOL	MASS (GRAMS)	MASS (AMU)	CHARGE (CHARGE UNITS)
Proton	p	$1.672\ 622 \times 10^{-24}$	1.007 276	+1
Neutron	n	$1.674\ 927 \times 10^{-24}$	1.008 665	0
Electron	e^-	$9.109\ 328 \times 10^{-28}$	$5.485\ 799 \times 10^{-4}$	−1

Atomic mass unit (amu) A convenient unit for describing the mass of an atom; 1 amu = ½ the mass of a carbon-12 atom.

Nucleus The dense, central core of an atom that contains protons and neutrons.

The masses of atoms and their constituent subatomic particles are so small when measured in grams that it is more convenient to express them on a *relative* mass scale. That is, one atom is assigned a mass, and all others are measured relative to it. The process is like deciding that a golf ball (46.0 g) will be assigned a mass of 1. A baseball (149 g), which is 149/46.0 = 3.24 times heavier than a golf ball, would then have a mass of about 3.24, a volleyball (270 g) would have a mass of 270/46.0 = 5.87, and so on.

The basis for the relative atomic mass scale is an atom of carbon that contains 6 protons and 6 neutrons. Such an atom is assigned a mass of exactly 12 **atomic mass units (amu;** also called a *dalton* in honor of the English scientist John Dalton, who proposed most of atomic theory as we know it), where 1 amu = $1.660\ 539 \times 10^{-24}$ g. Thus, for all practical purposes, both a proton and a neutron have a mass of 1 amu (Table 3.1). Hydrogen atoms are only about one-twelfth as heavy as carbon atoms and have a mass close to 1 amu, magnesium atoms are about twice as heavy as carbon atoms and have a mass close to 24 amu, and so forth.

Subatomic particles are not distributed at random throughout an atom. Rather, the protons and neutrons are packed closely together in a dense core called the **nucleus.** Surrounding the nucleus, the electrons move about rapidly through a large, mostly empty volume of space (Figure 3.1). Measurements show that the diameter of a nucleus is only about 10^{-15} m, whereas that of the atom itself is about 10^{-10} m. For comparison, if an atom were the size of a large domed stadium, the nucleus would be approximately the size of a small pea in the center of the playing field.

▲ The relative size of a nucleus in an atom is the same as that of a pea in the middle of this stadium.

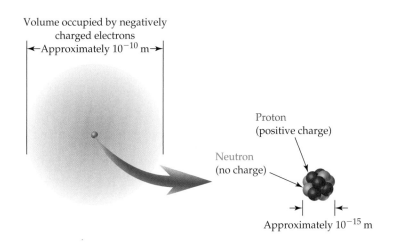

Volume occupied by negatively charged electrons
Approximately 10^{-10} m

Proton (positive charge)

Neutron (no charge)

Approximately 10^{-15} m

◀ **FIGURE 3.1 The structure of an atom.** Protons and neutrons are packed together in the nucleus, whereas electrons move about in the large surrounding volume. Virtually all the mass of an atom is concentrated in the nucleus.

The structure of the atom is determined by an interplay of different attractive and repulsive forces. Because unlike charges attract one another, the negatively charged electrons are held near the positively charged nucleus. But because like charges repel one another, the negatively charged electrons try to get as far away from one another as possible, accounting for the relatively large volume they occupy. The positively charged protons in the nucleus also repel one another, but are nevertheless held together by a unique attraction called the *nuclear strong force*, which is beyond the scope of this text.

Electrons repel one another

Protons repel one another

Protons and electrons attract one another

WORKED EXAMPLE **3.1** Atomic Mass Units: Gram-to-Atom Conversions

How many atoms are in a small piece of aluminum foil with a mass of 0.100 g? The mass of an atom of aluminum is 27.0 amu.

ANALYSIS We know the sample mass in grams and the mass of one atom in atomic mass units. To find the number of atoms in the sample, two conversions are needed, the first between grams and atomic mass units and the second between atomic mass units and the number of atoms. The conversion factor between atomic mass units and grams is 1 amu = $1.660\,539 \times 10^{-24}$ g.

BALLPARK ESTIMATE An atom of aluminum has a mass of 27.0 amu; since 1 amu $\sim 10^{-24}$ g, the mass of a single aluminum atom is very small ($\approx 10^{-23}$ g). A very *large* number of atoms, therefore (10^{22} ?), is needed to obtain a mass of 0.100 g.

SOLUTION

STEP 1: Identify known information.

Mass of aluminum foil = 0.100 g
1 Al atom = 27.0 amu

STEP 2: Identify unknown answer and units.

Number of Al atoms = ?

STEP 3: Identify needed conversion factors. Knowing the mass of foil (in g) and the mass of individual atoms (in amu) we need to convert from amu/atom to g/atom.

1 amu = $1.660\,539 \times 10^{-24}$ g
$$\rightarrow \frac{1\ \text{amu}}{1.660\,539 \times 10^{-24}\ \text{g}}$$

STEP 4: Solve. Set up an equation using known information and conversion factors so that unwanted units cancel.

$$(0.100\ \cancel{\text{g}})\left(\frac{1\ \cancel{\text{amu}}}{1.660\,539 \times 10^{-24}\ \cancel{\text{g}}}\right)\left(\frac{1\ \text{Al atom}}{27.0\ \cancel{\text{amu}}}\right)$$

$$= 2.23 \times 10^{21}\ \text{Al atoms}$$

BALLPARK CHECK: Our estimate was 10^{22}, which is within a factor of 10.

PROBLEM 3.1

What is the mass in atomic mass units of a nitrogen atom weighing 2.33×10^{-23} g?

PROBLEM 3.2

What is the mass in grams of 150×10^{12} iron atoms, each having a mass of 56 amu?

PROBLEM 3.3

How many atoms are in each of the following?

(a) 1.0 g of hydrogen atoms, each of mass 1.0 amu

(b) 12.0 g of carbon atoms, each of mass 12.0 amu

(c) 23.0 g of sodium atoms, each of mass 23.0 amu

PROBLEM 3.4

What pattern do you see in your answers to Problem 3.3? (We will return to this very important pattern in Chapter 6.)

APPLICATION ▶   Are Atoms Real?

Chemistry rests on the premise that matter is composed of the tiny particles we call atoms. Every chemical reaction and every physical law that governs the behavior of matter are explained by chemists in terms of atomic theory. But how do we know that atoms are real and not just an imaginary concept? And how do we know the structure of the atom? Our understanding of atomic structure is another example of the scientific method at work.

Dalton's atomic theory was originally published in 1808, but many prominent scientists dismissed it. Over the next century, however, several unrelated experiments provided insight into the nature of matter and the structure of the atom. Nineteenth-century investigations into electricity, for example, demonstrated that matter was composed of charged particles—rubbing a glass rod with a silk cloth would generate "static electricity," the same phenomenon that shocks you when you walk across a carpet and then touch a metal surface. It was also known that passing electricity through certain substances, such as water, decomposed the compounds into their constituent elements.

In 1897, J. J. Thomson used magnetic fields to deflect a beam of particles emitted from a cathode ray tube, demonstrating that these particles had a negative charge and were 1000 times lighter than the lightest charged particles found in aqueous solution (H^+). (⬤▭⬤ Section 6.10 and Chapter 10) This result implied that atoms were *not* the smallest particles of matter but could be divided into even smaller particles. In 1909, Robert Millikan studied the behavior of oil droplets in a

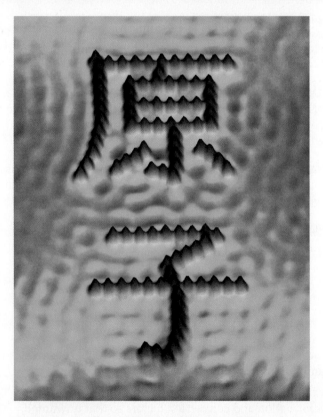

▲ Colored scanning tunneling micrograph of the surface of graphite, a form of the element carbon. The hexagonal pattern is related to an identical arrangement of the carbon atoms.

chamber containing electrically charged plates. When Millikan bombarded the atmosphere in the chamber with x-rays, the droplets acquired a negative charge. Millikan observed that by varying the strength of the electric field associated with the charged plates he could alter the rate of descent of the droplets or even suspend them in midair! From these results he was able to calculate the charge associated with the electron (16×10^{-19} coulombs). Finally, in 1910 Ernest Rutherford bombarded a gold foil with positively charged "alpha" particles emitted from radium during radioactive decay. The majority of these particles passed straight through the foil, but a small fraction of them were deflected, and a few even bounced backward. From these results Rutherford deduced that an atom consists mostly of empty space (occupied by the negatively charged electrons) and that most of the mass and all of the positive charge are contained in a relatively small, dense region that he called the nucleus.

We can now actually "see" and manipulate individual atoms through the use of a device called a *scanning tunneling microscope*, or STM (⬭ see Application on p. 28). With the STM, invented in 1981 by a research team at the IBM Corporation, magnifications of up to ten million have been achieved, allowing chemists to look directly at atoms. The accompanying photograph shows a computer-enhanced representation of carbon atoms in graphite that have been deposited on a copper surface.

Most present uses of the STM involve studies of surface chemistry, such as the events accompanying the corrosion of metals and the ordering of large molecules in polymers. Work is also under way using the STM to determine the structures of complex biological molecules.

See Additional Problems 3.90 and 3.91 at the end of the chapter.

3.2 Elements and Atomic Number

Atoms of different elements differ from one another according to how many protons they contain, a value called the element's **atomic number (Z)**. Thus, if we know the number of protons in an atom, we can identify the element. Any atom with 6 protons, for example, is a carbon atom because carbon has $Z = 6$.

Atoms are neutral overall and have no net charge because the number of positively charged protons in an atom is the same as the number of negatively charged electrons. Thus, the atomic number also equals the number of electrons in every atom of a given element. Hydrogen, $Z = 1$, has only 1 proton and 1 electron; carbon, $Z = 6$, has 6 protons and 6 electrons; sodium, $Z = 11$, has 11 protons and 11 electrons; and so on up to the newly discovered element with $Z = 118$. In a periodic table, elements are listed in order of increasing atomic number, beginning at the upper left and ending at the lower right.

Atomic number (Z)   The number of protons in atoms of a given element; the number of electrons in atoms of a given element

The sum of the protons and neutrons in an atom is called the atom's **mass number (A)**. Hydrogen atoms with 1 proton and no neutrons have mass number 1; carbon atoms with 6 protons and 6 neutrons have mass number 12; sodium atoms with 11 protons and 12 neutrons have mass number 23; and so on. Except for hydrogen, atoms generally contain at least as many neutrons as protons, and frequently contain more. There is no simple way to predict how many neutrons a given atom will have.

Mass number (A)   The total number of protons and neutrons in an atom

WORKED EXAMPLE   **3.2** Atomic Structure: Protons, Neutrons, and Electrons

Phosphorus has atomic number $Z = 15$. How many protons, electrons, and neutrons are there in phosphorus atoms, which have mass number $A = 31$?

ANALYSIS The atomic number gives the number of protons, which is the same as the number of electrons, and the mass number gives the total number of protons plus neutrons.

SOLUTION

Phosphorus atoms, with $Z = 15$, have 15 protons and 15 electrons. To find the number of neutrons, subtract the atomic number from the mass number:

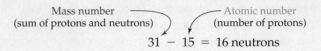

$$31 - 15 = 16 \text{ neutrons}$$

WORKED EXAMPLE 3.3 Atomic Structure: Atomic Number and Atomic Mass

An atom contains 28 protons and has $A = 60$. Give the number of electrons and neutrons in the atom, and identify the element.

ANALYSIS The number of protons and the number of electrons are the same and are equal to the atomic number Z, 28 in this case. Subtracting the number of protons (28) from the total number of protons plus neutrons (60) gives the number of neutrons.

SOLUTION

The atom has 28 electrons and $60 - 28 = 32$ neutrons. Looking at the list of elements inside the front cover shows that the element with atomic number 28 is nickel (Ni).

PROBLEM 3.5

Use the list inside the front cover to identify elements with the following atomic numbers:

(a) $Z = 75$

(b) $Z = 20$

(c) $Z = 52$

PROBLEM 3.6

The cobalt used in cancer treatments has $Z = 27$ and $A = 60$. How many protons, neutrons, and electrons are in these cobalt atoms?

PROBLEM 3.7

A certain atom has $A = 98$ and contains 55 neutrons. Identify the element.

3.3 Isotopes and Atomic Weight

All atoms of a given element have the same number of protons—the atomic number Z characteristic of that element—but different atoms of an element can have different numbers of neutrons and therefore different mass numbers. Atoms with identical atomic numbers but different mass numbers are called **isotopes**. Hydrogen, for example, has three isotopes. The most abundant hydrogen isotope, called *protium*, has no neutrons and thus has a mass number of 1. A second hydrogen isotope, called *deuterium*, has one neutron and a mass number of 2; and a third isotope, called *tritium*, has two neutrons and a mass number of 3. Tritium is unstable and does not occur naturally in significant amounts, although it can be made in nuclear reactors (⬤⬤, see Section 11.11).

Isotopes Atoms with identical atomic numbers but different mass numbers.

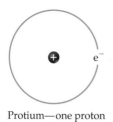

Protium—one proton
( ) and no neutrons;
mass number = 1

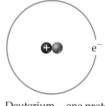

Deuterium—one proton
( ) and one neutron ( );
mass number = 2

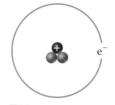

Tritium—one proton
( ) and two neutrons ( );
mass number = 3

A specific isotope is represented by showing its mass number (A) as a superscript and its atomic number (Z) as a subscript in front of the atomic symbol, for example, $_Z^A X$, where X represents the symbol for the element. Thus, protium is $_1^1 H$, deuterium is $_1^2 H$, and tritium is $_1^3 H$.

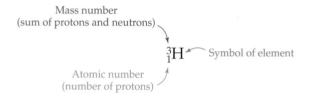

Unlike the three isotopes of hydrogen, the isotopes of most elements do not have distinctive names. Instead, the mass number of the isotope is given after the name of the element. The $_{92}^{235} U$ isotope used in nuclear reactors, for example, is usually referred to as uranium-235, or U-235.

Most naturally occurring elements are mixtures of isotopes. In a large sample of naturally occurring hydrogen atoms, for example, 99.985% have mass number $A = 1$ (protium) and 0.015% have mass number $A = 2$ (deuterium). It is therefore useful to know the *average* mass of the atoms in a large sample, a value called the element's **atomic weight**. For hydrogen, the atomic weight is 1.008 amu. Atomic weights for all elements are given inside the front cover of this book.

Atomic weight The weighted average mass of an element's atoms.

To calculate the atomic weight of an element, the individual masses of the naturally occurring isotopes and the percentage of each must be known. The atomic weight can then be calculated as the sum of the masses of the individual isotopes for that element, or

$$\text{Atomic weight} = \Sigma(\text{isotopic abundance}) \times (\text{isotopic mass})$$

where the Greek symbol Σ indicates the mathematical summing of terms.

Chlorine, for example, occurs on earth as a mixture of 75.77% Cl-35 atoms (mass = 34.97 amu) and 24.23% Cl-37 atoms (mass = 36.97 amu). The atomic weight is found by calculating the percentage of the mass contributed by each isotope. For chlorine, the calculation is done in the following way (to four significant figures), giving an atomic weight of 35.45 amu:

Contribution from ^{35}Cl: $(0.7577)(34.97 \text{ amu}) = 26.4968 \text{ amu}$

Contribution from ^{37}Cl: $(0.2423)(36.97 \text{ amu}) = \underline{\quad 8.9578 \text{ amu}}$

$$\text{Atomic weight} = 35.4546 = 35.45 \text{ amu}$$
$$\text{(rounded to four significant figures)}$$

The final number of significant figures in this case (four) was determined by the atomic masses. Note that the final rounding to four significant figures was not done until *after* the final answer was obtained.

WORKED EXAMPLE **3.4** Average Atomic Mass: Weighted-Average Calculation

Gallium is a metal with a very low melting point—it will melt in the palm of your hand. It has two naturally occurring isotopes: 60.4% is Ga-69, (mass = 68.9257 amu), and 39.6% is Ga-71, (mass = 70.9248 amu). Calculate the average atomic weight for gallium.

ANALYSIS We can calculate the average atomic mass for the element by summing up the contributions from each of the naturally occurring isotopes.

BALLPARK ESTIMATE The masses of the two naturally occurring isotopes of gallium differ by 2 amu (68.9 and 70.9 amu). Since slightly more than half of the Ga atoms are the lighter isotope (Ga-69), the average mass will be slightly less than halfway between the two isotopic masses; estimate = 69.8 amu.

SOLUTION

STEP 1: Identify known information.	Ga-69 (60.4% at 68.9257 amu)
	Ga-71 (39.6% at 70.9248 amu)
STEP 2: Identify the unknown answer and units.	Average atomic weight for Ga (in amu) = ?
STEP 3: Identify conversion factors or equations. This equation calculates the average atomic weight as a weighted average of all naturally occurring isotopes.	Atomic weight = Σ(isotopic abundance) $\times$ (isotopic mass)

$$\text{Atomic weight} = (0.604) \times (68.9257 \text{ amu}) = 41.6311 \text{ amu}$$

STEP 4: Solve. Substitute known information and solve.

$$+ (0.396) \times (70.9248 \text{ amu}) = 28.0862 \text{ amu}$$

$$\text{Atomic weight} = 69.7 \text{ amu}$$

$$(3 \text{ significant figures})$$

BALLPARK CHECK: Our estimate (69.8 amu) is close!

WORKED EXAMPLE **3.5** Identifying Isotopes from Atomic Mass and Atomic Number

Identify element X in the symbol $^{194}_{78}X$ and give its atomic number, mass number, number of protons, number of electrons, and number of neutrons.

ANALYSIS The identity of the atom corresponds to the atomic number—78.

SOLUTION
Element X has Z = 78, which shows that it is platinum. (Look inside the front cover for the list of elements.) The isotope $^{194}_{78}Pt$ has a mass number of 194, and we can subtract the atomic number from the mass number to get the number of neutrons. This platinum isotope therefore has 78 protons, 78 electrons, and $194 - 78 = 116$ neutrons.

PROBLEM 3.8

Potassium (K) has two naturally occurring isotopes: K-39 (93.12%; mass = 38.9637 amu), and K-41 (6.88%; 40.9618 amu). Calculate the atomic weight for potassium. How does your answer compare with the atomic mass given in the list inside the front cover of this book?

PROBLEM 3.9

Bromine, an element present in compounds used as sanitizers and fumigants (for example, ethylene bromide), has two naturally occurring isotopes, with mass numbers 79 and 81. Write the symbols for both, including their atomic numbers and mass numbers.

PROBLEM 3.10

Complete the following isotope symbols:

(a) $^{11}_{5}?$ (b) $^{56}_{?}Fe$ (c) $^{37}_{17}?$

3.4 The Periodic Table

Ten elements have been known since the beginning of recorded history: antimony (Sb), carbon (C), copper (Cu), gold (Au), iron (Fe), lead (Pb), mercury (Hg), silver (Ag), sulfur (S), and tin (Sn). It is worth noting that the symbols for many of these elements are derived from their Latin names, a reminder that they have been known since the time when Latin was the language used for all scholarly work. The first "new" element to be found in several thousand years was arsenic (As), discovered in about 1250. In fact, only 24 elements were known up to the time of the American Revolution in 1776.

As the pace of discovery quickened in the late 1700s and early 1800s, chemists began to look for similarities among elements that might make it possible to draw general conclusions. Particularly important was Johann Döbereiner's observation in 1829 that there were several *triads*, or groups of three elements, that appeared to have similar chemical and physical properties. For example, lithium, sodium, and potassium were all known to be silvery metals that react violently with water; chlorine, bromine, and iodine were all known to be colored nonmetals with pungent odors.

Numerous attempts were made in the mid-1800s to account for the similarities among groups of elements, but the great breakthrough came in 1869 when the Russian chemist Dmitri Mendeleev organized the elements into a forerunner of the modern periodic table, introduced previously in Section 1.6 and shown again in Figure 3.2. The table has boxes for each element that give the symbol, atomic number, and atomic weight of the element:

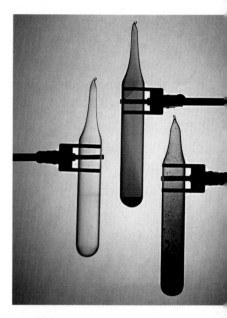

▲ Samples of chlorine, bromine, and iodine, one of Döbereiner's triads of elements with similar chemical properties.

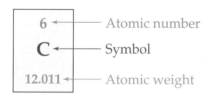

6 ← Atomic number
C ← Symbol
12.011 ← Atomic weight

Beginning at the upper left corner of the periodic table, elements are arranged by increasing atomic number into seven horizontal rows, called **periods**, and 18 vertical columns, called **groups**. When organized in this way, *the elements in a given group have similar chemical properties*. Lithium, sodium, potassium, and the other elements in group 1A behave similarly. Chlorine, bromine, iodine, and the other elements in group 7A behave similarly, and so on throughout the table.

Note that different periods (rows) contain different numbers of elements. The first period contains only 2 elements, hydrogen and helium; the second and third periods each contain 8 elements; the fourth and fifth periods each contain 18; the sixth period contains 32; and the seventh period (incomplete as yet) contains 31 elements. Note also that the 14 elements following lanthanum (the *lanthanides*) and the 14 following actinium (the *actinides*) are pulled out and shown below the others.

Groups are numbered in two ways, both shown in Figure 3.2. The two large groups on the far left and the six on the far right are called the **main group elements** and are numbered 1A through 8A. The ten smaller groups in the middle of the table are called the **transition metal elements** and are numbered 1B through 8B. Alternatively, all 18 groups are numbered sequentially from 1 to 18. The 14 groups shown separately at the bottom of the table are called the **inner transition metal elements** and are not numbered.

Period One of the 7 horizontal rows of elements in the periodic table.

Group One of the 18 vertical columns of elements in the periodic table.

Main group element An element in one of the two groups on the left or the six groups on the right of the periodic table.

Transition metal element An element in one of the 10 smaller groups near the middle of the periodic table.

Inner transition metal element An element in one of the 14 groups shown separately at the bottom of the periodic table.

Main groups

Main groups

Period	1A 1	2A 2		Transition metal groups									3A 13	4A 14	5A 15	6A 16	7A 17	8A 18
1	1 **H** 1.00794																	2 **He** 4.00260
2	3 **Li** 6.941	4 **Be** 9.01218	3B 3	4B 4	5B 5	6B 6	7B 7	— 8	8B 9	— 10	1B 11	2B 12	5 **B** 10.81	6 **C** 12.011	7 **N** 14.0067	8 **O** 15.9994	9 **F** 18.9984	10 **Ne** 20.1797
3	11 **Na** 22.98977	12 **Mg** 24.305											13 **Al** 26.98154	14 **Si** 28.0855	15 **P** 30.9738	16 **S** 32.066	17 **Cl** 35.4527	18 **Ar** 39948
4	19 **K** 39.0983	20 **Ca** 40.078	21 **Sc** 44.9559	22 **Ti** 47.88	23 **V** 50.9415	24 **Cr** 51.996	25 **Mn** 54.9380	26 **Fe** 55.847	27 **Co** 58.9332	28 **Ni** 58.69	29 **Cu** 63.546	30 **Zn** 65.39	31 **Ga** 69.72	32 **Ge** 72.61	33 **As** 74.9216	34 **Se** 78.96	35 **Br** 79.904	36 **Kr** 83.80
5	37 **Rb** 85.4678	38 **Sr** 87.62	39 **Y** 88.9059	40 **Zr** 91.224	41 **Nb** 92.9064	42 **Mo** 95.94	43 **Tc** (98)	44 **Ru** 101.07	45 **Rh** 102.9055	46 **Pd** 106.42	47 **Ag** 107.8682	48 **Cd** 112.41	49 **In** 114.82	50 **Sn** 118.710	51 **Sb** 121.757	52 **Te** 127.60	53 **I** 126.9045	54 **Xe** 131.29
6	55 **Cs** 132.9054	56 **Ba** 137.33	57 ***La** 138.9055	72 **Hf** 178.49	73 **Ta** 180.9479	74 **W** 183.85	75 **Re** 186.207	76 **Os** 190.2	77 **Ir** 192.22	78 **Pt** 195.08	79 **Au** 196.9665	80 **Hg** 200.59	81 **Tl** 204.383	82 **Pb** 207.2	83 **Bi** 208.9804	84 **Po** (209)	85 **At** (210)	86 **Rn** (222)
7	87 **Fr** (223)	88 **Ra** 226.0254	89 **†Ac** 227.0278	104 **Rf** (261)	105 **Db** (262)	106 **Sg** (266)	107 **Bh** (264)	108 **Hs** (269)	109 **Mt** (268)	110 **Ds** (271)	111 **Rg** (272)	112 (285)	113 (284)	114 (289)	115 (288)	116 (292)		118 (294)

Lanthanides

58 **Ce** 140.12	59 **Pr** 140.9077	60 **Nd** 144.24	61 **Pm** (145)	62 **Sm** 150.36	63 **Eu** 151.965	64 **Gd** 157.25	65 **Tb** 158.9254	66 **Dy** 162.50	67 **Ho** 164.9304	68 **Er** 167.26	69 **Tm** 168.9342	70 **Yb** 173.04	71 **Lu** 174.967

Actinides

90 **Th** 232.0381	91 **Pa** 231.0399	92 **U** 238.0289	93 **Np** 237.048	94 **Pu** (244)	95 **Am** (243)	96 **Cm** (247)	97 **Bk** (247)	98 **Cf** (251)	99 **Es** (252)	100 **Fm** (257)	101 **Md** (258)	102 **No** (259)	103 **Lr** (262)

Metals   Metalloids   Nonmetals

▲ **FIGURE 3.2** **The periodic table of the elements.** Each element is identified by a one- or two-letter symbol and is characterized by an *atomic number*. The table begins with hydrogen (H, atomic number 1) in the upper left-hand corner and continues to the yet unnamed element with atomic number 118. The 14 elements following lanthanum (La, atomic number 57) and the 14 elements following actinium (Ac, atomic number 89) are pulled out and shown below the others.

Elements are organized into 18 vertical columns, or *groups*, and 7 horizontal rows, or *periods*. The two groups on the left and the six on the right are the *main groups*; the ten in the middle are the *transition metal groups*. The 14 elements following lanthanum are the *lanthanides*, and the 14 elements following actinium are the *actinides*; together these are known as the *inner transition metals*. Two systems for numbering the groups are explained in the text.

Those elements (except hydrogen) on the left-hand side of the zigzag line running from boron (B) to astatine (At) are *metals*, those elements to the right of the line are *nonmetals*, and most elements abutting the line are *metalloids*.

▲ Sodium, an alkali metal, reacts violently with water to yield hydrogen gas and an alkaline (basic) solution.

PROBLEM 3.11

Locate aluminum in the periodic table, and give its group number and period number.

PROBLEM 3.12

Identify the group 1B element in period 5 and the group 2A element in period 4.

PROBLEM 3.13

There are five elements in group 5A of the periodic table. Identify them, and give the period of each.

3.5 Some Characteristics of Different Groups

To see why the periodic table has the name it does, look at the graph of atomic radius versus atomic number in Figure 3.3. The graph shows an obvious *periodicity*—a repeating, rise-and-fall pattern. Beginning on the left with atomic number 1 (hydrogen), the sizes of the atoms increase to a maximum at atomic number 3 (lithium), then decrease to a minimum, then increase again to a maximum at atomic number 11 (sodium), then decrease, and so on. It turns out that the maxima occur for atoms of group 1A elements—Li, Na, K, Rb, Cs, and Fr—and the minima occur for atoms of the group 7A elements.

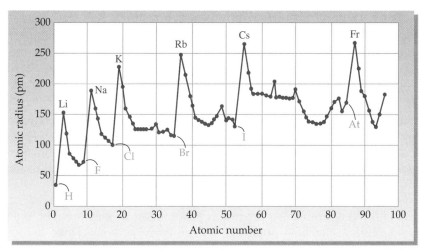

▲ **FIGURE 3.3** **A graph of atomic radius in picometers (pm) versus atomic number shows a periodic rise-and-fall pattern.** The maxima occur for atoms of the group 1A elements (Li, Na, K, Rb, Cs, Fr); the minima occur for atoms of the group 7A elements. Accurate data are not available for the group 8A elements.

There is nothing unique about the periodicity of atomic radii shown in Figure 3.3. The melting points of the first 100 elements, for example, exhibit similar periodic behavior, as shown in Figure 3.4. Many other physical and chemical properties can be plotted in a similar way with similar results. In fact, the various elements in a given group of the periodic table usually show remarkable similarities

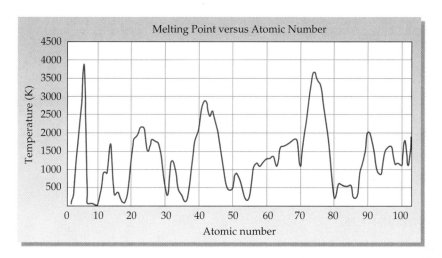

▲ **FIGURE 3.4** **A graph of melting point versus atomic number shows periodic properties similar to the trend in Figure 3.3.** While the maxima and minima are not as sharp as in Figure 3.3, the change in melting points of the elements still shows the same periodic trend.

Alkali metal An element in group 1A of the periodic table.

Alkaline earth metal An element in group 2A of the periodic table.

Halogen An element in group 7A of the periodic table.

Noble gas An element in group 8A of the periodic table.

▲ Magnesium, an alkaline earth metal, burns in air. Magnesium alloys are often used in welding rods.

▲ Chlorine, a halogen, is a toxic, corrosive green gas.

▲ Neon and other noble gases are used in neon lights, signs, and works of art.

in many of their chemical and physical properties. Look at the following four groups, for example:

- **Group 1A—Alkali metals:** Lithium (Li), sodium (Na), potassium (K), rubidium (Rb), cesium (Cs), and francium (Fr) are shiny, soft metals with low melting points. All react rapidly (often violently) with water to form products that are highly alkaline, or basic—hence the name *alkali metals*. Because of their high reactivity, the alkali metals are never found in nature in the pure state but only in combination with other elements.

- **Group 2A—Alkaline earth metals:** Beryllium (Be), magnesium (Mg), calcium (Ca), strontium (Sr), barium (Ba), and radium (Ra) are also lustrous, silvery metals, but are less reactive than their neighbors in group 1A. Like the alkali metals, the alkaline earths are never found in nature in the pure state.

- **Group 7A—Halogens:** Fluorine (F), chlorine (Cl), bromine (Br), iodine (I), and astatine (At) are colorful and corrosive nonmetals. All are found in nature only in combination with other elements, such as with sodium in table salt (sodium chloride, NaCl). In fact, the group name *halogen* is taken from the Greek word *hals*, meaning salt.

- **Group 8A—Noble gases:** Helium (He), neon (Ne), argon (Ar), krypton (Kr), xenon (Xe), and radon (Rn) are colorless gases. The elements in this group were labeled the "noble" gases because of their lack of chemical reactivity—helium, neon, and argon don't combine with any other elements, whereas krypton and xenon combine with very few.

Although the resemblances are not as pronounced as they are within a single group, *neighboring* elements often behave similarly as well. Thus, as noted in Section 1.6 and indicated in Figure 3.2, the periodic table can be divided into three major classes of elements—*metals*, *nonmetals*, and *metalloids* (metal-like). Metals, the largest category of elements, are found on the left side of the periodic table, bounded on the right by a zigzag line running from boron (B) at the top to astatine (At) at the bottom. Nonmetals are found on the right side of the periodic table, and seven of the elements adjacent to the zigzag boundary between metals and nonmetals are metalloids.

⊂⊃ Looking Ahead

Carbon, the element on which life is based, is a group 4A nonmetal near the top right of the periodic table. Clustered near carbon are other elements often found in living organisms, including oxygen, nitrogen, phosphorus, and sulfur. We will look at the subject of *organic chemistry*—the chemistry of carbon compounds—in Chapters 12–17, and move on to *biochemistry*—the chemistry of living things—in Chapters 18–29. ⊂⊃

PROBLEM 3.14

Identify the following elements as metals, nonmetals, or metalloids:

(a) Ti   (b) Te   (c) Se

(d) Sc   (e) At   (f) Ar

PROBLEM 3.15

Locate (a) krypton, (b) strontium, (c) nitrogen, and (d) cobalt in the periodic table. Indicate which categories apply to each: (i) metal, (ii) nonmetal, (iii) transition element, (iv) main group element, (v) noble gas.

APPLICATION ▶ The Origin of Chemical Elements

Astronomers believe that the universe began some 15 billion years ago in an extraordinary moment they call the "big bang." Initially, the temperature must have been inconceivably high, but after 1 second, it had dropped to about 10^{10} K and subatomic particles began to form: protons, neutrons, and electrons. After 3 minutes, the temperature had dropped to 10^9 K, and protons began fusing with neutrons to form helium nuclei, $^4_2$He.

Matter remained in this form for many millions of years until the expanding universe had cooled to about 10,000 K and electrons were then able to bind to protons and to helium nuclei, forming stable hydrogen and helium atoms.

The attractive force of gravity acting on regions of higher-than-average density slowly produced massive local concentrations of matter and ultimately formed billions of galaxies, each with many billions of stars. As the gas clouds of hydrogen and helium condensed under gravitational attraction and stars formed, their temperatures reached 10^7 K, and their densities reached 100 g/cm^3. Protons and neutrons again fused to yield helium nuclei, generating vast amounts of heat and light.

Most of these early stars probably burned out after a few billion years, but a few were so massive that, as their nuclear fuel diminished, gravitational attraction caused a rapid contraction leading to still higher core temperatures and higher densities—up to 5×10^8 K and 5×10^5 g/cm^3. Under such extreme conditions, larger nuclei were formed, including carbon, oxygen, silicon, magnesium, and iron. Ultimately, the

▲ The stars in the Milky Way galaxy condensed from gas clouds under gravitational attraction.

stars underwent a gravitational collapse resulting in the synthesis of still heavier elements and an explosion visible throughout the universe as a *supernova*.

Matter from exploding supernovas was blown throughout the galaxy, forming a new generation of stars and planets. Our own sun and solar system formed about 4.5 billion years ago from matter released by former supernovas. Except for hydrogen and helium, all the atoms in our bodies and our entire solar system were created more than five billion years ago in exploding stars. We and our world are made from the ashes of dying stars.

See Additional Problems 3.92 and 3.93 at the end of this chapter.

KEY CONCEPT PROBLEM 3.16

Identify the elements shown in red and in blue on the following periodic table. For each, tell its group number, its period number, and whether it is a metal, nonmetal, or metalloid.

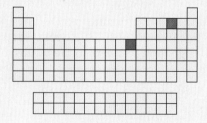

3.6 Electronic Structure of Atoms

Why does the periodic table have the shape it does, with periods of different length? Why are periodic variations observed in atomic radii and in so many other characteristics of the elements? And why do elements in a given group of the periodic table show similar chemical behavior? These questions occupied the thoughts of chemists for more than 50 years after Mendeleev, and it was not until well into the 1920s that the answers were established. Today, we know that *the properties of the elements are determined by the arrangement of electrons in their atoms.*

Our current understanding of the electronic structure of atoms is based on the now accepted *quantum mechanical model*, developed by Austrian physicist Erwin Schrödinger in 1926. Although a detailed discussion of the model is beyond the scope of this text, one of the fundamental assumptions of the model is that electrons have both particle-like and wave-like properties, and that the behavior of electrons can be described using a mathematical equation called a wave function. One consequence of this assumption is that electrons are not perfectly free to move about in an atom. Instead, each electron is restricted to moving about in only a certain region of space within the atom, depending on the energy level of the electron. Different electrons have different amounts of energy and thus occupy different regions within the atom. Furthermore, the energies of electrons are *quantized*, or restricted to having only certain values.

To understand the idea of quantization, think about the difference between stairs and a ramp. A ramp is *not* quantized because it changes height continuously. Stairs, by contrast, *are* quantized because they change height only by a fixed amount. You can climb one stair or two stairs, but you cannot climb 1.5 stairs. In the same way, the energy values available to electrons in an atom change only in steps rather than continuously.

The wave functions derived from the quantum mechanical model also provide important information about the location of electrons in an atom. Just as a person can be found by giving his or her address within a state, an electron can be found by giving its "address" within an atom. Furthermore, just as a person's address is composed of several successively narrower categories—city, street, and house number—an electron's address is also composed of successively narrower categories—*shell, subshell,* and *orbital,* which are defined by the quantum mechanical model.

The electrons in an atom are grouped around the nucleus into **shells**, roughly like the layers in an onion, according to the energy of the electrons. The farther a shell is from the nucleus, the larger it is, the more electrons it can hold, and the higher the energies of those electrons. The first shell (the one nearest the nucleus) can hold only 2 electrons, the second shell can hold 8, the third shell can hold 18, and the fourth shell can hold 32 electrons.

Shell number:	1	2	3	4
Electron capacity:	2	8	18	32

Within shells, electrons are further grouped into **subshells** of four different types, identified in order of increasing energy by the letters *s, p, d,* and *f*. The first shell has only an *s* subshell; the second shell has an *s* and a *p* subshell; the third shell has an *s*, a *p*, and a *d* subshell; and the fourth shell has an *s*, a *p*, a *d*, and an *f* subshell. Of the four types, we will be concerned mainly with *s* and *p* subshells because most of the elements found in living organisms use only these. A specific subshell is symbolized by writing the number of the shell, followed by the letter for the subshell. For example, the designation 3*p* refers to the *p* subshell in the third shell.

Shell number:	1	2	3	4
Subshell designation:	*s*	*s , p*	*s , p , d*	*s , p , d , f*

Note that the number of subshells in a given shell is equal to the shell number. For example, shell number 3 has 3 subshells.

Finally, within each subshell, electrons are grouped into **orbitals**, regions of space within an atom where the specific electrons are most likely to be found. There are different numbers of orbitals within the different kinds of subshells. A given *s* subshell has only 1 orbital, a *p* subshell has 3 orbitals, a *d* subshell has 5 orbitals, and an *f* subshell has 7 orbitals. Each orbital can hold only two electrons, which differ

▲ Stairs are *quantized* because they change height in discrete amounts. A ramp, by contrast, is not quantized because it changes height continuously.

Shell (electron) A grouping of electrons in an atom according to energy.

Subshell (electron) A grouping of electrons in a shell according to the shape of the region of space they occupy.

Orbital A region of space within an atom where an electron in a given subshell can be found.

in a property known as *spin*. If one electron in an orbital has a clockwise spin, the other electron in the same orbital must have a counterclockwise spin.

Shell number:	1	2	3	4
Subshell designation:	s	s , p	s , p , d	s , p , d , f
Number of orbitals:	1	1 , 3	1 , 3 , 5	1 , 3 , 5 , 7

Different orbitals have different shapes and orientations, which are described by the quantum mechanical model. Orbitals in s subshells are spherical regions centered about the nucleus, whereas orbitals in p subshells are roughly dumbbell-shaped regions (Figure 3.5). As shown in Figure 3.5(b), the three p orbitals in a given subshell are oriented at right angles to one another.

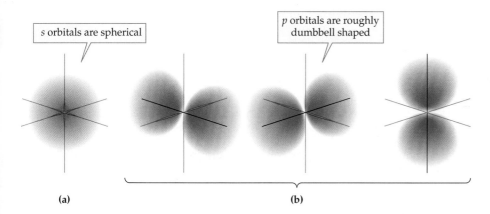

s orbitals are spherical

p orbitals are roughly dumbbell shaped

(a) (b)

▲ **FIGURE 3.5 The shapes of s and p orbitals.** (a) The s orbitals and (b) the p orbitals. The three p orbitals in a given subshell are oriented at right angles to one another. Each orbital can hold only two electrons.

The overall electron distribution within an atom is summarized in Table 3.2 and in the following list:

- The first shell holds only 2 electrons. The 2 electrons have different spins and are in a single 1s orbital.
- The second shell holds 8 electrons. Two are in a 2s orbital, and 6 are in the three different 2p orbitals (two per 2p orbital).
- The third shell holds 18 electrons. Two are in a 3s orbital, 6 are in three 3p orbitals, and 10 are in five 3d orbitals.
- The fourth shell holds 32 electrons. Two are in a 4s orbital, 6 are in three 4p orbitals, 10 are in five 4d orbitals, and 14 are in seven 4f orbitals.

TABLE 3.2 Electron Distribution in Atoms

SHELL NUMBER:	1	2	3	4
Subshell designation:	s	s , p	s , p , d	s , p , d , f
Number of orbitals:	1	1 , 3	1 , 3 , 5	1 , 3 , 5 , 7
Number of electrons:	2	2 , 6	2 , 6 , 10	2 , 6 , 10 , 14
Total electron capacity:	2	8	18	32

WORKED EXAMPLE **3.6** Atomic Structure: Electron Shells

How many electrons are present in an atom that has its first and second shells filled and has 4 electrons in its third shell? Name the element.

ANALYSIS The number of electrons in the atom is calculated by adding the total electrons in each shell. We can identify the element from the number of protons in the nucleus, which is equal to the number of electrons in the atom.

SOLUTION
The first shell of an atom holds 2 electrons in its $1s$ orbital, and the second shell holds 8 electrons (2 in a $2s$ orbital and 6 in three $2p$ orbitals). Thus, the atom has a total of $2 + 8 + 4 = 14$ electrons and must be silicon (Si).

PROBLEM 3.17

What is the maximum number of electrons that can occupy the following subshells?

(a) $3p$ subshell

(b) $2s$ subshell

(c) $2p$ subshell

PROBLEM 3.18

How many electrons are present in an atom in which the $1s$, $2s$, and $2p$ subshells are filled? Name the element.

PROBLEM 3.19

How many electrons are present in an atom in which the first and second shells and the $3s$ subshell are filled? Name the element.

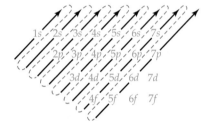

▲ Following the energy level diagram for the electronic orbitals, the orbital filling order can be predicted as indicated in this figure.

Electron configuration The specific arrangement of electrons in an atom's shells and subshells.

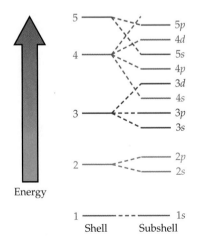

▲ **FIGURE 3.6 Order of orbital energy levels.** Above the $3p$ level, there is some crossover of energies among orbitals in different shells.

3.7 Electron Configurations

The exact arrangement of electrons in an atom's shells and subshells is called the atom's **electron configuration** and can be predicted by applying three rules:

RULE 1. **Electrons occupy the lowest-energy orbitals available, beginning with 1s and continuing in the order shown in Figure 3.6.** Within each shell, the orbital energies increase in the order s, p, d, f. The overall ordering is complicated, however, by the fact that some "crossover" of energies occurs between orbitals in different shells above the $3p$ level. The $4s$ orbital is lower in energy than the $3d$ orbitals, for example, and is therefore filled first.

8 electrons in second shell

2 electrons in first shell

2 electrons in third shell

Mg (atomic number 12): $1s^2\ 2s^2\ 2p^6\ 3s^2$

RULE 2. **Each orbital can hold only two electrons, which must be of opposite spin.**

RULE 3. **Two or more orbitals with the same energy—the three p orbitals or the five d orbitals in a given shell, for example—are each half filled by one electron before any one orbital is completely filled by addition of the second electron.**

- The first 2 electrons are placed in the 1s orbital ($1s^2$).
- The next 2 electrons are placed in the 2s orbital ($2s^2$).
- The next 6 electrons are placed in the three available 2p o
- The remaining 2 electrons are both put in the 3s orbital (3

SOLUTION

Magnesium has the configuration $1s^2\ 2s^2\ 2p^6\ 3s^2$ or [Ne] $3s^2$.

WORKED EXAMPLE **3.8** Electron Configurations: Orbital-Fill

Write the electron configuration of phosphorus, $Z = 15$, usin
arrows to show how the electrons in each orbital are paired.

ANALYSIS Phosphorus has 15 electrons, which occupy orbitals
order shown in Figure 3.6.

- The first 2 are paired and fill the first shell ($1s^2$).
- The next 8 fill the second shell ($2s^2\ 2p^6$). All electrons are
- The remaining 5 electrons enter the third shell, where 2 f
  ($3s^2$) and 3 occupy the 3p subshell, one in each of the thre

SOLUTION

$$P \quad \underset{1s^2}{\uparrow\downarrow}\ \underset{2s^2}{\uparrow\downarrow}\ \underset{\underbrace{\uparrow\downarrow\ \uparrow\downarrow\ \uparrow\downarrow}_{2p^6}}{}\ \underset{3s^2}{\uparrow\downarrow}\ \underset{\underbrace{\uparrow\ \uparrow\ \uparrow}_{3p^3}}{}$$

PROBLEM 3.20

Write electron configurations for the following elements. (You
answers in Table 3.3.)

(a) C (b) P (c) Cl (d) K

PROBLEM 3.21

Write electron configurations for the elements with atomic num

PROBLEM 3.22

For an atom containing 33 electrons, identify the incompletely
and show the paired and/or unpaired electrons in this subshe
down arrows.

KEY CONCEPT PROBLEM 3.23

Identify the atom with the following orbital-filling diagram.

$$1s^2\ 2s^2\ 2p^6\ 3s^2\ 3p^6 \quad \underset{4s}{\updownarrow} \quad \underset{3d}{\updownarrow\ \updownarrow\ \updownarrow\ \updownarrow\ \updownarrow}$$

TABLE 3.3 Electron Configurations of the First 20 Elements

	ELEMENT	ATOMIC NUMBER	ELECTRON CONFIGURATION
H	Hydrogen	1	$1s^1$
He	Helium	2	$1s^2$
Li	Lithium	3	$1s^2\ 2s^1$
Be	Beryllium	4	$1s^2\ 2s^2$
B	Boron	5	$1s^2\ 2s^2\ 2p^1$
C	Carbon	6	$1s^2\ 2s^2\ 2p^2$
N	Nitrogen	7	$1s^2\ 2s^2\ 2p^3$
O	Oxygen	8	$1s^2\ 2s^2\ 2p^4$
F	Fluorine	9	$1s^2\ 2s^2\ 2p^5$
Ne	Neon	10	$1s^2\ 2s^2\ 2p^6$
Na	Sodium	11	$1s^2\ 2s^2\ 2p^6\ 3s^1$
Mg	Magnesium	12	$1s^2\ 2s^2\ 2p^6\ 3s^2$
Al	Aluminum	13	$1s^2\ 2s^2\ 2p^6\ 3s^2\ 3p^1$
Si	Silicon	14	$1s^2\ 2s^2\ 2p^6\ 3s^2\ 3p^2$
P	Phosphorus	15	$1s^2\ 2s^2\ 2p^6\ 3s^2\ 3p^3$
S	Sulfur	16	$1s^2\ 2s^2\ 2p^6\ 3s^2\ 3p^4$
Cl	Chlorine	17	$1s^2\ 2s^2\ 2p^6\ 3s^2\ 3p^5$
Ar	Argon	18	$1s^2\ 2s^2\ 2p^6\ 3s^2\ 3p^6$
K	Potassium	19	$1s^2\ 2s^2\ 2p^6\ 3s^2\ 3p^6\ 4s^1$
Ca	Calcium	20	$1s^2\ 2s^2\ 2p^6\ 3s^2\ 3p^6\ 4s^2$

Electron configurations of the first 20 elements are shown in Table 3.3. Notice
that the number of electrons in each subshell is indicated by a superscript. For
example, the notation $1s^2\ 2s^2\ 2p^6\ 3s^2$ for magnesium means that magnesium atoms
have 2 electrons in the first shell, 8 electrons in the second shell, and 2 electrons
in the third shell.

As you read through the following electron configurations, check the atomic
number and the location of each element in the periodic table (Figure 3.2). See if you
can detect the relationship between electron configuration and position in the table.

- **Hydrogen ($Z = 1$):** The single electron in a hydrogen atom is in the lowest-energy,
  1s level. The configuration can be represented in either of two ways:

$$H \quad 1s^1 \quad \text{or} \quad \underset{1s^1}{\uparrow}$$

In the written representation, the superscript in the notation $1s^1$ means that the
1s orbital is occupied by one electron. In the graphic representation, the 1s
orbital is indicated by a line and the single electron in this orbital is shown by
an up arrow ($\uparrow$). A single electron in an orbital is often referred to as being
unpaired.

- **Helium ($Z = 2$):** The two electrons in helium are both in the lowest-energy, 1s
  orbital, and their spins are *paired*, as represented by up and down arrows ($\uparrow\downarrow$):

$$He \quad 1s^2 \quad \text{or} \quad \underset{1s^2}{\uparrow\downarrow}$$

- **Lithium ($Z = 3$):** With the first shell full, the second shell begins to fill. The third
  electron goes into the 2s orbital:

$$Li \quad 1s^2\ 2s^1 \quad \text{or} \quad \underset{1s^2}{\uparrow\downarrow}\ \underset{2s^1}{\uparrow}$$

Because [He] has the
tuted for the $1s^2$ orbi
shorthand notation, t

- **Beryllium (Z = 4):** An

                    Be

- **Boron (Z = 5), Carbon**
  the three $2p$ orbitals,
  with lines and arrows
  tion because the fillin
  p subshell is shown.

        B $1s^2 2s^2$

        C $1s^2 2s^2$

        N $1s^2 2s^2$

- **Oxygen (Z = 8), Fluor**
  one to fill the three 2

        O $1s^2 2s^2$

        F $1s^2 2s^2$

        Ne $1s^2 2s^2$

At this point we may
configuration for a co

- **Sodium to Calcium (**
  is seen again for sodi
  shells fill up. For eler
  sent a completely fil
  in subshell energies o
  energy than the $3d$ su
  (Z = 20) therefore ha

  K $1s^2 2s^2 2p^6 3s^2 3p$

Show how the electron

ANALYSIS Magnesium,
Assignments are made
order shown in Figure

s-Block element A main group
element that results from the filling
of an s orbital.

p-Block element A main group
element that results from the filling
of p orbitals.

d-Block element A transition
metal element that results from the
filling of d orbitals.

f-Block element An inner transition metal element that results from
the filling of f orbitals.

► **FIGURE 3.7 The blocks of elements in the periodic table correspond to filling the different types
of subshells.** Beginning at the top
left and going across successive
rows of the periodic table provides a
method for remembering the order of
orbital filling: $1s \rightarrow 2s \rightarrow 2p \rightarrow 3s \rightarrow$
$3p \rightarrow 4s \rightarrow 3d \rightarrow 4p$, and so on.

3.8 Electron Configurations and the Periodic Table

How is an atom's electron configuration related to its chemical behavior, and why
do elements with similar behavior occur in the same group of the periodic table? As
shown in Figure 3.7, the periodic table can be divided into four regions, or *blocks*,
of elements according to the electron shells and subshells occupied by *the subshell
filled last*.

- The main group 1A and 2A elements on the left side of the table (plus He) are
  called the **s-block elements** because an s subshell is filled last in these elements.
- The main group 3A–8A elements on the right side of the table (except He) are
  the **p-block elements** because a p subshell is filled last in these elements.
- The transition metals in the middle of the table are the **d-block elements**
  because a d subshell is filled last in these elements.
- The inner transition metals detached at the bottom of the table are the **f-block
  elements** because an f subshell is filled last in these elements.

Thinking of the periodic table as outlined in Figure 3.7 provides a simple way to
remember the order of orbital filling shown previously in Figure 3.6. Beginning at
the top left corner of the periodic table, the first row contains only two elements (H
and He) because only two electrons are required to fill the s orbital in the first shell,
$1s^2$. The second row begins with two s-block elements (Li and Be) and continues
with six p-block elements (B through Ne), so electrons fill the next available s orbital
($2s$) and then the first available p orbitals ($2p$). The third row is similar to the second
row, so the $3s$ and $3p$ orbitals are filled next. The fourth row again starts with two
s-block elements (K and Ca) but is then followed by ten d-block elements (Sc
through Zn) and six p-block elements (Ga through Kr). Thus, the order of orbital
filling is $4s$ followed by the first available d orbitals ($3d$) followed by $4p$. Continuing
through successive rows of the periodic table gives the entire filling order, identical
to that shown in Figure 3.6.

$$1s \rightarrow 2s \rightarrow 2p \rightarrow 3s \rightarrow 3p \rightarrow 4s \rightarrow 3d \rightarrow 4p \rightarrow 5s \rightarrow$$
$$4d \rightarrow 5p \rightarrow 6s \rightarrow 4f \rightarrow 5d \rightarrow 6p \rightarrow 7s \rightarrow 5f \rightarrow 6d$$

But why do the elements in a given group of the periodic table have similar
properties? The answer emerges when you look at Table 3.4, which gives electron

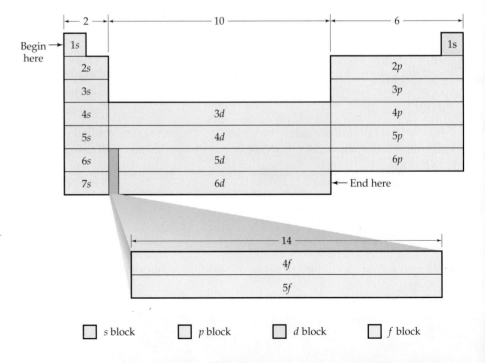

TABLE 3.4 Valence-Shell Electron Configurations for Group 1A, 2A, 7A, and 8A Elements

GROUP	ELEMENT	ATOMIC NUMBER	VALENCE-SHELL ELECTRON CONFIGURATION
1A	Li (lithium)	3	$2s^1$
	Na (sodium)	11	$3s^1$
	K (potassium)	19	$4s^1$
	Rb (rubidium)	37	$5s^1$
	Cs (cesium)	55	$6s^1$
2A	Be (beryllium)	4	$2s^2$
	Mg (magnesium)	12	$3s^2$
	Ca (calcium)	20	$4s^2$
	Sr (strontium)	38	$5s^2$
	Ba (barium)	56	$6s^2$
7A	F (fluorine)	9	$2s^2\,2p^5$
	Cl (chlorine)	17	$3s^2\,3p^5$
	Br (bromine)	35	$4s^2\,4p^5$
	I (iodine)	53	$5s^2\,5p^5$
8A	He (helium)	2	$1s^2$
	Ne (neon)	10	$2s^2\,2p^6$
	Ar (argon)	18	$3s^2\,3p^6$
	Kr (krypton)	36	$4s^2\,4p^6$
	Xe (xenon)	54	$5s^2\,5p^6$

configurations for elements in the main groups 1A, 2A, 7A, and 8A. Focusing only on the electrons in the outermost shell, or **valence shell**, *elements in the same group of the periodic table have similar electron configurations in their valence shells.* The group 1A elements, for example, all have one **valence electron**, ns^1 (where n represents the number of the valence shell: $n = 2$ for Li; $n = 3$ for Na; $n = 4$ for K; and so on). The group 2A elements have two valence electrons (ns^2); the group 7A elements have seven valence electrons ($ns^2\,np^5$); and the group 8A elements (except He) have eight valence electrons ($ns^2\,np^6$). You might also notice that the group numbers from 1A through 8A give the numbers of valence electrons for the elements in each main group.

What is true for the main group elements is also true for the other groups in the periodic table: Atoms within a given group have the same number of valence electrons and have similar electron configurations. *Because the valence electrons are the most loosely held, they are the most important in determining an element's properties.* Similar electron configurations thus explain why the elements in a given group of the periodic table have similar chemical behavior.

Valence shell   The outermost electron shell of an atom.

Valence electron   An electron in the valence shell of an atom.

⊂▢⊃ Looking Ahead

We have seen that elements in a given group have similar chemical behavior because they have similar valence electron configurations, and that many chemical properties exhibit periodic trends across the periodic table. The *chemical* behavior of nearly all the elements can be predicted based on their position in the periodic table, and will be examined in more detail in Chapters 4–6. Similarly, the *nuclear* behavior of the different isotopes of a given element is related to the configuration of the nucleus (that is, the number of neutrons and protons), and will be examined in Chapter 11.

⊂▢⊃

3.62 Americium, atomic number 95, is used in household smoke detectors. What is the symbol for americium? Is americium a metal, a nonmetal, or a metalloid?

3.63 Antimony, Z = 51, is alloyed with lead for use in automobile batteries. What is the symbol for antimony? Is antimony a metal, a nonmetal, or a metalloid?

3.64 Answer the following questions for the elements from scandium through zinc:

(a) Are they metals or nonmetals?
(b) To what general class of elements do they belong?
(c) What subshell is being filled by electrons in these elements?

3.65 Answer the following questions for the elements from cerium through lutetium:

(a) Are they metals or nonmetals?
(b) To what general class of elements do they belong?
(c) What subshell is being filled by electrons in these elements?

3.66 For (a) rubidium (b) tungsten, (c) germanium, and (d) krypton, which of the following terms apply? (i) metal, (ii) nonmetal, (iii) metalloid (iv) transition element, (v) main group element, (vi) noble gas, (vii) alkali metal, (viii) alkaline earth metal

3.67 For (a) calcium, (b) palladium, (c) carbon, and (d) radon, which of the following terms apply? (i) metal, (ii) nonmetal, (iii) metalloid (iv) transition element, (v) main group element, (vi) noble gas, (vii) alkali metal, (viii) alkaline earth metal

3.68 Name an element in the periodic table that you would expect to be chemically similar to sulfur.

3.69 Name an element in the periodic table that you would expect to be chemically similar to magnesium

3.70 What elements in addition to lithium make up the alkali metal family?

3.71 What elements in addition to fluorine make up the halogen family?

ELECTRON CONFIGURATIONS

3.72 What is the maximum number of electrons that can go into an orbital?

3.73 What are the shapes and locations within an atom of s and p orbitals?

3.74 What is the maximum number of electrons that can go into the first shell? The second shell? The third shell?

3.75 What is the total number of orbitals in the third shell? The fourth shell?

3.76 How many subshells are there in the third shell? The fourth shell? The fifth shell?

3.77 How many orbitals would you expect to find in the last subshell of the fifth shell? How many electrons would you need to fill this subshell?

3.78 How many electrons are present in an atom with its $1s$, $2s$, and $2p$ subshells filled? What is this element?

3.79 How many electrons are present in an atom with its $1s$, $2s$, $2p$, and $3s$ subshells filled and with two electrons in the $3p$ subshell? What is this element?

3.80 Use arrows to show electron pairing in the valence p subshell of:

(a) Sulfur
(b) Bromine
(c) Silicon

3.81 Use arrows to show electron pairing in the $5s$ and $4d$ orbitals of:

(a) Strontium
(b) Technetium
(c) Palladium

3.82 Determine the number of unpaired electrons for each of the atoms in Problems 3.80 and 3.81.

3.83 Without looking back in the text, write the electron configurations for the following:

(a) Calcium, Z = 20
(b) Sulfur, Z = 16
(c) Fluorine, Z = 9
(d) Cadmium, Z = 48

3.84 How many electrons does the element with Z = 12 have in its valence shell? Write the electron-dot symbol for this element.

3.85 How many valence electrons do group 4A elements have? Explain. Write a generic electron-dot symbol for elements in this group.

3.86 Identify the valence subshell occupied by electrons in beryllium and arsenic atoms.

3.87 What group in the periodic table has the valence-shell configuration $ns^2\,np^3$?

3.88 Give the number of valence electrons and draw electron-dot symbols for atoms of the following elements:

(a) Kr   (b) C
(c) Ca   (d) K
(e) B   (f) Cl

3.89 Using n for the number of the valence shell, write a general valence-shell configuration for the elements in group 7A and in group 1A.

Applications

3.90 What is the advantage of using a scanning tunneling microscope rather than a normal light microscope? [*Are Atoms Real? p. 52*]

3.91 Before Rutherford's experiments, atomic structure was represented using a *"plum pudding" model* proposed by Thomson, in which negatively charged electrons were embedded in diffuse, positively charged matter like raisins in plum pudding. How might Rutherford's experimental results have been different if this model were correct? [*Are Atoms Real? p. 52*]

3.92 What are the first two elements that are made in stars? [*The Origin of Chemical Elements, p. 61*]

3.93 How are elements heavier than iron made? [*The Origin of Chemical Elements, p. 61*]

3.94 Which type of electromagnetic energy in the following pairs is of higher energy? [*Atoms and Light, p. 72*]

(a) Infrared, ultraviolet
(b) Gamma waves, microwaves
(c) Visible light, X rays

3.95 Why do you suppose ultraviolet rays from the sun are more damaging to the skin than visible light? [*Atoms and Light*, p. 72]

General Questions and Problems

3.96 What elements in addition to helium make up the noble gas family?

3.97 Hydrogen is placed in group 1A on many periodic charts, even though it is not an alkali metal. On other periodic charts, however, hydrogen is included with group 7A even though it is not a halogen. Explain. (Hint: draw electron-dot symbols for H and for the 1A and 7A elements.)

3.98 Tellurium ($Z = 52$) has a *lower* atomic number than iodine ($Z = 53$), yet it has a *higher* atomic weight (127.60 amu for Te versus 126.90 amu for I). How is this possible?

3.99 What is the atomic number of the yet undiscovered element directly below francium (Fr) in the periodic table?

3.100 Give the number of electrons in each shell for lead.

3.101 Identify the highest-energy occupied subshell in atoms of the following elements:

(a) Argon
(b) Magnesium
(c) Technetium
(d) Iron

3.102 What is the atomic weight of naturally occurring bromine, which contains 50.69% Br-79 of mass 78.92 amu and 49.31% Br-81 of mass 80.91 amu?

3.103 Naturally occurring magnesium consists of three isotopes: 78.99% ^{24}Mg with a mass of 23.99 amu, 10.00% ^{25}Mg with a mass of 24.99 amu, and 11.01% ^{26}Mg with a mass of 25.98 amu. Calculate the atomic weight of magnesium.

3.104 If you had one atom of hydrogen and one atom of carbon, which would weigh more? Explain.

3.105 If you had a pile of 10^{23} hydrogen atoms and another pile of 10^{23} carbon atoms, which of the two piles would weigh more? (See Problem 3.104.)

3.106 If your pile of hydrogen atoms in Problem 3.105 weighed about 1 gram, how much would your pile of carbon atoms weigh?

3.107 Based on your answer to Problem 3.106, how much would you expect a pile of 10^{23} sodium atoms to weigh?

3.108 An unidentified element is found to have an electron configuration by shell of 2 8 18 8 2. To what group and period does this element belong? Is the element a metal or a non-metal? How many protons does an atom of the element have? What is the name of the element? Write its electron-dot symbol.

3.109 Germanium, atomic number 32, is used in building semiconductors for microelectronic devices. If germanium, has an electron configuration by shell of 2 8 18 4, in what orbital are the valence electrons?

3.110 Tin, atomic number 50, is directly beneath germanium (Problem 3.109) in the periodic table. What electron configuration by shell would you expect tin to have? Is tin a metal or a nonmetal?

3.111 A blood sample is found to contain 8.6 mg/dL of Ca. How many atoms of Ca are present in 8.6 mg? The atomic weight of Ca is 40.08 amu.

3.112 What is wrong with the following electron configurations?

(a) Ni $1s^2\ 2s^2\ 2p^6\ 3s^2\ 3p^6\ 3d^{10}$
(b) N $1s^2\ 2p^5$

(c) Si $1s^2\ 2s^2\ 2p\ \underline{\uparrow\downarrow}\ \underline{\ \ }\ \underline{\ \ }$

(d) Mg $1s^2\ 2s^2\ 2p^6\ 3s\ \underline{\uparrow\uparrow}$

3.113 Not all elements follow exactly the electron-filling order described in Figure 3.7. Atoms of which elements are represented by the following electron configurations? (Hint: count the total number of electrons!)

(a) $1s^2\ 2s^2\ 2p^6\ 3s^2\ 3p^6\ 3d^5\ 4s^1$
(b) $1s^2\ 2s^2\ 2p^6\ 3s^2\ 3p^6\ 3d^{10}\ 4s^1$
(c) $1s^2\ 2s^2\ 2p^6\ 3s^2\ 3p^6\ 3d^{10}\ 4s^2\ 4p^6\ 4d^5\ 5s^1$
(d) $1s^2\ 2s^2\ 2p^6\ 3s^2\ 3p^6\ 3d^{10}\ 4s^2\ 4p^6\ 4d^{10}\ 5s^1$

3.114 What similarities do you see in the electron configurations for the atoms in Problem 3.113? How might these similarities explain their anomalous electron configurations?

3.115 What orbital is filled last in the yet undiscovered element 117?

CHAPTER 4

Ionic Compounds

CONCEPTS TO REVIEW

The Periodic Table
(Sections 3.4 and 3.5)

Electron Configurations
(Sections 3.7 and 3.8)

▲ Stalagmites and stalactites, such as these in a cave in the Nangu Stone Forest in China, are composed of the ionic compounds calcium carbonate, $CaCO_3$, and magnesium carbonate, $MgCO_3$.

CONTENTS

CHAPTER GOALS

We will answer the following questions in this chapter:

1. What is an ion, what is an ionic bond, and what are the general characteristics of ionic compounds?

THE GOAL: Be able to describe ions and ionic bonds, and give the general properties of compounds that contain ionic bonds.

2. What is the octet rule, and how does it apply to ions?

THE GOAL: Be able to state the octet rule and use it to predict the electron configurations of ions of main group elements.

3. What is the relationship between an element's position in the periodic table and the formation of its ion?

THE GOAL: Be able to predict what ions are likely to be formed by atoms of a given element.

4. What determines the chemical formula of an ionic compound?

THE GOAL: Be able to write formulas for ionic compounds, given the identities of the ions.

5. How are ionic compounds named?

THE GOAL: Be able to name an ionic compound from its formula or give the formula of a compound from its name.

6. What are acids and bases?

THE GOAL: Be able to recognize common acids and bases.

There are more than 19 million known chemical compounds, ranging in size from small *diatomic* (two-atom) substances like carbon monoxide, CO, to deoxyribonucleic acid (DNA), which can contain several *billion* atoms linked together in a precise way. Clearly, there must be some force that holds atoms together in compounds; otherwise, the atoms would simply drift apart and no compounds could exist. The forces that hold atoms together are called *chemical bonds* and are of two major types: *ionic bonds* and *covalent bonds*. In this chapter, we look at ionic bonds and at the substances formed by them. In the next chapter, we will look at covalent bonds.

All chemical bonds result from the electrical attraction between opposite charges—between positively charged nuclei and negatively charged electrons. As a result, the way in which different elements form bonds is related to their different electron configurations.

4.1 Ions

A general rule noted by early chemists is that metals, on the left side of the periodic table, tend to form compounds with nonmetals, on the right side of the table. The alkali metals of group 1A, for instance, react with the halogens of group 7A to form a variety of compounds. Sodium chloride (table salt), formed by the reaction of sodium with chlorine, is a familiar example. The names and chemical formulas of some other compounds containing elements from groups 1A and 7A include:

Potassium iodide, KI — Added to table salt to provide iodide ion needed by the thyroid gland

Sodium fluoride, NaF — Added to many municipal water supplies to provide fluoride ion for the prevention of tooth decay

Sodium iodide, NaI — Used in laboratory scintillation counters to detect radiation (See Section 11.8)

Both the compositions and the properties of these alkali metal–halogen compounds are similar. For instance, the two elements always combine in a 1:1 ratio: one alkali metal atom for every halogen atom. Each compound has a high melting point (all are over 500 °C); each is a stable, white, crystalline solid; and each is soluble in water. Furthermore, the water solution of each compound conducts electricity, a property that gives a clue to the kind of chemical bond holding the atoms together.

Electricity can flow only through a medium containing charged particles that are free to move. The electrical conductivity of metals, for example, results from the

▲ A solution of sodium chloride in water conducts electricity, allowing the bulb to light.

movement of negatively charged electrons through the metal. But what charged particles might be present in the water solutions of alkali metal–halogen compounds? To answer this question, think about the composition of atoms. Atoms are electrically neutral because they contain equal numbers of protons and electrons. By gaining or losing one or more electrons, however, an atom can be converted into a charged particle called an **ion**.

The *loss* of one or more electrons from a neutral atom gives a *positively* charged ion called a **cation** (cat-ion). As we saw in Section 3.8, sodium and other alkali metal atoms have a single electron in their valence shell and an electron configuration symbolized as ns^1, where n represents the shell number. By losing this electron, an alkali metal is converted to a cation.

Ion An electrically charged atom or group of atoms.

Cation A positively charged ion.

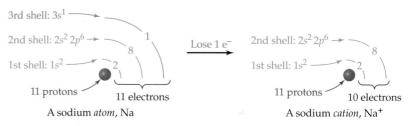

Conversely, the *gain* of one or more electrons by a neutral atom gives a *negatively* charged ion called an **anion** (an-ion). Chlorine and other halogen atoms have $ns^2 np^5$ valence electrons and can easily gain an additional electron to fill out their valence subshell, thereby forming anions.

Anion A negatively charged ion.

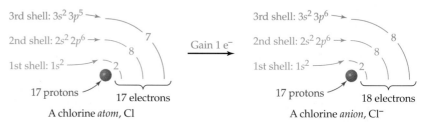

The symbol for a cation is written by adding the positive charge as a superscript to the symbol for the element; an anion symbol is written by adding the negative charge as a superscript. If one electron is lost or gained, the charge is $+1$ or -1 but the number 1 is omitted in the notation, as in Na^+ and Cl^-. If two or more electrons are lost or gained, however, the charge is ±2 or greater and the number *is* used, as in Ca^{2+} and N^{3-}.

PROBLEM 4.1

Magnesium atoms lose two electrons when they react. Write the symbol of the ion that results. Is it a cation or an anion?

PROBLEM 4.2

Sulfur atoms gain two electrons when they react. Write the symbol of the ion that results. Is it a cation or an anion?

⬤ KEY CONCEPT PROBLEM 4.3

Write the symbol for the ion depicted here. Is it a cation or an anion?

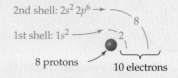

4.2 Periodic Properties and Ion Formation

The ease with which an atom loses an electron to form a positively charged cation is measured by a property called the atom's **ionization energy**, defined as the energy required to remove one electron from a single atom in the gaseous state. Conversely, the ease with which an atom *gains* an electron to form a negatively charged anion is measured by a property called **electron affinity**, defined as the energy released on adding an electron to a single atom in the gaseous state.

Ionization energy
(energy is added)   Atom + Energy ⟶ Cation + Electron

Electron affinity
(energy is released)   Atom + Electron ⟶ Anion + Energy

> **Ionization energy** The energy required to remove one electron from a single atom in the gaseous state.
>
> **Electron affinity** The energy released on adding an electron to a single atom in the gaseous state.

The relative magnitudes of ionization energies and electron affinities for elements in the first four rows of the periodic table are shown in Figure 4.1. Because ionization energy measures the amount of energy that must be *added* to pull an electron away from a neutral atom, the small values shown in Figure 4.1 for alkali metals (Li, Na, K) and other elements on the left side of the periodic table mean that these elements lose an electron easily. Conversely, the large values shown for halogens (F, Cl, Br) and noble gases (He, Ne, Ar, Kr) on the right side of the periodic table mean that these elements do not lose an electron easily. Electron affinities, however, measure the amount of energy *released* when an atom gains an electron. Although electron affinities are small compared to ionization energies, the halogens nevertheless have the largest values and therefore gain an electron most easily, whereas metals have the smallest values and do not gain an electron easily:

Alkali metal
{
Small ionization energy—electron easily lost
Small electron affinity—electron not easily gained
Net result: Cation formation is favored.
}

Halogen
{
Large ionization energy—electron not easily lost
Large electron affinity—electron easily gained
Net result: Anion formation is favored.
}

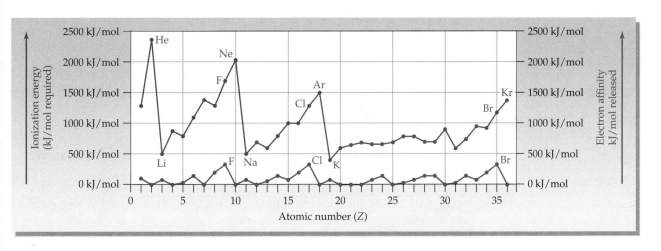

▲ **FIGURE 4.1** **Relative ionization energies (red) and electron affinities (blue) for elements in the first four rows of the periodic table.** Those elements having a value of zero for electron affinity do not accept an electron. Note that the alkali metals (Li, Na, K) have the lowest ionization energies and lose an electron most easily, whereas the halogens (F, Cl, Br) have the highest electron affinities and gain an electron most easily. The noble gases (He, Ne, Ar, Kr) neither gain nor lose an electron easily.

You might also note in Figure 4.1 that main group elements near the *middle* of the periodic table—boron (Z = 5), carbon (Z = 6, group 4A), and nitrogen (Z = 7, group 5A)—neither lose nor gain electrons easily and thus do not form ions easily. In the next chapter, we will see that these elements tend not to form ionic bonds but form covalent bonds instead.

Because alkali metals such as sodium tend to lose an electron, and halogens such as chlorine tend to gain an electron, these two elements (sodium and chlorine) will react with each other by transfer of an electron from the metal to the halogen (Figure 4.2). The product that results—sodium chloride (NaCl)—is electrically neutral because the positive charge of each Na^+ ion is balanced by the negative charge of each Cl^- ion.

▶ **FIGURE 4.2** (a) Chlorine is a toxic green gas, sodium is a reactive metal, and sodium chloride is a harmless white solid. (b) Sodium metal burns with an intense yellow flame when immersed in chlorine gas, yielding white sodium chloride "smoke."

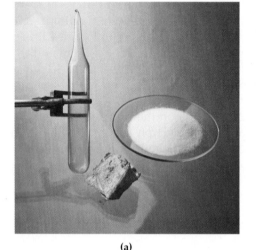

(a)

(b)

WORKED EXAMPLE   **4.1** Periodic Trends: Ionization Energy

Look at the periodic trends in Figure 4.1, and predict where the ionization energy of rubidium is likely to fall on the chart.

ANALYSIS Identify the group number of rubidium (group 1A), and find where other members of the group appear in Figure 4.1.

SOLUTION
Rubidium (Rb) is the alkali metal below potassium (K) in the periodic table. Since the alkali metals Li, Na, and K all have ionization energies near the bottom of the chart, the ionization energy of rubidium is probably similar.

WORKED EXAMPLE   **4.2** Periodic Trends: Formation of Anions and Cations

Which element is likely to lose an electron more easily, Mg or S?

ANALYSIS Identify the group numbers of the elements, and find where members of those groups appear in Figure 4.1.

SOLUTION
Magnesium, a group 2A element on the left side of the periodic table, has a relatively low ionization energy, and loses an electron easily. Sulfur, a group 6A element on the right side of the table, has a higher ionization energy, and loses an electron less easily.

PROBLEM 4.4

Look at the periodic trends in Figure 4.1, and predict approximately where the ionization energy of xenon is likely to fall.

PROBLEM 4.5

Which element in the following pairs is likely to lose an electron more easily?

(a) Be or B   **(b)** Ca or Co   **(c)** Sc or Se

PROBLEM 4.6

Which element in the following pairs is likely to gain an electron more easily?

(a) H or He   **(b)** S or Si   **(c)** Cr or Mn

4.3 Ionic Bonds

When sodium reacts with chlorine, the product is sodium chloride, a compound completely unlike either of the elements from which it is formed. Sodium is a soft, silvery metal that reacts violently with water, and chlorine is a corrosive, poisonous, green gas (Figure 4.2a). When chemically combined, however, they produce our familiar table salt containing Na^+ ions and Cl^- ions. Because opposite electrical charges attract each other, the positive Na^+ ion and negative Cl^- ion are said to be held together by an **ionic bond**.

When a vast number of sodium atoms transfer electrons to an equally vast number of chlorine atoms, a visible crystal of sodium chloride results. In this crystal, equal numbers of Na^+ and Cl^- ions are packed together in a regular arrangement. Each positively charged Na^+ ion is surrounded by six negatively charged Cl^- ions, and each Cl^- ion is surrounded by six Na^+ ions (Figure 4.3). This packing arrangement allows each ion to be stabilized by the attraction of unlike charges on its six nearest-neighbor ions, while being as far as possible from ions of like charge.

Because of the three-dimensional arrangement of ions in a sodium chloride crystal, we cannot speak of specific ionic bonds between specific pairs of ions. Rather, there are many ions attracted by ionic bonds to their nearest neighbors. We therefore speak of the whole NaCl crystal as being an **ionic solid** and of such compounds as being **ionic compounds**. The same is true of all compounds composed of ions.

Ionic bond The electrical attractions between ions of opposite charge in a crystal.

Ionic solid A crystalline solid held together by ionic bonds.

Ionic compound A compound that contains ionic bonds.

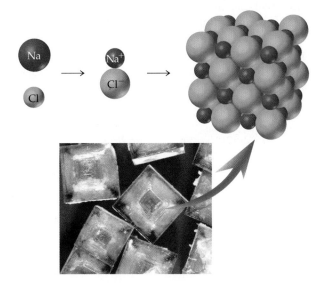

◀ **FIGURE 4.3 The arrangement of Na^+ and Cl^- ions in a sodium chloride crystal.** Each positively charged Na^+ ion is surrounded by six negatively charged Cl^- ions, and each Cl^- ion is surrounded by six Na^+ ions. The crystal is held together by ionic bonds—the attraction between oppositely charged ions.

▲ The melting point of sodium chloride is 801 °C.

4.4 Some Properties of Ionic Compounds

Like sodium chloride, ionic compounds are usually crystalline solids. Different ions vary in size and charge, however, and therefore are packed together in crystals in different ways. The ions in each compound settle into a pattern that efficiently fills space and maximizes ionic bonding.

Because the ions in an ionic solid are held rigidly in place by attraction to their neighbors, they cannot move about. Once an ionic solid is dissolved in water, however, the ions can move freely, thereby accounting for the electrical conductivity of these compounds in solution.

The high melting points and boiling points observed for ionic compounds are also accounted for by ionic bonding. The attractive force between oppositely charged particles is extremely strong, and the ions need to gain a large amount of energy by being heated to high temperatures for them to loosen their grip on one another. Sodium chloride, for example, melts at 801 °C and boils at 1413 °C; potassium iodide melts at 681 °C and boils at 1330 °C.

Despite the strength of ionic bonds, ionic solids shatter if struck sharply. A blow disrupts the orderly arrangement of cations and anions, and the electrical repulsion between ions of like charge that have been pushed together helps to split apart the crystal.

Ionic compounds dissolve in water if the attraction between water and the ions overcomes the attraction of the ions for one another. Compounds like sodium chloride are very soluble and can be dissolved to make solutions of high concentration. Do not be misled, however, by the ease with which sodium chloride and other familiar ionic compounds dissolve in water. Many other ionic compounds are not water-soluble, because water is unable to overcome the ionic forces in many crystals.

4.5 Ions and the Octet Rule

We have seen that alkali metal atoms have a single valence-shell electron, ns^1. The electron-dot symbol X· is consistent with this valence electron configuration. Halogens, having seven valence electrons, ns^2np^5, can be represented using :X· as the electron-dot symbol. Noble gases can be represented as :X:, since they have eight valence electrons, ns^2np^6. Both the alkali metals and the halogens are extremely reactive, undergoing many chemical reactions and forming many compounds. The noble gases, however, are quite different. They are the least reactive of all elements.

Now look at sodium chloride and similar ionic compounds. When sodium or any other alkali metal reacts with chlorine or any other halogen, the metal transfers an electron from its valence shell to the valence shell of the halogen. Sodium thereby changes its valence-shell electron configuration from $2s^22p^63s^1$ in the atom to $2s^22p^6(3s^0)$ in the Na$^+$ ion, and chlorine changes from $3s^23p^5$ in the atom to $3s^23p^6$ in the Cl$^-$ ion. *In so doing, both sodium and chlorine gain noble gas electron configurations, with 8 valence electrons.* The Na$^+$ ion has 8 electrons in the $n = 2$ shell, matching the electron configuration of neon. The Cl$^-$ ion has 8 electrons in the $n = 3$ shell, matching the electron configuration of argon.

$$\underset{1s^2\,2s^2\,2p^6\,3s^1}{\text{Na}} \quad + \quad \underset{1s^2\,2s^2\,2p^6\,3s^2\,3p^5}{\text{Cl}} \quad \longrightarrow \quad \underset{\substack{1s^2\,2s^2\,2p^63s^0 \\ \text{Neon} \\ \text{configuration}}}{\text{Na}^+} \quad + \quad \underset{\substack{1s^2\,2s^2\,2p^6\,3s^2\,3p^6 \\ \text{Argon} \\ \text{configuration}}}{\text{Cl}^-}$$

$$\text{Na}^\bullet \quad + \quad {\cdot}\overset{\cdots}{\underset{\cdots}{\text{Cl}}}{:} \quad \longrightarrow \quad \text{Na} \quad + \quad {:}\overset{\cdots}{\underset{\cdots}{\text{Cl}}}{:}$$

Evidently there is something special about having 8 valence electrons (filled s and p subshells) that leads to stability and lack of chemical reactivity. In fact,

APPLICATION ▶ Minerals and Gems

If you are wearing a sapphire, ruby, emerald, or zircon ring, you have a crystalline ionic compound on your finger. The gem came from the earth's crust, the source of most of our chemical raw materials. These gemstones are *minerals*, which to a geologist means that they are naturally occurring, crystalline chemical compounds. (To a nutritionist, by contrast, a "mineral" is one of the metal ions essential to human health.)

Sapphire and ruby are forms of the mineral *corundum*, or aluminum oxide (Al_2O_3). The blue of sapphire is due to traces of iron and titanium ions also present in the crystal, and the red of ruby is due to traces of chromium ions. Many minerals are *silicates*, meaning that their anions contain silicon and

oxygen combined in a variety of ways. Zircon is zirconium silicate ($ZrSiO_4$), and emerald is a form of the mineral beryl, $Be_3Al_2(Si_6O_{18})$, which is composed of Al^{3+}, Be^{2+}, and silicate rings.

Many minerals not sufficiently beautiful for use in jewelry are valuable as sources for the exotic metals so essential to our industrial civilization. Extraction of the metals from these minerals requires energy and a series of chemical reactions to convert the metal ions into free elements—the reverse of ion formation from atoms.

See Additional Problem 4.82 at the end of the chapter.

(a)

(b)

(c)

▲ Many minerals are silicates, which are compounds made up of polyatomic anions of silicon and oxygen. Their colors are determined largely by the cations they contain. (a) A crystal of tourmaline, a complex silicate of boron, aluminum, and other elements. (b) Dioptase from Namibia and (c) epidote from Pakistan.

observations of a great many chemical compounds have shown that main group elements frequently combine in such a way that each winds up with 8 valence electrons, a so-called *electron octet*. This conclusion is summarized in a statement called the **octet rule**:

> **Octet rule**   Main group elements tend to undergo reactions that leave them with 8 valence electrons.

Put another way, main group *metals* tend to lose electrons when they react so that they attain an electron configuration like that of the noble gas just *before* them in the periodic table, and reactive main group *nonmetals* tend to gain electrons when they react so that they attain an electron configuration like that of the noble gas just *after* them in the periodic table. In both cases, the product ions have filled *s* and *p* subshells in their valence electron shell.

lose one or more *d* electrons in addition to losing valence *s* electrons. For example, iron ($\ldots 3s^2 3p^6 3d^6 4s^2$) forms Fe^{2+} by losing two electrons from the $4s$ subshell and also forms Fe^{3+} by losing an additional electron from the $3d$ subshell. Looking at the iron configuration shows why the octet rule is limited to main group elements: Transition metal cations generally do not have noble gas configurations because they would have to lose *all* their *d* electrons.

Important Points about Ion Formation and the Periodic Table:

- Metals form cations by losing one or more electrons.
  - Group 1A and 2A metals form +1 and +2 ions, respectively (for example, Li^+ and Mg^{2+}) to achieve a noble gas configuration.
  - Transition metals can form cations of more than one charge (for example, Fe^{2+} and Fe^{3+}) by losing a combination of valence-shell *s* electrons and inner-shell *d* electrons.
- Reactive nonmetals form anions by gaining one or more electrons to achieve a noble gas configuration.
  - Group 6A nonmetals oxygen and sulfur form the anions O^{2-} and S^{2-}.
  - Group 7A elements (the halogens) form -1 ions; for example, F^- and Cl^-.
- Group 8A elements (the noble gases) are unreactive.
- Ionic charges of main group elements can be predicted using the group number and the octet rule.
  - For 1A and 2A metals, cation charge = group number
  - For nonmetals in groups 5A, 6A, and 7A, anion charge = 8 − (group number)

WORKED EXAMPLE **4.5** Formation of Ions: Gain/Loss of Valence Electrons

Which of the following ions is likely to form?

(a) S^{3-} (b) Si^{2+} (c) Sr^{2+}

ANALYSIS Count the number of valence electrons in each ion. For main group elements, only ions with a valence octet of electrons are likely to form.

SOLUTION

(a) Sulfur is in group 6A, has 6 valence electrons, and needs only two more to reach an octet. Gaining two electrons gives an S^{2-} ion with a noble gas configuration, but gaining three electrons does not. The S^{3-} ion is therefore unlikely to form.

(b) Silicon is a nonmetal in group 4A. Like carbon, it does not form ions because it would have to gain or lose too many (4) electrons to reach a noble gas electron configuration. The Si^{2+} ion does not have an octet and will not form.

(c) Strontium is a metal in group 2A, has only 2 outer-shell electrons, and can lose both to reach a noble gas configuration. The Sr^{2+} ion has an octet and therefore forms easily.

PROBLEM 4.10

Is molybdenum more likely to form a cation or an anion? Why?

PROBLEM 4.11

Which of the following elements can form more than one cation?

(a) Strontium   (b) Chromium   (c) Bromine

PROBLEM 4.12

Write symbols, both with and without electron dots, for the ions formed by the following processes:

(a) Gain of two electrons by selenium

(b) Loss of two electrons by barium

(c) Gain of one electron by bromine

APPLICATION ▶ Salt

I f you are like most people, you feel a little guilty about reaching for the salt shaker at mealtime. The notion that high salt intake and high blood pressure go hand in hand is surely among the most highly publicized pieces of nutritional lore ever to appear.

Salt has not always been held in such disrepute. Historically, salt has been prized since the earliest recorded times as a seasoning and a food preservative. Words and phrases in many languages reflect the importance of salt as a life-giving and life-sustaining substance. We refer to a kind and generous person as "the salt of the earth," for instance, and we speak of being "worth one's salt." In Roman times, soldiers were paid in salt; the English word "salary" is derived from the Latin word for paying salt wages (*salarium*).

Salt is perhaps the easiest of all minerals to obtain and purify. The simplest method, used for thousands of years throughout the world in coastal climates where sunshine is abundant and rainfall is scarce, is to evaporate seawater. Though the exact amount varies depending on the source, seawater contains an average of about 3.5% by mass of dissolved substances, most of which is sodium chloride. It has been estimated that evaporation of all the world's oceans would yield approximately *4.5 million cubic miles* of NaCl.

Only about 10% of current world salt production comes from evaporation of seawater. Most salt is obtained by mining the vast deposits of *halite*, or *rock salt*, formed by evaporation of ancient inland seas. These salt beds vary in thickness up to hundreds of meters and vary in depth from a few meters to thousands of meters below the earth's surface. Salt mining has gone on for at least 3400 years, and the Wieliczka mine in Galicia, Poland, has been worked continuously from A.D. 1000 to the present.

Now, back to the dinner table. What about the link between dietary salt intake and high blood pressure? There is no doubt that most people in industrialized nations have a relatively high salt intake, and also that high blood pressure among industrialized populations is on the rise. How closely, though, are the two observations related?

In a study called the DASH-Sodium study published in 2001, a strong correlation was found between a change in salt intake and a change in blood pressure. When volunteers cut back their salt intake from 8.3 g per day—roughly what Americans typically consume—to 3.8 g per day, significant

▲ In many areas of the world salt is still harvested by evaporation of ocean or tidal waters.

drops in blood pressure were found. The largest reduction in blood pressure was seen in people already diagnosed with hypertension, but subjects with normal blood pressure also lowered their readings by several percent.

What should an individual do? The best answer, as in so many things, is to use moderation and common sense. People with hypertension should make a strong effort to lower their sodium intake; others might be well advised to choose unsalted snacks, use less salt in preparing food, and read nutrition labels for sodium content.

See Additional Problems 4.83 and 4.84 at the end of this chapter.

4.7 Naming Ions

Main group metal cations in groups 1A, 2A, and 3A are named by identifying the metal, followed by the word "ion," as in the following examples:

$$K^+ \qquad\qquad Mg^{2+} \qquad\qquad Al^{3+}$$

Potassium ion   Magnesium ion   Aluminum ion

It is sometimes a little confusing to use the same name for both a metal and its ion, and you may occasionally have to stop and think about what is meant. For example, it is common practice in nutrition and health-related fields to talk about sodium or potassium in the bloodstream. Because both sodium and potassium *metals* react violently with water, however, they cannot possibly be present in blood. The references are to dissolved sodium and potassium *ions*.

For transition metals, such as iron or chromium, which can form more than one type of cation, a method is needed to differentiate these ions. Two systems are used. The first is an old system that gives the ion with the smaller charge the word ending -*ous* and the ion with the larger charge the ending -*ic*.

The second is a newer system in which the charge on the ion is given as a Roman numeral in parentheses right after the metal name. For example:

$$Cr^{2+} \qquad\qquad\qquad Cr^{3+}$$

Old name: Chrom*ous* ion   Chrom*ic* ion

New name: Chromium(II) ion   Chromium(III) ion

We will generally emphasize the new system in this book, but it is important to understand both because the old system is often found on labels of commercially supplied chemicals. The small differences between the names in either system illustrate the importance of reading a name very carefully before using a chemical. There are significant differences between compounds consisting of the same two elements but having different charges on the cation. In treating iron-deficiency anemia, for example, iron(II) compounds are preferable because the body absorbs them considerably better than iron(III) compounds.

The names of some common transition metal cations are listed in Table 4.1. Notice that the old names of the copper, iron, and tin ions are derived from their Latin names (*cuprum, ferrum,* and *stannum*).

Anions are named by replacing the ending of the element name with -*ide*, followed by the word "ion" (Table 4.2). For example, the anion formed by fluor*ine* is the fluor*ide* ion, and the anion formed by sulf*ur* is the sulf*ide* ion.

TABLE 4.1 Names of Some Transition Metal Cations

ELEMENT	SYMBOL	OLD NAME	NEW NAME
Chromium	Cr^{2+}	Chromous	Chromium(II)
	Cr^{3+}	Chromic	Chromium(III)
Copper	Cu^+	Cuprous	Copper(I)
	Cu^{2+}	Cupric	Copper(II)
Iron	Fe^{2+}	Ferrous	Iron(II)
	Fe^{3+}	Ferric	Iron(III)
Mercury	$*Hg_2^{2+}$	Mercurous	Mercury(I)
	Hg^{2+}	Mercuric	Mercury(II)
Tin	Sn^{2+}	Stannous	Tin(II)
	Sn^{4+}	Stannic	Tin(IV)

*This cation is composed of two mercury atoms, each of which has an average charge of +1.

TABLE 4.2 Names of Some Common Anions

ELEMENT	SYMBOL	NAME
Bromine	Br^-	Bromide ion
Chlorine	Cl^-	Chloride ion
Fluorine	F^-	Fluoride ion
Iodine	I^-	Iodide ion
Oxygen	O^{2-}	Oxide ion
Sulfur	S^{2-}	Sulfide ion

PROBLEM 4.13

Name the following ions:

(a) Cu^{2+} (b) F^- (c) Mg^{2+} (d) S^{2-}

PROBLEM 4.14

Write the symbols for the following ions:

(a) Silver(I) ion   (b) Iron(II) ion   (c) Cuprous ion   (d) Telluride ion

PROBLEM 4.15

Ringer's solution, which is used intravenously to adjust ion concentrations in body fluids, contains the ions of sodium, potassium, calcium, and chlorine. Give the names and symbols of these ions.

4.8 Polyatomic Ions

Ions that are composed of more than one atom are called **polyatomic ions**. Most polyatomic ions contain oxygen and another element, and their chemical formulas show by subscripts how many of each type of atom are combined. Sulfate ion, for example, is composed of one sulfur atom and four oxygen atoms, and has a -2 charge: SO_4^{2-}. The atoms in a polyatomic ion are held together by covalent bonds, of the sort discussed in the next chapter, and the entire group of atoms acts as a single unit. A polyatomic ion is charged because it contains a total number of electrons different from the total number of protons in the combined atoms.

The most common polyatomic ions are listed in Table 4.3. Note that the ammonium ion, NH_4^+, and the hydronium ion, H_3O^+, are the only cations; all the others

Polyatomic ion An ion that is composed of more than one atom.

TABLE 4.3 Some Common Polyatomic Ions

NAME	FORMULA	NAME	FORMULA
Hydronium ion	H_3O^+	Nitrate ion	NO_3^-
Ammonium ion	NH_4^+	Nitrite ion	NO_2^-
Acetate ion	$CH_3CO_2^-$	Oxalate ion	$C_2O_4^{2-}$
Carbonate ion	CO_3^{2-}	Permanganate ion	MnO_4^-
Hydrogen carbonate ion (bicarbonate ion)	HCO_3^-	Phosphate ion	PO_4^{3-}
		Hydrogen phosphate ion	HPO_4^{2-}
Chromate ion	CrO_4^{2-}	Dihydrogen phosphate ion	$H_2PO_4^-$
Dichromate ion	$Cr_2O_7^{2-}$	Sulfate ion	SO_4^{2-}
Cyanide ion	CN^-	Hydrogen sulfate ion (bisulfate ion)	HSO_4^-
Hydroxide ion	OH^-		
Hypochlorite ion	OCl^-	Sulfite ion	SO_3^{2-}

▲ The brilliant blue mineral chalcanthite consists of the hydrated ionic compound copper sulfate, $CuSO_4$ $5H_2O$.

APPLICATION ▶ Biologically Important Ions

The human body requires many different ions for proper functioning. Several of these ions, such as Ca^{2+}, Mg^{2+}, and HPO_4^{2-}, are used as structural materials in bones and teeth in addition to having other essential functions. Although 99% of Ca^{2+} is contained in bones and teeth, small amounts in body fluids play a vital role in transmission of nerve impulses. Other ions, including essential transition metal ions such as Fe^{2+}, are required for specific chemical reactions in the body. And still others, such as K^+, Na^+, and Cl^-, are present in fluids throughout the body.

Solutions containing ions must have overall neutrality, and several polyatomic anions, especially HCO_3^- and HPO_4^{2-}, are present in body fluids where they help balance the cation charges. Some of the most important ions and their functions are shown in the accompanying table.

See Additional Problems 4.85, 4.86, and 4.87 at the end of the chapter.

Some Biologically Important Ions

ION	LOCATION	FUNCTION	DIETARY SOURCE
Ca^{2+}	Outside cell; 99% of Ca^{2+} is in bones and teeth as $Ca_3(PO_4)_2$ and $CaCO_3$	Bone and tooth structure; necessary for blood clotting, muscle contraction, and transmission of nerve impulses	Milk, whole grains, leafy vegetables
Fe^{2+}	Blood hemoglobin	Transports oxygen from lungs to cells	Liver, red meat, leafy green vegetables
K^+	Fluids inside cells	Maintain ion concentrations in cells; regulate insulin release and heartbeat	Milk, oranges, bananas, meat
Na^+	Fluids outside cells	Protect against fluid loss; necessary for muscle contraction and transmission of nerve impulses	Table salt, seafood
Mg^{2+}	Fluids inside cells; bone	Present in many enzymes; needed for energy generation and muscle contraction	Leafy green plants, seafood, nuts
Cl^-	Fluids outside cells; gastric juice	Maintain fluid balance in cells; help transfer CO_2 from blood to lungs	Table salt, seafood
HCO_3^-	Fluids outside cells	Control acid–base balance in blood	By-product of food metabolism
HPO_4^{2-}	Fluids inside cells; bones and teeth	Control acid–base balance in cells	Fish, poultry, milk

are anions. These ions are encountered so frequently in chemistry, biology, and medicine that there is no alternative but to memorize their names and formulas. Fortunately, there are only a few of them.

Note in Table 4.3 that several pairs of ions— CO_3^{2-} and HCO_3^-, for example— are related by the presence or absence of a hydrogen ion, H^+. In such instances, the ion with the hydrogen is sometimes named using the prefix *bi-*. Thus, CO_3^{2-} is the carbonate ion and HCO_3^- is the bicarbonate ion; similarly, SO_4^{2-} is the sulfate ion and HSO_4^- is the bisulfate ion.

PROBLEM 4.16

Name the following ions:

(a) NO_3^- (b) CN^- (c) OH^- (d) HPO_4^{2-}

PROBLEM 4.17

Write the formulas of the following ions:

(a) Bicarbonate ion   (b) Ammonium ion

(c) Phosphate ion   (d) Permanganate ion

4.9 Formulas of Ionic Compounds

Since all chemical compounds are neutral, it is relatively easy to figure out the formulas of ionic compounds. Once the ions are identified, all we need to do is decide how many ions of each type give a total charge of zero. Thus, the chemical formula of an ionic compound tells the ratio of anions and cations.

If the ions have the same charge, only one of each ion is needed:

$$K^+ \quad \text{and} \quad F^- \quad \text{form} \quad KF$$
$$Ca^{2+} \quad \text{and} \quad O^{2-} \quad \text{form} \quad CaO$$

This makes sense when we look at how many electrons must be gained or lost by each atom in order to satisfy the octet rule:

$$K\cdot \; + \; \cdot \ddot{\underset{..}{F}} \colon \; \rightarrow \; K^+ \; + \; \colon \ddot{\underset{..}{F}} \colon^-$$

$$Ca\colon \; + \; \cdot \ddot{\underset{..}{O}} \cdot \; \rightarrow \; Ca^{2+} \; + \; \colon \ddot{\underset{..}{O}} \colon^{2-}$$

If the ions have different charges, however, unequal numbers of anions and cations must combine in order to have a net charge of zero. When potassium and oxygen combine, for example, it takes two K^+ ions to balance the -2 charge of the O^{2-} ion. Put another way, it takes two K atoms to provide the two electrons needed in order to complete the octet for the O atom:

$$2K\cdot \; + \; \cdot \ddot{\underset{..}{O}} \cdot \; \rightarrow \; 2K^+ \; + \; \colon \ddot{\underset{..}{O}} \colon^{2-}$$

$$2\,K^+ \quad \text{and} \quad O^{2-} \quad \text{form} \quad K_2O$$

The situation is reversed when a Ca^{2+} ion reacts with a Cl^- ion. One Ca atom can provide two electrons; each Cl atom requires only one electron to achieve a complete octet. Thus, there is one Ca^{2+} cation for every two Cl^- anions:

$$Ca\colon \; + \; 2\cdot \ddot{\underset{..}{Cl}} \colon \; \rightarrow \; Ca^{2+} \; + \; 2 \colon \ddot{\underset{..}{Cl}} \colon^-$$

$$Ca^{2+} \quad \text{and} \quad 2\,Cl^- \quad \text{form} \quad CaCl_2$$

It sometimes helps when writing the formulas for an ionic compound to remember that, when the two ions have different charges, the number of one ion is equal to the charge on the other ion. In magnesium phosphate, for example, the charge on the magnesium ion is $+2$ and the charge on the polyatomic phosphate ion is -3. Thus, there must be 3 magnesium ions with a total charge of $3 \times (+2) = +6$ and 2 phosphate ions with a total charge of $2 \times (-3) = -6$ for overall neutrality:

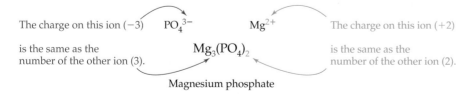

The charge on this ion (-3) $PO_4{}^{3-}$ Mg^{2+} The charge on this ion ($+2$)

is the same as the $Mg_3(PO_4)_2$ is the same as the
number of the other ion (3).   number of the other ion (2).

Magnesium phosphate

The formula of an ionic compound shows the lowest possible ratio of atoms in the compound and is thus known as a *simplest formula*. Because there is no such

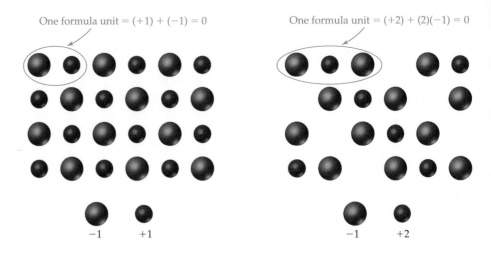

One formula unit $= (+1) + (-1) = 0$

One formula unit $= (+2) + (2)(-1) = 0$

-1 $+1$

-1 $+2$

▶ **FIGURE 4.5 Formula units of ionic compounds.** The sum of charges on the ions in a formula unit equals zero.

Formula unit The formula that identifies the smallest neutral unit of an ionic compound.

thing as a single neutral *particle* of an ionic compound, however, we use the term **formula unit** to identify the smallest possible neutral *unit* (Figure 4.5). For NaCl, the formula unit is one Na^+ ion and one Cl^- ion; for K_2SO_4, the formula unit is two K^+ ions and one SO_4^{2-} ion; for CaF_2, the formula unit is one Ca^{2+} ion and two F^- ions; and so on.

Once the numbers and kinds of ions in a compound are known, the formula is written using the following rules:

- List the cation first and the anion second; for example, NaCl rather than ClNa.
- Do not write the charges of the ions; for example, KF rather than K^+F^-.
- Use parentheses around a polyatomic ion formula if it has a subscript; for example, $Al_2(SO_4)_3$ rather than Al_2SO_{43}.

WORKED EXAMPLE **4.6** Ionic Compounds: Writing Formulas

Write the formula for the compound formed by calcium ions and nitrate ions.

ANALYSIS Knowing the formula and charges on the cation and anion (Table 4.4), we determine how many of each are needed to yield a neutral formula for the ionic compound.

SOLUTION
The two ions are Ca^{2+} and NO_3^-. Two nitrate ions, each with a -1 charge, will balance the $+2$ charge of the calcium ion.

Ca^{2+} Charge $= 1 \times (+2) = +2$
$2 NO_3^-$ Charge $= 2 \times (-1) = -2$

Since there are two nitrate ions, the nitrate formula must be enclosed in parentheses:

$Ca(NO_3)_2$ Calcium nitrate

PROBLEM 4.18

Write the formulas for the ionic compounds that silver(I) forms with each of the following:

(a) Iodide ion

(b) Oxide ion

(c) Phosphate ion

PROBLEM 4.19

Write the formulas for the ionic compounds that sulfate ion forms with the following:

(a) Sodium ion   **(b)** Iron(II) ion   **(c)** Chromium(III) ion

PROBLEM 4.20

The ionic compound containing ammonium ion and carbonate ion gives off the odor of ammonia, a property put to use in smelling salts for reviving someone who has fainted. Write the formula for this compound.

PROBLEM 4.21

An *astringent* is a compound that causes proteins in blood, sweat, and other body fluids to coagulate, a property put to use in deodorants. Two safe and effective astringents are the ionic compounds of aluminum with sulfate ion and with acetate ion. Write the formulas of both.

KEY CONCEPT PROBLEM 4.22

Three ionic compounds are represented on this periodic table—red cation with red anion, blue cation with blue anion, and green cation with green anion. Give a likely formula for each compound.

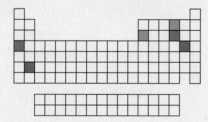

KEY CONCEPT PROBLEM 4.23

The ionic compound calcium nitride is represented here. What is the formula for calcium nitride, and what are the charges on the calcium and nitride ions?

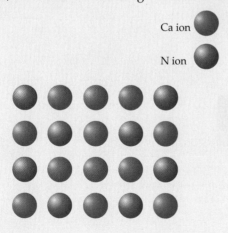

Ca ion

N ion

4.10 Naming Ionic Compounds

Just as in writing formulas for ionic compounds, these compounds are named by citing first the cation and then the anion, with a space between words. There are two kinds of ionic compounds, and the rules for naming them are slightly different.

Type I: Ionic compounds containing cations of main group elements (1A, 2A, aluminum). Since the charges on these cations do not vary, we do not need to specify the charge on the cation as discussed in Section 4.7.

Type II: Ionic compounds containing metals that can exhibit more than one charge. Since some metals, including the transition metals, often form more than one ion, we need to specify the charge on the cation in these compounds. Either the old (-ous, -ic) or the new (Roman numerals) system described in Section 4.7 can be used. Thus, $FeCl_2$ is called iron(II) chloride (or ferrous chloride), and $FeCl_3$ is called iron(III) chloride (or ferric chloride). Note that we do *not* name these compounds iron *di*chloride or iron *tri*chloride—once the charge on the metal is known, the number of anions needed to yield a neutral compound is also known and does not need to be included as part of the compound name. Ions of elements that form only one type of ion, such as Na^+ and Ca^{2+}, do not need Roman numerals. Table 4.4 lists some common ionic compounds and their uses.

⊂⊙⊃ **Looking Ahead**

Because the formula unit for an ionic compound must be neutral, we can unambiguously write the formula from the name of the compound, and vice versa. As we shall see in Chapter 5, covalent bonding between atoms can produce a much greater variety of compounds. The rules for naming covalent compounds must be able to accommodate multiple combinations of elements (for example, CO and CO_2).   ⊂⊙⊃

TABLE 4.4   Some Common Ionic Compounds and Their Applications

CHEMICAL NAME (COMMON NAME)	FORMULA	APPLICATIONS
Ammonium carbonate	$(NH_4)_2CO_3$	Smelling salts
Calcium hydroxide (hydrated lime)	$Ca(OH)_2$	Mortar, plaster, whitewash
Calcium oxide (lime)	CaO	Lawn treatment, industrial chemical
Lithium carbonate ("lithium")	Li_2CO_3	Treatment of manic depression
Magnesium hydroxide (milk of magnesia)	$Mg(OH)_2$	Antacid
Magnesium sulfate (Epsom salts)	$MgSO_4$	Laxative, anticonvulsant
Potassium permanganate	$KMnO_4$	Antiseptic, disinfectant*
Potassium nitrate (saltpeter)	KNO_3	Fireworks, matches, and desensitizer for teeth
Silver nitrate	$AgNO_3$	Antiseptic, germicide
Sodium bicarbonate (baking soda)	$NaHCO_3$	Baking powder, antacid, mouthwash, deodorizer
Sodium hypochlorite	$NaOCl$	Disinfectant; active ingredient in household bleach
Zinc oxide	ZnO	Skin protection, in calamine lotion

An antiseptic kills or inhibits growth of harmful microorganisms on the skin or in the body; a disinfectant kills harmful microorganisms but is generally not used on living tissue.

WORKED EXAMPLE   **4.7** Ionic Compounds: Formulas Involving Polyatomic Ions

Magnesium carbonate is used as an ingredient in Bufferin tablets. Write its formula.

ANALYSIS Since magnesium is a main group metal, we can determine its ionic compound formula by identifying the charges and formulas for the anion and the cation, remembering that the overall formula must be neutral.

SOLUTION
Look at the cation and the anion parts of the name separately. Magnesium, a group 2A element, forms the doubly positive Mg^{2+} cation; carbonate anion is doubly negative, CO_3^{2-}. Because the charges on the anion and cation are equal, a formula of $MgCO_3$ will be neutral.

WORKED EXAMPLE **4.8** Ionic Compounds: Formulas and Ionic Charges

Sodium and calcium both form a wide variety of ionic compounds. Write formulas for the following compounds:

(a) Sodium bromide and calcium bromide

(b) Sodium sulfide and calcium sulfide

(c) Sodium phosphate and calcium phosphate

ANALYSIS Using the formulas and charges for the cations and the anions (from Tables 4.2 and 4.3) we determine how many of each cation and anion are needed to yield a formula that is neutral.

SOLUTION

(a) Cations = Na^+ and Ca^{2+}; anion = Br^-: $NaBr$ and $CaBr_2$

(b) Cations = Na^+ and Ca^{2+}; anion = S^{2-}: Na_2S and CaS

(c) Cations = Na^+ and Ca^{2+}; anion = PO_4^{3-}: Na_3PO_4 and $Ca_3(PO_4)_2$

WORKED EXAMPLE **4.9** Naming Ionic Compounds

Name the following compounds, using Roman numerals to indicate the charges on the cations where necessary:

(a) KF   **(b)** $MgCl_2$ **(c)** $AuCl_3$ **(d)** Fe_2O_3

ANALYSIS For main group metals, the charge is determined from the group number and no Roman numerals are necessary. For transition metals, the charge on the metal can be determined from the total charge(s) on the anion(s).

SOLUTION

(a) Potassium fluoride. No Roman numeral is necessary because a group 1A metal forms only one cation.

(b) Magnesium chloride. No Roman numeral is necessary because magnesium (group 2A) forms only Mg^{2+}.

(c) Gold(III) chloride. The three Cl^- ions require a +3 charge on the gold for a neutral formula. Since gold is a transition metal that can form other ions, the Roman numeral is necessary to specify the +3 charge.

(d) Iron(III) oxide. Because the three oxide anions (O^{2-}) have a total negative charge of −6, the two iron cations must have a total charge of +6. Thus, each is Fe^{3+}, and the charge on each is indicated by the Roman numeral (III).

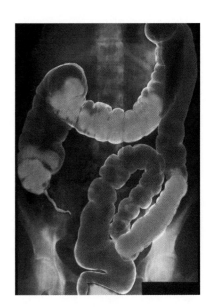

PROBLEM 4.24

Barium sulfate is an ionic compound swallowed by patients before having an X-ray of their gastrointestinal tract. Write its formula.

PROBLEM 4.25

The compound Ag_2S is responsible for much of the tarnish found on silverware. Name this compound, and give the charge on the silver ion.

▲ A barium sulfate "cocktail" is given to patients prior to an X-ray to help make the gastrointestinal tract visible on the film.

PROBLEM 4.26

Name the following compounds:

(a) SnO_2 (b) $Ca(CN)_2$ (c) Na_2CO_3

(d) Cu_2SO_4 (e) $Ba(OH)_2$ (f) $Fe(NO_3)_2$

PROBLEM 4.27

Write formulas for the following compounds:

(a) Lithium phosphate

(b) Copper(II) carbonate

(c) Aluminum sulfite

(d) Cuprous fluoride

(e) Ferric sulfate

(f) Ammonium chloride

KEY CONCEPT PROBLEM 4.28

The ionic compound formed between chromium and oxygen is shown here. Name the compound and write its formula.

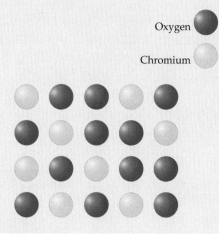

Oxygen

Chromium

4.11 H⁺ and OH⁻ Ions: An Introduction to Acids and Bases

Two of the most important ions we will be discussing in the remainder of this book are the hydrogen cation (H^+) and the hydroxide anion (OH^-). Since a hydrogen *atom* contains one proton and one electron, a hydrogen *cation* is simply a proton. When an acid dissolves in water, the proton typically attaches to a molecule of water to form the hydronium ion (H_3O^+), but chemists routinely use the H^+ and H_3O^+ ions interchangeably. A hydroxide anion, by contrast, is a polyatomic ion in which an oxygen atom is covalently bonded to a hydrogen atom. Although much of Chapter 10 is devoted to the chemistry of H^+ and OH^- ions, it is worth taking a preliminary look now.

The importance of the H^+ cation and the OH^- anion is that they are fundamental to the concepts of *acids* and *bases*. In fact, one definition of an **acid** is a substance that provides H$^+$ ions when dissolved in water, and one definition of a **base** is a substance that provides OH$^-$ ions when dissolved in water.

Acid   A substance that provides H$^+$ ions in water; for example, HCl, HNO$_3$, H$_2$SO$_4$, H$_3$PO$_4$

Base   A substance that provides OH$^-$ ions in water; for example, NaOH, KOH, Ba(OH)$_2$

Hydrochloric acid (HCl), nitric acid (HNO$_3$), sulfuric acid (H$_2$SO$_4$), and phosphoric acid (H$_3$PO$_4$) are among the most common acids. When any of these substances is dissolved in water, H$^+$ ions are formed along with the corresponding anion (Table 4.5).

TABLE 4.5   Some Common Acids and Ions Derived from Them

ACIDS		IONS	
Acetic acid	CH$_3$COOH	Acetate ion	*CH$_3$COO$^-$
Carbonic acid	H$_2$CO$_3$	Hydrogen carbonate ion (bicarbonate ion)	HCO$_3^-$
		Carbonate ion	CO$_3^{2}$
Hydrochloric acid	HCl	Chloride ion	Cl$^-$
Nitric acid	HNO$_3$	Nitrate ion	NO$_3^-$
Nitrous acid	HNO$_2$	Nitrite ion	NO$_2^-$
Phosphoric acid	H$_3$PO$_4$	Dihydrogen phosphate ion	H$_2$PO$_4^-$
		Hydrogen phosphate ion	HPO$_4^{2-}$
		Phosphate ion	PO$_4^{3-}$
Sulfuric acid	H$_2$SO$_4$	Hydrogen sulfate ion	HSO$_4^-$
		Sulfate ion	SO$_4^{2-}$

*Sometimes written C$_2$H$_3$O$_2^-$ or as CH$_3$CO$_2^-$.

Different acids can provide different numbers of H$^+$ ions per acid molecule. Hydrochloric acid, for instance, provides one H$^+$ ion per acid molecule; sulfuric acid can provide two H$^+$ ions per acid molecule; and phosphoric acid can provide three H$^+$ ions per acid molecule.

Sodium hydroxide (NaOH; also known as *lye* or *caustic soda*), potassium hydroxide (KOH; also known as *caustic potash*), and barium hydroxide [Ba(OH)$_2$] are examples of bases. When any of these compounds dissolves in water, OH$^-$ anions go into solution along with the corresponding metal cation. Sodium hydroxide and potassium hydroxide provide one OH$^-$ ion per formula unit; barium hydroxide provides two OH$^-$ ions per formula unit, as indicated by its formula, Ba(OH)$_2$.

PROBLEM 4.29

Which of the following compounds are acids, and which are bases? Explain.

(a) HF

(b) Ca(OH)$_2$

(c) LiOH

(d) HCN

◆○ KEY CONCEPT PROBLEM 4.30

One of these pictures represents a solution of HCl, and one represents a solution of H_2SO_4. Which is which?

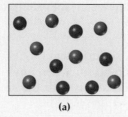
(a)

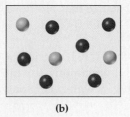
(b)

APPLICATION ▶ Osteoporosis

Bone consists primarily of two components, one mineral and one organic. About 70% of bone is the ionic compound *hydroxyapatite*, $Ca_{10}(PO_4)_6(OH)_2$, called the *trabecular*, or spongy, bone. This mineral component is intermingled in a complex matrix with about 30% by mass of fibers of the protein *collagen*, called the *cortical*, or compact, bone. Hydroxyapatite gives bone its hardness and strength, whereas collagen fibers add flexibility and resistance to breaking.

Total bone mass in the body increases from birth until reaching a maximum in the mid 30s. By the early 40s, however, an age-related decline in bone mass begins to occur in both sexes. Should this thinning of bones become too great and the bones become too porous and brittle, a clinical condition called *osteoporosis* can result. Osteoporosis is, in fact, the most common of all bone diseases, affecting approximately 25 million people in the United States. Approximately 1.5 million bone fractures each year are caused by osteoporosis at an estimated health-care cost of $14 billion.

Although both sexes are affected by osteoporosis, the condition is particularly common in postmenopausal women, who undergo cortical bone loss at a rate of 2–3% per year over and above that of the normal age-related loss. The cumulative lifetime bone loss, in fact, may approach 40–50% in women versus 20–30% in men. It has been estimated that half of all women over age 50 will have an osteoporosis-related bone fracture at some point in their life. Other risk factors in addition to sex include being thin, being sedentary, having a family history of osteoporosis, smoking, and having a diet low in calcium.

No cure yet exists for osteoporosis, but treatment for its prevention and management includes estrogen replacement therapy for postmenopausal women as well as several approved medications called *bisphosphonates* to prevent further bone loss. Calcium supplements are also recommended, as is appropriate weight-bearing exercise. In addition, treatment with sodium fluoride is under active investigation and shows considerable promise. Fluoride ion reacts with hydroxyapatite to give *fluorapatite*, in which OH^- ions are replaced by F^-, increasing both bone strength and density.

$$Ca_{10}(PO_4)_6(OH)_2 + 2\ F^- \longrightarrow Ca_{10}(PO_4)_6F_2$$
Hydroxyapatite   Fluorapatite

See Additional Problems 4.88 and 4.89 at the end of the chapter.

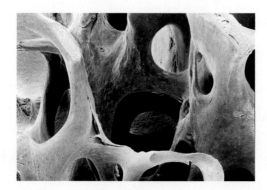

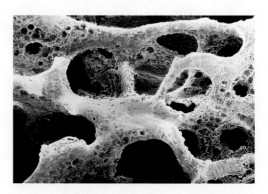

▲ Normal bone is strong and dense; a bone affected by osteoporosis is weak and spongy in appearance.

SUMMARY: REVISITING THE CHAPTER GOALS

1. **What is an ion, what is an ionic bond, and what are the general characteristics of ionic compounds?** Atoms are converted into *cations* by the loss of one or more electrons and into *anions* by the gain of one or more electrons. Ionic compounds are composed of cations and anions held together by *ionic bonds*, which result from the attraction between opposite electrical charges. Ionic compounds conduct electricity when dissolved in water, and they are generally crystalline solids with high melting points and high boiling points.

2. **What is the octet rule, and how does it apply to ions?** A valence-shell electron configuration of 8 electrons in filled *s* and *p* subshells leads to stability and lack of reactivity, as typified by the noble gases in group 8A. According to the *octet rule*, atoms of main group elements tend to form ions in which they have gained or lost the appropriate number of electrons to reach a noble gas configuration.

3. **What is the relationship between an element's position in the periodic table and the formation of its ion?** Periodic variations in *ionization energy*, the amount of energy that must be supplied to remove an electron from an atom, show that metals lose electrons more easily than nonmetals. As a result, metals usually form cations. Similar periodic variations in *electron affinity*, the amount of energy released on adding an electron to an atom, show that reactive nonmetals gain electrons more easily than metals. As a result, reactive nonmetals usually form anions. The ionic charge can be predicted from the group number and the octet rule. For main group metals, the charge on the cation is equal to the group number. For nonmetals, the charge on the anion is equal to 8 − (group number).

4. **What determines the chemical formula of an ionic compound?** Ionic compounds contain appropriate numbers of anions and cations to maintain overall neutrality, thereby providing a means of determining their chemical formulas.

5. **How are ionic compounds named?** Cations have the same name as the metal from which they are derived. Monatomic anions have the name ending *-ide*. For metals that form more than one ion, a Roman numeral equal to the charge on the ion is added to the name of the cation. Alternatively, the ending *-ous* is added to the name of the cation with the lesser charge and the ending *-ic* is added to the name of the cation with the greater charge. To name an ionic compound, the cation name is given first, with the charge of the metal ion indicated if necessary, and the anion name is given second.

6. **What are acids and bases?** The hydrogen ion (H^+) and the hydroxide ion (OH^-) are among the most important ions in chemistry because they are fundamental to the idea of acids and bases. According to one common definition, an *acid* is a substance that yields H^+ ions when dissolved in water, and a *base* is a substance that yields OH^- ions when dissolved in water.

KEY WORDS

Acid, *p. 99*

Anion, *p. 80*

Base, *p. 99*

Cation, *p. 80*

Electron affinity, *p. 81*

Formula unit, *p. 94*

Ion, *p. 80*

Ionic bond, *p. 83*

Ionic compound, *p. 83*

Ionic solid, *p. 83*

Ionization energy, *p. 81*

Octet rule, *p. 85*

Polyatomic ion, *p. 91*

UNDERSTANDING KEY CONCEPTS

4.31 Where on the blank outline of the periodic table are the following elements found?

   (a) Elements that commonly form only one type of cation

   (b) Elements that commonly form anions

   (c) Elements that can form more than one type of cation

   (d) Elements that do not readily form either anions or cations

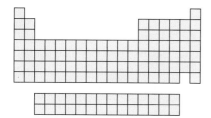

4.32 Where on the blank outline of the periodic table are the following elements found?

   (a) Elements that commonly form +2 ions

   (b) Elements that commonly form −2 ions

   (c) An element that forms a +3 ion

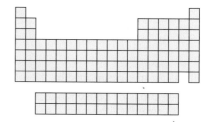

4.33 Which of these drawings represents a Ca atom, which an Na$^+$ ion, and which an O^{2-} ion?

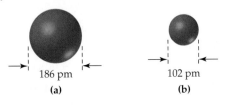

(a)   (b)   (c)

4.34 One of these drawings represents an Na atom, and one represents an Na$^+$ ion. Tell which is which, and explain why there is a difference in size.

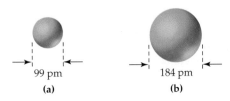

186 pm   102 pm
(a)   (b)

4.35 One of these drawings represents a Cl atom, and one represents a Cl$^-$ ion. Tell which is which, and explain why there is a difference in size.

99 pm   184 pm
(a)   (b)

4.36 Three ionic compounds are represented in this outline of the periodic table—red cation with red anion, blue cation with blue anion, and green cation with green anion. Give a likely formula for each compound, and tell the name of each.

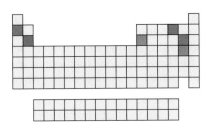

4.37 Each of these drawings (a)–(d) represents one of the following ionic compounds: PbBr$_2$, ZnS, CrF$_3$, Al$_2$O$_3$. Which is which?

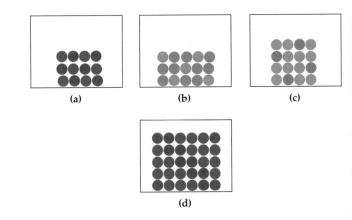

(a)   (b)   (c)

(d)

ADDITIONAL PROBLEMS

IONS AND IONIC BONDING

4.38 Write electron-dot symbols for the following atoms:

(a) Beryllium
(b) Neon
(c) Strontium
(d) Aluminum

4.39 Write electron-dot symbols for the following atoms:

(a) Nitrogen
(b) Selenium
(c) Iodine
(d) Strontium

4.40 Write equations for loss or gain of electrons by atoms that result in formation of the following ions from the corresponding atoms:

(a) Ca^{2+}
(b) Au$^+$
(c) F$^-$
(d) Cr^{3+}

4.41 Write symbols for the ions formed by the following:

(a) Gain of 3 electrons by phosphorus
(b) Loss of 1 electron by lithium
(c) Loss of 2 electrons by cobalt
(d) Loss of 3 electrons by thallium

4.42 Tell whether each statement about ions is true or false:

(a) A cation is formed by addition of one or more electrons to an atom.
(b) Group 4A elements tend to lose 4 electrons to yield ions with a +4 charge.
(c) Group 4A elements tend to gain 4 electrons to yield ions with a −4 charge.
(d) The individual atoms in a polyatomic ion are held together by covalent bonds.

4.43 Tell whether each statement about ionic solids is true or false:

(a) Ions are randomly arranged in ionic solids.
(b) All ions are the same size in ionic solids.
(c) Ionic solids can often be shattered by a sharp blow.
(d) Ionic solids have low boiling points.

IONS AND THE OCTET RULE

4.44 What is the *octet rule*?

4.45 Why do H and He not obey the octet rule?

4.46 What is the charge of an ion that contains 34 protons and 36 electrons?

4.47 What is the charge of an ion that contains 20 protons and 18 electrons?

4.48 Identify the element X in the following ions, and tell which noble gas has the same electron configuration.

(a) X^{2+}, a cation with 36 electrons

(b) X^-, an anion with 36 electrons

4.49 Element Z forms an ion Z^{3+}, which contains 31 protons. What is the identity of Z, and how many electrons does Z^{3+} have?

4.50 Write the electron configuration for the following ions:

(a) Rb^+

(b) Br^-

(c) S^{2-}

(d) Ba^{2+}

(e) Al^{3+}

4.51 The following ions have a noble gas configuration. Identify the noble gas.

(a) Ca^{2+}

(b) Li^+

(c) O^{2-}

(d) F^-

(e) Mg^{2+}

PERIODIC PROPERTIES AND ION FORMATION

4.52 Looking only at the periodic table, tell which member of each pair of atoms has the larger ionization energy and thus loses an electron less easily:

(a) Li and O

(b) Li and Cs

(c) K and Zn

(d) Mg and N

4.53 Looking only at the periodic table, tell which member of each pair of atoms has the larger electron affinity and thus gains an electron more easily:

(a) Li and S

(b) Ba and I

(c) Ca and Br

4.54 Which of the following ions are likely to form? Explain.

(a) Li^{2+}

(b) K^-

(c) Mn^{3+}

(d) Zn^{4+}

(e) Ne^+

4.55 Which of the following elements are likely to form more than one cation?

(a) Magnesium

(b) Silicon

(c) Manganese

4.56 Write the electron configurations of Cr^{2+} and Cr^{3+}.

4.57 Write the electron configurations of Co, Co^{2+}, and Co^{3+}.

4.58 Would you expect the ionization energy of Li^+ to be less than, greater than, or the same as the ionization energy of Li? Explain.

4.59 (a) Write equations for the loss of an electron by a K atom and the gain of an electron by a K^+ ion.

(b) What is the relationship between the equations?

(c) What is the relationship between the ionization energy of a K atom and the electron affinity of a K^+ ion?

SYMBOLS, FORMULAS, AND NAMES FOR IONS

4.60 Name the following ions:

(a) S^{2-}

(b) Sn^{2+}

(c) Sr^{2+}

(d) Mg^{2+}

(e) Au^+

4.61 Name the following ions in both the old and the new systems:

(a) Cu^{2+}

(b) Fe^{2+}

(c) Hg_2^{2+}

4.62 Write symbols for the following ions:

(a) Selenide ion

(b) Oxide ion

(c) Silver(I) ion

4.63 Write symbols for the following ions:

(a) Ferric ion

(b) Cobalt(II) ion

(c) Lead (IV) ion

4.64 Write formulas for the following ions:

(a) Hydroxide ion

(b) Bisulfate ion

(c) Acetate ion

(d) Permanganate ion

(e) Hypochlorite ion

(f) Nitrate ion

(g) Carbonate ion

(h) Dichromate ion

4.65 Name the following ions:

(a) SO_3^{2-}

(b) CN^-

(c) H_3O^+

(d) $PO_4{}^{3-}$

NAMES AND FORMULAS FOR IONIC COMPOUNDS

4.66 Write formulas for the compounds formed by the sulfate ion with the following cations:

(a) Aluminum

(b) Silver(I)

(c) Zinc

(d) Barium

4.67 Write formulas for the compounds formed by the carbonate ion with the following cations:

(a) Strontium

(b) Fe(III)

(c) Ammonium

(d) Sn(IV)

4.68 Write the formula for the following substances:

(a) Sodium bicarbonate (baking soda)

(b) Potassium nitrate (a backache remedy)

(c) Calcium carbonate (an antacid)

(d) Ammonium nitrate (first aid cold packs)

4.69 Write the formula for the following compounds:

(a) Calcium hypochlorite, used as a swimming pool disinfectant

CHAPTER 5

Molecular Compounds

CONCEPTS TO REVIEW

The Periodic Table
(Sections 3.4 and 3.5)

Electron Configurations
(Sections 3.7 and 3.8)

The Octet Rule
(Section 4.5)

Electron-Dot Symbols
(Section 3.9)

▲ In living systems, as in this print by the Dutch artist M. C. Escher (1898–1972), the shapes of the component parts determine their contribution to the whole.

CONTENTS

CHAPTER GOALS

In this chapter, we will explore the following questions about molecules and covalent bonds:

1. What is a covalent bond?

THE GOAL: Be able to describe the nature of covalent bonds and how they are formed.

2. How does the octet rule apply to covalent bond formation?

THE GOAL: Be able to use the octet rule to predict the numbers of covalent bonds formed by common main group elements.

3. How are molecular compounds represented?

THE GOAL: Be able to interpret molecular formulas and draw Lewis structures for molecules.

4. What is the influence of valence-shell electrons on molecular shape?

THE GOAL: Be able to use Lewis structures to predict molecular geometry.

5. When are bonds and molecules polar?

THE GOAL: Be able to use electronegativity and molecular geometry to predict bond and molecular polarity.

6. What are the major differences between ionic and molecular compounds?

THE GOAL: Be able to compare the structures, compositions, and properties of ionic and molecular compounds.

We saw in the preceding chapter that ionic compounds are crystalline solids composed of positively and negatively charged ions. Not all substances, however, are ionic. In fact, with the exception of table salt (NaCl), baking soda ($NaHCO_3$), lime for the garden (CaO), and a few others, most of the compounds around us are *not* crystalline, brittle, high-melting ionic solids. We are much more likely to encounter gases (like those in air), liquids (such as water), low-melting solids (such as butter), and flexible solids like plastics. All these materials are composed of *molecules* rather than ions, all contain *covalent* bonds rather than ionic bonds, and all consist primarily of nonmetal atoms rather than metals.

5.1 Covalent Bonds

How do we describe the bonding in carbon dioxide, water, polyethylene, and the many millions of nonionic compounds that make up our bodies and much of the world around us? Simply put, the bonds in such compounds are formed by the *sharing* of electrons between atoms (in contrast to ionic bonds, which involve the complete transfer of electrons from one atom to another). The bond formed when atoms share electrons is called a **covalent bond**, and the group of atoms held together by covalent bonds is called a **molecule**. A single molecule of water, for example, contains two hydrogen atoms and one oxygen atom covalently bonded to one another. We might visualize a water molecule using a space-filling model as shown here:

Covalent bond A bond formed by sharing electrons between atoms.

Molecule A group of atoms held together by covalent bonds.

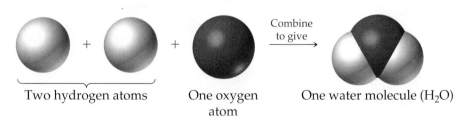

Two hydrogen atoms + One oxygen atom → (Combine to give) One water molecule (H_2O)

Recall that according to the *octet rule* (Section 4.5), main group elements tend to undergo reactions that leave them with completed outer subshells with eight valence electrons (or two for hydrogen), so that they have a noble gas electron configuration. (⬤▭, p. 85) Although metals and reactive nonmetals can achieve an electron octet by gaining or losing an appropriate number of electrons to form ions, the nonmetals can also achieve an electron octet by *sharing* an appropriate number of electrons in covalent bonds.

As another example, acetylene, the gas used in welding, has the formula C_2H_2. To achieve octets, the two acetylene carbons share six electrons in a carbon—carbon triple bond:

$$H : C :: C : H \quad or \quad H—C\equiv C—H$$

Acetylene—the carbon atoms share
6 electrons in a triple bond.

Note that in compounds with multiple bonds like ethylene and acetylene, each carbon atom still forms a total of 4 covalent bonds.

▲ Acetylene is frequently used for welding metal because it burns with such a hot flame.

WORKED EXAMPLE 5.4 Molecular Compounds: Multiple Bonds

The compound 1-butene contains a multiple bond. In the following representation, however, only the connections between atoms are shown; the multiple bond is not specifically indicated. Identify the position of the multiple bond.

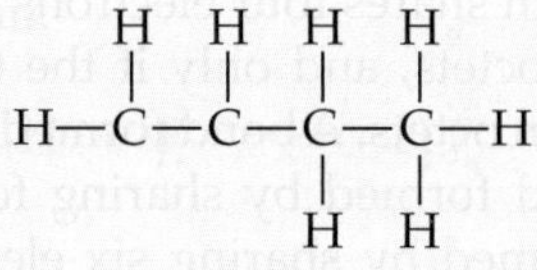

$$\begin{array}{cccc} H & H & H & H \\ | & | & | & | \\ H—C—C—C—C—H \\ | & | \\ H & H \end{array}$$

1-Butene

ANALYSIS Look for two adjacent atoms that appear to have fewer than the typical number of covalent bonds, and connect those atoms by a double or triple bond. Refer to Figure 5.4 to see how many bonds will typically be formed by hydrogen and carbon atoms.

SOLUTION

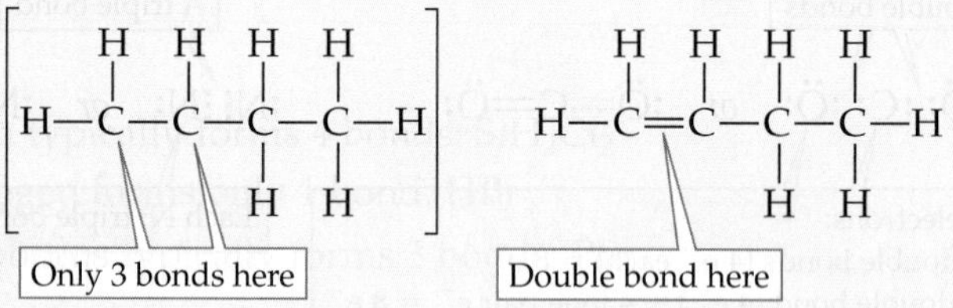

$$\left[\begin{array}{cccc} H & H & H & H \\ | & | & | & | \\ H—C—C—C—C—H \\ | & | \\ H & H \end{array}\right] \qquad \begin{array}{cccc} H & H & H & H \\ | & | & | & | \\ H—C=C—C—C—H \\ | & | \\ H & H \end{array}$$

Only 3 bonds here   Double bond here

WORKED EXAMPLE 5.5 Multiple Bonds: Electron-Dot and Line Structures

Draw the oxygen molecule (a) using the electron-dot symbols, and (b) using lines rather than dots to indicate covalent bonds.

ANALYSIS Each oxygen atom has six valence electrons, and will tend to form two covalent bonds to reach an octet. Thus, each oxygen will need to share four electrons to form a double bond.

SOLUTION

$$:\ddot{O}::\ddot{O}: \quad or \quad :\ddot{O}=\ddot{O}:$$

PROBLEM 5.5

Acetic acid, the organic constituent of vinegar, can be drawn using electron-dot symbols as shown below. How many outer-shell electrons are associated with each atom? Draw the structure using lines rather than dots to indicate covalent bonds.

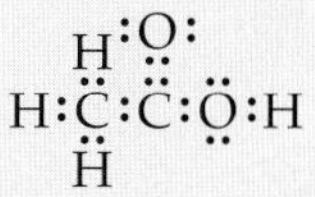

$$
\begin{array}{c}
\text{H} \overset{\displaystyle ..}{\underset{\displaystyle ..}{\text{O}}} \\
\text{H} \overset{..}{\text{C}} \overset{..}{\text{C}} \overset{..}{\underset{..}{\text{O}}} \text{H} \\
\overset{..}{\text{H}}
\end{array}
$$

PROBLEM 5.6

Identify the position of the double bond in methyl ethyl ketone, a common industrial solvent with the following connections among atoms.

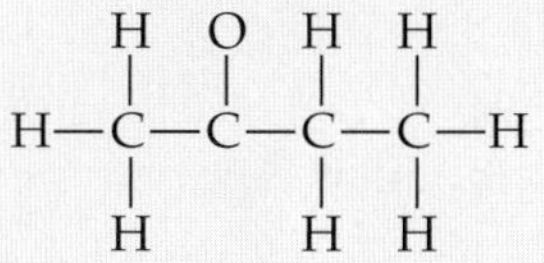

$$
\begin{array}{ccccc}
\text{H} & \text{O} & \text{H} & \text{H} \\
| & | & | & | \\
\text{H} - \text{C} - \text{C} - \text{C} - \text{C} - \text{H} \\
| & & | & | \\
\text{H} & & \text{H} & \text{H}
\end{array}
$$

Methyl ethyl ketone

5.4 Coordinate Covalent Bonds

In the covalent bonds we have seen thus far, the shared electrons have come from different atoms. That is, the bonds result from the overlap of two singly occupied valence orbitals, one from each atom. Sometimes, though, a bond is formed by the overlap of a filled orbital on one atom with a vacant orbital on another atom so that both electrons come from the *same* atom. The bond that results in this case is called a **coordinate covalent bond**.

Coordinate covalent bond The covalent bond that forms when both electrons are donated by the same atom.

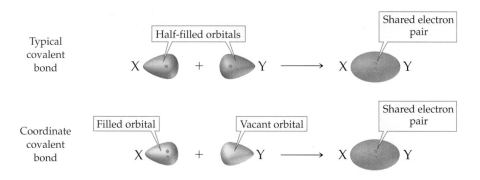

The ammonium ion, NH_4^+, is an example of a species with a coordinate covalent bond. When ammonia reacts in water solution with a hydrogen ion, H^+, the nitrogen atom donates two electrons from a filled valence orbital to form a coordinate covalent bond to the hydrogen ion, which has a vacant $1s$ orbital.

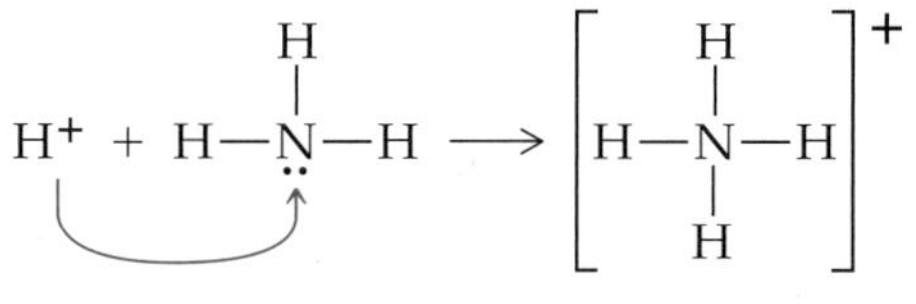

$$
\text{H}^+ + \begin{array}{c} \text{H} \\ | \\ \text{H} - \text{N} - \text{H} \\ .. \end{array} \longrightarrow \left[\begin{array}{c} \text{H} \\ | \\ \text{H} - \text{N} - \text{H} \\ | \\ \text{H} \end{array} \right]^+
$$

Once formed, a coordinate covalent bond contains two shared electrons and is no different from any other covalent bond. All four covalent bonds in NH_4^+ are identical, for example. Note, however, that formation of a coordinate covalent bond results in unusual bonding patterns, such as an N atom with four covalent bonds rather than the usual three.

APPLICATION ▶ CO and NO: Pollutants or Miracle Molecules?

Carbon monoxide (CO) is a killer; everyone knows that. It is to blame for an estimated 3500 accidental deaths and suicides each year in the United States and is the number one cause of all deaths by poisoning. Nitric oxide (NO) is formed in combustion engines and reacts with oxygen to form nitrogen dioxide (NO_2), the reddish-brown gas associated with urban smog. What most people do not know, however, is that our bodies cannot function *without* these molecules. A startling discovery made in 1992 showed that CO and NO are key chemical messengers in the body, used by cells to regulate critical metabolic processes.

The toxicity of CO in moderate concentration is due to its ability to bind to hemoglobin molecules in the blood, thereby preventing the hemoglobin from carrying oxygen to tissues. The high reactivity of NO leads to the formation of compounds that are toxic irritants. At the same time, though, low concentrations of CO and NO are produced in cells throughout the body. Both CO and NO are highly soluble in water and can diffuse from one cell to another, where they stimulate production of a substance called *guanylyl cyclase*. Guanylyl cyclase, in turn, controls the production of another substance called *cyclic GMP*, which regulates many cellular functions.

Levels of CO production are particularly high in certain regions of the brain, including those associated with long-term memory. Evidence from experiments with rat brains suggests that a special kind of cell in the brain's hippocampus is signaled by transfer of a molecular messenger from a neighboring cell. The receiving cell responds back to the signaling cell by releasing CO, which causes still more messenger molecules to be sent. After several rounds of this back-and-forth communication, the receiving cell undergoes some sort of change that serves as a memory. When CO production is blocked, long-term memories are no longer stored, and those memories that previously existed are erased. When CO production is stimulated, however, memories are again laid down.

NO controls a seemingly limitless range of functions in the body. The immune system uses NO to fight infections and tumors. It also is used to transmit messages between nerve cells and is associated with the processes involved in learning and memory, sleeping, and depression. Its most advertised role, however, is as a *vasodilator*, a substance that allows blood vessels to relax and dilate. This discovery led to

▲ Los Angeles at sunset. Carbon monoxide is a major component of photochemical smog, but it also functions as an essential chemical messenger in our bodies.

the development of a new class of drugs that stimulate production of enzymes called nitric oxide synthases (NOS). These drugs can be used to treat conditions from erectile dysfunction (Viagra) to hypertension. Given the importance of NO in the fields of neuroscience, physiology, and immunology, it is not surprising that it was named "Molecule of the Year" in 1992.

See Additional Problems 5.91 and 5.92 at the end of the chapter.

⊂⊃ Looking Ahead

An entire class of substances is based on the ability of transition metals to form coordinate covalent bonds with nonmetals. Called *coordination compounds*, many of these substances have important roles in living organisms. For example, toxic metals can be removed from the bloodstream by forming water-soluble coordination compounds. As another example, we will see in Chapter 19 that essential metal ions are held in enzyme molecules by coordinate covalent bonds. ⊂⊃

5.5 Molecular Formulas and Lewis Structures

Formulas such as H_2O, NH_3, and CH_4, which show the numbers and kinds of atoms in one molecule of a compound, are called **molecular formulas**. Though important, molecular formulas are limited in their use because they do not provide information about how the atoms in a given molecule are connected.

Much more useful are **structural formulas**, which use lines to show how atoms are connected, and **Lewis structures**, which show both the connections among atoms and the placement of unshared valence electrons. In a water molecule, for instance, the oxygen atom shares two electron pairs in covalent bonds with two hydrogen atoms and has two other pairs of valence electrons that are not shared in bonds. Such unshared pairs of valence electrons are called **lone pairs**. In an ammonia molecule, three electron pairs are used in bonding and there is one lone pair. In methane, all four electron pairs are bonding.

▲ Ammonia is used as a fertilizer to supply nitrogen to growing plants.

Molecular formula A formula that shows the numbers and kinds of atoms in one molecule of a compound.

Structural formula A molecular representation that shows the connections among atoms by using lines to represent covalent bonds.

Lewis structure A molecular representation that shows both the connections among atoms and the locations of lone-pair valence electrons.

Lone pair A pair of electrons that is not used for bonding.

Note how a molecular formula differs from an ionic formula, described previously in Section 4.10. A *molecular* formula gives the number of atoms that are combined in one molecule of a compound, whereas an *ionic* formula gives only a ratio of ions (Figure 5.5). The formula C_2H_4 for ethylene, for example, says that every ethylene molecule consists of two carbon atoms and four hydrogen atoms. The formula NaCl for sodium chloride, however, says only that there are equal numbers of Na^+ and Cl^- ions in the crystal; the formula says nothing about how the ions interact with one another.

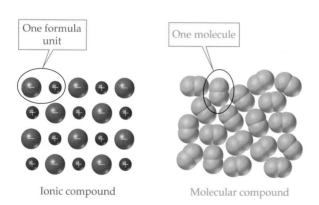

Ionic compound   Molecular compound

◄ **FIGURE 5.5 The distinction between ionic and molecular compounds.** In ionic compounds, the smallest particle is an ion. In molecular compounds, the smallest particle is a molecule.

5.6 Drawing Lewis Structures

To draw a Lewis structure, you first need to know the connections among atoms. Sometimes the connections are obvious. Water, for example, can only be $H-O-H$ because only oxygen can be in the middle and form two covalent bonds. Other times, you will have to be told how the atoms are connected.

Two approaches are used for drawing Lewis structures once the connections are known. The first is particularly useful for organic molecules like those found in living organisms because common bonding patterns are followed by the atoms. The second approach is a more general, stepwise procedure that works for all molecules.

WORKED EXAMPLE **5.9** Lewis Structures: Molecular Shape

What shape do you expect for the hydronium ion, H_3O^+?

ANALYSIS Draw the Lewis structure for the molecular ion and count the number of charge clouds around the central oxygen atom; imagine the clouds orienting as far away from one another as possible.

SOLUTION

The Lewis structure for the hydronium ion shows that the oxygen atom has four charge clouds (three single bonds and one lone pair). The hydronium ion is therefore pyramidal with bond angles of approximately 109.5°:

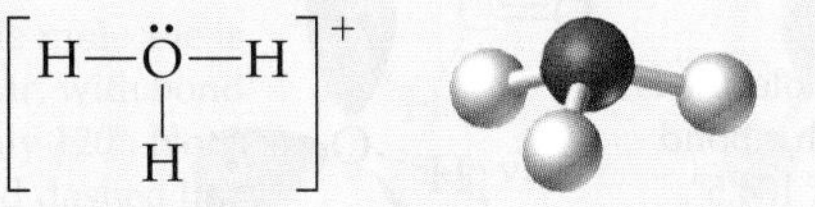

$$\left[\begin{array}{c} H{-}\ddot{O}{-}H \\ | \\ H \end{array} \right]^+$$

WORKED EXAMPLE **5.10** Lewis Structures: Charge Cloud Geometry

Predict the geometry around each of the carbon atoms in an acetaldehyde molecule, CH_3CHO.

ANALYSIS Draw the Lewis structure and identify the number of charge clouds around each of the central carbon atoms.

SOLUTION

The Lewis structure of acetaldehyde shows that the CH_3 carbon has four charge clouds (four single bonds) and the CHO carbon atom has three charge clouds (two single bonds, one double bond). Table 5.1 indicates that the CH_3 carbon is tetrahedral, but the CHO carbon is planar triangular.

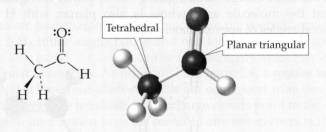

PROBLEM 5.12

Boron typically only forms three covalent bonds because it only has three valence electrons, but can form coordinate covalent bonds. Draw the Lewis structure for BF_4^- and predict the molecular shape of the ion.

PROBLEM 5.13

Predict shapes for the organic molecules chloroform, $CHCl_3$, and dichloroethylene, $Cl_2C{=}CH_2$.

PROBLEM 5.14

Electron-pair repulsion influences the shapes of polyatomic *ions* in the same way it influences neutral molecules. Draw electron-dot symbols and predict the shape of the ammonium ion, NH_4^+, and the sulfate ion, SO_4^{2-}.

APPLICATION ▶ VERY Big Molecules

How big can a molecule be? The answer is very, *very* big. The really big molecules in our bodies and in many items we buy are all *polymers*. Like a string of beads, a polymer is formed of many repeating units connected in a long chain. Each "bead" in the chain comes from a simple molecule that has formed chemical bonds at both ends, linking it to other molecules. The repeating units can be the same:

$$-a-a-a-a-a-a-a-a-a-a-a-a-$$

or they can be different. If different, they can be connected in an ordered pattern:

$$-a-b-a-b-a-b-a-b-a-b-a-b-$$

or in a random pattern:

$$-a-b-b-a-b-a-a-a-b-a-b-b-$$

Furthermore, the polymer chains can have branches, and the branches can have either the same repeating unit as the main chain or a different one:

```
        a
        |
  a-a-a-a-
        |
        a
        |
        a
        |
        a
        |
  a-a-a-a-
        |
        a
        |
        a
        |
  a-a-a-a-
        |
        a
        |
```

or

```
        a
        |
  a-b-b-b-
        |
        a
        |
        a
        |
        a
        |
  a-b-b-b-
        |
        a
        |
        a
        |
  a-b-b-b-
        |
        a
        |
```

Still other possible variations include complex, three-dimensional networks of "cross-linked" chains. The rubber used in tires, for example, contains polymer chains connected by cross-linking atoms of sulfur to impart greater rigidity.

We all use synthetic polymers every day—we usually call them "plastics." Common synthetic polymers are made by connecting up to several hundred thousand smaller molecules together, producing giant polymer molecules with masses up to several million atomic mass units. Polyethylene, for example, is made by combining as many as 50,000 ethylene molecules ($H_2C{=}CH_2$) to give a polymer with repeating $-CH_2CH_2-$ units:

$$\text{Many } H_2C{=}CH_2 \longrightarrow -CH_2CH_2CH_2CH_2CH_2CH_2-$$

Ethylene   Polyethlene

The product is used in such items as chairs, toys, drain pipes, milk bottles, and packaging films.

Nature began to exploit the extraordinary variety of polymer properties long before humans did. In fact, despite great progress in recent years, there is still much to be learned about the polymers in living things. Carbohydrates and proteins are polymers, as are the giant molecules of deoxyribonucleic acid (DNA) that govern the reproduction of viruses, bacteria, plants, and all living creatures. Nature's polymer molecules, though, are larger and more complex than any that chemists have yet created. We will see the structures of these natural polymers in later chapters.

▲ The protective gear used by these firefighters is composed of advanced materials based on polymers.

See Additional Problems 5.93 and 5.94 at the end of the chapter.

| **WORKED EXAMPLE** | **5.13** Naming Molecular Compounds |

Name the following compounds:

(a) N_2O_3 (b) $GeCl_4$ (c) PCl_5

SOLUTION

(a) Dinitrogen trioxide

(b) Germanium tetrachloride

(c) Phosphorus pentachloride

| **WORKED EXAMPLE** | **5.14** Writing Formulas for Molecular Compounds |

Write molecular formulas for the following compounds:

(a) Nitrogen triiodide

(b) Silicon tetrachloride

(c) Carbon disulfide

SOLUTION

(a) NI_3 (b) $SiCl_4$ (c) CS_2

PROBLEM 5.23

Name the following compounds:

(a) S_2Cl_2 (b) ICl (c) ICl_3

PROBLEM 5.24

Write formulas for the following compounds:

(a) Selenium tetrafluoride

(b) Diphosphorus pentoxide

(c) Bromine trifluoride

5.11 Characteristics of Molecular Compounds

We saw in Section 4.4 that ionic compounds have high melting and boiling points because the attractive forces between oppositely charged ions are so strong that the ions are held tightly together. *Molecules*, however, are neutral, so there is no strong electrical attraction between different molecules to hold them together. There are, however, several weaker forces between molecules, called *intermolecular forces*, that we will look at in more detail in Chapter 8.

When intermolecular forces are very weak, molecules of a substance are so weakly attracted to one another that the substance is a gas at ordinary temperatures. If the forces are somewhat stronger, the molecules are pulled together into a liquid; and if the forces are still stronger, the substance becomes a molecular solid. Even so, the melting points and boiling points of molecular solids are usually lower than those of ionic solids.

In addition to having lower melting points and boiling points, molecular compounds differ from ionic compounds in other ways. Most molecular compounds are insoluble in water, for instance, because they have little attraction to strongly polar water molecules. In addition, they do not conduct electricity when melted because they have no charged particles. Table 5.3 provides a comparison of the properties of ionic and molecular compounds.

APPLICATION ▶

Damascenone by Any Other Name Would Smell as Sweet

What's in a name? According to Shakespeare's *Romeo and Juliet*, a rose by any other name would smell as sweet. Chemical names, however, often provoke less favorable responses: "It's unpronounceable." "It's too complicated." "It must be something bad."

Regarding pronunciation, chemical names are usually pronounced using every possible syllable. *Phenylpropanolamine*, for instance, a substance used in over-the-counter decongestants, is spoken with seven syllables: phen-yl-pro-pa-**nol**-a-mine.

Regarding complexity, the reason is obvious once you realize that there are more than 19 *million* known chemical compounds: The full name of a chemical compound has to include enough information to tell chemists the composition and structure of the compound. It is as if every person on earth had to have his or her own unique name that described height, hair color, and other identifying characteristics.

But does it really follow that a chemical with a really complicated name must be bad? These days, it seems that a different chemical gets into the news every week, often in a story describing some threat to health or the environment. The unfortunate result is that people sometimes conclude that everything with a chemical name is unnatural and dangerous. Neither is true, though. Acetaldehyde, for instance, is present naturally in most tart, ripe fruits and is often added in small amounts to artificial flavorings. When *pure*, however, acetaldehyde is also a flammable gas that is toxic and explosive in high concentrations.

Similar comparisons of desirable and harmful properties can be made for almost all chemicals, including water, sugar, and salt. The properties of a substance and the conditions surrounding its use must be evaluated before judgments are made. And damascenone, by the way, is the chemical largely responsible for the wonderful odor of roses.

▲ The scent of these roses contains the following: β-damascenone, β-ionone, citronellol, geraniol, nerol, eugenol, methyl eugenol, β-phenylethyl, alcohol, farnesol, linalool, terpineol, rose oxide, carvone, and many other natural substances.

See Additional Problems 5.95 and 5.96 at the end of the chapter.

TABLE 5.3 A Comparison of Ionic and Molecular Compounds

IONIC COMPOUNDS	MOLECULAR COMPOUNDS
Smallest components are ions (e.g., Na^+, Cl^-)	Smallest components are molecules (e.g., CO_2, H_2O)
Usually composed of metals combined with nonmetals	Usually composed of nonmetals with nonmetals
Crystalline solids	Gases, liquids, or low-melting solids
High melting points (e.g., NaCl = 801 °C)	Low melting points (H_2O = 0.0 °C)
High boiling points (above 700 °C) (e.g., NaCl = 1413 °C)	Low boiling points (e.g. H_2O = 100 °C; CH_3CH_2OH = 76 °C)
Conduct electricity when molten or dissolved in water	Do not conduct electricity
Many are water-soluble	Relatively few are water-soluble
Not soluble in organic liquids	Many are soluble in organic liquids

PROBLEM 5.25

A white crystalline solid has a melting point of 128 °C. It is soluble in water, but the resulting solution does not conduct electricity. Is the substance ionic or molecular? Explain.

PROBLEM 5.26

Aluminum chloride ($AlCl_3$) has a melting point of 190 °C, whereas aluminum oxide (Al_2O_3) has a melting point of 2070 °C. Explain.

KEY WORDS

Binary compound, *p. 132*

Bond angle, *p. 123*

Bond length, *p. 109*

Condensed structure, *p. 118*

Coordinate covalent bond, *p. 115*

Covalent bond, *p. 107*

Double bond, *p. 113*

Electronegativity, *p. 129*

Lewis structure, *p. 117*

Lone pair, *p. 117*

Molecular compound, *p. 110*

Molecular formula, *p. 117*

Molecule, *p. 107*

Polar covalent bond, *p. 128*

Regular tetrahedron, *p. 124*

Single bond, *p. 113*

Structural formula, *p. 117*

Triple bond, *p. 113*

Valence-shell electron-pair repulsion (VSEPR) model, *p. 122*

SUMMARY: REVISITING THE CHAPTER GOALS

1. **What is a covalent bond?** A *covalent bond* is formed by the sharing of electrons between atoms rather than by the complete transfer of electrons from one atom to another. Atoms that share two electrons are joined by a *single bond* (such as C—C), atoms that share four electrons are joined by a *double bond* (such as C=C), and atoms that share six electrons are joined by a *triple bond* (such as C≡C). The group of atoms held together by covalent bonds is called a *molecule*.

   Electron sharing typically occurs when a singly occupied valence orbital on one atom *overlaps* a singly occupied valence orbital on another atom. The two electrons occupy both overlapping orbitals and belong to both atoms, thereby bonding the atoms together. Alternatively, electron sharing can occur when a filled orbital containing an unshared, *lone pair* of electrons on one atom overlaps a vacant orbital on another atom to form a *coordinate covalent bond*.

2. **How does the octet rule apply to covalent bond formation?** Depending on the number of valence electrons, different atoms form different numbers of covalent bonds. In general, an atom shares enough electrons to reach a noble gas configuration. Hydrogen, for instance, forms one covalent bond because it needs to share one more electron to achieve the helium configuration ($1s^2$). Carbon and other group 4A elements form four covalent bonds because they need to share four more electrons to reach an octet. In the same way, nitrogen and other group 5A elements form three covalent bonds, oxygen and other group 6A elements form two covalent bonds, and halogens (group 7A elements) form one covalent bond.

3. **How are molecular compounds represented?** Formulas such as H_2O, NH_3, and CH_4, which show the numbers and kinds of atoms in a molecule, are called *molecular formulas*. More useful are *Lewis structures*, which show how atoms are connected in molecules. Covalent bonds are indicated as lines between atoms, and valence electron lone pairs are shown as dots. Lewis structures are drawn by counting the total number of valence electrons in a molecule or polyatomic ion and then placing shared pairs (bonding) and lone pairs (nonbonding) so that all electrons are accounted for.

4. **What is the influence of valence-shell electrons on molecular shape?** Molecules have specific shapes that depend on the number of electron charge clouds (bonds and lone pairs) surrounding the various atoms. These shapes can often be predicted using the *valence-shell electron-pair repulsion (VSEPR)* model. Atoms with two electron charge clouds adopt linear geometry, atoms with three charge clouds adopt planar triangular geometry, and atoms with four charge clouds adopt tetrahedral geometry.

5. **When are bonds and molecules polar?** Bonds between atoms are *polar covalent* if the bonding electrons are not shared equally between the atoms. The ability of an atom to attract electrons in a covalent bond is the atom's *electronegativity* and is highest for reactive nonmetal elements on the upper right of the periodic table and lowest for metals on the lower left. Comparing electronegativities allows a prediction of whether a given bond is covalent, polar covalent, or ionic. Just as individual bonds can be polar, entire molecules can be polar if electrons are attracted more strongly to one part of the molecule than to another. Molecular polarity is due to the sum of all individual bond polarities and lone-pair contributions in the molecule.

6. **What are the major differences between ionic and molecular compounds?** *Molecular compounds* can be gases, liquids, or low-melting solids. They usually have lower melting points and boiling points than ionic compounds, many are water insoluble, and they do not conduct electricity when melted or dissolved.

UNDERSTANDING KEY CONCEPTS

5.27 Which of the drawings shown here is more likely to represent an ionic compound and which a covalent compound?

(a)   (b)

5.28 If yellow spheres represent sulfur atoms and red spheres represent oxygen atoms, which of the following drawings depicts a collection of sulfur dioxide molecules?

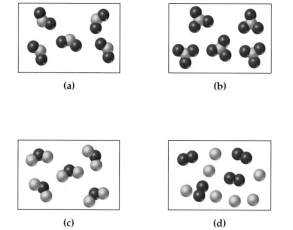

(a)   (b)

(c)   (d)

5.29 What is the geometry around the central atom in the following molecular models? (There are no "hidden" atoms; all atoms in each model are visible.)

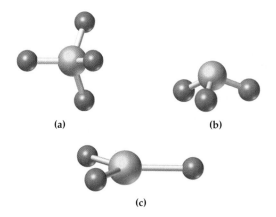

(a)   (b)

(c)

5.30 Three of the following molecular models have a tetrahedral central atom, and one does not. Which is the odd one?

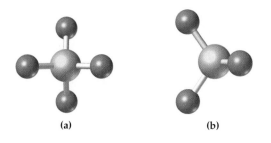

(a)   (b)

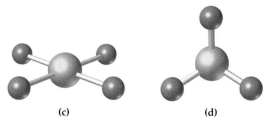

(c)   (d)

5.31 The ball-and-stick molecular model shown here is a representation of acetaminophen, the active ingredient in such over-the-counter headache remedies as Tylenol. The lines indicate only the connections between atoms, not whether the bonds are single, double, or triple (red = O, gray = C, blue = N, ivory = H).

(a) What is the molecular formula of acetaminophen?

(b) Indicate the positions of the multiple bonds in acetaminophen.

(c) What is the geometry around each carbon and each nitrogen?

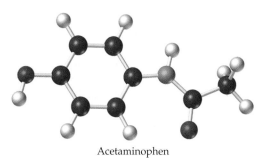

Acetaminophen

5.32 The atom-to-atom connections in vitamin C (ascorbic acid) are as shown here. Convert this skeletal drawing to a Lewis electron-dot structure for vitamin C by showing the positions of any multiple bonds and lone pairs of electrons.

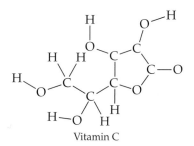

Vitamin C

5.33 The ball-and-stick molecular model shown here is a representation of thalidomide, a drug that causes terrible birth defects when taken by expectant mothers but has been approved for treating leprosy. The lines indicate only the connections between atoms, not whether the bonds are single, double, or triple (red = O, gray = C, blue = N, ivory = H).

(a) What is the molecular formula of thalidomide?

(b) Indicate the positions of the multiple bonds in thalidomide.

(c) What is the geometry around each carbon and each nitrogen?

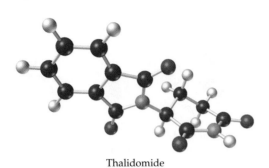

Thalidomide

5.34 Show the position of any electron lone pairs in this structure of acetamide, and indicate the electron-rich and electron-poor regions.

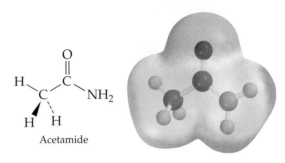

Acetamide

ADDITIONAL PROBLEMS

COVALENT BONDS

5.35 What is a covalent bond, and how does it differ from an ionic bond?

5.36 What is a coordinate covalent bond and how does it differ from a covalent bond?

5.37 Which of the following elements would you expect to form (i) diatomic molecules, (ii) mainly covalent bonds, (iii) mainly ionic bonds, (iv) both covalent and ionic bonds? (More than one answer may apply.)

(a) Oxygen
(b) Potassium
(c) Phosphorus
(d) Iodine
(e) Hydrogen
(f) Cesium

5.38 Identify the bonds formed between the following pairs of atoms as either covalent or ionic.

(a) Aluminum and bromine
(b) Carbon and fluorine
(c) Cesium and iodine
(d) Zinc and fluorine
(e) Lithium and chlorine

5.39 Write electron-dot symbols to show the number of covalent bonds in the molecules that are formed by reactions between the atoms in Problem 5.38.

5.40 Look up tellurium ($Z = 52$) in the periodic table and predict how many covalent bonds it is likely to form. Explain.

5.41 Germanium (atomic number 32) is an element used in the manufacture of transistors. Judging from its position in the periodic table, how many covalent bonds does it usually form?

5.42 Which of the following contains a coordinate covalent bond?

(a) $PbCl_2$ **(b)** $Cu(NH_3)_4{}^{2+}$ **(c)** $NH_4{}^+$

5.43 Which of the following contain a coordinate covalent bond?

(a) H_2O **(b)** $BF_4{}^-$ **(c)** H_3O^+

5.44 Tin forms both an ionic compound and a covalent compound with chlorine. The ionic compound is $SnCl_2$. Is the covalent compound more likely to be $SnCl_3$, $SnCl_4$, or $SnCl_5$? Explain.

5.45 A compound of gallium with chlorine has a melting point of 77 °C and a boiling point of 201 °C. Is the compound ionic or covalent? What is a likely formula?

5.46 Nitrous oxide, N_2O, has the following structure. Which bond in N_2O is a coordinate covalent bond?

$$:N\!\equiv\!N\!-\!\ddot{\underset{..}{O}}:$$

Nitrous oxide

5.47 Thionyl chloride, $SOCl_2$, has the following structure. Which bond in $SOCl_2$ is a coordinate covalent bond?

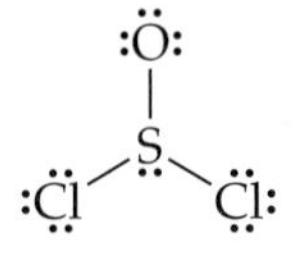

Thionyl chloride

STRUCTURAL FORMULAS

5.48 Distinguish between the following:

(a) A molecular formula and a structural formula
(b) A structural formula and a condensed structure
(c) A lone pair and a shared pair of electrons

5.49 Assume that you are given samples of two white, crystalline compounds, one of them ionic and one covalent. Describe how you might tell which is which.

5.50 Give the total number of valence electrons in the following molecules:

(a) N_2 **(b)** CO
(c) CH_3CH_2CHO **(d)** OF_2

5.51 Add lone pairs where appropriate to the following structures:

(a) $C\!\equiv\!O$ **(b)** CH_3SH

(c) 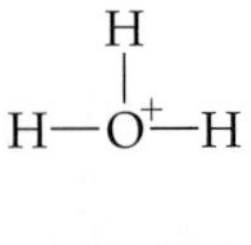 $H\!-\!\overset{H}{\underset{|}{O}}{}^+\!\!-\!H$ **(d)** 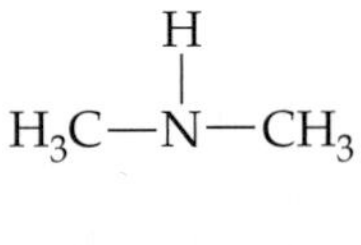 $H_3C\!-\!\overset{H}{\underset{|}{N}}\!-\!CH_3$

5.52 If a research paper appeared reporting the structure of a new molecule with formula C_2H_8, most chemists would be highly skeptical. Why?

5.53 Which of these possible structural formulas for $C_3H_6O_2$ is correct? Explain.

(a)

(b)

(c)

5.54 Convert the following Lewis structures into structural formulas in which lines replace the bonding electrons. Include the lone pairs.

(a) $H:\ddot{O}:\ddot{N}::\ddot{O}:$ (b) $H:\ddot{C}:C:::N:$ with H below   (c) $H:\ddot{F}:$

5.55 Convert the following Lewis structure for the nitrate ion into a line structure that includes the lone pairs. Why does the nitrate ion have a −1 charge?

5.56 Convert the following structural formulas into condensed structures.

(a)   (b)

(c)

5.57 Expand the following condensed structures into the correct structural formulas.

(a) $CH_3COCH_2CH_3$
(b) CH_3CH_2COOH
(c) $CH_3CH_2OCH_3$

5.58 Acetic acid is the major organic constituent of vinegar. Convert the following structural formula of acetic acid into a condensed structure.

DRAWING LEWIS STRUCTURES

5.59 Draw a Lewis structure for the following molecules:
(a) SiF_4
(b) $AlCl_3$
(c) CH_2O
(d) SO_2
(e) BBr_3
(f) NF_3

5.60 Draw a Lewis structure for the following molecules:
(a) Nitrous acid, HNO_2 (H is bonded to an O atom)
(b) Ozone, O_3
(c) Acetaldehyde, CH_3CHO

5.61 Ethanol, or "grain alcohol," has the formula C_2H_6O and contains an O—H bond. Propose a structure for ethanol that is consistent with common bonding patterns.

5.62 Dimethyl ether has the same molecular formula as ethanol (Problem 5.61) but very different properties. Propose a structure for dimethyl ether in which the oxygen is bonded to two carbons.

5.63 Hydrazine, a substance used to make rocket fuel, has the formula N_2H_4. Propose a structure for hydrazine.

5.64 Tetrachloroethylene, C_2Cl_4, is used commercially as a dry cleaning solvent. Propose a structure for tetrachloroethylene based on the common bonding patterns expected in organic molecules. What kind of carbon–carbon bond is present?

5.65 Draw a Lewis structure for carbon disulfide, CS_2, a foul-smelling liquid used as a solvent for fats. What kind of carbon–sulfur bonds are present?

5.66 Draw a Lewis structure for hydroxylamine, NH_2OH.

5.67 The nitrate ion, NO_3^-, contains a double bond. Draw a Lewis structure for the ion and show why it has a negative charge.

5.68 Draw a Lewis structure for the following polyatomic ions:
(a) Formate, HCO_2^-
(b) Carbonate, CO_3^{2-}
(c) Sulfite, SO_3^{2-}
(d) Thiocyanate, SCN^-
(e) Phosphate, PO_4^{3-}
(f) Chlorite, ClO_2^- (chloride is the central atom)

MOLECULAR GEOMETRY

5.69 Predict the geometry and bond angles around atom A for molecules with the general formulas AB_3 and AB_2E, where B represents another atom and E represents an electron pair.

5.70 Predict the geometry and bond angles around atom A for molecules with the general formulas AB_4, AB_3E, and AB_2E_2, where B represents another atom and E represents an electron pair.

5.71 Sketch the three-dimensional shape of the following molecules:
(a) Chloroform, $CHCl_3$
(b) Hydrogen sulfide, H_2S
(c) Ozone, O_3
(d) Nitrogen triiodide, NI_3
(e) Chlorous acid, $HClO_2$

CHAPTER 6

Chemical Reactions: Classification and Mass Relationships

CONCEPTS TO REVIEW

Problem Solving: Converting a Quantity from One Unit to Another
(Section 2.7)

Periodic Properties and Ion Formation
(Section 4.2)

H^+ and OH^- Ions: An Introduction to Acids and Bases
(Section 4.11)

▲ The A320 Airbus shown on the assembly line in Toulouse, France. Commercial air transport relies on oxidation-reduction reactions, from the production of lightweight materials used for construction to the generation of energy required for flight.

CONTENTS

CHAPTER GOALS

Among the questions we will answer are the following:

1. How are chemical reactions written?

THE GOAL: Given the identities of reactants and products, be able to write a balanced chemical equation or net ionic equation.

2. What is the mole, and why is it useful in chemistry?

THE GOAL: Be able to explain the meaning and uses of the mole and Avogadro's number.

3. How are molar quantities and mass quantities related?

THE GOAL: Be able to convert between molar and mass quantities of an element or compound.

4. What are the limiting reagent, theoretical yield, and percent yield of a reaction?

THE GOAL: Be able to take the amount of product actually formed in a reaction, calculate the amount that could form theoretically, and express the results as a percent yield.

5. How are chemical reactions of ionic compounds classified?

THE GOAL: Be able to recognize precipitation, acid–base neutralization, and redox reactions.

6. What are oxidation numbers, and how are they used?

THE GOAL: Be able to assign oxidation numbers to atoms in compounds and identify the substances oxidized and reduced in a given reaction.

A log burns in the fireplace, an oyster makes a pearl, a seed grows into a plant—these and almost all other changes you see taking place around you are the result of *chemical reactions*. The study of how and why chemical reactions happen is a major part of chemistry, providing information that is both fascinating and practical. In this chapter, we will begin to look at chemical reactions, starting with a discussion of how to represent them in writing. Next we will describe the mass relationships among substances involved in chemical reactions, and then introduce a few easily recognized classes of chemical reactions.

6.1 Chemical Equations

One way to view chemical reactions is to think of them as "recipes." Like recipes, all the "ingredients" in a chemical equation and their relative amounts are given, as well as the amount of product that would be obtained. Take, for example, a recipe for making s'mores, a concoction of chocolate, marshmallows, and graham crackers, which could be written as

Graham crackers + Roasted marshmallows + Chocolate bars $\longrightarrow$ S'mores

This recipe, however, is simply a list of ingredients and gives no indication of the relative amounts of each ingredient, or how many s'mores we would obtain. A more detailed recipe would be

2 Graham crackers + 1 Roasted marshmallow + $\frac{1}{4}$ Chocolate bar $\longrightarrow$ 1 S'more

In this case, the relative amounts of each ingredient are given, as well as the amount of the final product.

Let us extend this analogy to a typical chemical reaction. When sodium bicarbonate is heated in the range 50–100 °C, sodium carbonate, water, and carbon dioxide are produced. In words, we might write the reaction as

Sodium bicarbonate $\xrightarrow{\text{Heat}}$ Sodium carbonate + Water + Carbon dioxide

Just as in the recipe, the starting materials and final products are listed. Replacing the chemical names with formulas converts the word description of this reaction into a **chemical equation**:

$$\underbrace{2\,NaHCO_3}_{\text{Reactant}} \xrightarrow{\text{Heat}} \underbrace{Na_2CO_3 + H_2O + CO_2}_{\text{Products}}$$

Chemical equation An expression in which symbols and formulas are used to represent a chemical reaction.

Reactant A substance that undergoes change in a chemical reaction and is written on the left side of the reaction arrow in a chemical equation.

Product A substance that is formed in a chemical reaction and is written on the right side of the reaction arrow in a chemical equation.

Balanced equation A chemical equation in which the numbers and kinds of atoms are the same on both sides of the reaction arrow.

Coefficient A number placed in front of a formula to balance a chemical equation.

Look at how this equation is written. The **reactants** are written on the left, the **products** are written on the right, and an arrow is placed between them to indicate a chemical change. Conditions necessary for the reaction to occur—heat in this particular instance—are often specified above the arrow.

Why is the number 2 placed before $NaHCO_3$ in the equation? The 2 is necessary because of a fundamental law of nature called the *law of conservation of mass*:

Law of conservation of mass Matter is neither created nor destroyed in chemical reactions.

The bonds between atoms in the reactants are rearranged to form new compounds in chemical reactions, but none of the atoms disappear and no new ones are formed. As a consequence, chemical equations must be **balanced**, meaning that *the numbers and kinds of atoms must be the same on both sides of the reaction arrow*.

The numbers placed in front of formulas to balance equations are called **coefficients**, and they multiply all the atoms in a formula. Thus, the symbol "$2\,NaHCO_3$" indicates two units of sodium bicarbonate, which contain 2 Na atoms, 2 H atoms, 2 C atoms, and 6 O atoms ($2 \times 3 = 6$, the coefficient times the subscript for O). Count the numbers of atoms on the right side of the equation to convince yourself that it is indeed balanced.

The substances that take part in chemical reactions may be solids, liquids, or gases, or they may be dissolved in a solvent. Ionic compounds, in particular, frequently undergo reaction in *aqueous solution*— that is, dissolved in water. Sometimes this information is added to an equation by placing the appropriate symbols after the formulas:

(s)	(l)	(g)	(aq)
Solid	Liquid	Gas	Aqueous solution

Thus, the decomposition of solid sodium bicarbonate can be written as

$$2\,NaHCO_3(s) \xrightarrow{\text{Heat}} Na_2CO_3(s) + H_2O(l) + CO_2(g)$$

WORKED EXAMPLE **6.1** Balancing Chemical Reactions

Interpret in words the following equation for the reaction used in extracting lead metal from its ores. Show that the equation is balanced.

$$2\,PbS(s) + 3\,O_2(g) \longrightarrow 2\,PbO(s) + 2\,SO_2(g)$$

SOLUTION
The equation can be read as, "Solid lead(II) sulfide plus gaseous oxygen yields solid lead(II) oxide plus gaseous sulfur dioxide."

To show that the equation is balanced, count the atoms of each element on each side of the arrow:

On the left:	2 Pb	2 S	$(3 \times 2)\,O = 6\,O$
On the right:	2 Pb	2 S	$2\,O + (2 \times 2)\,O = 6\,O$

From 2 PbO   From 2 SO$_2$

The numbers of atoms of each element are the same in the reactants and products, so the equation is balanced.

PROBLEM 6.1

Interpret the following equations in words:

(a) $CoCl_2(s) + 2\,HF(g) \longrightarrow CoF_2(s) + 2\,HCl(g)$

(b) $Pb(NO_3)_2(aq) + 2\,KI(aq) \longrightarrow PbI_2(s) + 2\,KNO_3(aq)$

PROBLEM 6.2

Which of the following equations are balanced?

(a) $HCl + KOH \longrightarrow H_2O + KCl$

(b) $CH_4 + Cl_2 \longrightarrow CH_2Cl_2 + HCl$

(c) $H_2O + MgO \longrightarrow Mg(OH)_2$

(d) $Al(OH)_3 + H_3PO_4 \longrightarrow AlPO_4 + 2\,H_2O$

6.2 Balancing Chemical Equations

Just as a recipe indicates the appropriate amounts of each ingredient needed to make a given product, a balanced chemical equation indicates the appropriate amounts of reactants needed to generate a given amount of product. Balancing chemical equations can often be done using a mixture of common sense and trial-and-error. There are four steps:

STEP 1: Write an unbalanced equation, using the correct formulas for all reactants and products. For example, hydrogen and oxygen must be written as H_2 and O_2, rather than as H and O, since we know that both elements exist as diatomic molecules. Remember that *the subscripts in chemical formulas cannot be changed in balancing an equation because doing so would change the identity of the substances in the reaction.*

STEP 2: Add appropriate coefficients to balance the numbers of atoms of each element. It helps to begin with elements that appear in only one formula on each side of the equation, which usually means leaving oxygen and hydrogen until last. For example, in the reaction of sulfuric acid with sodium hydroxide to give sodium sulfate and water, we might balance first for sodium. We could do this by adding a coefficient of 2 for NaOH:

$$H_2SO_4 + NaOH \longrightarrow Na_2SO_4 + H_2O \quad \text{(Unbalanced)}$$
$$H_2SO_4 + 2\,NaOH \longrightarrow Na_2SO_4 + H_2O \quad \text{(Balanced for Na)}$$

Add this coefficient . . . . . . to balance these 2 Na.

If a polyatomic ion appears on both sides of an equation, it is treated as a single unit. For example, the sulfate ion ($SO_4{}^{2-}$) in our example is balanced because there is one on the left and one on the right:

$$H_2SO_4 + 2\,NaOH \longrightarrow Na_2SO_4 + H_2O \quad \text{(Balanced for Na and sulfate)}$$

One sulfate here . . . . . . and one here.

At this point, the equation can be balanced for H and O by adding a coefficient of 2 for H_2O

$$H_2SO_4 + 2\,NaOH \longrightarrow Na_2SO_4 + 2\,H_2O \quad \text{(Completely balanced)}$$

4 H and 2 O here. 4 H and 2 O here.

STEP 3: Check the equation to make sure the numbers and kinds of atoms on both sides of the equation are the same.

STEP 4: Make sure the coefficients are reduced to their lowest whole-number values. For example, the equation

$$2\,H_2SO_4 + 4\,NaOH \longrightarrow 2\,Na_2SO_4 + 4\,H_2O$$

is balanced but can be simplified by dividing all coefficients by 2:

$$H_2SO_4 + 2\,NaOH \longrightarrow Na_2SO_4 + 2\,H_2O$$

WORKED EXAMPLE **6.2** Balancing Chemical Equations

Write a balanced chemical equation for the Haber process, an important industrial reaction in which elemental nitrogen and hydrogen combine to form ammonia according to the following unbalanced reaction:

$$N_2(g) + H_2(g) \longrightarrow NH_3(g)$$

SOLUTION

STEP 1: Write an unbalanced equation, using the correct formulas for all reactants and products. The unbalanced equation is provided above. By examination, we see that only two elements, N and H, need to be balanced. Both these elements exist in nature as diatomic gases, as indicated on the reactant side of the unbalanced equation.

STEP 2: Add appropriate coefficients to balance the numbers of atoms of each element. Remember that the subscript 2 in N_2 and H_2 indicates that these are diatomic molecules (that is, two N atoms or two H atoms per molecule). Since there are two nitrogen atoms on the left, we must add a coefficient of 2 in front of the NH_3 on the right side of the equation to balance the equation with respect to N:

$$N_2(g) + H_2(g) \longrightarrow 2\,NH_3(g)$$

Now we see that there are two H atoms on the left, but six H atoms on the right. We can balance the equation with respect to hydrogen by adding a coefficient of 3 in front of the $H_2(g)$ on the left side:

$$N_2(g) + 3\,H_2(g) \longrightarrow 2\,NH_3(g)$$

STEP 3: Check the equation to make sure the numbers and kinds of atoms on both sides of the equation are the same.

On the left: $(1 \times 2)\,N = 2\,N$ $(3 \times 2)\,H = 6\,H$

On the right: $(2 \times 1)\,N = 2\,N$ $(2 \times 3)\,H = 6\,H$

STEP 4: Make sure the coefficients are reduced to their lowest whole-number values. In this case, the coefficients already represent the lowest whole-number ratios.

WORKED EXAMPLE **6.3** Balancing Chemical Equations

Natural gas (methane, CH_4) burns in oxygen to yield water and carbon dioxide (CO_2). Write a balanced equation for the reaction.

SOLUTION

STEP 1: Write the unbalanced equation, using correct formulas for all substances:

$$CH_4 + O_2 \longrightarrow CO_2 + H_2O \text{ (Unbalanced)}$$

STEP 2: Since carbon appears in one formula on each side of the arrow, let us begin with that element. In fact, there is only one carbon atom in each formula, so the equation is already balanced for that element. Next, note that there are four hydrogen atoms on the left (in CH_4) and only two on the right (in H_2O). Placing a coefficient of 2 before H_2O gives the same number of hydrogen atoms on both sides:

$$CH_4 + O_2 \longrightarrow CO_2 + 2\,H_2O \text{ (Balanced for C and H)}$$

Finally, look at the number of oxygen atoms. There are two on the left (in O_2) but four on the right (two in CO_2 and one in each H_2O). If we place a 2 before the O_2, the number of oxygen atoms will be the same on both sides, but the numbers of other elements will not change:

$$CH_4 + 2\,O_2 \longrightarrow CO_2 + 2\,H_2O \text{ (Balanced for C, H, and O)}$$

STEP 3: Check to be sure the numbers of atoms on both sides are the same.

On the left: 1 C $\qquad$ 4 H $\qquad$ $(2 \times 2)\,O = 4\,O$

On the right: 1 C $\quad$ $(2 \times 2)\,H = 4\,H$ $\qquad$ $2\,O + 2\,O = 4\,O$

From CO_2 $\qquad$ From 2 H_2O

STEP 4: Make sure the coefficients are reduced to their lowest whole-number values. In this case, the answer is already correct.

WORKED EXAMPLE **6.4** Balancing Chemical Equations

Sodium chlorate ($NaClO_3$) decomposes when heated to yield sodium chloride and oxygen, a reaction used to provide oxygen for the emergency breathing masks in airliners. Write a balanced equation for this reaction.

▲ The oxygen in emergency breathing masks comes from heating sodium chlorate.

SOLUTION

STEP 1: The unbalanced equation is

$$NaClO_3 \longrightarrow NaCl + O_2$$

STEP 2: Both the Na and the Cl are already balanced, with only one atom of each on the left and right sides of the equation. There are three O atoms on the left, but only two on the right. The O atoms can be balanced by placing a coefficient of 1½ in front of O_2 on the right side of the equation:

$$NaClO_3 \longrightarrow NaCl + 1^1/_2 O_2$$

STEP 3: Checking to make sure the same number of atoms of each type occurs on both sides of the equation, we see one atom of Na and Cl on both sides, and three O atoms on both sides.

STEP 4: In this case, obtaining all coefficients in their smallest whole-number values requires that we multiply all coefficients by 2 to obtain

$$2\,NaClO_3 \longrightarrow 2\,NaCl + 3\,O_2$$

Checking gives

On the left: 2 Na 2 Cl $(2 \times 3)\,O = 6\,O$

On the right: 2 Na 2 Cl $(3 \times 2)\,O = 6\,O$

PROBLEM 6.3

Ozone (O_3) is formed in the earth's upper atmosphere by the action of solar radiation on oxygen molecules (O_2). Write a balanced equation for the formation of ozone from oxygen.

PROBLEM 6.4

Balance the following equations:

(a) $Ca(OH)_2 + HCl \longrightarrow CaCl_2 + H_2O$

(b) $Al + O_2 \longrightarrow Al_2O_3$

(c) $CH_3CH_3 + O_2 \longrightarrow CO_2 + H_2O$

(d) $AgNO_3 + MgCl_2 \longrightarrow AgCl + Mg(NO_3)_2$

KEY CONCEPT PROBLEM 6.5

The following diagram represents the reaction of A (red spheres) with B_2 (blue spheres). Write a balanced equation for the reaction.

6.3 Avogadro's Number and the Mole

The balanced chemical equation indicates what is happening at the molecular level. Now let us imagine a laboratory experiment: the reaction of ethylene (C_2H_4) with hydrogen chloride (HCl) to prepare ethyl chloride (C_2H_5Cl), a colorless, low-boiling liquid used by doctors and athletic trainers as a spray-on anesthetic. The reaction is represented as

$$C_2H_4(g) + HCl(g) \rightarrow C_2H_5Cl(g)$$

In this reaction, one molecule of ethylene reacts with one molecule of hydrogen chloride to produce one molecule of ethyl chloride.

How, though, can you be sure you have a 1 to 1 ratio of reactant molecules in your reaction flask? Since it is impossible to hand-count the number of molecules correctly, you must weigh them instead. (This is a common method for dealing with all kinds of small objects: Nails, nuts, and grains of rice are all weighed rather than counted.) But the weighing approach leads to another problem. How many molecules are there in one gram of ethylene, hydrogen chloride, or any other substance? The answer depends on the identity of the substance because different molecules have different masses.

To determine how many molecules of a given substance are in a certain mass, it is helpful to define a quantity called *molecular weight*. Just as the *atomic* weight of an element is the average mass of the element's *atoms* (Section 3.3), the **molecular weight (MW)** of a molecule is the average mass of a substance's *molecules*. (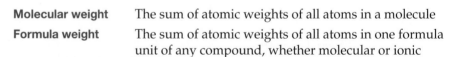 p. 55) Numerically, a substance's molecular weight (or **formula weight** for an ionic compound) is equal to the sum of the atomic weights for all the atoms in the molecule or formula unit.

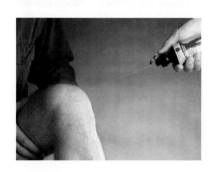

▲ Ethyl chloride is often used as a spray-on anesthetic for athletic injuries.

| **Molecular weight** | The sum of atomic weights of all atoms in a molecule |
| **Formula weight** | The sum of atomic weights of all atoms in one formula unit of any compound, whether molecular or ionic |

For example, the molecular weight of ethylene (C_2H_4) is 28.0 amu, the molecular weight of HCl is 36.5 amu, and the molecular weight of ethyl chloride (C_2H_5Cl) is 64.5 amu. (The actual values are known more precisely but are rounded off here for convenience.)

For ethylene, C_2H_4:

Atomic weight of 2 C = 2 × 12.0 amu = 24.0 amu

Atomic weight of 4 H = 4 × 1.0 amu = 4.0 amu

MW of C_2H_4 = 28.0 amu

For hydrogen chloride, HCl:

Atomic weight of H = 1.0 amu

Atomic weight of Cl = 35.5 amu

MW of HCl   = 36.5 amu

For ethyl chloride, C_2H_5Cl:

Atomic weight of 2 C = 2 × 12.0 amu = 24.0 amu

Atomic weight of 5 H = 5 × 1.0 amu = 5.0 amu

Atomic weight of Cl   = 35.5 amu

MW of C_2H_5Cl = 64.5 amu

How are molecular weights used? Since the mass ratio of *one* ethylene molecule to *one* HCl molecule is 28.0 to 36.5, the mass ratio of *any* given number of ethylene molecules to the same number of HCl molecules is also 28.0 to 36.5. In other words, a 28.0 to 36.5 *mass* ratio of ethylene and HCl always guarantees a 1 to 1 *number* ratio. *Samples of different substances always contain the same number of molecules or formula units whenever their mass ratio is the same as their molecular or formula weight ratio* (Figure 6.1).

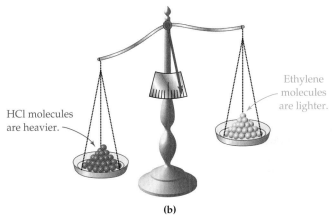

HCl molecules are heavier.

Ethylene molecules are lighter.

(a)   (b)

▲ **FIGURE 6.1**   (a) Because one gumdrop weighs more than one jellybean, you cannot get equal numbers by taking equal weights. The same is true for atoms or molecules of different substances. (b) Equal numbers of ethylene and HCL molecules always have a mass ratio equal to the ratio of their molecular weights, 28.0 to 36.5.

A particularly convenient way to use this mass/number relationship for molecules is to measure amounts in grams that are numerically equal to molecular weights. If, for instance, you were to carry out your experiment with 28.0 g of ethylene and 36.5 g of HCl, you could be certain that you would have a 1 to 1 ratio of reactant molecules.

◀ These samples of water, sulfur, table sugar, mercury, and copper each contain 1 mol. Do they all weigh the same?

When referring to the vast numbers of molecules or formula units that take part in a visible chemical reaction, it is convenient to use a counting unit called a **mole**, abbreviated *mol*. One mole of any substance is the amount whose mass in

Alternatively, suppose we need to know how many moles of water are in 27 g of water. The conversion factor is 1 mol/18.0 g:

> Molar mass used as conversion factor

$$27 \text{ g } H_2O \times \frac{1 \text{ mol } H_2O}{18.0 \text{ g } H_2O} = 1.5 \text{ mol } H_2O$$

Worked Examples 6.7 and 6.8 give more practice in gram–mole conversions.

WORKED EXAMPLE **6.7** Molar Mass: Mole to Gram Conversion

The nonprescription pain relievers Advil and Nuprin contain ibuprofen ($C_{13}H_{18}O_2$), whose molecular weight is 206.3 amu (Problem 6.6a). If all the tablets in a bottle of pain reliever together contain 0.082 mol of ibuprofen, what is the number of grams of ibuprofen in the bottle?

ANALYSIS We are given a number of moles and asked to find the mass. Molar mass is the conversion factor between the two.

BALLPARK ESTIMATE Since 1 mol of ibuprofen has a mass of about 200 g, 0.08 mol has a mass of about $0.08 \times 200 \text{ g} = 16 \text{ g}$.

SOLUTION

STEP 1: Identify known information.	0.082 mol ibuprofen in bottle
STEP 2: Identify answer and units.	mass ibuprofen in bottle = ?? g
STEP 3: Identify conversion factor. We use the molecular weight of ibuprofen to convert from moles to grams.	1 mol ibuprofen = 206.3 g $$\frac{206.3 \text{ g ibuprofen}}{1 \text{ mol ibuprofen}}$$
STEP 4: Solve. Set up an equation using the known information and conversion factor so that unwanted units cancel.	$$0.082 \text{ mol } C_{13}H_{18}O_2 \times \frac{206.3 \text{ g ibuprofen}}{1 \text{ mol ibuprofen}} = 17 \text{ g } C_{13}H_{18}O_2$$

BALLPARK CHECK: The calculated answer is consistent with our estimate of 16 g.

WORKED EXAMPLE **6.8** Molar Mass: Gram to Mole Conversion

The maximum dose of sodium hydrogen phosphate (Na_2HPO_4, MW = 142.0 g/mol) that should be taken in one day for use as a laxative is 3.8 g. How many moles of sodium hydrogen phosphate, how many moles of Na^+ ions, and how many total moles of ions are in this dose?

ANALYSIS Molar mass is the conversion factor between mass and number of moles. The chemical formula Na_2HPO_4 shows that each formula unit contains 2 Na^+ ions and 1 HPO_4^{2-} ion.

BALLPARK ESTIMATE The maximum dose is about two orders of magnitude smaller than the molecular weight (approximately 4 g compared to 142 g). Thus, the number of moles of sodium hydrogen phosphate in 3.8 g should be about two orders of magnitude less than one mole. The number of moles of $NaHPO_4$ and total moles of ions, then, should be on the order of 10^{-2}.

SOLUTION

STEP 1: Identify known information. We are given the mass and molecular weight of Na_2HPO_4.	3.8 g Na_2HPO_4; MW = 142.0 amu
STEP 2: Identify answer and units. We need to find the number of moles of Na_2HPO_4, and the total number of moles of ions.	Moles of Na_2HPO_4 = ?? mol Moles of Na^+ ions = ?? mol Total moles of ions = ?? mol

6.7 Limiting Reagent and

All the calculations we have done in th
100% of the reactants are converted to pr
tice, though. Let us return to the recipe f

2 Graham crackers + 1 Roasted marshr

When you check your supplies, you
marshmallows, and 3 chocolate bars
(Answer = 8!) You have enough graham
but you will run out of marshmallows af
ilar way, when running a chemical re
amounts of reagents to allow all of ther
exhausted first in such a reaction is calle
uct you obtain if the limiting reagen
theoretical yield of the reaction.

Suppose that, while you are making
gets burned to a crisp. If this happens, th
be less than what you predicted base
Similarly, chemical reactions do not alwa
dicted by the initial amount of reactants.
molecules behave as written but other p
addition, some of the product may be lc
product actually formed—the reaction's
theoretical yield. The amount of produc
expressed as a **percent yield**:

$$\text{Percent yield} = \frac{A}{\text{The}}$$

A reaction's actual yield is found by
The theoretical yield is found by using tl
mass calculation like those illustrated
Example 6.11). Worked Examples 6.12–6.
actual yield, and theoretical yield calcula

WORKED EXAMPLE 6.12 Percent Yi

The combustion of acetylene gas (C_2H_2
indicated in the following reaction:

$$2\,C_2H_2(g) + 5\,O_2(g) —$$

When 26.0 g of acetylene is burned in
the theoretical yield of CO_2 is 88.0 g. (
tion if the actual yield is only 72.4 g C(

ANALYSIS The percent yield is calcula
theoretical yield and multiplying by 1(

BALLPARK ESTIMATE The theoretical y
yield (72.4 g) is about 15 g less than the
about 15% less than the theoretical yiel

SOLUTION

$$\text{Percent yield} = \frac{\text{Actual yield}}{\text{Theoretical yield}}$$

BALLPARK CHECK The calculated perc
mate of 85%.

STEP 3: Identify conversion factor. We can use the molecular weight of Na_2HPO_4 to convert from grams to moles.

$$\frac{1\ \text{mol Na}_2\text{HPO}_4}{142.0\ \text{g Na}_2\text{HPO}_4}$$

STEP 4: Solve. We use the known information and conversion factor to obtain moles of Na_2HPO_4; since 1 mol of Na_2HPO_4 contains 2 mol of Na^+ ions and 1 mol of HPO_4^{2-} ions, we multiply these values by the number of moles in the sample.

$$3.8\ \text{g Na}_2\text{HPO}_4 \times \frac{1\ \text{mol Na}_2\text{HPO}_4}{142.0\ \text{g Na}_2\text{HPO}_4} = 0.027\ \text{mol Na}_2\text{HPO}_4$$

$$\frac{2\ \text{mol Na}^+}{1\ \text{mol Na}_2\text{HPO}_4} \times 0.027\ \text{mol Na}_2\text{HPO}_4 = 0.054\ \text{mol Na}^+$$

$$\frac{3\ \text{mol ions}}{1\ \text{mol Na}_2\text{HPO}_4} \times 0.027\ \text{mol Na}_2\text{HPO}_4 = 0.081\ \text{mol ions}$$

BALLPARK CHECK: The calculated answers (0.027 mol Na_2HPO_4, 0.081 mol ions) are on the order of 10^{-2}, consistent with our estimate.

PROBLEM 6.10

How many moles of ethyl alcohol, C_2H_6O, are in a 10.0 g sample? How many grams are in a 0.10 mol sample of ethyl alcohol?

PROBLEM 6.11

Which weighs more, 5.00 g or 0.0225 mol of acetaminophen ($C_8H_9NO_2$)?

6.5 Mole Relationships and Chemical Equations

In a typical recipe, the amount of ingredients needed are specified using a variety of units: The amount of flour, for example, is usually specified in cups, whereas the amount of salt or vanilla flavoring might be indicated in teaspoons. In chemical reactions, the appropriate unit to specify the relationship between reactants and products is the mole.

The coefficients in a balanced chemical equation tell how many *molecules*, and thus how many *moles*, of each reactant are needed and how many molecules, and thus moles, of each product are formed. You can then use molar mass to calculate reactant and product masses. If, for example, you saw the following balanced equation for the industrial synthesis of ammonia, you would know that 3 mol of H_2 (3 mol × 2.0 g/mol = 6.0 g) are required for reaction with 1 mol of N_2 (28.0 g) to yield 2 mol of NH_3 (2 mol × 17.0 g/mol = 34.0 g).

This number of moles of hydrogen . . . . . . reacts with this number of moles of nitrogen . . . to yield this number of moles of ammonia.

$$3\,H_2 \; + \; 1\,N_2 \longrightarrow 2\,NH_3$$

The coefficients can be put in the form of *mole ratios*, which act as conversion factors when setting up factor-label calculations. In the ammonia synthesis, for example, the mole ratio of H_2 to N_2 is 3:1, the mole ratio of H_2 to NH_3 is 3:2, and the mole ratio of N_2 to NH_3 is 1:2:

$$\frac{3\ \text{mol H}_2}{1\ \text{mol N}_2} \qquad \frac{3\ \text{mol H}_2}{2\ \text{mol NH}_3} \qquad \frac{1\ \text{mol N}_2}{2\ \text{mol NH}_3}$$

Worked Example 6.9 shows how to set up and use mole ratios.

STEP 3: Set up factor labels. Ider
mole-ratio factor labels to convert
moles HNO_3, and moles HNO_3 to

STEP 4: BALLPARK CHECK

WORKED EXAMPLE 6.11 Mole

The following reaction produced (
reactant? (The molar mass of CaC_2

$$CaC$$

ANALYSIS Both the known inform
lem. The mass of CaC_2O_4 is first c
of moles of $CaCl_2$ is converted into

BALLPARK ESTIMATE The balance
Because the formula weights of the
CaC_2O_4.

SOLUTION

STEP 1: Write the balanced equat

STEP 2: Identify conversion facto
the mass of CaC_2O_4 into moles, us
to find moles of $CaCl_2$, and conver
of moles of $CaCl_2$ to mass. We will
conversion factors.

STEP 3: Set up factor-labels. We
perform gram to mole and mole to
sions to get from grams CaC_2O_4 to

STEP 4: BALLPARK CHECK

▲ The floral pattern on this glass was
created by *etching*, a process based
on the reaction of HF with glass.

APPLICATION ▶ Anemia – A Limiting Reagent Problem?

Anemia is the most commonly diagnosed blood disorder, with symptoms typically including lethargy, fatigue, poor concentration, and sensitivity to cold. While anemia has many causes, including genetic factors, the most common cause is insufficient dietary intake or absorption of iron.

Hemoglobin (abbreviated Hb), the iron-containing protein found in red blood cells, is responsible for oxygen transport throughout the body (⬭, p. 266) Low iron levels in the body result in decreased production and incorporation of Hb in red blood cells. In addition, blood loss due to injury or to menstruation in women increases the body's demand for iron in order to replace lost Hb. In the United States, nearly 20% of women of child-bearing age suffer from iron-deficiency anemia compared to only 2% of adult men.

The recommended minimum daily iron intake is 8 mg for adult men and 18 mg for pre-menopausal women. One way to ensure sufficient iron intake is a well-balanced diet that includes iron-fortified grains and cereals, red meat, egg yolks, leafy green vegetables, tomatoes, and raisins. Vegetarians should pay extra attention to their diet since the iron in fruits and vegetables is not as readily absorbed by the body as the iron in meat, poultry, and fish. Vitamin supplements containing folic acid and either ferrous sulfate or ferrous glutonate can decrease iron deficiencies, and vitamin C increases the absorption of iron by the body.

▲ Can cooking in cast iron pots decrease anemia?

However, the simplest way to increase dietary iron may be to use cast iron cookware. Studies have demonstrated that the iron content of many foods increases when cooked in an iron pot. Other studies involving Ethiopian children showed that those who ate food cooked in iron cookware were less likely to suffer from iron-deficiency anemia than their playmates who ate similar foods prepared in aluminum cookware.

See Additional Problem 6.94 at the end of the chapter.

Salt An ionic compound formed from reaction of an acid with a base.

Oxidation–reduction (redox) reaction A reaction in which electrons are transferred from one atom to another.

▲ Reaction of aqueous $Pb(NO_3)_2$ with aqueous KI gives a yellow precipitate of PbI_2.

partners. For example, an aqueous solution of lead(II) nitrate reacts with an aqueous solution of potassium iodide to yield an aqueous solution of potassium nitrate plus an insoluble yellow precipitate of lead iodide:

$$Pb(NO_3)_2(aq) + 2\,KI(aq) \longrightarrow 2\,KNO_3(aq) + PbI_2(s)$$

- **Acid–base neutralization reactions** are processes in which an acid reacts with a base to yield water plus an ionic compound called a **salt**. We will look at both acids and bases in more detail in Chapter 10, but you might recall for the moment that we previously defined acids as compounds that produce H^+ ions and bases as compounds that produce OH^- ions when dissolved in water (Section 4.11). (⬭, p. 99) Thus, a neutralization reaction removes H^+ and OH^- ions from solution and yields neutral H_2O. The reaction between hydrochloric acid and sodium hydroxide is a typical example:

$$HCl(aq) + NaOH(aq) \longrightarrow H_2O(l) + NaCl(aq)$$

Note that in this reaction, the "salt" produced is sodium chloride, or common table salt. In a general sense, however, *any* ionic compound produced in an acid–base reaction is also called a salt.

- **Oxidation–reduction reactions**, or **redox reactions**, are processes in which one or more electrons are transferred between reaction partners (atoms, molecules, or ions). As a result of this transfer, the number of electrons assigned to individual atoms in the various reactants change. When metallic magnesium reacts with iodine vapor, for instance, a magnesium atom gives an electron to each of two iodine atoms, forming an Mg^{2+} ion and two I^- ions. The charge on the magnesium changes from 0 to +2, and the charge on each iodine changes from 0 to -1:

$$Mg(s) + I_2(g) \longrightarrow MgI_2(s)$$

WORKED EXAMPLE **6.15** Classifying Chemical Reactions

Classify the following processes as a precipitation, acid–base neutralization, or redox reaction.

(a) $Ca(OH)_2(aq) + 2\,HBr(aq) \longrightarrow 2\,H_2O(l) + CaBr_2(aq)$

(b) $Pb(ClO_4)_2(aq) + 2\,NaCl(aq) \longrightarrow PbCl_2(s) + 2\,NaClO_4(aq)$

(c) $2\,AgNO_3(aq) + Cu(s) \longrightarrow 2\,Ag(s) + Cu(NO_3)_2(aq)$

ANALYSIS One way to identify the class of reaction is to examine the products that form and match them with the descriptions for the types of reactions provided in this section. By process of elimination, we can readily identify the appropriate reaction classification.

SOLUTION

(a) The products of this reaction are water and an ionic compound, or salt ($CaBr_2$). This is consistent with the description of an acid–base neutralization reaction.

(b) This reaction involves two aqueous reactants, $Pb(ClO_4)_2$ and $NaCl$, which combine to form a solid product, $PbCl_2$. This is consistent with a precipitation reaction.

(c) The products of this reaction are a solid, $Ag(s)$, and an aqueous ionic compound, $Cu(NO_3)_2$. This does not match the description of a neutralization reaction, which would form *water* and an ionic compound. One of the products *is* a solid, but the reactants are not both aqueous compound; one of the reactants is *also* a solid (Cu). Therefore, this reaction would not be classified as a precipitation reaction. By process of elimination, then, it must be a redox reaction.

PROBLEM 6.19

Classify each of the following processes as a precipitation, acid–base neutralization, or redox reaction.

(a) $AgNO_3(aq) + KCl(aq) \longrightarrow AgCl(s) + KNO_3(aq)$

(b) $2\,Al(s) + 3\,Br_2(l) \longrightarrow 2\,AlBr_3(s)$

(c) $Ca(OH)_2(aq) + 2\,HNO_3(aq) \longrightarrow 2\,H_2O(l) + Ca(NO_3)_2(aq)$

6.9 Precipitation Reactions and Solubility Guidelines

Now let us look at precipitation reactions in more detail. To predict whether a precipitation reaction will occur on mixing aqueous solutions of two ionic compounds, you must know the **solubilities** of the potential products—how much of each compound will dissolve in a given amount of solvent at a given temperature. If a substance has a low solubility in water, then it is likely to precipitate from an aqueous solution. If a substance has a high solubility in water, then no precipitate will form.

Solubility is a complex matter, and it is not always possible to make correct predictions. As a rule of thumb, though, the following solubility guidelines for ionic compounds are useful.

Solubility The amount of a compound that will dissolve in a given amount of solvent at a given temperature.

General Rules on Solubility

RULE 1. **A compound is probably soluble if it contains one of the following** *cations*:

- Group 1A cation: Li^+, Na^+, K^+, Rb^+, Cs^+
- Ammonium ion: NH_4^+

Oxidizing agent Gains one or more electrons
Causes oxidation
Undergoes reduction
Becomes more negative (or less positive)

Among the simplest of redox processes is the reaction of an element, usually a metal, with an aqueous cation to yield a different element and a different ion. Iron metal reacts with aqueous copper(II) ion, for example, to give iron(II) ion and copper metal. Similarly, magnesium metal reacts with aqueous acid to yield magnesium ion and hydrogen gas. In both cases, the reactant element (Fe or Mg) is oxidized, and the reactant ion (Cu^{2+} or H^+) is reduced.

$$Fe(s) + Cu^{2+}(aq) \longrightarrow Fe^{2+}(aq) + Cu(s)$$
$$Mg(s) + 2\,H^+(aq) \longrightarrow Mg^{2+}(aq) + H_2(g)$$

The reaction of a metal with water or aqueous acid (H^+) to release H_2 gas is a particularly important process. As you might expect based on the periodic properties discussed in Section 4.2, the alkali metals and alkaline earth metals (on the left side of the periodic table) are the most powerful reducing agents (electron donors), so powerful that they even react with pure water, in which the concentration of H^+ is very low. Ionization energy, which is a measure of how easily an element will lose an electron, tends to decrease as we move to the left and down in the periodic table. In contrast, metals toward the middle of the periodic table, such as iron and chromium, do not lose electrons as readily; they react only with aqueous acids but not with water. Those metals near the bottom right of the periodic table, such as platinum and gold, react with neither aqueous acid nor water. At the other extreme, the reactive nonmetals at the top right of the periodic table are extremely weak reducing agents and instead are powerful oxidizing agents (electron acceptors). This is, again, predictable based on the periodic property of electron affinity (, Section 4.2) which becomes more energetically favored as we move up and to the right in the periodic table.

We can make a few generalizations about the redox behavior of metals and nonmetals.

1. In reactions involving metals and nonmetals, metals tend to lose electrons while nonmetals tend to gain electrons. The number of electrons lost or gained can often be predicted based on the position of the element in the periodic table. (, Section 4.5)

2. In reactions involving nonmetals, the "more metallic" element (farther down and/or to the left in the periodic table) tends to lose electrons, and the "less metallic" element (up and/or to the right) tends to gain electrons.

   Redox reactions involve almost every element in the periodic table, and they occur in a vast number of processes throughout nature, biology, and industry. Here are just a few examples:

- **Corrosion** is the deterioration of a metal by oxidation, such as the rusting of iron in moist air. The economic consequences of rusting are enormous: It has been estimated that up to one-fourth of the iron produced in the United States is used to replace bridges, buildings, and other structures that have been destroyed by corrosion. (The raised dot in the formula $Fe_2O_3 \cdot H_2O$ for rust indicates that one water molecule is associated with each Fe_2O_3 in an undefined way.)

- **Combustion** is the burning of a fuel by rapid oxidation with oxygen in air. Gasoline, fuel oil, natural gas, wood, paper, and other organic substances of carbon and hydrogen are the most common fuels that burn in air. Even some metals, though, will burn in air. Magnesium and calcium are examples.

$$CH_4(g) + 2\,O_2(g) \longrightarrow CO_2(g) + 2\,H_2O(l)$$

Methane
(natural gas)

$$2\,Mg(s) + O_2(g) \longrightarrow 2\,MgO(s)$$

▲ Magnesium metal reacts with aqueous acid to give hydrogen gas and Mg^{2+} ion.

- **Respiration** is the process of breathing and using oxygen for the many biological redox reactions that provide the energy that living organisms need. We will see in Chapters 21–22 that energy is released from food molecules slowly and in complex, multistep pathways, but the overall result of respiration is similar to that of combustion reactions. For example, the simple sugar glucose ($C_6H_{12}O_6$) reacts with O_2 to give CO_2 and H_2O according to the following equation:

$$C_6H_{12}O_6 + 6\,O_2 \longrightarrow 6\,CO_2 + 6\,H_2O + Energy$$
Glucose
(a carbohydrate)

- **Bleaching** makes use of redox reactions to decolorize or lighten colored materials. Dark hair is bleached to turn it blond, clothes are bleached to remove stains, wood pulp is bleached to make white paper, and so on. The oxidizing agent used depends on the situation: hydrogen peroxide (H_2O_2) is used for hair, sodium hypochlorite (NaOCl) for clothes, and elemental chlorine for wood pulp, but the principle is always the same. In all cases, colored organic materials are destroyed by reaction with strong oxidizing agents.
- **Metallurgy,** the science of extracting and purifying metals from their ores, makes use of numerous redox processes. Worldwide, approximately 800 million tons of iron is produced each year by reduction of the mineral hematite, Fe_2O_3, with carbon monoxide.

$$Fe_2O_3(s) + 3\,CO(g) \longrightarrow 2\,Fe(s) + 3\,CO_2(g)$$

WORKED EXAMPLE   **6.18** Chemical Reactions: Redox Reactions

For the following reactions, indicate which atom is oxidized and which is reduced, based on the definitions provided in this section. Identify the oxidizing and reducing agents.

(a) $Cu(s) + Pt^{2+}(aq) \rightarrow Cu^{2+}(aq) + 2\,Pt(s)$
(b) $2\,Mg(s) + CO_2(g) \rightarrow 2\,MgO(s) + C(s)$

ANALYSIS The definitions for oxidation include a loss of electrons, an increase in charge, and a gain of oxygen atoms; reduction is defined as a gain of electrons, a decrease in charge, or a loss of oxygen atoms.

SOLUTION

(a) In this reaction, the charge on the Cu atom increases from 0 to 2+. This corresponds to a loss of 2 electrons. The Cu is therefore oxidized, and acts as the reducing agent. Conversely, each Pt^{2+} ion undergoes a decrease in charge from 2+ to 0, corresponding to a gain of 2 electrons per Pt^{2+} ion. The Pt^{2+} is reduced, and acts as the oxidizing agent.

(b) In this case, the gain or loss of oxygen atoms is the easiest way to identify which atoms are oxidized and reduced. The Mg atom is gaining oxygen to form MgO; therefore, the Mg is being oxidized and acts as the reducing agent. The C atom in CO_2 is losing oxygen. Therefore, the C atom is being reduced and acts as the oxidizing agent.

WORKED EXAMPLE   **6.19** Chemical Reactions: Identifying Oxidizing/ Reducing Agents

For the respiration and metallurgy examples discussed above, identify the atoms being oxidized and reduced, and label the oxidizing and reducing agents.

ANALYSIS Again, using the definitions of oxidation and reduction provided in this section, we can determine which atom(s) are gaining/losing electrons or gaining/losing oxygen atoms.

SOLUTION

$$\textit{Respiration:} \quad C_6H_{12}O_6 + 6\,O_2 \longrightarrow 6\,CO_2 + 6\,H_2O$$

Since the charge associated with the individual atoms is not evident, we will use the definition of oxidation/reduction as the gaining/losing of oxygen atoms. In this reaction, there is only one reactant besides oxygen ($C_6H_{12}O_6$), so we must determine *which* atom in the compound is changing. The ratio of carbon to oxygen in $C_6H_{12}O_6$ is 1:1, while the ratio in CO_2 is 1:2. Therefore, the C atoms are gaining oxygen and are oxidized; the C is the reducing agent. The O_2 is the oxidizing agent. Note that the ratio of hydrogen to oxygen in $C_6H_{12}O_6$ and in H_2O is 2:1. The H atoms are neither oxidized nor reduced.

$$\textit{Metallurgy:} \quad Fe_2O_3(s) + 3\,CO(g) \longrightarrow 2\,Fe(s) + 3\,CO_2(g)$$

The Fe_2O_3 is losing oxygen to form Fe(s); it is being reduced, and acts as the oxidizing agent. In contrast, the CO is gaining oxygen to form CO_2; it is being oxidized and acts as the reducing agent.

WORKED EXAMPLE **6.20** Chemical Reactions: Identifying Redox Reactions

For the following reactions, identify the atom(s) being oxidized and reduced:

(a) $2\,Al(s) + 3\,Cl_2(g) \longrightarrow 2\,AlCl_3(s)$

(b) $C(s) + 2\,Cl_2(g) \longrightarrow CCl_4(l)$

ANALYSIS Again, there is no obvious increase or decrease in charge to indicate a gain or loss of electrons. Also, the reactions do not involve a gain or loss of oxygen. We can, however, evaluate the reactions in terms of the typical behavior of metals and nonmetals in reactions.

SOLUTION

(a) In this case, we have the reaction of a metal (Al) with a nonmetal (Cl_2). Since metals tend to lose electrons and nonmetals tend to gain electrons, we can assume that the Al atom is oxidized (loss of electrons), and the Cl_2 is reduced (gains electrons).

(b) In this case, we have a reaction involving two nonmetals. The carbon is the more metallic element (farther to the left) and is more likely to lose electrons (oxidized). The less metallic element (Cl) will tend to gain electrons and be reduced.

PROBLEM 6.23

Identify the oxidized reactant, the reduced reactant, the oxidizing agent, and the reducing agent in the following reactions:

(a) $Fe(s) + Cu^{2+}(aq) \longrightarrow Fe^{2+}(aq) + Cu(s)$

(b) $Mg(s) + Cl_2(g) \longrightarrow MgCl_2(s)$

(c) $2\,Al(s) + Cr_2O_3(s) \longrightarrow 2\,Cr(s) + Al_2O_3(s)$

PROBLEM 6.24

Potassium, a silvery metal, reacts with bromine, a corrosive, reddish liquid, to yield potassium bromide, a white solid. Write the balanced equation, and identify the oxidizing and reducing agents.

APPLICATION ▶ **Batteries**

I magine life without batteries: no cars (they do not start very easily without their batteries!), no heart pacemakers, no flashlights, no hearing aids, no portable computers, radios, cellular phones, or thousands of other things. Modern society cannot exist without batteries.

Although they come in many types and sizes, all batteries are based on redox reactions. In a typical redox reaction carried out in the laboratory—say, the reaction of zinc metal with Ag^+ to yield Zn^{2+} and silver metal—the reactants are simply mixed in a flask and electrons are transferred by direct contact between the reactants. In a battery, however, the two reactants are kept in separate compartments and the electrons are transferred through a wire running between them.

The common household battery used for flashlights and radios is the *dry-cell*, developed in 1866. One reactant is a can of zinc metal, and the other is a paste of solid manganese dioxide. A graphite rod sticks into the MnO_2 paste to provide electrical contact, and a moist paste of ammonium chloride separates the two reactants. When the zinc can and the graphite rod are connected by a wire, zinc sends electrons flowing through the wire toward the MnO_2 in a redox reaction. The resultant electrical current can then be used to light a bulb or power a radio. The accompanying figure shows a cutaway view of a dry-cell battery.

$$Zn(s) + 2\,MnO_2(s) + 2\,NH_4Cl(s) \longrightarrow$$
$$ZnCl_2(aq) + Mn_2O_3(s) + 2\,NH_3(aq) + H_2O(l)$$

Closely related to the dry-cell battery is the familiar *alkaline* battery, in which the ammonium chloride paste is replaced by an alkaline, or basic, paste of NaOH or KOH. The alkaline battery has a longer life than the standard dry-cell battery because the zinc container corrodes less easily under basic conditions. The redox reaction is

$$Zn(s) + 2\,MnO_2(s) \longrightarrow ZnO(aq) + Mn_2O_3(s)$$

The batteries used in implanted medical devices such as pacemakers must be small, corrosion-resistant, reliable, and able to last up to 10 years. Nearly all pacemakers being implanted today—about 750,000 each year—use titanium-encased, lithium-iodine batteries, whose redox reaction is

$$2\,Li(s) + I_2(s) \longrightarrow 2\,LiI(aq)$$

See Additional Problem 6.96 at the end of the chapter.

▲ **Think of all the devices we use every day–laptop computers, cell phones, iPods—that depend on batteries.**

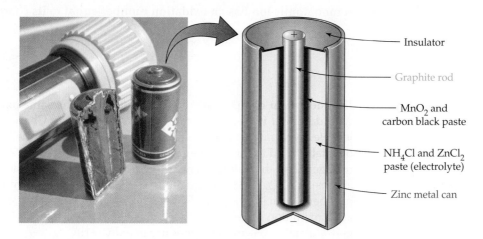

Insulator

Graphite rod

MnO_2 and carbon black paste

NH_4Cl and $ZnCl_2$ paste (electrolyte)

Zinc metal can

▲ **A dry-cell battery. The cutaway view shows the two reactants that make up the redox reaction.**

▲ Sulfur burns in air to yield SO_2. Is this a redox reaction?

Oxidation number A number that indicates whether an atom is neutral, electron-rich, or electron-poor.

6.12 Recognizing Redox Reactions

How can you tell when a redox reaction is taking place? When ions are involved, it is simply a matter of determining whether there is a change in the charges. For reactions involving metals and nonmetals, we can predict gain or loss of electrons as discussed previously. When molecular substances are involved, though, it is not as obvious. Is the combining of sulfur with oxygen a redox reaction? If so, which partner is the oxidizing agent and which is the reducing agent?

$$S(s) + O_2(g) \longrightarrow SO_2(g)$$

One way to evaluate this reaction is in terms of the oxygen gain by sulfur, indicating that S atoms are oxidized and O atoms are reduced. But can we also look at this reaction in terms of the gain or loss of electrons by the S and O atoms? Because oxygen is more electronegative than sulfur (Section 5.8), the oxygen atoms in SO_2 attract the electrons in the S—O bonds more strongly than sulfur does, giving the oxygen atoms a larger share of the electrons than sulfur. (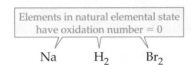, p. 129) By extending the ideas of oxidation and reduction to an increase or decrease in electron *sharing* instead of complete electron *transfer*, we can say that the sulfur atom is oxidized in its reaction with oxygen because it loses a share in some electrons, whereas the oxygen atoms are reduced because they gain a share in some electrons.

A formal system has been devised for keeping track of changes in electron sharing, and thus for determining whether atoms are oxidized or reduced in reactions. To each atom in a substance, we assign a value called an **oxidation number** (or *oxidation state*), which indicates whether the atom is neutral, electron-rich, or electron-poor. By comparing the oxidation number of an atom before and after reaction, we can tell whether the atom has gained or lost shares in electrons. Note that *oxidation numbers do not necessarily imply ionic charges*. They are simply a convenient device for keeping track of electrons in redox reactions.

The rules for assigning oxidation numbers are straightforward:

- **An atom in its elemental state has an oxidation number of 0.**

Elements in natural elemental state
have oxidation number = 0

Na   H₂   Br₂

- **A monatomic ion has an oxidation number equal to its charge.**

Oxidation number +1 — Na⁺   Oxidation number +2 — Ca²⁺   Oxidation number −1 — Cl⁻   Oxidation number −2 — O²⁻

- **In a molecular compound, an atom usually has the same oxidation number it would have if it were a monatomic ion.** Recall from Chapters 4 and 5 that the less electronegative elements (hydrogen and metals) on the left side of the periodic table tend to form cations, and the more electronegative elements (oxygen, nitrogen, and the halogens) near the top right of the periodic table tend to form anions. (, p. 88) Hydrogen and metals therefore have positive oxidation numbers in most compounds, whereas reactive nonmetals generally have negative oxidation numbers. Hydrogen is usually +1, oxygen is usually −2, nitrogen is usually −3, and halogens are usually −1:

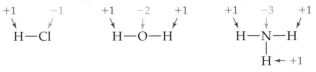

$$\overset{+1}{H}—\overset{-1}{Cl} \qquad \overset{+1}{H}—\overset{-2}{O}—\overset{+1}{H} \qquad \overset{+1}{H}—\overset{-3}{N}—\overset{+1}{H}$$
$$\underset{H}{\overset{|}{}} \leftarrow +1$$

For compounds with more than one nonmetal element, such as SO_2, NO, or CO_2, the more electronegative element—oxygen in these examples—has a negative oxidation number and the less electronegative element has a positive oxidation number. Thus, in answer to the question posed at the beginning of this section, combining sulfur with oxygen to form SO_2 is a redox reaction because the oxidation number of sulfur increases from 0 to +4 and that of oxygen decreases from 0 to −2.

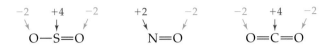

- **The sum of the oxidation numbers in a neutral compound is 0.** Using this rule, the oxidation number of any atom in a compound can be found if the oxidation numbers of the other atoms are known. In the SO_2 example just mentioned, each of the two O atoms has an oxidation number of −2, so the S atom must have an oxidation number of +4. In HNO_3, the H atom has an oxidation number of +1 and the strongly electronegative O atom has an oxidation number of −2, so the N atom must have an oxidation number of +5. In a polyatomic ion, the sum of the oxidation numbers equals the charge on the ion.

$$\overset{+1}{H}-\overset{-2}{O}-\overset{+5}{N}=\overset{-2}{O} \qquad \text{Total} = 1 + 5 + 3(-2) = 0$$
$$\underset{O}{\overset{\ \ }{\big|}}{\scriptstyle -2}$$

Worked Examples 6.21 and 6.22 show further instances of assigning and using oxidation numbers.

WORKED EXAMPLE **6.21** Redox Reactions: Oxidation Numbers

What is the oxidation number of the titanium atom in $TiCl_4$? Name the compound using a Roman numeral (Section 4.11).

SOLUTION
Chlorine, a reactive nonmetal, is more electronegative than titanium and has an oxidation number of −1. Because there are four chlorine atoms in $TiCl_4$, the oxidation number of titanium must be +4. The compound is named titanium(IV) chloride. Note that the Roman numeral IV in the name of this molecular compound refers to the oxidation number +4 rather than to a true ionic charge.

WORKED EXAMPLE **6.22** Redox Reactions: Identifying Redox Reactions

Use oxidation numbers to show that the production of iron metal from its ore (Fe_2O_3) by reaction with charcoal (C) is a redox reaction. Which reactant has been oxidized, and which has been reduced? Which reactant is the oxidizing agent, and which is the reducing agent?

$$2\,Fe_2O_3(s) + 3\,C(s) \longrightarrow 4\,Fe(s) + 3\,CO_2(g)$$

SOLUTION
The idea is to assign oxidation numbers to both reactants and products, and see if there has been a change. In the production of iron from Fe_2O_3, the oxidation number of Fe changes from +3 to 0, and the oxidation number of C changes from 0 to +4. Iron has thus been reduced (decrease in oxidation number), and carbon has been oxidized (increase in oxidation number). Oxygen is neither oxidized nor reduced because its oxidation number does not change. Carbon is the reducing agent and Fe_2O_3 is the oxidizing agent.

$$2\,\overset{+3}{Fe_2}\overset{-2}{O_3} + 3\,\overset{0}{C} \longrightarrow 4\,\overset{0}{Fe} + 3\,\overset{+4}{C}\overset{-2}{O_2}$$

PROBLEM 6.25

What are the oxidation numbers of the metal atoms in the following compounds? Name each, using the oxidation number as a Roman numeral.

(a) VCl_3 **(b)** $SnCl_4$ **(c)** CrO_3 **(d)** $Cu(NO_3)_2$ **(e)** $NiSO_4$

PROBLEM 6.26

Assign an oxidation number to each atom in the reactants and products shown here to determine which of the following reactions are redox reactions:

(a) $Na_2S(aq) + NiCl_2(aq) \longrightarrow 2\,NaCl(aq) + NiS(s)$
(b) $2\,Na(s) + 2\,H_2O(l) \longrightarrow 2\,NaOH(aq) + H_2(g)$
(c) $C(s) + O_2(g) \longrightarrow CO_2(g)$
(d) $CuO(s) + 2\,HCl(aq) \longrightarrow CuCl_2(aq) + H_2O(l)$
(e) $2\,MnO_4^-(aq) + 5\,SO_2(g) + 2\,H_2O(l) \longrightarrow 2\,Mn^{2+}(aq) + 5\,SO_4^{2-}(aq) + 4\,H^+(aq)$

6.13 Net Ionic Equations

In the equations we have been writing up to this point, all the substances involved in reactions have been written using their full formulas. In the precipitation reaction of lead(II) nitrate with potassium iodide mentioned in Section 6.8, for example, only the parenthetical (aq) indicated that the reaction actually takes place in aqueous solution, and nowhere was it explicitly indicated that ions are involved:

$$Pb(NO_3)_2(aq) + 2\,KI(aq) \longrightarrow 2\,KNO_3(aq) + PbI_2(s)$$

In fact, lead(II) nitrate, potassium iodide, and potassium nitrate dissolve in water to yield solutions of ions. Thus, it is more accurate to write the reaction as an **ionic equation**, in which all the ions are explicitly shown:

Ionic equation An equation in which ions are explicitly shown.

An ionic equation: $Pb^{2+}(aq) + 2\,NO_3^-(aq) + 2\,K^+(aq) + 2\,I^-(aq) \longrightarrow$
$$2\,K^+(aq) + 2\,NO_3^-(aq) + PbI_2(s)$$

A look at this ionic equation shows that the NO_3^- and K^+ ions undergo no change during the reaction. They appear on both sides of the reaction arrow and act merely as **spectator ions**, that is, they are present but play no role. The actual reaction, when stripped to its essentials, can be described more simply by writing a **net ionic equation**, which includes only the ions that undergo change and ignores all spectator ions:

Spectator ion An ion that appears unchanged on both sides of a reaction arrow.

Net ionic equation An equation that does not include spectator ions.

Ionic equation: $Pb^{2+}(aq) + 2\,\cancel{NO_3^-}(aq) + 2\,\cancel{K^+}(aq) + 2\,I^-(aq) \longrightarrow$
$$2\,\cancel{K^+}(aq) + 2\,\cancel{NO_3^-}(aq) + PbI_2(s)$$

Net Ionic equation: $Pb^{2+}(aq) + 2\,I^-(aq) \longrightarrow PbI_2(s)$

Note that a net ionic equation, like all chemical equations, must be balanced both for atoms and for charge, with all coefficients reduced to their lowest whole numbers. Note also that all compounds that do *not* give ions in solution—all insoluble compounds and all molecular compounds—are represented by their full formulas.

We can apply the concept of ionic equations to acid–base neutralization reactions and redox reactions as well. Consider the neutralization reaction between KOH and HNO_3:

$$KOH(aq) + HNO_3(aq) \longrightarrow H_2O(l) + KNO_3(aq)$$

Since acids and bases are identified based on the ions they form when dissolved in aqueous solutions, we can write an ionic equation for this reaction:

Ionic equation: $K^+(aq) + OH^-(aq) + H^+(aq) + NO_3^-(aq) \longrightarrow$

$$H_2O(l) + K^+(aq) + NO_3^-(aq)$$

Eliminating the spectator ions (K^+ and NO_3^-) we obtain the net ionic equation for the neutralization reaction:

Net ionic equation: $OH^-(aq) + H^+(aq) \longrightarrow H_2O(l)$

The net ionic equation confirms the basis of the acid–base neutralization; the OH^- from the base and the H^+ from the acid neutralize each other to form water.

Similarly, many redox reactions can be viewed in terms of ionic equations. Consider the reaction between $Cu(s)$ and $AgNO_3$ from Section 6.11:

$$Cu(s) + 2\,AgNO_3(aq) \longrightarrow 2\,Ag^+(aq) + Cu(NO_3)_2(aq)$$

The aqueous products and reactants can be written as dissolved ions:

Ionic equation: $Cu(s) + 2\,Ag^+(aq) + 2\,NO_3^-(aq) \longrightarrow$

$$2\,Ag(s) + Cu^{2+}(aq) + 2\,NO_3^-(aq)$$

Again, eliminating the spectator ions (NO_3^-), we obtain the net ionic equation for this redox reaction:

Net ionic equation: $Cu(s) + 2\,Ag^+(aq) \longrightarrow 2\,Ag(s) + Cu^{2+}(aq)$

It is now clear that the $Cu(s)$ loses two electrons and is oxidized, whereas each Ag^+ ion gains an electron and is reduced.

WORKED EXAMPLE   **6.23** Chemical Reactions: Net Ionic Reactions

Write balanced net ionic equations for the following reactions:

(a) $AgNO_3(aq) + ZnCl_2(aq) \longrightarrow$
(b) $HCl(aq) + Ca(OH)_2(aq) \longrightarrow$
(c) $6\,HCl(aq) + 2\,Al(s) \longrightarrow 2\,AlCl_3(aq) + 3\,H_2(g)$

SOLUTION

(a) The solubility guidelines discussed in Section 6.9 predict that a precipitate of insoluble AgCl forms when aqueous solutions of Ag^+ and Cl^- are mixed. Writing all the ions separately gives an ionic equation, and eliminating spectator ions Zn^{2+} and NO_3^- gives the net ionic equation.

Ionic equation: $2\,Ag^+(aq) + 2\,NO_3^-(aq) + Zn^{2+}(aq) + 2\,Cl^-(aq) \longrightarrow$

$$2\,AgCl(s) + Zn^{2+}(aq) + 2\,NO_3^-(aq)$$

Net ionic equation: $2\,Ag^+(aq) + 2\,Cl^-(aq) \longrightarrow 2\,AgCl(s)$

The coefficients can all be divided by 2 to give

Net ionic equation: $Ag^+(aq) + Cl^-(aq) \longrightarrow AgCl(s)$

A check shows that the equation is balanced for atoms and charge (zero on each side).

(b) Allowing the acid HCl to react with the base $Ca(OH)_2$ leads to a neutralization reaction. Writing the ions separately, and remembering to write a complete formula for water, gives an ionic equation. Then eliminating the spectator ions and dividing the coefficients by 2 gives the net ionic equation.

Ionic equation: $2\,H^+(aq) + \cancel{2\,Cl^-(aq)} + \cancel{Ca^{2+}(aq)} + 2\,OH^-(aq) \longrightarrow$
$2\,H_2O(l) + \cancel{Ca^{2+}(aq)} + \cancel{2\,Cl^-(aq)}$

Net ionic equation: $H^+(aq) + OH^-(aq) \longrightarrow H_2O(l)$

A check shows that atoms and charges are the same on both sides of the equation.

(c) The reaction of Al metal with acid (HCl) is a redox reaction. The Al is oxidized, since the oxidation number increases from $0 \rightarrow +3$, whereas the H in HCl is reduced from $+1 \rightarrow 0$. We write the ionic equation by showing the ions that are formed for each aqueous ionic species. Eliminating the spectator ions yields the net ionic equation.

Ionic equation: $6\,H^+(aq) + \cancel{6\,Cl^-(aq)} + 2\,Al(s) \longrightarrow$
$2\,Al^{3+}(aq) + \cancel{6\,Cl^-(aq)} + 3\,H_2(g)$

Net ionic equation: $6\,H^+(aq) + 2\,Al(s) \longrightarrow 2\,Al^{3+}(aq) + 3\,H_2(g)$

A check shows that atoms and charges are the same on both sides of the equation.

PROBLEM 6.27

Write net ionic equations for the following reactions:

(a) $Zn(s) + Pb(NO_3)_2(aq) \longrightarrow Zn(NO_3)_2(aq) + Pb(s)$
(b) $2\,KOH(aq) + H_2SO_4(aq) \longrightarrow K_2SO_4(aq) + 2\,H_2O(l)$
(c) $2\,FeCl_3(aq) + SnCl_2(aq) \longrightarrow 2\,FeCl_2(aq) + SnCl_4(aq)$

KEY WORDS

Actual yield, *p. 159*

Avogadro's number (N_A), *p. 150*

Balanced equation, *p. 144*

Chemical equation, *p. 143*

Coefficient, *p. 144*

Formula weight, *p. 148*

Ionic equation, *p. 174*

Law of conservation of mass, *p. 144*

Limiting reagent, *p. 159*

Molar mass, *p. 152*

Mole, *p. 150*

Molecular weight (MW), *p. 148*

Net ionic equation, *p. 174*

Neutralization reaction, *p. 165*

SUMMARY: REVISITING THE CHAPTER GOALS

1. **How are chemical reactions written?** Chemical equations must be *balanced;* that is, the numbers and kinds of atoms must be the same in both the reactants and the products. To balance an equation, *coefficients* are placed before formulas but the formulas themselves cannot be changed.

2. **What is the mole, and why is it useful in chemistry?** A *mole* refers to *Avogadro's number* (6.022×10^{23}) of formula units of a substance. One mole of any substance has a mass (a *molar mass*) equal to the molecular or formula weight of the substance in grams. Because equal numbers of moles contain equal numbers of formula units, molar masses act as conversion factors between numbers of molecules and masses in grams.

3. **How are molar quantities and mass quantities related?** The coefficients in a balanced chemical equation represent the numbers of moles of reactants and products in a reaction. Thus, the ratios of coefficients act as *mole ratios* that relate amounts of reactants and/or products. By using molar masses and mole ratios in factor-label calculations, unknown masses or molar amounts can be found from known masses or molar amounts.

4. **What are the limiting reagent, theoretical yield, and percent yield of a reaction?** The *limiting reagent* is the reactant that runs out first. The *theoretical yield* is the amount of product that would be formed based on the amount of the limiting reagent. The *actual yield* of a reaction is the amount of product obtained. The *percent yield* is the amount of product obtained divided by the amount theoretically possible and multiplied by 100%.

5. How are chemical reactions of ionic compounds classified? There are three common types of reactions of ionic compounds: *Precipitation reactions* are processes in which an insoluble solid called a *precipitate* is formed. Most precipitations take place when the anions and cations of two ionic compounds change partners. Solubility guidelines for ionic compounds are used to predict when precipitation will occur.

Acid–base neutralization reactions are processes in which an acid reacts with a base to yield water plus an ionic compound called a *salt*. Since acids produce H^+ ions and bases produce OH^- ions when dissolved in water, a neutralization reaction removes H^+ and OH^- ions from solution and yields neutral H_2O.

Oxidation–reduction (redox) reactions are processes in which one or more electrons are transferred between reaction partners. An *oxidation* is defined as the loss of one or more electrons by an atom, and a *reduction* is the gain of one or more electrons. An *oxidizing agent* causes the oxidation of another reactant by accepting electrons, and a *reducing agent* causes the reduction of another reactant by donating electrons.

6. What are oxidation numbers, and how are they used? *Oxidation numbers* are assigned to atoms in reactants and products to provide a measure of whether an atom is neutral, electron-rich, or electron-poor. By comparing the oxidation number of an atom before and after reaction, we can tell whether the atom has gained or lost shares in electrons and thus whether a redox reaction has occurred.

UNDERSTANDING KEY CONCEPTS

6.28 Assume that the mixture of substances in drawing (a) undergoes a reaction. Which of the drawings (b)–(d) represents a product mixture consistent with the law of conservation of mass?

(a)

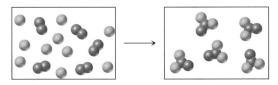

(b)　　　　(c)　　　　(d)

6.29 Reaction of A (green spheres) with B (blue spheres) is shown in the following diagram:

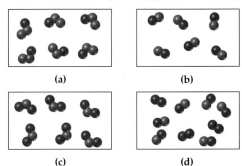

Which equation best describes the reaction?

(a) $A_2 + 2B \longrightarrow A_2B$　　(b) $10A + 5B_2 \longrightarrow 5A_2B_2$
(c) $2A + B_2 \longrightarrow A_2B$　　(d) $5A + 5B_2 \longrightarrow 5A_2B_2$

6.30 If blue spheres represent nitrogen atoms and red spheres represent oxygen atoms in the following diagrams, which box represents reactants and which represents products for the reaction $2NO(g) + O_2(g) \longrightarrow 2NO_2(g)$?

(a)　　　　　　　(b)

(c)　　　　　　　(d)

6.31 Methionine, an amino acid used by organisms to make proteins, can be represented by the following ball-and-stick molecular model. Write the formula for methionine, and give its molecular weight (red = O, gray = C, blue = N, yellow = S, ivory = H).

Methionine

6.32 The following diagram represents the reaction of A_2 (red spheres) with B_2 (blue spheres):

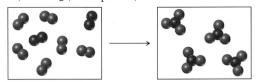

(a) Write a balanced equation for the reaction.

(b) How many moles of product can be made from 1.0 mol of A_2? From 1.0 mol of B_2?

6.33 Assume that an aqueous solution of a cation (represented as red spheres in the diagram) is allowed to mix with a solution of an anion (represented as yellow spheres). Three possible outcomes are represented by boxes (1)–(3):

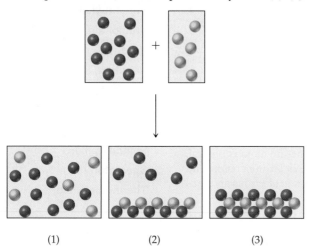

(1)   (2)   (3)

Which outcome corresponds to each of the following reactions?

(a) $2 Na^+(aq) + CO_3{}^{2-}(aq) \longrightarrow$

(b) $Ba^{2+}(aq) + CrO_4{}^{2-}(aq) \longrightarrow$

(c) $2 Ag^+(aq) + SO_3{}^{2-}(aq) \longrightarrow$

6.34 An aqueous solution of a cation (represented as blue spheres in the diagram) is allowed to mix with a solution of an anion (represented as green spheres) and the following result is obtained:

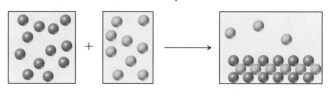

Which combinations of cation and anion, chosen from the following lists, are compatible with the observed results? Explain.

Cations: $Na^+, Ca^{2+}, Ag^+, Ni^{2+}$

Anions: $Cl^-, CO_3{}^{2-}, CrO_4{}^{2-}, NO_3{}^-$

6.35 The following drawing represents the reaction of ethylene oxide with water to give ethylene glycol, a compound used as automobile antifreeze. What mass in grams of ethylene oxide is needed to react with 9.0 g of water, and what mass in grams of ethylene glycol is formed?

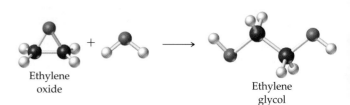

Ethylene
oxide

Ethylene
glycol

ADDITIONAL PROBLEMS

BALANCING CHEMICAL EQUATIONS

6.36 What is meant by the term "balanced equation"?

6.37 Why is it not possible to balance an equation by changing the subscript on a substance, say from H_2O to H_2O_2?

6.38 Write balanced equations for the following reactions:

(a) Gaseous sulfur dioxide reacts with water to form aqueous sulfurous acid (H_2SO_3).

(b) Liquid bromine reacts with solid potassium metal to form solid potassium bromide.

(c) Gaseous propane (C_3H_8) burns in oxygen to form gaseous carbon dioxide and water vapor.

6.39 Balance the following equation for the synthesis of hydrazine, N_2H_4, a substance used as rocket fuel.

$$NH_3(g) + Cl_2(g) \longrightarrow N_2H_4(l) + NH_4Cl(s)$$

6.40 Which of the following equations are balanced? Balance those that need it.

(a) $2 C_2H_6(g) + 5 O_2(g) \longrightarrow 2 CO_2(g) + 6 H_2O(l)$

(b) $3 Ca(OH)_2(aq) + 2 H_3PO_4(aq) \longrightarrow$
$Ca_3(PO_4)_2(aq) + 6 H_2O(l)$

(c) $Mg(s) + O_2(g) \longrightarrow 2 MgO(s)$

(d) $K(s) + H_2O(l) \longrightarrow KOH(aq) + H_2(g)$

6.41 Which of the following equations are balanced? Balance those that need it.

(a) $CaC_2 + 2 H_2O \longrightarrow Ca(OH)_2 + C_2H_2$

(b) $C_2H_8N_2 + 2 N_2O_4 \longrightarrow 2 N_2 + 2 CO_2 + 4 H_2O$

(c) $3 MgO + 2 Fe \longrightarrow Fe_2O_3 + 3 Mg$

(d) $N_2O \longrightarrow N_2 + O_2$

6.42 Balance the following equations:

(a) $Hg(NO_3)_2(aq) + LiI(aq) \longrightarrow LiNO_3(aq) + HgI_2(s)$

(b) $I_2(s) + Cl_2(g) \longrightarrow ICl_5(s)$

(c) $Al(s) + O_2(g) \longrightarrow Al_2O_3(s)$

(d) $CuSO_4(aq) + AgNO_3(aq) \longrightarrow$
$Ag_2SO_4(s) + Cu(NO_3)_2(aq)$

(e) $Mn(NO_3)_3(aq) + Na_2S(aq) \longrightarrow$
$Mn_2S_3(s) + NaNO_3(aq)$

(f) $NO_2(g) + O_2(g) \longrightarrow N_2O_5(g)$

(g) $P_4O_{10}(s) + H_2O(l) \longrightarrow H_3PO_4(aq)$

6.43 Write a balanced equation for the reaction of aqueous sodium carbonate (Na_2CO_3) with aqueous nitric acid (HNO_3) to yield CO_2, $NaNO_3$, and H_2O.

6.44 When organic compounds are burned, they react with oxygen to form CO_2 and H_2O. Write balanced equations for the combustion of the following:

(a) C_4H_{10} (butane, used in lighters)

(b) C_2H_6O (ethyl alcohol, used in gasohol and as race car fuel)

(c) C_8H_{18} (octane, a component of gasoline)

MOLAR MASSES AND MOLES

6.45 What is a mole of a substance? How many molecules are in 1 mol of a molecular compound?

6.46 What is the difference between molecular weight and formula weight? Between molecular weight and molar mass?

6.47 How many Na^+ ions are in a mole of Na_2SO_4? How many SO_4^{2-} ions?

6.48 How many moles of ions are in 1.75 mol of K_2SO_4?

6.49 How many calcium atoms are in 16.2 g of calcium?

6.50 What is the mass in grams of 2.68×10^{22} atoms of uranium?

6.51 Calculate the molar mass of each of the following compounds:

(a) Calcium carbonate, $CaCO_3$
(b) Urea, $CO(NH_2)_2$
(c) Ethylene glycol, $C_2H_6O_2$

6.52 How many moles of carbon atoms are there in 1 mol of each compound in Problem 6.51?

6.53 How many atoms of carbon and how many grams of carbon are there in 1 mol of each compound in Problem 6.51?

6.54 Caffeine has the formula $C_8H_{10}N_4O_2$. If an average cup of coffee contains approximately 125 mg of caffeine, how many moles of caffeine are in one cup?

6.55 How many moles of aspirin, $C_9H_8O_4$, are in a 500 mg tablet?

6.56 What is the molar mass of diazepam (Valium), $C_{16}H_{13}ClN_2O$?

6.57 Calculate the molar masses of the following substances:

(a) Aluminum sulfate, $Al_2(SO_4)_3$
(b) Sodium bicarbonate, $NaHCO_3$
(c) Diethyl ether, $(C_2H_5)_2O$
(d) Penicillin V, $C_{16}H_{18}N_2O_5S$

6.58 How many moles are present in a 4.50 g sample of each compound listed in Problem 6.57?

6.59 The recommended daily dietary intake of calcium for adult men and pre-menopausal women is 1000 mg/day. Calcium citrate , $Ca_3(C_6H_5O_7)_2$ (MW = 498.5 g/mol), is a common dietary supplement. What mass of calcium citrate would be needed to provide the recommended daily intake of calcium?

6.60 What is the mass in grams of 0.0015 mol of aspirin, $C_9H_8O_4$? How many aspirin molecules are there in this 0.0015 mol sample?

6.61 How many grams are present in a 0.075 mol sample of each compound listed in Problem 6.57?

6.62 The principal component of many kidney stones is calcium oxalate, CaC_2O_4. A kidney stone recovered from a typical patient contains 8.5×10^{20} formula units of calcium oxalate. How many moles of CaC_2O_4 are present in this kidney stone? What is the mass of the kidney stone in grams?

MOLE AND MASS RELATIONSHIPS FROM CHEMICAL EQUATIONS

6.63 At elevated temperatures in an automobile engine, N_2 and O_2 can react to yield NO, an important cause of air pollution.

(a) Write a balanced equation for the reaction.
(b) How many moles of N_2 are needed to react with 7.50 mol of O_2?
(c) How many moles of NO can be formed when 3.81 mol of N_2 reacts?

(d) How many moles of O_2 must react to produce 0.250 mol of NO?

6.64 Ethyl acetate reacts with H_2 in the presence of a catalyst to yield ethyl alcohol:

$$C_4H_8O_2(l) + H_2(g) \longrightarrow C_2H_6O(l)$$

(a) Write a balanced equation for the reaction.
(b) How many moles of ethyl alcohol are produced by reaction of 1.5 mol of ethyl acetate?
(c) How many grams of ethyl alcohol are produced by reaction of 1.5 mol of ethyl acetate with H_2?
(d) How many grams of ethyl alcohol are produced by reaction of 12.0 g of ethyl acetate with H_2?
(e) How many grams of H_2 are needed to react with 12.0 g of ethyl acetate?

6.65 The active ingredient in Milk of Magnesia (an antacid) is magnesium hydroxide, $Mg(OH)_2$. A typical dose (one tablespoon) contains 1.2 g of $Mg(OH)_2$. Calculate (a) the molar mass of magnesium hydroxide, and (b) the amount of magnesium hydroxide (in moles) in one teaspoon.

6.66 Ammonia, NH_3, is prepared for use as a fertilizer by reacting N_2 with H_2.

(a) Write a balanced equation for the reaction.
(b) How many moles of N_2 are needed for reaction to make 16.0 g of NH_3?
(c) How many grams of H_2 are needed to react with 75.0 g of N_2?

6.67 Hydrazine, N_2H_4, a substance used as rocket fuel, reacts with oxygen as follows:

$$N_2H_4(l) + O_2(g) \longrightarrow NO_2(g) + H_2O(g)$$

(a) Balance the equation.
(b) How many moles of oxygen are needed to react with 165 g of hydrazine?
(c) How many grams of oxygen are needed to react with 165 g of hydrazine?

6.68 One method for preparing pure iron from Fe_2O_3 is by reaction with carbon monoxide:

$$Fe_2O_3(s) + CO(g) \longrightarrow Fe(s) + CO_2(g)$$

(a) Balance the equation.
(b) How many grams of CO are needed to react with 3.02 g of Fe_2O_3?
(c) How many grams of CO are needed to react with 1.68 mol of Fe_2O_3?

6.69 Magnesium metal burns in oxygen to form magnesium oxide, MgO.

(a) Write a balanced equation for the reaction.
(b) How many grams of oxygen are needed to react with 25.0 g of Mg? How many grams of MgO will result?
(c) How many grams of Mg are needed to react with 25.0 g of O_2? How many grams of MgO will result?

6.70 Titanium metal is obtained from the mineral rutile, TiO_2. How many kilograms of rutile are needed to produce 95 kg of Ti?

6.71 In the preparation of iron from hematite (Problem 6.68) how many moles of carbon monoxide are needed to react completely with 105 kg of Fe_2O_3.

LIMITING REAGENT AND PERCENT YIELD

6.72 Once made by heating wood in the absence of air, methanol (CH_3OH) is now made by reacting carbon monoxide and hydrogen at high pressure:

$$CO(g) + 2 H_2(g) \longrightarrow CH_3OH(l)$$

(a) If 25.0 g of CO is reacted with 6.00 g of H_2, which is the limiting reagent?

(b) How many grams of CH_3OH can be made from 10.0 g of CO if it all reacts?

(c) If 9.55 g of CH_3OH is recovered when the amounts in part (b) are used, what is the percent yield?

6.73 In Problem 6.67 hydrazine reacted with oxygen according to the (unbalanced) equation:

$$N_2H_4(l) + O_2(g) \longrightarrow NO_2(g) + H_2O(g)$$

(a) If 75.0 kg of hydrazine are reacted with 75.0 kg of oxygen, which is the limiting reagent?

(b) How many kilograms of NO_2 are produced from the reaction of 75.0 kg of the limiting reagent?

(c) If 59.3 kg of NO_2 are obtained from the reaction in part (a), what is the percent yield?

6.74 Dichloromethane, CH_2Cl_2, the solvent used to decaffeinate coffee beans, is prepared by reaction of CH_4 with Cl_2.

(a) Write the balanced equation. (HCl is also formed.)

(b) How many grams of Cl_2 are needed to react with 50.0 g of CH_4?

(c) How many grams of dichloromethane are formed from 50.0 g of CH_4 if the percent yield for the reaction is 76%?

6.75 Cisplatin $[Pt(NH_3)_2Cl_2]$, a compound used in cancer treatment, is prepared by reaction of ammonia with potassium tetrachloroplatinate:

$$K_2PtCl_4 + 2 NH_3 \longrightarrow 2 KCl + Pt(NH_3)_2Cl_2$$

(a) How many grams of NH_3 are needed to react with 55.8 g of K_2PtCl_4?

(b) How many grams of cisplatin are formed from 55.8 g of K_2PtCl_4 if the percent yield for the reaction is 95%?

TYPES OF CHEMICAL REACTIONS

6.76 Identify the following reactions as a precipitation, neutralization, or redox reaction:

(a) $Mg(s) + 2 HCl(aq) \longrightarrow MgCl_2(aq) + H_2(g)$

(b) $KOH(aq) + HNO_3(aq) \longrightarrow KNO_3(aq) + H_2O(l)$

(c) $Pb(NO_3)_2(aq) + 2 HBr(aq) \longrightarrow$ $PbBr_2(s) + 2 HNO_3(aq)$

(d) $Ca(OH)_2(aq) + 2 HCl(aq) \longrightarrow 2 H_2O(l) + CaCl_2(aq)$

6.77 Write balanced ionic equations and net ionic equations for the following reactions:

(a) Aqueous sulfuric acid is neutralized by aqueous potassium hydroxide.

(b) Aqueous magnesium hydroxide is neutralized by aqueous hydrochloric acid.

6.78 Write balanced ionic equations and net ionic equations for the following reactions:

(a) A precipitate of barium sulfate forms when aqueous solutions of barium nitrate and potassium sulfate are mixed.

(b) Zinc ion and hydrogen gas form when zinc metal reacts with aqueous sulfuric acid.

6.79 Which of the following substances are likely to be soluble in water?

(a) $ZnSO_4$ (b) $NiCO_3$

(c) $PbCl_2$ (d) $Ca_3(PO_4)_2$

6.80 Which of the following substances are likely to be soluble in water?

(a) Ag_2O (b) $Ba(NO_3)_2$

(c) $SnCO_3$ (d) Al_2S_3

6.81 Use the solubility guidelines in Section 6.9 to predict whether a precipitation reaction will occur when aqueous solutions of the following substances are mixed.

(a) $NaOH + HClO_4$ (b) $FeCl_2 + KOH$

(c) $(NH_4)_2SO_4 + NiCl_2$

6.82 Use the solubility guidelines in Section 6.9 to predict whether precipitation reactions will occur between the listed pairs of reactants. Write balanced equations for those reactions that should occur.

(a) $NaBr$ and $Hg_2(NO_3)_2$ (b) $CuCl_2$ and K_2SO_4

(c) $LiNO_3$ and $Ca(CH_3CO_2)_2$ (d) $(NH_4)_2CO_3$ and $CaCl_2$

(e) KOH and $MnBr_2$ (f) Na_2S and $Al(NO_3)_3$

6.83 Write net ionic equations for the following reactions:

(a) $Mg(s) + CuCl_2(aq) \longrightarrow MgCl_2(aq) + Cu(s)$

(b) $2 KCl(aq) + Pb(NO_3)_2(aq) \longrightarrow$ $PbCl_2(s) + 2 KNO_3(aq)$

(c) $2 Cr(NO_3)_3(aq) + 3 Na_2S(aq) \longrightarrow$ $Cr_2S_3(s) + 6 NaNO_3(aq)$

6.84 Write net ionic equations for the following reactions:

(a) $2 AuCl_3(aq) + 3 Sn(s) \longrightarrow 3 SnCl_2(aq) + 2 Au(s)$

(b) $2 NaI(aq) + Br_2(l) \longrightarrow 2 NaBr(aq) + I_2(s)$

(c) $2 AgNO_3(aq) + Fe(s) \longrightarrow Fe(NO_3)_2(aq) + 2 Ag(s)$

REDOX REACTIONS AND OXIDATION NUMBERS

6.85 Where in the periodic table are the best reducing agents found? The best oxidizing agents?

6.86 Where in the periodic table are the most easily reduced elements found? The most easily oxidized?

6.87 In each of the following, tell whether the substance gains electrons or loses electrons in a redox reaction:

(a) An oxidizing agent

(b) A reducing agent

(c) A substance undergoing oxidation

(d) A substance undergoing reduction

6.88 For the following substances, tell whether the oxidation number increases or decreases in a redox reaction:

(a) An oxidizing agent

(b) A reducing agent

(c) A substance undergoing oxidation

(d) A substance undergoing reduction

6.89 Assign an oxidation number to each element in the following compounds or ions:

(a) N_2O_5 (b) SO_3^{2-}

(c) CH_2O (d) $HClO_3$

6.90 Assign an oxidation number to the metal in the following compounds:

(a) $CoCl_3$ (b) $FeSO_4$ (c) UO_3

(d) CuF_2 (e) TiO_2 (f) SnS

6.91 Which element is oxidized and which is reduced in the following reactions?

(a) $Si(s) + 2 Cl_2(g) \longrightarrow SiCl_4(l)$

(b) $Cl_2(g) + 2 NaBr(aq) \longrightarrow Br_2(aq) + 2 NaCl(aq)$

(c) $SbCl_3(s) + Cl_2(g) \longrightarrow SbCl_5(s)$

6.92 Which element is oxidized and which is reduced in the following reactions?

(a) $2 SO_2(g) + O_2(g) \longrightarrow 2 SO_3(g)$

(b) $2 Na(s) + Cl_2(g) \longrightarrow 2 NaCl(s)$

(c) $CuCl_2(aq) + Zn(s) \longrightarrow ZnCl_2(aq) + Cu(s)$

(d) $2 NaCl(aq) + F_2(g) \longrightarrow 2 NaF(aq) + Cl_2(g)$

Applications

6.93 What do you think are some of the errors involved in calculating Avogadro's number by spreading oil on a pond? [*Did Ben Franklin Have Avogadro's Number?*, p. 153]

6.94 Ferrous sulfate is one dietary supplement used to treat iron-deficiency anemia. What are the molecular formula and molecular weight of this compound? How many milligrams of iron are in 250 mg of ferrous sulfate? [*Anemia— A Limiting Reagent Problem?*, p. 162]

6.95 Sodium urate, the principal constituent of some kidney stones, has the formula $NaC_5H_3N_4O_3$. In aqueous solution, the solubility of sodium urate is only 0.067 g/L. How many moles of sodium urate dissolve in 1.00 L of water? [*Gout and Kidney Stones*, p. 165]

6.96 Identify the oxidizing and reducing agents in a typical dry-cell battery. [*Batteries*, p. 171]

General Questions and Problems

6.97 Zinc metal reacts with hydrochloric acid (HCl) according to the equation:

$$Zn(s) + 2 HCl(aq) \longrightarrow ZnCl_2(aq) + H_2(g)$$

(a) How many grams of hydrogen are produced if 15.0 g of zinc reacts?

(b) Is this a redox reaction? If so, tell what is reduced, what is oxidized, and reducing and oxidizing agents.

6.98 Lithium oxide is used aboard the space shuttle to remove water from the atmosphere according to the equation

$$Li_2O(s) + H_2O(g) \longrightarrow 2 LiOH(s)$$

(a) How many grams of Li_2O must be carried on board to remove 80.0 kg of water?

(b) Is this a redox reaction? Why or why not?

6.99 Balance the following equations.

(a) The thermite reaction, used in welding:

$$Al(s) + Fe_2O_3(s) \longrightarrow Al_2O_3(l) + Fe(l)$$

(b) The explosion of ammonium nitrate:

$$NH_4NO_3(s) \longrightarrow N_2(g) + O_2(g) + H_2O(g)$$

6.100 Batrachotoxin, $C_{31}H_{42}N_2O_6$, an active component of South American arrow poison, is so toxic that 0.05 μg can kill a person. How many molecules is this?

6.101 Look at the solubility guidelines in Section 6.9 and predict whether a precipitate forms when $CuCl_2(aq)$ and $Na_2CO_3(aq)$ are mixed. If so, write both the balanced equation and the net ionic equation for the process.

6.102 When table sugar (sucrose, $C_{12}H_{22}O_{11}$) is heated, it decomposes to form C and H_2O.

(a) Write a balanced equation for the process.

(b) How many grams of carbon are formed by the breakdown of 60.0 g of sucrose?

(c) How many grams of water are formed when 6.50 g of carbon are formed?

6.103 Although Cu is not sufficiently active to react with acids, it can be dissolved by concentrated nitric acid, which functions as an oxidizing agent according to the following equation:

$$Cu(s) + 4 HNO_3(aq) \longrightarrow$$
$$Cu(NO_3)_2(aq) + 2 NO_2(g) + 2 H_2O(l)$$

(a) Write the net ionic equation for this process.

(b) Is 35.0 g of HNO_3 sufficient to dissolve 5.00 g of copper?

6.104 The net ionic equation for the Breathalyzer test used to indicate alcohol concentration in the body is

$$16 H^+(aq) + 2 Cr_2O_7{}^{2-}(aq) + 3 C_2H_6O(aq) \longrightarrow$$
$$3 C_2H_4O_2(aq) + 4 Cr^{3+}(aq) + 11 H_2O(l)$$

(a) How many grams of $K_2Cr_2O_7$ must be used to consume 1.50 g of C_2H_6O?

(b) How many grams of $C_2H_4O_2$ can be produced from 80.0 g of C_2H_6O?

6.105 Ethyl alcohol is formed by enzyme action on sugars and starches during fermentation:

$$C_6H_{12}O_6 \longrightarrow 2 CO_2 + 2 C_2H_6O$$

If the density of ethyl alcohol is 0.789 g/mL, how many quarts can be produced by the fermentation of 100.0 lb of sugar?

6.106 Balance the following equations:

(a) $Al(OH)_3(aq) + HNO_3(aq) \longrightarrow$
$Al(NO_3)_3(aq) + H_2O(l)$

(b) $AgNO_3(aq) + FeCl_3(aq) \longrightarrow$
$AgCl(s) + Fe(NO_3)_3(aq)$

(c) $(NH_4)_2Cr_2O_7(s) \longrightarrow Cr_2O_3(s) + H_2O(g) + N_2(g)$

(d) $Mn_2(CO_3)_3(s) \longrightarrow Mn_2O_3(s) + CO_2(g)$

6.107 White phosphorus (P_4) is a highly reactive form of elemental phosphorus that reacts with oxygen to form a variety of molecular compounds, including diphosphorus pentoxide.

(a) Write the balanced chemical equation for this reaction.

(b) Calculate the oxidation number for P and O on both sides of the reaction, and identify the oxidizing and reducing agents.

6.108 The combustion of fossil fuels containing sulfur contributes to the phenomenon known as acid rain. The combustion process releases sulfur in the form of sulfur dioxide, which is converted to sulfuric acid in a process involving two reactions.

(a) In the first reaction, sulfur dioxide reacts with molecular oxygen to form sulfur trioxide. Write the balanced chemical equation for this reaction.

(b) In the second reaction, sulfur trioxide reacts with water in the atmosphere to form sulfuric acid. Write the balanced chemical equation for this reaction.

(c) Calculate the oxidation number for the S atom in each compound in these reactions.

CHAPTER 7

Chemical Reactions: Energy, Rates, and Equilibrium

CONCEPTS TO REVIEW

Energy and Heat
(Section 2.10)

Ionic Bonds
(Section 4.3)

Covalent Bonds
(Section 5.1)

Chemical Equations
(Section 6.1)

▲ Many spontaneous chemical reactions are accompanied by the release of energy, in some cases explosively.

CONTENTS

CHAPTER GOALS

In this chapter, we will look more closely at chemical reactions and answer the following questions:

1. What energy changes take place during reactions?

THE GOAL: Be able to explain the factors that influence energy changes in chemical reactions.

2. What is "free energy," and what is the criterion for spontaneity in chemistry?

THE GOAL: Be able to define enthalpy, entropy, and free-energy changes, and explain how the values of these quantities affect chemical reactions.

3. What determines the rate of a chemical reaction?

THE GOAL: Be able to explain activation energy and other factors that determine reaction rate.

4. What is chemical equilibrium?

THE GOAL: Be able to describe what occurs in a reaction at equilibrium and write the equilibrium equation for a given reaction.

5. What is Le Châtelier's principle?

THE GOAL: Be able to state Le Châtelier's principle and use it to predict the effect of changes in temperature, pressure, and concentration on reactions.

We have yet to answer many questions about reactions. Why, for instance, do reactions occur? Just because a balanced equation can be written does not mean it will take place. We can write a balanced equation for the reaction of gold with water, for example, but the reaction does not occur in practice, so your gold jewelry is safe in the shower.

Balanced, but does not occur $2 \, Au(s) + 3 \, H_2O(l) \longrightarrow Au_2O_3(s) + 3 \, H_2(g)$

To describe reactions more completely, several fundamental questions are commonly asked: Is energy released or absorbed when a reaction occurs? Is a given reaction fast or slow? Does a reaction continue until all reactants are converted to products or is there a point beyond which no additional product forms?

7.1 Energy and Chemical Bonds

There are two fundamental and interconvertible kinds of energy: *potential* and *kinetic*. **Potential energy** is stored energy. The water in a reservoir behind a dam, an automobile poised to coast downhill, and a coiled spring have potential energy waiting to be released. **Kinetic energy**, by contrast, is the energy of motion. When the water falls over the dam and turns a turbine, when the car rolls downhill, or when the spring uncoils and makes the hands on a clock move, the potential energy in each is converted to kinetic energy. Of course, once all the potential energy is converted, nothing further occurs. The water at the bottom of the dam, the car at the bottom of the hill, and the uncoiled spring no longer have potential energy and thus undergo no further change.

In chemical compounds, the attractive forces between ions (ionic bonds) or atoms (covalent bonds) are a form of potential energy. In many chemical reactions, this potential energy is often converted into **heat**—the kinetic energy of the moving particles that make up the compound. Because the reaction products have less potential energy than the reactants, we say that the products are *more stable* than the reactants. The term "stable" is used in chemistry to describe a substance that has little remaining potential energy and consequently little tendency to undergo further change. Whether a reaction occurs, and how much energy or heat is associated with the reaction, depends on the amount of potential energy contained in the reactants and products.

Potential energy Stored energy.

Kinetic energy The energy of an object in motion.

Heat A measure of the transfer of thermal energy.

7.2 Heat Changes during Chemical Reactions

Why does chlorine react so easily with many elements and compounds but nitrogen does not? What difference between Cl_2 molecules and N_2 molecules accounts for their different reactivities? The answer is that the nitrogen–nitrogen triple bond

Bond dissociation energy The amount of energy that must be supplied to break a bond and separate the atoms in an isolated gaseous molecule.

is much *stronger* than the chlorine–chlorine single bond and cannot be broken as easily in chemical reactions.

The strength of a covalent bond is measured by its **bond dissociation energy**, defined as the amount of energy that must be supplied to break the bond and separate the atoms in an isolated gaseous molecule. The triple bond in N_2, for example, has a bond dissociation energy of 226 kcal/mol, whereas the single bond in chlorine has a bond dissociation energy of only 58 kcal/mol:

$$:N:::N: \xrightarrow{226 \text{ kcal/mol}} :\dot{N}\cdot + \cdot\dot{N}: \qquad N_2 \text{ bond dissociation energy} = 226 \text{ kcal/mol}$$

$$:\ddot{Cl}:\ddot{Cl}: \xrightarrow{58 \text{ kcal/mol}} :\ddot{Cl}\cdot + \cdot\ddot{Cl}: \qquad Cl_2 \text{ bond dissociation energy} = 58 \text{ kcal/mol}$$

Endothermic A process or reaction that absorbs heat and has a positive ΔH.

Exothermic A process or reaction that releases heat and has a negative ΔH.

A chemical change like bond breaking that absorbs heat is said to be **endothermic**, from the Greek words *endon* (within) and *therme* (heat), meaning that *heat* is put *in*. The reverse of bond breaking is bond formation, a process that *releases* heat and is described as **exothermic**, from the Greek *exo* (outside), meaning that heat goes *out*. The amount of energy released in forming a bond is numerically the same as that absorbed in breaking it. When nitrogen atoms combine to give N_2, 226 kcal/mol of heat is released. Similarly, when Cl_2 molecules are pulled apart into atoms, 58 kcal/mol of heat is absorbed; when chlorine atoms combine to give Cl_2, 58 kcal/mol of heat is released.

$$:\dot{N}\cdot + \cdot\dot{N}: \longrightarrow :N:::N: + 226 \text{ kcal/mol heat released}$$

$$:\ddot{Cl}\cdot + \cdot\ddot{Cl}: \longrightarrow :\ddot{Cl}:\ddot{Cl}: + 58 \text{ kcal/mol heat released}$$

The same energy relationships that govern bond breaking and bond formation apply to every physical or chemical change. That is, the amount of heat transferred during a change in one direction is numerically equal to the amount of heat transferred during the change in the opposite direction. Only the *direction* of the heat transfer is different. This relationship reflects a fundamental law of nature called the *law of conservation of energy:*

Law of conservation of energy Energy can be neither created nor destroyed in any physical or chemical change.

If more energy could be released by an exothermic reaction than was consumed in its reverse, the law would be violated and we could "manufacture" energy out of nowhere by cycling back and forth between forward and reverse reactions—a clear impossibility.

In every chemical reaction, some bonds in the reactants are broken and new bonds are formed in the products. The difference between the energy absorbed in breaking bonds and the energy released in forming bonds is called the **heat of reaction** and is a quantity that we can measure. Heats of reaction that are measured when a reaction is held at constant pressure are represented by the abbreviation ΔH, where Δ (the Greek capital letter delta) is a general symbol used to indicate "a change in" and H is a quantity called **enthalpy**. Thus, the value of ΔH represents the **enthalpy change** that occurs during a reaction. The terms *enthalpy change* and *heat of reaction* are often used interchangeably, but we will generally use the latter term in this book.

Enthalpy (H) A measure of the amount of energy associated with substances involved in a reaction.

Heat of reaction ΔH = Energy of bonds formed in products minus
(Enthalpy change)   energy of bonds broken in reactants

7.3 Exothermic and Endothermic Reactions

When the total strength of the bonds formed in the products is *greater* than the total strength of the bonds broken in the reactants, energy is released and a reaction is exothermic. All combustion reactions are exothermic; for example, burning 1 mol of methane releases 213 kcal of energy in the form of heat. The heat released in an exothermic reaction can be thought of as a reaction product, and ΔH is assigned a *negative* value because heat *leaves*.

An exothermic reaction—negative **ΔH**

Heat is a product.

$$CH_4(g) + 2\,O_2(g) \longrightarrow CO_2(g) + 2\,H_2O(l) + 213\ kcal$$

or

$$CH_4(g) + 2\,O_2(g) \longrightarrow CO_2(g) + 2\,H_2O(l) \qquad \Delta H = -213\ kcal/mol$$

Note that ΔH is given in units of kilocalories per mole, where "per mole" means the reaction of *molar amounts of products and reactants as represented by the coefficients of the balanced equation.* Thus, the value $\Delta H = -213$ kcal/mol refers to the amount of heat released when 1 mol (16.0 g) of methane reacts with O_2 to give 1 mol of CO_2 gas and 2 mol of liquid H_2O. If we were to double the amount of methane from 1 mol to 2 mol, the amount of heat released would also double.

The quantities of heat released in the combustion of several fuels, including natural gas (which is primarily methane), are compared in Table 7.1. The values are given in kilocalories per gram to make comparisons easier. You can see from the table why there is interest in the potential of hydrogen as a fuel.

TABLE 7.1   Energy Values of Some Common Fuels

FUEL	ENERGY VALUE (kcal/g)
Wood (pine)	4.3
Ethyl alcohol	7.1
Coal (anthracite)	7.4
Crude oil (Texas)	10.5
Gasoline	11.5
Natural gas	11.7
Hydrogen	34.0

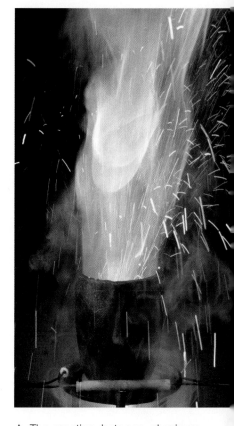

▲ The reaction between aluminum metal and iron(III) oxide, called the *thermite reaction*, is so strongly exothermic that it melts iron.

When the total energy of the bonds formed in the products is *less* than the total energy of the bonds broken in the reactants, energy is absorbed and a reaction is endothermic. The combination of nitrogen and oxygen to give nitrogen oxide (also known as nitric oxide), a gas present in automobile exhaust, is such a reaction. The heat added in an endothermic reaction is like a reactant, and ΔH is assigned a *positive* value because heat is *added*.

An endothermic reaction—positive **ΔH**

Heat is a reactant.

$$N_2(g) + O_2(g) + 43\ kcal \longrightarrow 2\,NO(g)$$

or

$$N_2(g) + O_2(g) \longrightarrow 2\,NO(g) \qquad \Delta H = +43\ kcal/mol$$

Important points about heat transfers and chemical reactions

- An exothermic reaction releases heat to the surroundings; ΔH is negative.
- An endothermic reaction absorbs heat from the surroundings; ΔH is positive.

- The reverse of an exothermic reaction is endothermic.
- The reverse of an endothermic reaction is exothermic.
- The amount of heat absorbed or released in the reverse of a reaction is equal to that released or absorbed in the forward reaction, but ΔH has the opposite sign.

Worked Examples 7.1-7.3 show how to calculate the amount of heat absorbed or released for reaction of a given amount of reactant. All that is needed is the balanced equation and its accompanying ΔH. Mole ratios and molar masses are used to convert between masses and moles of reactants or products, as discussed in Sections 6.5 and 6.6.

▲ Methane produced from rotting refuse is trapped and used for energy production to ease the energy crisis in California.

WORKED EXAMPLE **7.1** Heat of Reaction

Methane undergoes combustion with O_2 according to the following equation:

$$CH_4(g) + 2\,O_2(g) \longrightarrow CO_2(g) + 2\,H_2O(l) \quad \Delta H = -213\frac{kcal}{mol\ CH_4}$$

How much heat is released during the combustion of 0.35 mol of methane?

ANALYSIS Since the value of ΔH for the reaction (213 kcal/mol) is negative, it indicates the amount of heat released when 1 mol of methane reacts with O_2. We need to find the amount of heat released when an amount other than 1 mol reacts, using appropriate factor-label calculations to convert from our known or given units to kilocalories.

BALLPARK ESTIMATE Since 213 kcal is released for each mole of methane that reacts, 0.35 mol of methane should release about one-third of 213 kcal, or about 70 kcal.

SOLUTION
To find the amount of heat released (in kilocalories) by combustion of 0.35 mol of methane, we use a conversion factor of kcal/mol:

$$0.35\ \cancel{mol\ CH_4} \times \frac{-213\ kcal}{1\ \cancel{mol\ CH_4}} = -75\ kcal$$

The negative sign indicates that the 75 kcal of heat is released.

BALLPARK CHECK The calculated answer is consistent with our estimate (70 kcal).

WORKED EXAMPLE **7.2** Heat of Reaction: Mass to Mole Conversion

How much heat is released during the combustion of 7.50 g of methane (MW = 16.0 g/mol)?

$$CH_4(g) + 2\,O_2(g) \longrightarrow CO_2(g) + 2\,H_2O(l) \quad \Delta H = -213\frac{kcal}{mol\ CH_4}$$

ANALYSIS We can find the moles of methane involved in the reaction by using the molecular weight in a mass to mole conversion, and then use ΔH to find the heat released.

BALLPARK ESTIMATE Since 1 mol of methane (MW = 16.0 g/mol) has a mass of 16.0 g, 7.50 g of methane is a little less than 0.5 mol. Thus, less than half of 213 kcal, or about 100 kcal, is released from combustion of 7.50 g.

SOLUTION
Going from a given mass of methane to the amount of heat released in a reaction requires that we first find the number of moles of methane by including

molar mass (in mol/g) in the calculation and then converting moles to kilocalories:

$$7.50 \text{ g CH}_4 \times \frac{1 \text{ mol CH}_4}{16.0 \text{ g CH}_4} \times \frac{-213 \text{ kcal}}{1 \text{ mol CH}_4} = -99.8 \text{ kcal}$$

The negative sign indicates that the 99.8 kcal of heat is released.

BALLPARK CHECK Our estimate was −100 kcal!

WORKED EXAMPLE **7.3** Heat of Reaction: Mole Ratio Calculations

How much heat is released when 2.50 mol of O_2 reacts completely with methane?

$$CH_4(g) + 2 O_2(g) \longrightarrow CO_2(g) + 2 H_2O(l) \quad \Delta H = -213\frac{\text{kcal}}{\text{mol CH}_4}$$

ANALYSIS Since the ΔH for the reaction is based on the combustion of 1 mol of methane, we will need to perform a mole ratio calculation.

BALLPARK ESTIMATE The balanced equation shows that 213 kcal is released for each 2 mol of oxygen that reacts. Thus, 2.50 mol of oxygen should release a bit more than 213 kcal, perhaps about 250 kcal.

SOLUTION
To find the amount of heat released by combustion of 2.50 mol of oxygen, we include in our calculation a mole ratio based on the balanced chemical equation:

$$2.50 \text{ mol O}_2 \times \frac{1 \text{ mol CH}_4}{2 \text{ mol O}_2} \times \frac{-213 \text{ kcal}}{1 \text{ mol CH}_4} = -266 \text{ kcal}$$

The negative sign indicates that the 266 kcal of heat is released.

BALLPARK CHECK The calculated answer is close to our estimate (250 kcal).

PROBLEM 7.1

In photosynthesis, green plants convert carbon dioxide and water into glucose ($C_6H_{12}O_6$) according to the following equation:

$$6 CO_2(g) + 6 H_2O(l) + 678 \text{ kcal} \longrightarrow C_6H_{12}O_6(aq) + 6 O_2(g)$$

(a) Is the reaction exothermic or endothermic?
(b) What is the value of ΔH for the reaction?
(c) Write the equation for the reverse of the reaction, including heat as a reactant or product.

PROBLEM 7.2

The following equation shows the conversion of aluminum oxide (from the ore bauxite) to aluminum:

$$2 Al_2O_3(s) \longrightarrow 4 Al(s) + 3 O_2(g) \quad \Delta H = +801 \text{ kcal/mol}$$

(a) Is the reaction exothermic or endothermic?
(b) How many kilocalories are required to produce 1.00 mol of aluminum?
(c) How many kilocalories are required to produce 10.0 g of aluminum?

▲ Events that lead to lower energy tend to occur spontaneously. Thus, water always flows *down* a waterfall, not up.

Spontaneous process A process or reaction that, once started, proceeds on its own without any external influence.

Entropy (S) A measure of the amount of molecular disorder in a system.

PROBLEM 7.3

How much heat is absorbed during production of 127 g of NO by the combination of nitrogen and oxygen?

$$N_2(g) + O_2(g) \longrightarrow 2\,NO(g) \quad \Delta H = +43 \text{ kcal/mol}$$

7.4 Why Do Chemical Reactions Occur? Free Energy

Events that lead to lower energy tend to occur spontaneously. Water falls downhill, for instance, releasing its stored (potential) energy and reaching a lower-energy, more stable position. Similarly, a wound-up spring uncoils when set free. Applying this lesson to chemistry, the obvious conclusion is that exothermic processes—those that release heat energy—should be spontaneous. A log burning in a fireplace is just one example of a spontaneous reaction that releases heat. At the same time, endothermic processes, which absorb heat energy, should not be spontaneous. Often, these conclusions are correct, but not always. Many, but not all, exothermic processes take place spontaneously, and many, but not all, endothermic processes are nonspontaneous.

Before exploring the situation further, it is important to understand what the word "spontaneous" means in chemistry, which is not quite the same as in everyday language. A **spontaneous process** is one that, once started, proceeds on its own without any external influence. The change does not necessarily happen quickly, like a spring suddenly uncoiling or a car coasting downhill. It can also happen slowly, like the gradual rusting away of an abandoned bicycle. A *nonspontaneous process*, by contrast, takes place only in the presence of a continuous external influence: Energy must be continually expended to rewind a spring or push a car uphill. The reverse of a spontaneous process is always nonspontaneous.

As an example of a process that takes place spontaneously yet absorbs heat, think about what happens when you take an ice cube out of the refrigerator. The ice spontaneously melts to give liquid water above 0 °C, even though it *absorbs* heat energy from the surroundings. What this and other spontaneous processes that absorb heat energy have in common is *an increase in molecular disorder, or randomness*. When the solid ice melts, the H_2O molecules are no longer locked in position but are now free to move around randomly in the liquid water.

The amount of disorder in a system is called the system's **entropy**, symbolized S and expressed in units of calories per mole-kelvin [cal/(mol · K)]. The greater the disorder, or randomness, of the particles in a substance or mixture, the larger the value of S (Figure 7.1). Gases have more disorder and therefore higher entropy than liquids because particles in the gas move around more freely than particles in the liquid. Similarly, liquids have higher entropy than solids. In chemical reactions, entropy increases when, for example, a gas is produced from a solid or when 2 mol of reactants split into 4 mol of products.

$$\left.\begin{array}{c}\text{Solid} \longrightarrow \text{Liquid} \longrightarrow \text{Gas} \\ \\ \text{Fewer moles} \longrightarrow \text{More moles} \\ \text{of reactants} \qquad \text{of products}\end{array}\right.$$

Lower entropy { ... } Higher entropy

The entropy *change* for a process, ΔS, has a *positive* value if disorder increases because the process adds disorder to the system. The melting of ice to give water is an example. Conversely, ΔS has a *negative* value if the disorder of a system decreases. The freezing of water to give ice is an example.

It thus appears that two factors determine the spontaneity of a chemical or physical change: the release or absorption of heat, ΔH, and the increase or decrease in entropy, ΔS. *To decide whether a process is spontaneous, both the enthalpy change and*

APPLICATION ▶   Energy from Food

Any serious effort to lose weight usually leads to studying the caloric values of foods. Have you ever wondered how the numbers quoted on food labels are obtained?

Food is "burned" in the body to yield H_2O, CO_2, and energy, just as natural gas is burned in furnaces to yield the same products. In fact, the "caloric value" of a food is just the heat of reaction for complete combustion of the food (minus a small correction factor). The value is the same whether the food is burned in the body or in the laboratory. One gram of protein releases 4 kcal, 1 g of table sugar (a carbohydrate) releases 4 kcal, and 1 g of fat releases 9 kcal (see Table).

The caloric value of a food is usually given in "Calories" (note the capital C), where 1 Cal = 1000 cal = 1 kcal. To determine these values experimentally, a carefully dried and weighed food sample is placed together with oxygen into an instrument called a *calorimeter*, the food is ignited, the temperature change is measured, and the amount of heat given off is calculated from the temperature change. In the calorimeter, the heat from the food is released very quickly and the temperature rises dramatically. Clearly, though, something a bit different goes on when food is burned in the body, otherwise we would burst into flames after a meal!

It is a fundamental principle of chemistry that the total heat released or absorbed in going from reactants to products is the same, no matter how many reactions are involved.

Caloric Values of Some Foods

SUBSTANCE, SAMPLE SIZE	CALORIC VALUE (kcal)
Protein, 1 g	4
Carbohydrate, 1 g	4
Fat, 1 g	9
Alcohol, 1 g	7.1
Cola drink, 12 fl oz (369 g)	160
Apple, one medium (138 g)	80
Iceberg lettuce, 1 cup shredded (55 g)	5
White bread, 1 slice (25 g)	65
Hamburger patty, 3 oz (85 g)	245
Pizza, 1 slice (120 g)	290
Vanilla ice cream, 1 cup (133 g)	270

The body applies this principle by withdrawing energy from food a bit at a time in a long series of interconnected reactions rather than all at once in a single reaction. These and other reactions continually taking place in the body—called the body's *metabolism*—will be examined in later chapters.

See Additional Problems 7.70 and 7.71 at the end of the chapter.

▲ Eating this dessert gives your body 550 Calories. Burning the dessert in a calorimeter releases 550 kcal as heat.

Stir

Entropy increases (positive ΔS)

▶ **FIGURE 7.1 Entropy and values of S.** The mixture on the right has more disorder and a higher entropy than the mixture on the left, and has a higher value of S. The value of the entropy change, ΔS, for converting the mixture on the left to that on the right is positive because entropy increases.

the entropy change must be taken into account. We have already seen that a negative ΔH favors spontaneity, but what about ΔS? The answer is that an increase in molecular disorder (ΔS positive) favors spontaneity. A good analogy is the bedroom or office that seems to spontaneously become more messy over time (increase in disorder means increase in entropy, ΔS positive); to clean it up (a decrease in disorder, ΔS negative) requires an input of energy, a nonspontaneous process. Using our chemical example, the combustion of a log spontaneously converts large, complex molecules like lignin and cellulose (high molecular order, low entropy) into CO_2 and H_2O (smaller molecules with less molecular order and higher entropy). For this process, the level of disorder increases, and so ΔS is positive. The reverse process—turning CO_2 and H_2O back into cellulose—does occur in photosynthesis, but it requires a significant input of energy in the form of sunlight.

When enthalpy and entropy are both favorable (ΔH negative, ΔS positive), a process is spontaneous; when both are unfavorable, a process is nonspontaneous. Clearly, however, the two factors do not have to operate in the same direction. It is possible for a process to be *unfavored* by enthalpy (the process absorbs heat and so has a positive ΔH) and yet be *favored* by entropy (there is an increase in disorder and so ΔS is positive). The melting of an ice cube above 0 °C, for which ΔH = +1.44 kcal/mol and ΔS = +5.26 cal/(mol·K) is just such a process. To take both heat of reaction (ΔH) and change in disorder (ΔS) into account when determining the spontaneity of a process, a quantity called the **free-energy change (ΔG)** is needed:

Free-energy change

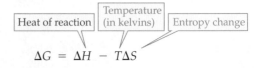

| Heat of reaction | Temperature (in kelvins) | Entropy change |

$$\Delta G = \Delta H - T\Delta S$$

The value of the free-energy change ΔG determines spontaneity. A negative value for ΔG means that free energy is released and the reaction or process is spontaneous. Such events are said to be **exergonic**. A positive value for ΔG means that free energy must be added and the process is nonspontaneous. Such events are said to be **endergonic**.

Exergonic A spontaneous reaction or process that releases free energy and has a negative ΔG.

Endergonic A nonspontaneous reaction or process that absorbs free energy and has a positive ΔG.

Spontaneous process	ΔG is negative; free energy is released; process is exergonic.
Nonspontaneous process	ΔG is positive; free energy is added; process is endergonic.

The equation for the free-energy change shows that spontaneity also depends on temperature (T). At low temperatures, the value of $T\Delta S$ is often small so that ΔH is the dominant factor. At a high enough temperature, however, the value of $T\Delta S$ can become larger than ΔH. Thus, an endothermic process that is nonspontaneous at low temperature can become spontaneous at a higher temperature. An example is the industrial synthesis of hydrogen by reaction of carbon with water:

$$C(s) + H_2O(l) \longrightarrow CO(g) + H_2(g) \qquad \begin{array}{ll} \Delta H = +31.3\,\text{kcal/mol} & \text{(Unfavorable)} \\ \Delta S = +32\,\text{cal/(mol}\cdot\text{K)} & \text{(Favorable)} \end{array}$$

The reaction has an unfavorable (positive) ΔH term but a favorable (positive) ΔS term because disorder increases when a solid and a liquid are converted into two gases. No reaction occurs if carbon and water are mixed together at 25 °C (298 K) because the unfavorable ΔH is larger than the favorable $T\,\Delta S$. Above about 700 °C (973 K), however, the favorable $T\,\Delta S$ becomes larger than the unfavorable ΔH, so the reaction becomes spontaneous.

Important points about spontaneity and free energy

- A spontaneous process, once begun, proceeds without any external assistance and is exergonic; that is, it has a negative value of ΔG.

- A nonspontaneous process requires continuous external influence and is endergonic; that is, it has a positive value of ΔG.

- The value of ΔG for the reverse of a reaction is numerically equal to the value of ΔG for the forward reaction, but has the opposite sign.

- Some nonspontaneous processes become spontaneous with a change in temperature.

⫘ Looking Ahead

In later chapters, we will see that a knowledge of free-energy changes is especially important for understanding how metabolic reactions work. Living organisms cannot raise their temperatures to convert nonspontaneous reactions into spontaneous reactions, so they must resort to other strategies, which we will explore in Chapter 21. ⫘

WORKED EXAMPLE **7.4** Entropy Change of Processes

Does entropy increase or decrease in the following processes?

    (a) Smoke from a cigarette disperses throughout a room rather than remaining in a cloud over the smoker's head.

    (b) Water boils, changing from liquid to vapor.

    (c) A chemical reaction occurs: $3\,H_2(g) + N_2(g) \longrightarrow 2\,NH_3(g)$

ANALYSIS Entropy is a measure of molecular disorder. Entropy increases when the products are more disordered than the reactants; entropy decreases when the products are less disordered than the reactants.

SOLUTION

    (a) Entropy increases because smoke particles are more disordered when they are randomly distributed in the larger volume.

    (b) Entropy increases because H_2O molecules have more freedom and disorder in the gas phase than in the liquid phase.

    (c) Entropy decreases because 4 mol of reactant gas particles become 2 mol of product gas particles, with a consequent decrease in freedom and disorder.

WORKED EXAMPLE **7.5** Spontaneity of Reactions: Enthalpy, Entropy, and Free Energy

The industrial method for synthesizing hydrogen by reaction of carbon with water has $\Delta H = +31.3$ kcal/mol and $\Delta S = +32$ cal/(mol·K). What is the value of ΔG for the reaction at 27 °C (300 K)? Is the reaction spontaneous or nonspontaneous at this temperature?

$$C(s) + H_2O(l) \longrightarrow CO(g) + H_2(g)$$

ANALYSIS The reaction is endothermic (ΔH positive) and does not favor spontaneity, whereas the ΔS indicates an increase in disorder (ΔS positive), which *does* favor spontaneity. Calculate ΔG to determine spontaneity.

BALLPARK ESTIMATE The unfavorable ΔH (+31.3 kcal/mol) is 1000 times greater than the favorable ΔS (+32 cal/mol·K), so the reaction will be spontaneous (ΔG negative) only when the temperature is high enough to make the $T\Delta S$ term in the equation for ΔG larger than the ΔH term. This happens at $T \geq 1000$ K. Since $T = 300$ K, expect ΔG to be positive and the reaction to be nonspontaneous.

SOLUTION
Use the free-energy equation to determine the value of ΔG at this temperature. (Remember that ΔS has units of *calories* per mole-kelvin, not kilocalories per mole-kelvin.)

$$\Delta G = \Delta H - T\,\Delta S$$
$$= +31.3\frac{\text{kcal}}{\text{mol}} - (300\,\cancel{K})\left(+32\frac{\cancel{\text{cal}}}{\text{mol}\cdot\cancel{K}}\right)\left(\frac{1\,\text{kcal}}{1000\,\cancel{\text{cal}}}\right)$$
$$= +21.7\frac{\text{kcal}}{\text{mol}}$$

BALLPARK CHECK Because ΔG is positive, the reaction is nonspontaneous at 300 K, consistent with our estimate.

PROBLEM 7.4

Does entropy increase or decrease in the following processes?

(a) After raking your leaves into a neat pile, a breeze blows them all over your lawn.

(b) Gasoline fumes escape as the fuel is pumped into your car.

(c) $Mg(s) + Cl_2(g) \longrightarrow MgCl_2(s)$

PROBLEM 7.5

Lime (CaO) is prepared by the decomposition of limestone ($CaCO_3$).

$$CaCO_3(s) \longrightarrow CaO(s) + CO_2(g) \quad \Delta G = +31 \text{ kcal/mol at 25 °C}$$

(a) Does the reaction occur spontaneously at 25 °C?

(b) Does entropy increase or decrease in this reaction?

(c) Would you expect the reaction to be spontaneous at higher temperatures?

PROBLEM 7.6

The melting of solid ice to give liquid water has $\Delta H = 1.44$ kcal/mol and $\Delta S = +5.26$ cal/(mol·K). What is the value of ΔG for the melting process at the following temperatures? Is the melting spontaneous or nonspontaneous at these temperatures?

(a) −10 °C (263 K)

(b) 0 °C (273 K)

(c) +10 °C (283 K)

◄● KEY CONCEPT PROBLEM 7.7

The following diagram portrays a reaction of the type A(s) ⟶ B(s) + C(g), where the different colored spheres represent different molecular structures. Assume that the reaction has $\Delta H = -23.5$ kcal/mol.

(a) What is the sign of ΔS for the reaction?

(b) Is the reaction likely to be spontaneous at all temperatures, nonspontaneous at all temperatures, or spontaneous at some but nonspontaneous at others?

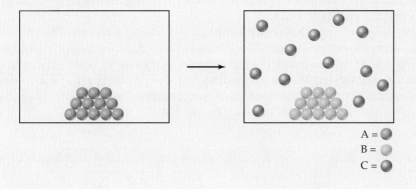

A = ●
B = ●
C = ●

7.5 How Do Chemical Reactions Occur? Reaction Rates

Just because a chemical reaction has a favorable free-energy change does not mean that it occurs rapidly. The value of ΔG tells us only whether a reaction *can* occur; it says nothing about how *fast* the reaction will occur or about the details of the molecular changes that take place during the reaction. It is now time to look into these other matters.

For a chemical reaction to occur, reactant particles must collide, some chemical bonds have to break, and new bonds have to form. Not all collisions lead to products, however. One requirement for a productive collision is that the colliding molecules must approach with the correct orientation so that the atoms about to form new bonds can connect. In the reaction of ozone (O_3) with nitric oxide (NO) to give oxygen (O_2) and nitrogen dioxide (NO_2), for example, the two reactants must collide so that the nitrogen atom of NO strikes a terminal oxygen atom of O_3 (Figure 7.2).

Another requirement for a reaction to occur is that the collision must take place with enough energy to break the appropriate bonds in the reactant. If the reactant particles are moving slowly, collisions might be too gentle to overcome the repulsion between electrons in the different reactants, and the particles will simply bounce apart. Only if the collisions are sufficiently energetic will a reaction ensue.

For this reason, many reactions with a favorable free-energy change do not occur at room temperature. To get such a reaction started, energy (heat) must be

▲ Matches are unreactive at room temperature but burst into flames when struck. The frictional heat produced on striking provides enough energy to start the combustion.

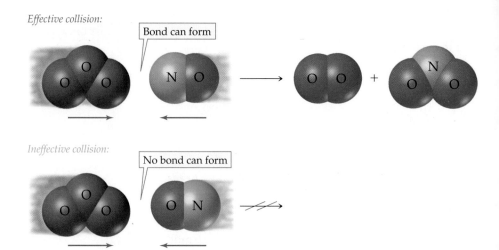

Effective collision:

Bond can form

Ineffective collision:

No bond can form

▶ **FIGURE 7.2 How do chemical reactions occur?** For a collision between NO and O_3 molecules to give O_2 and NO_2, the molecules must collide so that the correct atoms come into contact. No bond forms if the molecules collide with the wrong orientation.

added. The heat causes the reactant particles to move faster, thereby increasing both the frequency and the force of the collisions. We all know that matches burn, for instance, but we also know that they do not burst into flame until struck. The heat of friction provides enough energy for a few molecules to react. Once started, the reaction sustains itself as the energy released by reacting molecules gives other molecules enough energy to react.

The energy change that occurs during the course of a chemical reaction can be visualized in an energy diagram like that in Figure 7.3. At the beginning of the reaction (left side of the diagram), the reactants are at the energy level indicated. At the end of the reaction (right side of the diagram), the products are at a lower energy level than the reactants if the reaction is exergonic (Figure 7.3a) but higher than the reactants if the reaction is endergonic (Figure 7.3b).

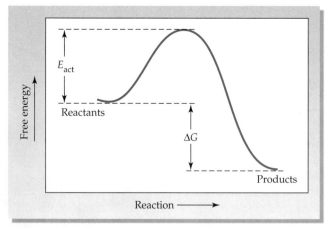

(a) An exergonic reaction

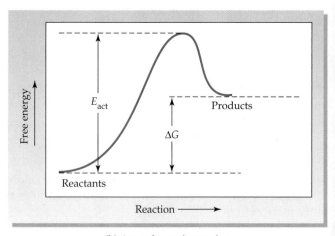

(b) An endergonic reaction

▲ **FIGURE 7.3 Reaction energy diagrams show energy changes during a chemical reaction.** A reaction begins on the left and proceeds to the right. (a) In an exergonic reaction, the product energy level is lower than that of reactants. (b) In an endergonic reaction, the situation is reversed. The height of the barrier between reactant and product energy levels is the activation energy, E_{act}. The difference between reactant and product energy levels is the free-energy change, ΔG.

Activation energy (E_{act}) The amount of energy necessary for reactants to surmount the energy barrier to reaction; determines reaction rate.

Reaction rate A measure of how rapidly a reaction occurs; determined by E_{act}.

Lying between the reactants and the products is an energy "barrier" that must be surmounted. The height of this barrier represents the amount of energy the colliding particles must have for productive collisions to occur, an amount called the **activation energy (E_{act})** of the reaction. The size of the activation energy determines the **reaction rate**, or how fast the reaction occurs. The lower the activation energy, the greater the number of productive collisions in a given amount of time, and the faster the reaction. Conversely, the higher the activation energy, the lower the number of productive collisions, and the slower the reaction.

Note that the size of the activation energy and the size of the free-energy change are unrelated. A reaction with a large E_{act} takes place very slowly even if it has a large negative ΔG. Every reaction is different; each has its own characteristic activation energy and free-energy change.

WORKED EXAMPLE **7.6** Energy of Reactions: Energy Diagrams

Draw an energy diagram for a reaction that is very fast but has a small negative free-energy change.

ANALYSIS A very fast reaction has a small E_{act}. A reaction with a small negative free-energy change is a favorable reaction with a small energy difference between starting materials and products.

SOLUTION

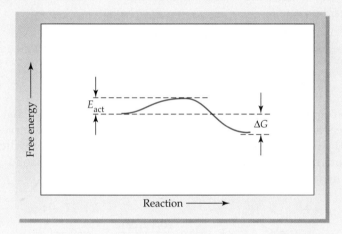

PROBLEM 7.8

Draw an energy diagram for a reaction that is very slow but highly favorable.

PROBLEM 7.9

Draw an energy diagram for a reaction that is slightly unfavorable.

7.6 Effects of Temperature, Concentration, and Catalysts on Reaction Rates

Several things can be done to help reactants over an activation energy barrier and thereby speed up a reaction. Let us look at some possibilities.

Temperature

One way to increase reaction rate is to add energy to the reactants by raising the temperature. With more energy in the system, the reactants move faster, so the frequency of collisions increases. Furthermore, the force with which collisions occur increases, making them more likely to overcome the activation barrier. As a rule of thumb, a 10 °C rise in temperature causes a reaction rate to double.

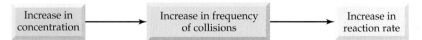

Concentration

Concentration A measure of the amount of a given substance in a mixture.

A second way to speed up a reaction is to increase the **concentrations** of the reactants. As the concentration increases reactants are crowded together, and collisions between reactant molecules become more frequent. As the frequency of collisions increases, reactions between molecules become more likely. Flammable materials burn more rapidly in pure oxygen than in air, for instance, because the concentration of O_2 molecules is higher (air is approximately 21% oxygen). Hospitals must therefore take extraordinary precautions to ensure that no flames are used near patients receiving oxygen. Although different reactions respond differently to concentration changes, doubling or tripling a reactant concentration often doubles or triples the reaction rate.

Increase in concentration	→	Increase in frequency of collisions	→	Increase in reaction rate

Catalysts

Catalyst A substance that speeds up the rate of a chemical reaction but is itself unchanged.

A third way to speed up a reaction is to add a **catalyst**—a substance that accelerates a chemical reaction but is itself unchanged in the process. For example, such metals as nickel, palladium, and platinum catalyze the addition of hydrogen to the carbon–carbon double bonds in vegetable oils to yield semisolid margarine. Without the metal catalyst, the reaction does not occur.

$$\underset{\substack{\text{A double bond in}\\\text{vegetable oil}}}{\text{C}=\text{C}} \quad + \quad \text{H}_2 \quad \xrightarrow[\text{catalyst}]{\text{Ni, Pd, or Pt}} \quad \underset{\substack{\text{A single bond}\\\text{in margarine}}}{-\text{C}-\text{C}-}$$

A catalyst does not affect the energy level of either reactants or products. Rather, it increases reaction rate either by letting a reaction take place through an alternative pathway with a lower energy barrier, or by orienting the reacting molecules appropriately. In a reaction energy diagram, the catalyzed reaction has a lower activation energy (Figure 7.4). It is worth noting that the free-energy change

▶ **FIGURE 7.4** A reaction energy diagram for a reaction in the presence (green curve) and absence (red curve) of a catalyst. The catalyzed reaction has a lower (E_{act}) because it uses an alternative pathway with a lower energy barrier. The free-energy change ΔG is unaffected by the presence of a catalyst.

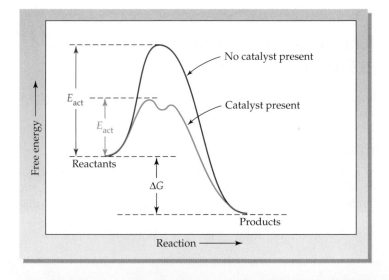

for a reaction depends *only* on the difference in the energy levels of the reactants and products, and *not* on the pathway of the reaction. Therefore, a catalyzed reaction releases (or absorbs) the same amount of energy as an uncatalyzed reaction. It simply occurs more rapidly.

In addition to their widespread use in industry, we also rely on catalysts to reduce the air pollution created by exhaust from automobile engines. The catalytic converters in most automobiles are tubes packed with catalysts of two types (Figure 7.5). One catalyst accelerates the complete combustion of hydrocarbons and CO in the exhaust to give CO_2 and H_2O, and the other decomposes NO to N_2 and O_2.

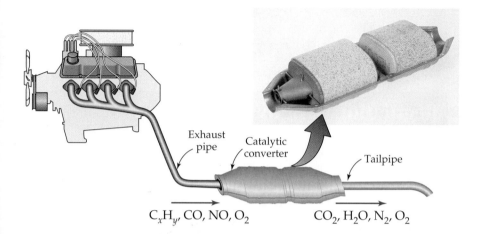

◀ FIGURE 7.5 A catalytic converter. The exhaust gases from an automobile pass through a two-stage catalytic converter. In one stage, carbon monoxide and unburned hydrocarbons are converted to CO_2 and H_2O. In the second stage, NO is converted to N_2 and O_2.

Table 7.2 summarizes the effects of changing conditions on reaction rates.

TABLE 7.2 Effects of Changes in Reaction Conditions on Reaction Rate

CHANGE	EFFECT
Concentration	Increase in reactant concentration increases rate.
	Decrease in reactant concentration decreases rate.
Temperature	Increase in temperature increases rate.
	Decrease in temperature decreases rate.
Catalyst added	Increases reaction rate.

Looking Ahead

The thousands of biochemical reactions continually taking place in our bodies are catalyzed by large protein molecules called *enzymes*, which promote reaction by controlling the orientation of the reacting molecules. Since almost every reaction is catalyzed by its own specific enzyme, the study of enzyme structure, activity, and control is a central part of biochemistry. We will look more closely at enzymes and how they work in Chapters 19 and 20.

PROBLEM 7.10

Ammonia is synthesized industrially by reaction of nitrogen and hydrogen in the presence of an iron catalyst according to the equation $3\,H_2(g) + N_2(g) \longrightarrow 2\,NH_3(g)$.

What effect will the following changes have on the reaction rate?

(a) The temperature is raised from 600 K to 700 K.

(b) The iron catalyst is removed.

(c) The concentration of H_2 gas is halved.

7.7 Reversible Reactions and Chemical Equilibrium

Many chemical reactions result in the virtually complete conversion of reactants into products. When sodium metal reacts with chlorine gas, for example, both are entirely consumed. The sodium chloride product is so much more stable than the reactants that, once started, the reaction keeps going until it is complete.

What happens, though, when the reactants and products are of approximately equal stability? This is the case, for example, in the reaction of acetic acid (the main organic constituent of vinegar) with ethyl alcohol to yield ethyl acetate, a solvent used in nail-polish remover and glue.

$$
\underset{\text{Acetic acid}}{CH_3\overset{\displaystyle O}{\overset{\displaystyle \|}{C}}OH} + \underset{\text{Ethyl alcohol}}{HOCH_2CH_3} \underset{\text{Or this direction?}}{\overset{\text{This direction?}}{\rightleftarrows}} \underset{\text{Ethyl acetate}}{CH_3\overset{\displaystyle O}{\overset{\displaystyle \|}{C}}OCH_2CH_3} + \underset{\text{Water}}{H_2O}
$$

APPLICATION ▶ Regulation of Body Temperature

Maintaining normal body temperature is crucial. If the body's thermostat is unable to maintain a temperature of 37 °C, the rates of the many thousands of chemical reactions that take place constantly in the body will change accordingly, with potentially disastrous consequences.

If, for example, a skater fell through the ice of a frozen lake, *hypothermia* could soon result. Hypothermia is a dangerous state that occurs when the body is unable to generate enough heat to maintain normal temperature. All chemical reactions in the body slow down because of the lower temperature, energy production drops, and death can result. Slowing the body's reactions can also be used to advantage, however. During open-heart surgery, the heart is stopped and maintained at about 15 °C, while the body, which receives oxygenated blood from an external pump, is cooled to 25–32 °C.

Conversely, a marathon runner on a hot, humid day might become overheated, and *hyperthermia* could result. Hyperthermia, also called *heat stroke*, is an uncontrolled rise in temperature as the result of the body's inability to lose sufficient heat. Chemical reactions in the body are accelerated at higher temperatures, the heart struggles to pump blood faster to supply increased oxygen, and brain damage can result if the body temperature rises above 41 °C.

Body temperature is maintained both by the thyroid gland and by the hypothalamus region of the brain, which act together to regulate metabolic rate. When the body's environment changes, temperature receptors in the skin, spinal cord, and abdomen send signals to the hypothalamus, which contains both heat-sensitive and cold-sensitive neurons.

Stimulation of the heat-sensitive neurons on a hot day causes a variety of effects: Impulses are sent to stimulate the sweat glands, dilate the blood vessels of the skin, decrease muscular activity, and reduce metabolic rate. Sweating cools the body through evaporation; approximately 540 cal is removed by evaporation of 1.0 g of sweat. Dilated blood vessels cool the body by allowing more blood to flow close to

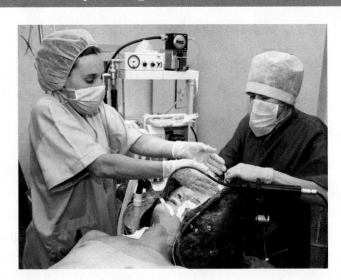

▲ The body is cooled to 25–32 °C by immersion in ice prior to open-heart surgery to slow down metabolism.

the surface of the skin where heat is removed by contact with air. Decreased muscular activity and a reduced metabolic rate cool the body by lowering internal heat production.

Stimulation of the cold-sensitive neurons on a cold day also causes a variety of effects: The hormone epinephrine is released to stimulate metabolic rate; peripheral blood vessels contract to decrease blood flow to the skin and prevent heat loss; and muscular contractions increase to produce more heat, resulting in shivering and "goosebumps."

One further comment: Drinking alcohol to warm up on a cold day actually has the opposite effect. Alcohol causes blood vessels to dilate, resulting in a warm feeling as blood flow to the skin increases. Although the warmth feels good temporarily, body temperature ultimately drops as heat is lost through the skin at an increased rate.

See Problems 7.72 and 7.73 at the end of the chapter.

Imagine the situation if you mix acetic acid and ethyl alcohol. The two begin to form ethyl acetate and water. But as soon as ethyl acetate and water form, they begin to go back to acetic acid and ethyl alcohol. Such a reaction, which easily goes in either direction, is said to be **reversible** and is indicated by a double arrow ($\rightleftharpoons$) in equations. The reaction read from left to right as written is referred to as the *forward reaction*, and the reaction from right to left is referred to as the *reverse reaction*.

Now suppose you mix some ethyl acetate and water. The same thing occurs: As soon as small quantities of acetic acid and ethyl alcohol form, the reaction in the other direction begins to take place. No matter which pair of reactants is mixed together, both reactions occur until ultimately the concentrations of reactants and products reach constant values and undergo no further change. At this point, the reaction vessel contains all four substances—acetic acid, ethyl acetate, ethyl alcohol, and water—and the reaction is said to be in a state of **chemical equilibrium**.

Since the reactant and product concentrations undergo no further change once equilibrium is reached, you might conclude that the forward and reverse reactions have stopped. That is not the case, however. The forward reaction takes place rapidly at the beginning of the reaction but then slows down as reactant concentrations decrease. At the same time, the reverse reaction takes place slowly at the beginning but then speeds up as product concentrations increase (Figure 7.6). Ultimately, the forward and reverse rates become equal and change no further.

Reversible reaction A reaction that can go in either direction, from products to reactants or reactants to products.

Chemical equilibrium A state in which the rates of forward and reverse reactions are the same.

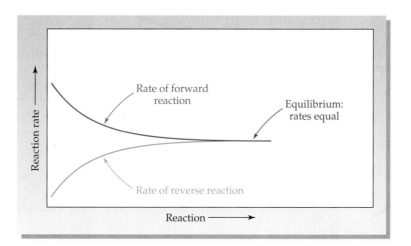

▲ **FIGURE 7.6 Reaction rates in an equilibrium reaction.** The forward rate is large initially but decreases as the concentrations of reactants drop. The reverse rate is small initially but increases as the concentrations of products increase. At equilibrium, the forward and reverse reaction rates are equal.

Chemical equilibrium is an active, dynamic condition. All substances present are continuously being made and unmade at the same rate, so their concentrations are constant at equilibrium. As an analogy, think of two floors of a building connected by up and down escalators. If the number of people moving up is the same as the number of people moving down, the numbers of people on each floor remain constant. *Individual people* are continuously changing from one floor to the other, but the *total populations* of the two floors are in equilibrium.

Note that it is not necessary for the concentrations of reactants and products at equilibrium to be equal (just as it is not necessary for the numbers of people on two floors connected by escalators to be equal). Equilibrium can be reached at any point between pure products and pure reactants. The extent to which the forward or reverse reaction is favored over the other is a characteristic property of a given reaction under given conditions.

▲ When the number of people moving up is the same as the number of people moving down, the number of people on each floor remains constant, and the two populations are in equilibrium.

7.8 Equilibrium Equations and Equilibrium Constants

Remember that the rate of a reaction depends on the number of collisions between molecules (Section 7.5), and that the number of collisions in turn depends on concentration, i.e., the number of molecules in a given volume (Section 7.6). For a reversible reaction, then, the rates of both the forward *and* the reverse reactions must depend on the concentration of reactants and products, respectively. When a reaction reaches equilibrium the rates of the forward and reverse reactions are equal, and the concentration of reactants and products remain constant. We can use this fact to obtain useful information about a reaction.

Let us look at the details of a specific equilibrium reaction. Suppose that you allow various mixtures of sulfur dioxide and oxygen to come to equilibrium with sulfur trioxide at a temperature of 727 °C and then measure the concentrations of all three gases in the mixtures.

$$2\,SO_2(g) + O_2(g) \rightleftharpoons 2\,SO_3(g)$$

In one experiment, we start with only 1.00 mol of SO_2 and 1.00 mol of O_2 in a 1.00 L container. In other words, the initial concentrations of reactants are 1.00 mol/L. When the reaction reaches equilibrium, we have 0.0620 mol/L of SO_2, 0.538 mol/L of O_2, and 0.938 mol/L of SO_3. In another experiment, we start with only 1.00 mol/L of SO_3. When this reaction reaches equilibrium, we have 0.150 mol/L of SO_2, 0.0751 mol/L of O_2, and 0.850 mol/L of SO_3. In both cases, we see that there is substantially more product than reactants when the reaction reaches equilibrium, regardless of the starting conditions. Is it possible to predict what the equilibrium conditions will be for any given reaction?

As it turns out, the answer is YES! No matter what the original concentrations, and no matter what concentrations remain at equilibrium, we find that a constant numerical value is obtained if the equilibrium concentrations are substituted into the expression

$$\frac{[SO_3]^2}{[SO_2]^2[O_2]} = 429 \quad \text{(at a constant temperature of 72 °C)}$$

The square brackets in this expression indicate the concentration of each substance expressed as moles per liter. Using the equilibrium concentrations for each of the experiments described above, we can verify that this is true:

$$\text{Experiment 1.} \quad \frac{[SO_3]^2}{[SO_2]^2[O_2]} = \frac{(0.938 \text{ mol/L})^2}{(0.0620 \text{ mol/L})^2(0.538 \text{ mol/L})} = 425$$

$$\text{Experiment 2.} \quad \frac{[SO_3]^2}{[SO_2]^2[O_2]} = \frac{(0.850 \text{ mol/L})^2}{(0.150 \text{ mol/L})^2(0.0751 \text{ mol/L})} = 428$$

Within experimental error, the ratios of product and reactant concentrations at equilibrium yield the same result. Numerous experiments like those just described have led to a general equation that is valid for any reaction. Consider a general reversible reaction:

$$a\text{A} + b\text{B} + \cdots \rightleftharpoons m\text{M} + n\text{N} + \cdots$$

where A, B, ... are reactants; M, N, ... are products; and $a, b, \ldots, m, n, \ldots$ are coefficients in the balanced equation. At equilibrium, the composition of the reaction mixture obeys the following *equilibrium equation*, where K is the **equilibrium constant**.

Equilibrium equation $\qquad K = \dfrac{[M]^m[N]^n \cdots}{[A]^a[B]^b \cdots}$ ⟵ Product concentrations ⟵ Reactant concentrations

Equilibrium constant

The equilibrium constant K is the number obtained by multiplying the equilibrium concentrations of the products and dividing by the equilibrium concentrations of the reactants, with the concentration of each substance raised to a power equal to its coefficient in the balanced equation. If we take another look at the reaction between sulfur dioxide and oxygen, we can now see how the equilibrium constant was obtained:

$$2\, SO_2\,(g) + O_2\,(g) \rightleftharpoons 2\, SO_3\,(g)$$

$$K = \frac{[SO_3]^2}{[SO_2]^2\,[O_2]}$$

Note that if there is no coefficient for a reactant or product in the reaction equation it is assumed to be 1. The value of K varies with temperature—25 °C is assumed unless otherwise specified—and units are usually omitted.

The value of the equilibrium constant indicates the position of a reaction at equilibrium. If the forward reaction is favored, the product term $[M]^m[N]^n$ is larger than the reactant term $[A]^a[B]^b$, and the value of K is larger than 1. If instead the reverse reaction is favored, $[M]^m[N]^n$ is smaller than $[A]^a[B]^b$ at equilibrium, and the value of K is smaller than 1.

For a reaction such as the combination of hydrogen and oxygen to form water vapor, the equilibrium constant is enormous (3.1×10^{81}), showing how greatly the formation of water is favored. Equilibrium is effectively nonexistent for such reactions, and the reaction is described as *going to completion*.

On the other hand, the equilibrium constant is very small for a reaction such as the combination of nitrogen and oxygen at 25 °C to give NO (4.7×10^{-31}), showing what we know from observation—that N_2 and O_2 in the air do not combine noticeably at room temperature:

$$N_2(g) + O_2(g) \rightleftharpoons 2\, NO(g) \quad K = \frac{[NO]^2}{[N_2][O_2]} = 4.7 \times 10^{-31}$$

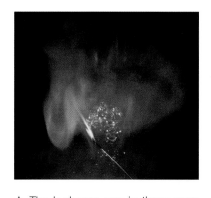

▲ The hydrogen gas in these soap bubbles reacts completely with oxygen when ignited to form water.

When K is close to 1, say between 10^3 and 10^{-3}, significant amounts of both reactants and products are present at equilibrium. An example is the reaction of acetic acid with ethyl alcohol to give ethyl acetate (Section 7.7). For this reaction, $K = 3.4$.

$$CH_3CO_2H + CH_3CH_2OH \rightleftharpoons CH_3CO_2CH_2CH_3 + H_2O$$

$$K = \frac{[CH_3CO_2CH_2CH_3][H_2O]}{[CH_3CO_2H][CH_3CH_2OH]} = 3.4$$

We can summarize the meaning of equilibrium constants in the following way:

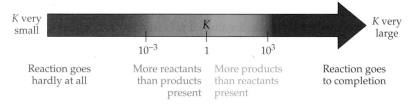

K very small				K very large
	10^{-3}	1	10^3	
Reaction goes hardly at all	More reactants than products present	More products than reactants present		Reaction goes to completion

K much smaller than 0.001 Only reactants are present at equilibrium; essentially no reaction occurs.

K between 0.001 and 1 More reactants than products are present at equilibrium.

Effect of Changes in Concentration

Let us look at the effect of a concentration change by considering the reaction of CO with H_2 to form CH_3OH (methanol). Once equilibrium is reached, the concentrations of the reactants and product are constant, and the forward and reverse reaction rates are equal.

$$CO(g) + 2\,H_2(g) \rightleftharpoons CH_3OH(g)$$

What happens if the concentration of CO is increased? To relieve the "stress" of added CO, according to Le Châtelier's principle, the extra CO must be used up. In other words, the rate of the forward reaction must increase to consume CO. Think of the CO added on the left as "pushing" the equilibrium to the right:

$$[CO \longrightarrow]$$
$$CO(g) + 2\,H_2(g) \rightleftharpoons CH_3OH(g)$$

Of course, as soon as more CH_3OH forms, the reverse reaction also speeds up, and so some CH_3OH converts back to CO and H_2. Ultimately, the forward and reverse reaction rates adjust until they are again equal, and equilibrium is reestablished. At this new equilibrium state, the value of $[H_2]$ is lower because some of the H_2 reacted with the added CO and the value of $[CH_3OH]$ is higher because CH_3OH formed as the reaction was driven to the right by the addition of CO. The changes offset each other, however, so that the value of the equilibrium constant K remains constant.

$$CO(g) + 2\,H_2(g) \rightleftharpoons CH_3OH(g)$$

If this increases . . .   . . . then this decreases . . .   . . . and this increases . . .

. . . but this remains constant. $K = \dfrac{[CH_3OH]}{[CO]\,[H_2]^2}$

What happens if CH_3OH is added to the reaction at equilibrium? Some of the methanol reacts to yield CO and H_2, making the values of $[CO]$, $[H_2]$, and $[CH_3OH]$ higher when equilibrium is reestablished. As before, the value of K does not change.

If this increases . . .

$$CO(g) + 2\,H_2(g) \rightleftharpoons CH_3OH(g)$$

. . . then this increases . . .   . . . and this increases . . .

. . . but this remains constant. $K = \dfrac{[CH_3OH]}{[CO]\,[H_2]^2}$

Alternatively, we can view chemical equilibrium as a *balance* between the energy of the reactants (on the left) and the products (on the right). Adding more reactants tips the balance in favor of the reactants. In order to restore the balance, reactants must be converted to products, or the reaction must shift to the right. If, instead, we remove reactants, then the balance is too heavy on the products side and the reaction must shift left, generating more reactants to restore balance.

Finally, what happens if a reactant is continuously supplied or a product is continuously removed? Because the concentrations are continuously changing, equilibrium can never be reached. As a result, it is sometimes possible to force a reaction to produce large quantities of a desirable product even when the equilibrium constant is unfavorable. Take the reaction of acetic acid with ethanol to yield ethyl

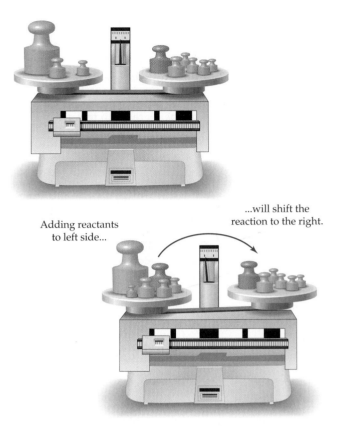

Adding reactants
to left side...

...will shift the
reaction to the right.

▲ Equilibrium represents a balance between the energy of reactants and products. Adding reactants (or products) to one side upsets the balance, and the reaction will proceed in a direction to restore the balance.

acetate, for example. As discussed in the preceding section, the equilibrium constant K for this reaction is 3.4, meaning that substantial amounts of reactants and products are both present at equilibrium. If, however, the ethyl acetate is removed as soon as it is formed, the production of more and more product is forced to occur, in accord with Le Châtelier's principle.

Continuously removing this
product from the reaction
forces more of it to be produced.

$$\underset{\text{Acetic acid}}{CH_3\overset{\displaystyle O}{\overset{\|}{C}}OH} + \underset{\text{Ethyl alcohol}}{CH_3CH_2OH} \rightleftharpoons \underset{\text{Ethyl acetate}}{CH_3\overset{\displaystyle O}{\overset{\|}{C}}OCH_2CH_3} + H_2O$$

Metabolic reactions sometimes take advantage of this effect, with one reaction prevented from reaching equilibrium by the continuous consumption of its product in a further reaction.

Effect of Changes in Temperature and Pressure

We noted in Section 7.2 that the reverse of an exothermic reaction is always endothermic. Equilibrium reactions are therefore exothermic in one direction and endothermic in the other. Le Châtelier's principle predicts that an increase in temperature will cause an equilibrium to shift in favor of the endothermic reaction so the additional heat is absorbed. Conversely, a decrease in temperature will cause an equilibrium to shift in favor of the exothermic reaction so additional heat is released. In other words, you can think of heat as a reactant or product whose increase or decrease stresses an equilibrium just as a change in reactant or product concentration does.

Endothermic reaction
(Heat is absorbed)   Favored by increase in temperature

Exothermic reaction
(Heat is released)   Favored by decrease in temperature

In the exothermic reaction of N_2 with H_2 to form NH_3, for example, raising the temperature favors the reverse reaction, which absorbs the heat:

$$[\longleftarrow \text{Heat}]$$
$$N_2(g) + 3\,H_2(g) \rightleftarrows 2\,NH_3(g) + \text{Heat}$$

We can also use the balance analogy to predict the effect of temperature on an equilibrium mixture; this time we think of heat as a reactant or product. Increasing the temperature of the reaction is the same as adding heat to the left side (for an endothermic reaction) or to the right side (for an exothermic reaction). The reaction then proceeds in the appropriate direction to restore "balance" to the system.

What about changing the pressure? Pressure influences an equilibrium only if one or more of the substances involved is a gas. As predicted by Le Châtelier's principle, decreasing the volume to increase the pressure in such a reaction shifts the equilibrium in the direction that decreases the number of molecules in the gas phase and thus decreases the pressure. For the ammonia synthesis, decreasing the volume *increases* the concentration of reactants and products, but has a greater effect on the reactant side of the equilibrium since there are more moles of gas phase reactants. Increasing the pressure, therefore, favors the forward reaction because 4 mol of gas is converted to 2 mol of gas.

$$[\text{Pressure} \longrightarrow]$$
$$\underbrace{N_2(g) + 3\,H_2(g)}_{\text{4 mol of gas}} \rightleftarrows \underbrace{2\,NH_3(g)}_{\text{2 mol of gas}}$$

The effects of changing reaction conditions on equilibria are summarized in Table 7.3.

TABLE 7.3   Effects of Changes in Reaction Conditions on Equilibria

CHANGE	EFFECT
Concentration	Increase in reactant concentration or decrease in product concentration favors forward reaction.
	Increase in product concentration or decrease in reactant concentration favors reverse reaction.
Temperature	Increase in temperature favors endothermic reaction.
	Decrease in temperature favors exothermic reaction.
Pressure	Increase in pressure favors side with fewer moles of gas.
	Decrease in pressure favors side with more moles of gas.
Catalyst added	Equilibrium reached more quickly; value of K unchanged.

⬤⬤ Looking Ahead

In Chapter 21, we will see how Le Châtelier's principle is exploited to keep chemical "traffic" moving through the body's metabolic pathways. It often happens that one reaction in a series is prevented from reaching equilibrium because its product is continuously consumed in another reaction.

APPLICATION ▶ Nitrogen Fixation

All plants and animals need nitrogen—it is present in all proteins and nucleic acids, and is the fourth most abundant element in the human body. Because the triple bond in the N_2 molecule is so strong, however, plants and animals cannot use the free element directly. It is up to nature and the fertilizer industry to convert N_2, which makes up 78% of the atmosphere, into usable nitrogen compounds in a process called *nitrogen fixation*. Plants use ammonia (NH_3), nitrates (NO_3^-), urea (H_2NCONH_2), and other simple, water-soluble compounds as their sources of nitrogen. Animals then get their nitrogen by eating plants or other plant-eating animals. All these processes contribute to the global *nitrogen cycle* (see figure).

Natural Nitrogen Fixation

Because of the very strong triple bond in the N_2 molecule, the rate of conversion of nitrogen to ammonia or nitrate is very slow under normal conditions. However, lightning in the atmosphere supplies sufficient energy to overcome the large activation energy and drive the endothermic reaction between N_2 and O_2 to form NO. Further reactions with O_2 or O_3 ultimately produce water-soluble nitrates that can be used by plants. Lightning produces small amounts of ammonia as well.

Nitrogen fixation also occurs as a result of bacterial activity in the soil. These bacteria are either free-living, such as *cyanobacteria*, or are associated symbiotically with plants, such as the *Rhizobium* found in the root nodules of legumes

(peas, beans, and clover). The biological fixation of nitrogen is represented by the following equation:

$$N_2 + 8\,H^+ + 8\,e^- + 16\,ATP \longrightarrow 2\,NH_3 + H_2 + 16\,ADP$$

where ATP and ADP are adenosine triphosphate and adenosine diphosphate respectively, in the reaction that serves as the major source of energy in many organisms (Chapter 21). This reaction is made possible by an enzyme complex called *nitrogenase*, which acts as a catalyst to lower the energy barrier.

Industrial Nitrogen Fixation

Most industrial nitrogen fixation results from fertilizer production utilizing the *Haber process*, the reaction between nitrogen and hydrogen to give ammonia:

The Haber process

$$N_2(g) + 3\,H_2(g) \longrightarrow 2\,NH_3(g)$$

This reaction is performed at high temperatures and pressures in the presence of an iron-based catalyst to increase the rate of reaction and shift the equilibrium in favor of ammonia. Since the reaction is reversible, an equilibrium would quickly be established between products and reactants; by removing ammonia as it forms, the reaction is continuously shifted to the right according to Le Châtelier's principle to maximize ammonia production.

See Additional Problems 7.74 and 7.75 at the end of the chapter.

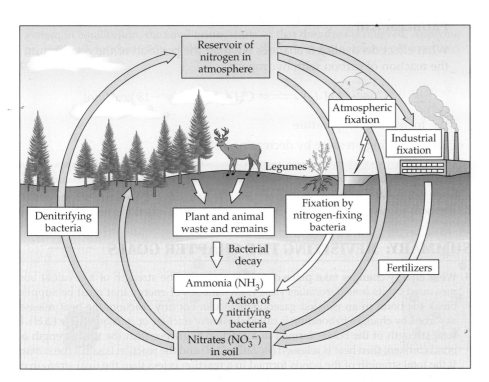

◀ The nitrogen cycle, showing how N_2 in the atmosphere is fixed, used by plants and animals, and then returned to the atmosphere.

CHAPTER 8

Gases, Liquids, and Solids

CONCEPTS TO REVIEW

Ionic Bonds
(Section 4.3)

Polar Covalent Bonds and Polar Molecules
(Sections 5.8 and 5.9)

Enthalpy, Entropy, and Free Energy
(Sections 7.2–7.4)

▲ The three states of matter—solid (rock), liquid (lava, water), and gas (steam)—all come together as this lava stream flows into the ocean.

CONTENTS

CHAPTER GOALS

In this chapter, we will answer the following questions:

1. How do scientists explain the behavior of gases?

THE GOAL: Be able to state the assumptions of the kinetic–molecular theory and use these assumptions to explain the behavior of gases.

2. How do gases respond to changes in temperature, pressure, and volume?

THE GOAL: Be able to use Boyle's law, Charles's law, Gay-Lussac's law, and Avogadro's law to explain the effect on gases of a change in pressure, volume, or temperature.

3. What is the ideal gas law?

THE GOAL: Be able to use the ideal gas law to find the pressure, volume, temperature, or molar amount of a gas sample.

4. What is partial pressure?

THE GOAL: Be able to define partial pressure and use Dalton's law of partial pressures.

5. What are the major intermolecular forces, and how do they affect the states of matter?

THE GOAL: Be able to explain dipole–dipole forces, London dispersion forces, and hydrogen bonding, and recognize which of these forces affect a given molecule.

6. What are the various kinds of solids, and how do they differ?

THE GOAL: Be able to recognize the different kinds of solids and describe their characteristics.

7. What factors affect a change of state?

THE GOAL: Be able to apply the concepts of heat change, equilibrium, and vapor pressure to changes of state.

The previous seven chapters dealt with matter at the atomic level. We have seen that all matter is composed of atoms, ions, or molecules; that these particles are in constant motion; that atoms combine to make compounds using chemical bonds; and that physical and chemical changes are accompanied by the release or absorption of energy. Now it is time to look at a different aspect of matter, concentrating not on the properties and small-scale behavior of individual atoms but on the properties and large-scale behavior of visible amounts of matter.

8.1 States of Matter and Their Changes

Matter exists in any of three phases, or *states*—solid, liquid, and gas. The state in which a compound exists under a given set of conditions depends on the relative strength of the attractive forces between particles compared to the kinetic energy of the particles. Kinetic energy (Section 7.1) is energy associated with motion, and is related to the temperature of the substance. In gases, the attractive forces between particles are very weak compared to their kinetic energy, so the particles move about freely, are far apart, and have almost no influence on one another. In liquids, the attractive forces between particles are stronger, pulling the particles close together but still allowing them considerable freedom to move about. In solids, the attractive forces are much stronger than the kinetic energy of the particles, so the atoms, molecules, or ions are held in a specific arrangement and can only wiggle around in place (Figure 8.1).

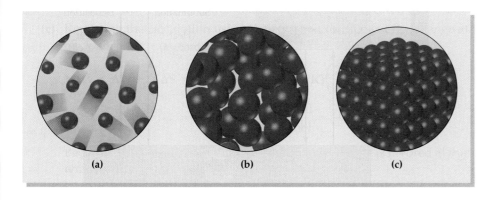

(a) (b) (c)

◀ **FIGURE 8.1** **A molecular comparison of gases, liquids, and solids.** (a) In gases, the particles feel little attraction for one another and are free to move about randomly. (b) In liquids, the particles are held close together by attractive forces but are free to slide over one another. (c) In solids, the particles still move slightly, but are held in a specific arrangement with respect to one another.

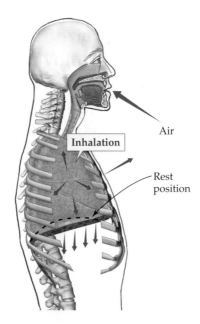

Air

Inhalation

Rest position

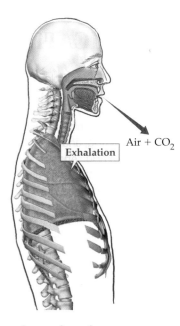

Air + CO_2

Exhalation

▶ **FIGURE 8.8 Boyle's law in breathing.** During inhalation, the diaphragm moves down and the rib cage moves up and out, thus increasing lung volume, decreasing pressure, and drawing in air. During exhalation, lung volume decreases, pressure increases, and air moves out.

Lung volume increases, causing pressure in lungs to *decrease*. Air flows *in*.

Lung volume decreases, causing pressure in lungs to *increase*. Air flows *out*.

WORKED EXAMPLE **8.4** Using Boyle's Law: Finding Volume at a Given Pressure

In a typical automobile engine, the fuel/air mixture in a cylinder is compressed from 1.0 atm to 9.5 atm. If the uncompressed volume of the cylinder is 750 mL, what is the volume when fully compressed?

ANALYSIS This is a Boyle's law problem because the volume and pressure in the cylinder change but the amount of gas and the temperature remain constant. According to Boyle's law, the pressure of the gas times its volume is constant:

$$P_1V_1 = P_2V_2$$

Knowing three of the four variables in this equation, we can solve for the unknown.

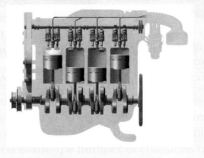

◀ A cut-away diagram of internal combustion engine shows movement of pistons during expansion and compression cycles.

BALLPARK ESTIMATE Since the pressure *increases* approximately tenfold (from 1.0 atm to 9.5 atm), the volume must *decrease* to approximately one-tenth, from 750 mL to about 75 mL.

SOLUTION

STEP 1: Identify known information. Of the four variables in Boyle's law, we know P_1, V_1, and P_2.

$P_1 = 1.0$ atm
$V_1 = 750$ mL
$P_2 = 9.5$ atm

STEP 2: Identify answer and units.

$V_2 = ??$ mL

STEP 3: Identify equation. In this case, we simply substitute the known variables into Boyle's law and rearrange to isolate the unknown.

$$P_1V_1 = P_2V_2 \implies V_2 = \frac{P_1V_1}{P_2}$$

STEP 4: Solve. Substitute the known information into the equation. Make sure units cancel so that the answer is given in the units of the unknown variable.

$$V_2 = \frac{P_1V_1}{P_2} = \frac{(1.0 \text{ atm})(750 \text{ mL})}{(9.5 \text{ atm})} = 79 \text{ mL}$$

BALLPARK CHECK Our estimate was 75 mL.

PROBLEM 8.4

An oxygen cylinder used for breathing has a volume of 5.0 L at 90 atm pressure. What is the volume of the same amount of oxygen at the same temperature if the pressure is 1.0 atm? (Hint: Would you expect the volume of gas at this pressure to be greater or less than the volume at 90 atm?)

PROBLEM 8.5

A sample of hydrogen gas at 273 K has a volume of 3.2 L at 4.0 atm pressure. What is its pressure if its volume is changed to 10.0 L? To 0.20 L?

8.5 Charles's Law: The Relation between Volume and Temperature

Imagine that you again have a sample of gas inside a cylinder with a plunger at one end. What happens if you double the sample's Kelvin temperature while letting the plunger move freely to keep the pressure constant? The gas particles move with twice as much energy and collide twice as forcefully with the walls. To maintain a constant pressure, the volume of the gas in the cylinder must double (Figure 8.9).

▲ The volume of the gas in the balloon increases as it is heated, causing a decrease in density and allowing the balloon to rise.

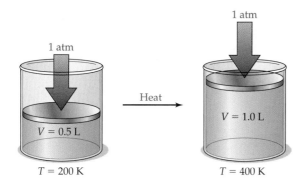

▲ **FIGURE 8.9 Charles's law.** The volume of a gas is directly proportionately to its Kelvin temperature at constant *n* and *P*. If the Kelvin temperature of the gas is doubled, its volume doubles.

According to **Charles's law**, the volume of a fixed amount of gas at constant pressure is directly proportional to its Kelvin temperature. Note the difference between *directly* proportional in Charles's law and *inversely* proportional in Boyle's law. Directly proportional quantities change in the same direction: As temperature goes up or down, volume also goes up or down (Figure 8.10).

Charles's law   The volume of a gas is directly proportional to its Kelvin temperature for a fixed amount of gas at a constant pressure. That is, *V* divided by *T* is constant when *n* and *P* are held constant.

$$V \propto T \quad \text{(In kelvins)}$$

$$\text{or } \frac{V}{T} = k \quad \text{(A constant value)}$$

$$\text{or } \frac{V_1}{T_1} = \frac{V_2}{T_2}$$

This observation is consistent with the kinetic–molecular theory. As temperature increases, the average kinetic energy of the gas molecules increases, as does the

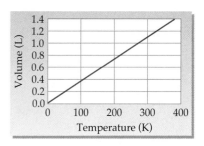

▲ **FIGURE 8.10 Charles's law.** Volume is directly proportional to the Kelvin temperature for a fixed amount of gas at a constant pressure. As the temperature goes up, the volume also goes up.

energy of molecular collisions with the interior surface of the container. The volume of the container must increase to maintain a constant pressure. As an example of Charles's law, think about what happens when a hot-air balloon is inflated. Heating causes the air inside to expand and fill the balloon. The air inside the balloon is less dense than the air outside the balloon, creating the buoyancy effect.

WORKED EXAMPLE **8.5** Using Charles's Law: Finding Volume at a Given Temperature

An average adult inhales a volume of 0.50 L of air with each breath. If the air is warmed from room temperature (20 °C = 293 K) to body temperature (37 °C = 310 K) while in the lungs, what is the volume of the air exhaled?

ANALYSIS This is a Charles's law problem because the volume and temperature of the air change while the amount and pressure remain constant. Knowing three of the four variables, we can rearrange Charles's law to solve for the unknown.

BALLPARK ESTIMATE Charles's Law predicts an increase in volume directly proportional to the increase in temperature from 273 K to 310 K. The increase of less than 20 K represents a relatively small change compared to the initial temperature of 273 K. A 10% increase, for example, would be equal to a temperature change of 27 K; so a 20 K change would be less than 10%. We would therefore expect the volume to increase by less than 10%, from 0.50 L to a little less than 0.55 L.

SOLUTION

STEP 1: Identify known information. Of the four variables in Charles's law, we know T_1, V_1, and T_2.

$T_1 = 293$ K
$V_1 = 0.50$ L
$T_2 = 310$ K

STEP 2: Identify answer and units.

$V_2 = ??$ L

STEP 3: Identify equation. Substitute the known variables into Charles's law and rearrange to isolate the unknown.

$$\frac{V_1}{T_1} = \frac{V_2}{T_2} \implies V_2 = \frac{V_1 T_2}{T_1}$$

STEP 4: Solve. Substitute the known information into Charles's law; check to make sure units cancel.

$$V_2 = \frac{V_1 T_2}{T_1} = \frac{(0.50 \text{ L})(310 \text{ K})}{293 \text{ K}} = 0.53 \text{ L}$$

BALLPARK CHECK This is consistent with our estimate!

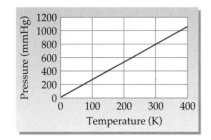

▲ **FIGURE 8.11 Gay-Lussac's law.** Pressure is directly proportional to the temperature in kelvins for a fixed amount of gas at a constant volume. As the temperature goes up, the pressure also goes up.

PROBLEM 8.6

A sample of chlorine gas has a volume of 0.30 L at 273 K and 1 atm pressure. What is its volume at 250 K and 1 atm pressure? At 525 °C and 1 atm?

8.6 Gay-Lussac's Law: The Relation between Pressure and Temperature

Imagine next that you have a fixed amount of gas in a sealed container whose volume remains constant. What happens if you double the temperature (in kelvins)? The gas particles move with twice as much energy and collide with the walls of the container with twice as much force. Thus, the pressure in the container doubles. According to **Gay-Lussac's law**, the pressure of a fixed amount of gas at constant volume is directly proportional to its Kelvin temperature. As temperature goes up or down, pressure also goes up or down (Figure 8.11).

Gay-Lussac's law The pressure of a gas is directly proportional to its Kelvin temperature for a fixed amount of gas at a constant volume. That is, P divided by T is constant when n and V are held constant.

$$P \propto T \quad \text{(In kelvins)}$$

$$\text{or } \frac{P}{T} = k \quad \text{(A constant value)}$$

$$\text{or } \frac{P_1}{T_1} = \frac{P_2}{T_2}$$

▲ Because of the possibility of explosion (see warning label), aerosol containers cannot be incinerated, requiring disposal in landfills.

According to the kinetic–molecular theory, the kinetic energy of molecules is directly proportional to absolute temperature. As the average kinetic energy of the molecules increases, the energy of collisions with the interior surface of the container increases, causing an increase in pressure. As an example of Gay-Lussac's law, think of what happens when an aerosol can is thrown into an incinerator. As the can gets hotter, pressure builds up inside and the can explodes (hence the warning statement on aerosol cans).

WORKED EXAMPLE **8.6** Using Gay-Lussac's Law: Finding Pressure at a Given Temperature

What does the inside pressure become if an aerosol can with an initial pressure of 4.5 atm is heated in a fire from room temperature (20 °C) to 600 °C?

ANALYSIS This is a Gay-Lussac's law problem because the pressure and temperature of the gas inside the can change while its amount and volume remain constant. We know three of the four variables in the equation for Gay-Lussac's law, and can find the unknown by substitution and rearrangement.

BALLPARK ESTIMATE Gay-Lussac's law states that pressure is directly proportional to temperature. Since the Kelvin temperature increases approximately threefold (from about 300 K to about 900 K), we expect the pressure to also increase by approximately threefold, from 4.5 atm to about 14 atm.

SOLUTION

STEP 1: **Identify known information.** Of the four variables in Gay-Lussac's law, we know P_1, T_1 and T_2. (Note that T must be in kelvins.)

$P_1 = 4.5$ atm
$T_1 = 20\ °C = 293$ K
$T_2 = 600\ °C = 873$ K

STEP 2: **Identify answer and units.**

$P_2 = ??$ atm

STEP 3: **Identify equation.** Substituting the known variables into Gay-Lussac's law, we rearrange to isolate the unknown.

$$\frac{P_1}{T_1} = \frac{P_2}{T_2} \implies P_2 = \frac{P_1 T_2}{T_1}$$

STEP 4: **Solve.** Substitute the known information into Gay-Lussac's law, check to make sure units cancel.

$$P_2 = \frac{P_1 T_2}{T_1} = \frac{(4.5\ \text{atm})(873\ \text{K})}{293\ \text{K}} = 13\ \text{atm}$$

BALLPARK CHECK Our estimate was 14 atm.

PROBLEM 8.7

Driving on a hot day causes tire temperature to rise. What is the pressure inside an automobile tire at 45 °C if the tire has a pressure of 30 psi at 15 °C? Assume that the volume and amount of air in the tire remain constant.

8.7 The Combined Gas Law

Since PV, V/T, and P/T all have constant values for a fixed amount of gas, these relationships can be merged into a **combined gas law**, which holds true whenever the amount of gas is fixed.

COMBINED GAS LAW $\quad \dfrac{PV}{T} = k \quad$ (A constant value)

$$\text{or} \quad \frac{P_1 V_1}{T_1} = \frac{P_2 V_2}{T_2}$$

If any five of the six quantities in this equation are known, the sixth quantity can be calculated. Furthermore, if any of the three variables T, P, or V is constant, that variable drops out of the equation, leaving behind Boyle's law, Charles's law, or Gay-Lussac's law. As a result, *the combined gas law is the only equation you need to remember for a fixed amount of gas.* Worked Example 8.7 gives a sample calculation.

Since $\qquad \dfrac{P_1 V_1}{T_1} = \dfrac{P_2 V_2}{T_2}$

At constant T: $\quad \dfrac{P_1 V_1}{T} = \dfrac{P_2 V_2}{T} \quad$ gives $\quad P_1 V_1 = P_2 V_2 \quad$ (Boyle's law)

At constant P: $\quad \dfrac{P V_1}{T_1} = \dfrac{P V_2}{T_2} \quad$ gives $\quad \dfrac{V_1}{T_1} = \dfrac{V_2}{T_2} \quad$ (Charles's law)

At constant V: $\quad \dfrac{P_1 V}{T_1} = \dfrac{P_2 V}{T_2} \quad$ gives $\quad \dfrac{P_1}{T_1} = \dfrac{P_2}{T_2} \quad$ (Gay-Lussac's law)

WORKED EXAMPLE 8.7 Using the Combined Gas Law: Finding Temperature

A 6.3 L sample of helium gas stored at 25 °C and 1.0 atm pressure is transferred to a 2.0 L tank and maintained at a pressure of 2.8 atm. What temperature is needed to maintain this pressure?

ANALYSIS This is a combined gas law problem because pressure, volume, and temperature change while the amount of helium remains constant. Of the six variables in this equation, we know P_1, V_1, T_1, P_2, and V_2, and we need to find T_2.

BALLPARK ESTIMATE Since the volume goes down by a little more than a factor of about 3 (from 6.3 L to 2.0 L) and the pressure goes up by a little less than a factor of about 3 (from 1.0 atm to 2.8 atm), the two changes roughly offset each other, and so the temperature should not change much. Since the volume-decrease factor (3.2) is slightly greater than the pressure-increase factor (2.8), the temperature will drop slightly ($T \propto V$).

SOLUTION

STEP 1: Identify known information. Of the six variables in combined-gas-law we know P_1, V_1, T_1, P_2, and V_2. (As always, T must be converted from Celsius degrees to kelvins.)

$P_1 = 1.0$ atm, $P_2 = 2.8$ atm
$V_1 = 6.3$ L, $V_2 = 2.0$ L
$T_1 = 25$ °C $= 298$ K

STEP 2: Identify answer and units.

$T_2 = $?? kelvin

STEP 3: Identify the equation. Substituting the known variables into the equation for the combined gas law and rearrange to isolate the unknown.

$$\frac{P_1 V_1}{T_1} = \frac{P_2 V_2}{T_2} \implies T_2 = \frac{P_2 V_2 T_1}{P_1 V_1}$$

STEP 4: Solve. Solve the combined gas law equation for T_2; check to make sure units cancel.

$$T_2 = \frac{P_2 V_2 T_1}{P_1 V_1} = \frac{(2.8 \text{ atm})(2.0 \text{ L})(298 \text{ K})}{(1.0 \text{ atm})(6.3 \text{ L})} = 260 \text{ K}(\Delta T = -38 \text{ °C})$$

BALLPARK CHECK The relatively small decrease in temperature (38 °C, or 13% compared to the original temperature) is consistent with our prediction.

PROBLEM 8.8

A weather balloon is filled with helium to a volume of 275 L at 22 °C and 752 mmHg. The balloon ascends to an altitude where the pressure is 480 mmHg, and the temperature is −32 °C. What is the volume of the balloon at this altitude?

◀ KEY CONCEPT PROBLEM 8.9

A balloon is filled under the initial conditions indicated below. If the pressure is then increased to 2 atm while the temperature is increased to 50 °C, which balloon on the right, (a) or (b), represents the new volume of the balloon?

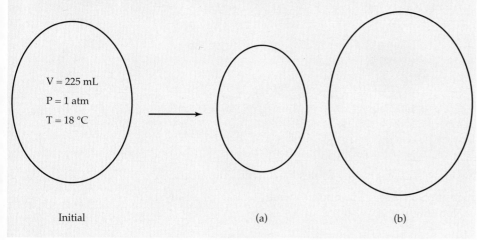

V = 225 mL

P = 1 atm

T = 18 °C

Initial   (a)   (b)

8.8 Avogadro's Law: The Relation between Volume and Molar Amount

Here we look at one final gas law, which takes changes in amount of gas into account. Imagine that you have two different volumes of a gas at the same temperature and pressure. How many moles does each sample contain? According to **Avogadro's law**, the volume of a gas is directly proportional to its molar amount at a constant pressure and temperature (Figure 8.12). A sample that contains twice the molar amount has twice the volume.

Avogadro's law   The volume of a gas is directly proportional to its molar amount at a constant pressure and temperature. That is, V divided by n is constant when P and T are held constant.

Volume $(V) \propto$ Number of moles (n)

or $\dfrac{V}{n} = k$ (A constant value; the same for all gases)

or $\dfrac{V_1}{n_1} = \dfrac{V_2}{n_2}$

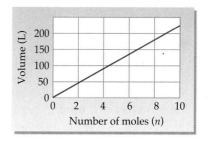

▲ FIGURE 8.12 Avogadro's law. Volume is directly proportional to the molar amount, n, at a constant temperature and pressure. As the number of moles goes up, the volume also goes up.

Because the particles in a gas are so tiny compared to the empty space surrounding them, there is no interaction among gas particles as proposed by the kinetic–molecular theory. As a result, the chemical identity of the particles does not matter and the value of the constant k in the equation $V/n = k$ is the same for all gases. It is therefore possible to compare the molar amounts of *any* two gases simply by comparing their volumes at the same temperature and pressure.

Notice that the *values* of temperature and pressure do not matter; it is only necessary that T and P be the same for both gases. To simplify comparisons of gas samples, however, it is convenient to define a set of conditions called **standard temperature and pressure (STP)**:

Standard temperature and pressure (STP)   0 °C (273.15 K); 1 atm (760 mmHg)

At standard temperature and pressure, 1 mol of any gas (6.02×10^{23} particles) has a volume of 22.4 L, a quantity called the **standard molar volume** (Figure 8.13).

Standard molar volume of any ideal gas at STP   22.4 L/mol

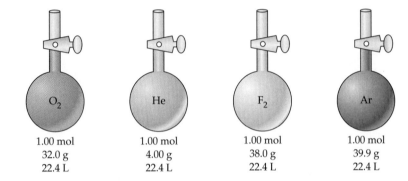

▶ **FIGURE 8.13 Avogadro's law.** Each of these 22.4 L bulbs contains 1.00 mol of gas at 0 °C and 1 atm pressure. Note that the volume occupied by 1 mol of gas is the same even though the mass of 1 mol of each gas is different.

O_2
1.00 mol
32.0 g
22.4 L

He
1.00 mol
4.00 g
22.4 L

F_2
1.00 mol
38.0 g
22.4 L

Ar
1.00 mol
39.9 g
22.4 L

WORKED EXAMPLE   **8.8** Using Avogadro's Law: Finding Moles in a Given Volume at STP

Use the standard molar volume of a gas at STP (22.4 L) to find how many moles of air at STP are in a room measuring 4.11 m wide by 5.36 m long by 2.58 m high.

ANALYSIS We first find the volume of the room and then use standard molar volume as a conversion factor to find the number of moles.

SOLUTION

STEP 1: Identify known information. We are given the room dimensions.

Length = 5.36 m
Width = 4.11 m
Height = 2.58 m

STEP 2: Identify answer and units.

Moles of air = ?? mol

STEP 3: Identify the equation. The volume of the room is the product of its three dimensions. Once we have the volume (in m³), we can convert to liters and use the molar volume at STP as a conversion factor to obtain moles of air.

$$\text{Volume} = (4.11 \text{ m})(5.36 \text{ m})(2.58 \text{ m}) = 56.8 \text{ m}^3$$

$$= 56.8 \text{ m}^3 \times \frac{1000 \text{ L}}{1 \text{ m}^3} = 5.68 \times 10^4 \text{ L}$$

$$1 \text{ mol} = 22.4 \text{ L} \rightarrow \frac{1 \text{ mol}}{22.4 \text{ L}}$$

STEP 4: Solve. Use the room volume and the molar volume at STP to set up an equation, making sure unwanted units cancel.

$$5.68 \times 10^4 \cancel{\text{ L}} \times \frac{1 \text{ mol}}{22.4 \cancel{\text{ L}}} = 2.54 \times 10^3 \text{ mol}$$

PROBLEM 8.10

How many moles of methane gas, CH_4, are in a 1.00×10^5 L storage tank at STP? How many grams of methane is this? How many grams of carbon dioxide gas could the same tank hold?

8.9 The Ideal Gas Law

The relationships among the four variables P, V, T, and n for gases can be combined into a single expression called the **ideal gas law**. If you know the values of any three of the four quantities, you can calculate the value of the fourth.

Ideal gas law $\dfrac{PV}{nT} = R$ (A constant value)

or $PV = nRT$

The constant R in the ideal gas law (instead of the usual k) is called the **gas constant**. Its value depends on the units chosen for pressure, with the two most common values

Gas constant (R) The constant R in the ideal gas law, $PV = nRT$.

For P in atmospheres: $R = 0.0821 \dfrac{L \cdot atm}{mol \cdot K}$

For P in millimeters Hg: $R = 62.4 \dfrac{L \cdot mmHg}{mol \cdot K}$

In using the ideal gas law, it is important to choose the value of R having pressure units that are consistent with the problem and, if necessary, to convert volume into liters and temperature into kelvins.

Table 8.1 summarizes the various gas laws, and Worked Example 8.9 shows how to use the ideal gas law.

TABLE 8.1   A Summary of the Gas Laws

	GAS LAW	VARIABLES	CONSTANT
Boyle's law	$P_1V_1 = P_2V_2$	P, V	n, T
Charles's law	$V_1/T_1 = V_2/T_2$	V, T	n, P
Gay-Lussac's law	$P_1/T_1 = P_2/T_2$	P, T	n, V
Combined gas law	$P_1V_1/T_1 = P_2V_2/T_2$	P, V, T	n
Avogadro's law	$V_1/n_1 = V_2/n_2$	V, n	P, T
Ideal gas law	$PV = nRT$	P, V, T, n	R

WORKED EXAMPLE   **8.9** Using Ideal Gas Law: Finding Moles

How many moles of air are in the lungs of an average person with a total lung capacity of 3.8 L? Assume that the person is at 1.0 atm pressure and has a normal body temperature of 37 °C.

ANALYSIS This is an ideal gas law problem because it asks for a value of n when P, V, and T are known: $n = PV/RT$. The volume is given in the correct unit of liters, but temperature must be converted to kelvins.

SOLUTION

STEP 1: **Identify known information.** We know three of the four variables in the ideal gas law.	$P = 1.0$ atm $V = 3.8$ L $T = 37\,°C = 310$ K
STEP 2: **Identify answer and units.**	Moles of air, $n = $?? mol

WORKED EXAMPLE **8.11** Using Dalton's Law: Finding Partial Pressures

Humid air on a warm summer day is approximately 20% oxygen, 75% nitrogen, 4% water vapor, and 1% argon. What is the partial pressure of each component if the atmospheric pressure is 750 mmHg?

ANALYSIS According to Dalton's law, the partial pressure of any gas in a mixture is equal to the percent concentration of the gas times the total gas pressure (750 mmHg). In this case,

$$P_{total} = P_{O_2} + P_{N_2} + P_{H_2O} + P_{Ar}$$

SOLUTION

Oxygen partial pressure (P_{O_2}):	0.20×750 mmHg $= 150$ mmHg
Nitrogen partial pressure (P_{N_2}):	0.75×750 mmHg $= 560$ mmHg
Water vapor partial pressure (P_{H_2O}):	0.04×750 mmHg $= 30$ mmHg
Argon partial pressure (P_{Ar}):	0.01×750 mmHg $= 8$ mmHg

Total pressure $= 748$ mmHg $\rightarrow 750$ mmHg (rounding to 2 significant figures!)

Note that the sum of the partial pressures must equal the total pressure (within rounding error).

▲ Because of the lack of sufficient oxygen at the top of Mt. Everest, most climbers rely on bottled oxygen supplies.

PROBLEM 8.14

Assuming a total pressure of 9.5 atm, what is the partial pressure of each component in the mixture of 98% helium and 2.0% oxygen breathed by deep-sea divers? How does the partial pressure of oxygen in diving gas compare with its partial pressure in normal air?

PROBLEM 8.15

Determine the percent composition of air in the lungs from the following composition in partial pressures: $P_{N_2} = 573$ mmHg, $P_{O_2} = 100$ mmHg, $P_{CO_2} = 40$ mmHg, $P_{H_2O} = 47$ mmHg; all at 37 °C and 1 atm pressure.

PROBLEM 8.16

The atmospheric pressure on the top of Mt. Everest, an altitude of 29,035 ft, is only 265 mmHg. What is the partial pressure of oxygen in the lungs at this altitude?

⚷ KEY CONCEPT PROBLEM 8.17

Assume that you have a mixture of He (MW = 4 amu) and Xe (MW = 131 amu) at 300 K. Which of the drawings (a)–(c) best represents the mixture (blue = He; green = Xe)?

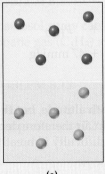

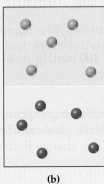

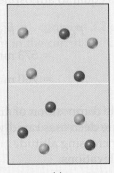

(a)	(b)	(c)

8.11 Intermolecular Forces

What determines whether a substance is a gas, a liquid, or a solid at a given temperature? Why does rubbing alcohol evaporate much more readily than water? Why do molecular compounds have lower melting points than ionic compounds? To answer these and a great many other such questions, we need to look into the nature of **intermolecular forces**—the forces that act *between different molecules* rather than within an individual molecule.

In gases, the intermolecular forces are negligible, so the gas molecules act independently of one another. In liquids and solids, however, intermolecular forces are strong enough to hold the molecules in close contact. As a general rule, the stronger the intermolecular forces in a substance, the more difficult it is to separate the molecules, and the higher the melting and boiling points of the substance.

There are three major types of intermolecular forces: *dipole–dipole, London dispersion*, and *hydrogen bonding*. We will discuss each in turn.

Intermolecular force   A force that acts between molecules and holds molecules close to one another.

Dipole–Dipole Forces

Recall from Sections 5.8 and 5.9 that many molecules contain polar covalent bonds and may therefore have a net molecular polarity. (, pp. 128, 130) In such cases, the positive and negative ends of different molecules are attracted to one another by what is called a **dipole–dipole force**. (Figure 8.14).

Dipole–dipole force   The attractive force between positive and negative ends of polar molecules.

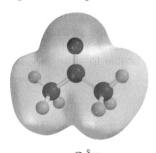

▲ **FIGURE 8.14   Dipole–dipole forces.**   The positive and negative ends of polar molecules are attracted to one another by dipole–dipole forces. As a result, polar molecules have higher boiling points than nonpolar molecules of similar size.

Dipole–dipole forces are weak, with strengths on the order of 1 kcal/mol compared to the 70–100 kcal/mol typically found for the strength of a covalent bond. Nevertheless, the effects of dipole–dipole forces are important, as can be seen by looking at the difference in boiling points between polar and nonpolar molecules. Butane, for instance, is a nonpolar molecule with a molecular weight of 58 amu and a boiling point of −0.5 °C, whereas acetone has the same molecular weight yet boils 57 °C higher because it is polar. (Recall from Section 5.8 how molecular polarities can be visualized using electrostatic potential maps. (, p. 128)

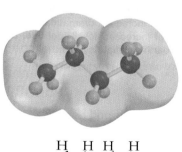

Butane (C$_4$H$_{10}$)

Mol wt = 58 amu
bp = −0.5 °C

Acetone (C$_3$H$_6$O)

Mol wt = 58 amu
bp = 56.2 °C

the volume of air in the tank at 0 °C and 1.00 atm pressure (STP)?

8.58 What is the effect on the pressure of a gas if you simultaneously:

(a) Halve its volume and double its Kelvin temperature?
(b) Double its volume and halve its Kelvin temperature?

8.59 What is the effect on the volume of a gas if you simultaneously:

(a) Halve its pressure and double its Kelvin temperature?
(b) Double its pressure and double its Kelvin temperature?

8.60 A sample of oxygen produced in a laboratory experiment had a volume of 590 mL at a pressure of 775 mmHg and a temperature of 352 K. What is the volume of this sample at 25 °C and 800.0 mmHg pressure?

8.61 A small cylinder of helium gas used for filling balloons has a volume of 2.30 L and a pressure of 1850 atm at 25 °C. How many balloons can you fill if each one has a volume of 1.5 L and a pressure of 1.25 atm at 25 °C?

AVOGADRO'S LAW AND STANDARD MOLAR VOLUME

8.62 Explain Avogadro's law using the kinetic–molecular theory of gases.

8.63 What conditions are defined as standard temperature and pressure (STP)?

8.64 How many liters does 1 mol of gas occupy at STP?

8.65 How many moles of gas are in a volume of 48.6 L at STP?

8.66 Which sample contains more molecules: 1.0 L of O_2 at STP or 1.0 L of H_2 at STP? Which sample has the larger mass?

8.67 How many milliliters of Cl_2 gas must you have to obtain 0.20 g at STP?

8.68 What is the mass of CH_4 in a sample that occupies a volume of 16.5 L at STP?

8.69 Assume that you have 1.75 g of the deadly gas hydrogen cyanide, HCN. What is the volume of the gas at STP?

8.70 A typical room is 4.0 m long, 5.0 m wide, and 2.5 m high. What is the total mass of the oxygen in the room assuming that the gas in the room is at STP and that air contains 21% oxygen and 79% nitrogen?

8.71 What is the total mass of nitrogen in the room described in Problem 8.70?

IDEAL GAS LAW

8.72 What is the ideal gas law?

8.73 How does the ideal gas law differ from the combined gas law?

8.74 Which sample contains more molecules: 2.0 L of Cl_2 at STP, or 3.0 L of CH_4 at 300 K and 1.5 atm? Which sample weighs more?

8.75 Which sample contains more molecules: 2.0 L of CO_2 at 300 K and 500 mmHg, or 1.5 L of N_2 at 57 °C and 760 mmHg? Which sample weighs more?

8.76 If 2.3 mol of He has a volume of 0.15 L at 294 K, what is the pressure in atm?

8.77 If 3.5 mol of O_2 has a volume of 27.0 L at a pressure of 1.6 atm, what is its temperature in kelvins?

8.78 If 15.0 g of CO_2 gas has a volume of 0.30 L at 310 K, what is its pressure in mmHg?

8.79 If 20.0 g of N_2 gas has a volume of 4.00 L and a pressure of 6.0 atm, what is its temperature in degrees Celsius?

8.80 If 18.0 g of O_2 gas has a temperature of 350 K and a pressure of 550 mmHg, what is its volume?

8.81 How many moles of a gas will occupy a volume of 0.55 L at a temperature of 347 K and a pressure of 2.5 atm?

DALTON'S LAW AND PARTIAL PRESSURE

8.82 What is meant by *partial pressure*?

8.83 What is Dalton's law?

8.84 If the partial pressure of oxygen in air at 1.0 atm is 160 mmHg, what is the partial pressure on the summit of Mt. Whitney, where atmospheric pressure is 440 mmHg? Assume that the percent oxygen is the same.

8.85 Patients suffering from respiratory disorders are often treated in oxygen tents in which the atmosphere is enriched in oxygen. What is the partial pressure of O_2 in an oxygen tent consisting of 45% O_2 for an atmospheric pressure of 753 mmHg?

LIQUIDS AND INTERMOLECULAR FORCES

8.86 What is the vapor pressure of a liquid?

8.87 What is the value of a liquid's vapor pressure at its normal boiling point?

8.88 What is the effect of pressure on a liquid's boiling point?

8.89 What is a liquid's heat of vaporization?

8.90 What characteristic must a compound have to experience the following intermolecular forces?

(a) London dispersion forces
(b) Dipole–dipole forces
(c) Hydrogen bonding

8.91 In which of the following compounds are dipole–dipole attractions the most important intermolecular force?

(a) N_2 (b) HCN   (c) CCl_4
(d) $MgBr_2$ (e) CH_3Cl (f) CH_3CO_2H

8.92 Dimethyl ether (CH_3OCH_3) and ethanol (C_2H_5OH) have the same formula (C_2H_6O), but the boiling point of dimethyl ether is −25 °C while that of ethanol is 78 °C. Explain.

8.93 Iodine is a solid at room temperature (mp = 113.5 °C) while bromine is a liquid (mp = −7 °C). Explain in terms of intermolecular forces.

8.94 The heat of vaporization of water is 9.72 kcal/mol.

(a) How much heat (in kilocalories) is required to vaporize 3.00 mol of H_2O?
(b) How much heat (in kilocalories) is released when 320 g of steam condenses?

8.95 Patients with a high body temperature are often given "alcohol baths." The heat of vaporization of isopropyl alcohol (rubbing alcohol) is 159 cal/g. How much heat is removed from the skin by the evaporation of 190 g (about ½ cup) of isopropyl alcohol?

SOLIDS

8.96 What is the difference between an amorphous and a crystalline solid?

8.97 List three kinds of crystalline solids, and give an example of each.

8.98 The heat of fusion of acetic acid, the principal organic component of vinegar, is 45.9 cal/g. How much heat (in kilocalories) is required to melt 1.75 mol of solid acetic acid?

8.99 The heat of fusion of sodium metal is 630 cal/mol. How much heat (in kilocalories) is required to melt 262 g of sodium?

Applications

8.100 What is the difference between a systolic and a diastolic pressure reading? Is a blood pressure of 180/110 within the normal range? [*Blood Pressure, p. 223*]

8.101 What are the three most important greenhouse gases? [*Greenhouse Gases and Global Warming, p. 236*]

8.102 What evidence is there that global warming is occurring? [*Greenhouse Gases and Global Warming, p. 236*]

8.103 What is the mass ratio of calcium to phosphate in calcium phosphate, $Ca_3(PO_4)_2$? In hydroxyapatite, $Ca_{10}(PO_4)_6(OH)_2$? [*Biomaterials for Joint Replacement, p. 246*]

8.104 What is a supercritical fluid? [*CO_2 as an Environmentally Friendly Solvent, p. 248*]

8.105 What are the environmental advantages of using supercritical CO_2 in place of chlorinated organic solvents? [*CO_2 as an Environmentally Friendly Solvent, p. 248*]

General Questions and Problems

8.106 Use the kinetic–molecular theory to explain why gas pressure increases if the temperature is raised and the volume is kept constant.

8.107 Hydrogen and oxygen react according to the equation $2\,H_2 + O_2 \longrightarrow 2\,H_2O$. According to Avogadro's law, how many liters of hydrogen are required to react with 2.5 L of oxygen at STP?

8.108 If 3.0 L of hydrogen and 1.5 L of oxygen at STP react to yield water, how many moles of water are formed? What gas volume does the water have at a temperature of 100 °C and 1 atm pressure?

8.109 Approximately 240 mL/min of CO_2 is exhaled by an average adult at rest. Assuming a temperature of 37 °C and 1 atm pressure, how many moles of CO_2 is this?

8.110 How many grams of CO_2 are exhaled by an average resting adult in 24 hours? (See Problem 8.109.)

8.111 Imagine that you have two identical containers, one containing hydrogen at STP and the other containing oxygen at STP. How can you tell which is which without opening them?

8.112 When fully inflated, a hot-air balloon has a volume of 1.6×10^5 L at an average temperature of 375 K and 0.975 atm. Assuming that air has an average molar mass of 29 g/mol, what is the density of the air in the hot-air balloon? How does this compare with the density of air at STP?

8.113 A 10.0 g sample of an unknown gas occupies 14.7 L at a temperature of 25 °C and a pressure of 745 mmHg. What is the molar mass of the gas?

8.114 One mole of any gas has a volume of 22.4 L at STP. What are the molecular weights of the following gases, and what are their densities in grams per liter at STP?

(a) CH_4 (b) CO_2 (c) O_2

8.115 Gas pressure outside the space shuttle is approximately 1×10^{-14} mm Hg at a temperature of approximately 1 K. If the gas is almost entirely hydrogen atoms (H, not H_2), what volume of space is occupied by 1 mol of atoms? What is the density of H gas in atoms per liter?

8.116 Ethylene glycol, $C_2H_6O_2$, has one OH bonded to each carbon.

(a) Draw the Lewis dot structure of ethylene glycol.

(b) Draw the Lewis dot structure of chloroethane, C_2H_5Cl.

(c) Chloroethane has a slightly higher molar mass than ethylene glycol, but a much lower boiling point (3 °C versus 198 °C). Explain.

8.117 A rule of thumb for scuba diving is that the external pressure increases by 1 atm for every 10 m of depth. A diver using a compressed air tank is planning to descend to a depth of 25 m.

(a) What is the external pressure at this depth? (Remember that the pressure at sea level is 1 atm.)

(b) Assuming that the tank contains 20% oxygen and 80% nitrogen, what is the partial pressure of each gas in the diver's lungs at this depth?

8.118 The *Rankine* temperature scale used in engineering is to the Fahrenheit scale as the Kelvin scale is to the Celsius scale. That is, 1 Rankine degree is the same size as 1 Fahrenheit degree, and 0 °R = absolute zero .

(a) What temperature corresponds to the freezing point of water on the Rankine scale?

(b) What is the value of the gas constant R on the Rankine scale in $(L \cdot atm)/(°R \cdot mol)$?

8.119 Isooctane, C_8H_{18}, is the component of gasoline from which the term *octane rating* derives.

(a) Write a balanced equation for the combustion of isooctane to yield CO_2 and H_2O.

(b) Assuming that gasoline is 100% isooctane and that the density of isooctane is 0.792 g/mL, what mass of CO_2 (in kilograms) is produced each year by the annual U.S. gasoline consumption of 4.6×10^{10} L?

(c) What is the volume (in liters) of this CO_2 at STP?

CHAPTER 9

Solutions

▲ The giant sequoia relies on osmotic pressure—a colligative property of solutions—to transport water and nutrients from the roots to the treetops 300 ft up.

CONTENTS

CHAPTER GOALS

Among the questions we will answer are the following:

1. What are solutions, and what factors affect solubility?

THE GOAL: Be able to define the different kinds of mixtures and explain the influence on solubility of solvent and solute structure, temperature, and pressure.

2. How is the concentration of a solution expressed?

THE GOAL: Be able to define, use, and convert between the most common ways of expressing solution concentrations.

3. How are dilutions carried out?

THE GOAL: Be able to calculate the concentration of a solution prepared by dilution and explain how to make a desired dilution.

4. What is an electrolyte?

THE GOAL: Be able to recognize strong and weak electrolytes and nonelectrolytes, and express electrolyte concentrations.

5. How do solutions differ from pure solvents in their behavior?

THE GOAL: Be able to explain vapor pressure lowering, boiling point elevation, and freezing point depression for solutions.

6. What is osmosis?

THE GOAL: Be able to describe osmosis and some of its applications.

U p to this point, we have been concerned primarily with pure substances, both elements and compounds. In day-to-day life, however, most of the materials we come in contact with are mixtures. Air, for example, is a gaseous mixture of primarily oxygen and nitrogen; blood is a liquid mixture of many different components; and many rocks are solid mixtures of different minerals. In this chapter, we look closely at the characteristics and properties of mixtures, with particular attention to the uniform mixtures we call *solutions*.

9.1 Mixtures and Solutions

As we saw in Section 1.3, a *mixture* is an intimate combination of two or more substances, both of which retain their chemical identities. (⬤━⬤, p. 6) Mixtures can be classified as either *heterogeneous* or *homogeneous* as indicated in Figure 9.1, depending on their appearance. **Heterogeneous mixtures** are those in which the mixing is

Heterogeneous mixture A nonuniform mixture that has regions of different composition.

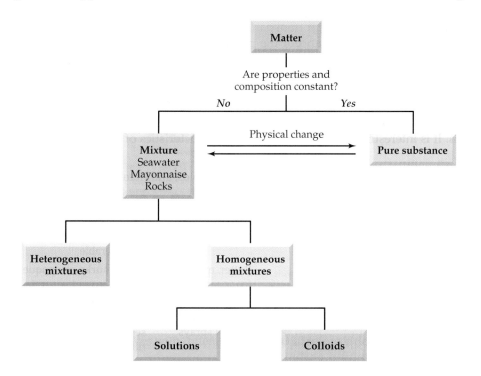

◀ **FIGURE 9.1 Classification of mixtures.** The components in heterogeneous mixtures are not uniformly mixed, and the composition varies with location. In homogeneous mixtures, the components are uniformly mixed at the molecular level.

APPLICATION ▶ Breathing and Oxygen Transport

Like all other animals, humans need oxygen. When we breathe, the freshly inspired air travels through the bronchial passages and into the lungs. The oxygen then diffuses through the delicate walls of the approximately 150 million alveolar sacs of the lungs and into arterial blood, which transports it to all body tissues.

Only about 3% of the oxygen in blood is dissolved; the rest is chemically bound to *hemoglobin* molecules, large proteins with *heme* groups embedded in them. Each hemoglobin molecule contains four heme groups, and each heme group contains an iron atom that is able to bind one O_2 molecule. Thus, a single hemoglobin molecule can bind up to four molecules of oxygen. The entire system of oxygen transport and delivery in the body depends on the pickup and release of O_2 by hemoglobin (Hb) according to the following series of equilibria:

$$O_2(lungs) \rightleftharpoons O_2(blood) \quad \text{(Henry's law)}$$
$$Hb + 4\ O_2(blood) \rightleftharpoons Hb(O_2)_4$$
$$Hb(O_2)_4 \rightleftharpoons Hb + 4\ O_2 \quad \text{(cell)}$$

The delivery of oxygen depends on the concentration of O_2 in the various tissues, as measured by partial pressure (P_{O_2}, Table 9.4). The amount of oxygen carried by hemoglobin at any given value of P_{O_2} is usually expressed as a percent saturation and can be found from the curve shown in the accompanying figure. When $P_{O_2} = 100$ mmHg, the saturation in the lungs is 97.5%, meaning that each hemoglobin is carrying close to its maximum of four O_2 molecules. When $P_{O_2} = 26$ mmHg, however, the saturation drops to 50%.

So, how does the body ensure that enough oxygen is available to the various tissues? When large amounts of oxygen are needed—during a strenuous workout, for example—oxygen is released from hemoglobin to the hardworking, oxygen-starved muscle cells, where P_{O_2} is low. Increasing the

▲ At high altitudes, the partial pressure of oxygen in the air is too low to saturate hemoglobin sufficiently. Additional oxygen is therefore needed.

supply of oxygen to the blood (by breathing harder and faster) shifts all the equilibria toward the right, according to Le Châtelier's principle (Section 7.9), to supply the additional O_2 needed by the muscles.

What about people living at high altitudes? In Leadville, CO, for example, where the altitude is 10,156 ft, the P_{O_2} in the lungs is only about 68 mmHg. Hemoglobin is only 90% saturated with O_2 at this pressure, meaning that less oxygen is available for delivery to the tissues. The body responds by producing erythropoietin (EPO), a hormone (Chapter 20) that stimulates the bone marrow to produce more red blood cells and hemoglobin molecules. The increase in Hb provides more capacity for O_2 transport and drives the Hb + O_2 equilibria to the right.

World-class athletes use the mechanisms of increased oxygen transport associated with higher levels of hemoglobin to enhance their performance. High-altitude training centers have sprung up, with living and training regimens designed to increase blood EPO levels. Unfortunately, some athletes have also tried to "cheat" by using injections of EPO and synthetic analogs, and "blood doping" to boost performance. This has led the governing bodies of many sports federations, including the Olympic Committee, to start testing for such abuse.

See Additional Problem 9.92 at the end of the chapter.

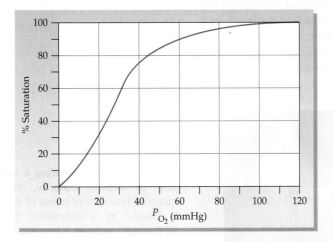

▲ An oxygen-carrying curve for hemoglobin. The percent saturation of the oxygen binding sites on hemoglobin depends on the partial pressure of oxygen (P_{O_2}).

Molarity can be used as a conversion factor to relate the volume of a solution to the number of moles of solute it contains. If we know the molarity and volume of a solution, we can calculate the number of moles of solute. If we know the number of moles of solute and the molarity of the solution, we can find the solution's volume.

$$\text{Molarity} = \frac{\text{Moles of solute}}{\text{Volume of solution (L)}}$$

$$\text{Moles of solute} = \text{Molarity} \times \text{Volume of solution}$$

$$\text{Volume of solution} = \frac{\text{Moles of solute}}{\text{Molarity}}$$

The flow diagram in Figure 9.7 shows how molarity is used in calculating the quantities of reactants or products in a chemical reaction, and Worked Examples 9.5 and 9.6 show how the calculations are done. Note that Problem 9.10 employs *millimolar* (mM) concentrations, which are useful in healthcare fields for expressing low concentrations such as are often found in body fluids (1 mM = 0.001 M).

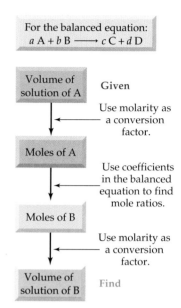

▶ **FIGURE 9.7 Molarity and conversions.** A flow diagram summarizing the use of molarity for conversions between solution volume and moles to find quantities of reactants and products for chemical reactions in solution.

WORKED EXAMPLE **9.4** Solution Concentration: Molarity

What is the molarity of a solution made by dissolving 2.355 g of sulfuric acid (H_2SO_4) in water and diluting to a final volume of 50.0 mL? The molar mass of H_2SO_4 is 98.1 g/mol.

ANALYSIS Molarity is defined as moles of solute per liter of solution: M = mol/L. Thus, we must first find the number of moles of sulfuric acid by doing a mass to mole conversion, and then divide the number of moles by the volume of the solution.

BALLPARK ESTIMATE The molar mass of sulfuric acid is about 100 g/mol, so 2.355 g is roughly 0.025 mol. The volume of the solution is 50.0 mL, or 0.05 L, so we have about 0.025 mol of acid in 0.05 L of solution, which is a concentration of about 0.5 M.

SOLUTION

STEP 1: Identify known information. We know the mass of sulfuric acid and the final volume of solution.

Mass of H_2SO_4 = 2.355 g

Volume of solution = 50.0 mL

STEP 2: Identify answer including units. We need to find the molarity (M) in units of moles per liter.

STEP 3: Identify conversion factors and equations. We know both the amount of solute and the volume of solution, but first we must make two conversions: convert mass of H_2SO_4 to moles of H_2SO_4, using molar mass as a conversion factor, and convert volume from milliliters to liters:

$$\text{Molarity} = \frac{\text{Moles } H_2SO_4}{\text{Liters of solution}}$$

$$(2.355 \ \text{g } H_2SO_4)\left(\frac{1 \ \text{mol } H_2SO_4}{98.1 \ \text{g } H_2SO_4}\right) = 0.0240 \ \text{mol } H_2SO_4$$

$$(50.0 \ \text{mL})\left(\frac{1 \ \text{L}}{1000 \ \text{mL}}\right) = 0.0500 \ \text{L}$$

STEP 4: Solve. Substitute the moles of solute and volume of solution into the molarity expression.

$$\text{Molarity} = \frac{0.0240 \ \text{mol } H_2SO_4}{0.0500 \ \text{L}} = 0.480 \ \text{M}$$

BALLPARK CHECK: The calculated answer is close to our estimate, which was 0.5 M.

WORKED EXAMPLE **9.5** Molarity as Conversion Factor: Molarity to Mass

A blood concentration of 0.065 M ethyl alcohol (EtOH) is sufficient to induce a coma. At this concentration, what is the total mass of alcohol (in grams) in an adult male whose total blood volume is 5.6 L? The molar mass of ethyl alcohol is 46.0 g/mol. (Refer to the flow diagram in Figure 9.7 to identify which conversions are needed.)

Acids and Bases

CONCEPTS TO REVIEW

Acids, Bases, and Neutralization Reactions

(Sections 4.11 and 6.10)

Reversible Reactions and Chemical Equilibrium

(Section 7.7)

Equilibrium Equations and Equilibrium Constants

(Section 7.8)

Units of Concentration; Molarity

(Section 9.7)

Ion Equivalents

(Section 9.10)

▲ Acids are found in many of the foods we eat, including tomatoes, peppers, and these citrus fruits.

CONTENTS

CHAPTER GOALS

We have already touched on the subject of acids and bases on several occasions, but the time has come for a more detailed study that will answer the following questions:

1. What are acids and bases?

THE GOAL: Be able to recognize acids and bases and write equations for common acid–base reactions.

2. What effect does the strength of acids and bases have on their reactions?

THE GOAL: Be able to interpret acid strength using acid dissociation constants K_a and predict the favored direction of acid–base equilibria.

3. What is the ion-product constant for water?

THE GOAL: Be able to write the equation for this constant and use it to find the concentration of H_3O^+ or OH^-.

4. What is the pH scale for measuring acidity?

THE GOAL: Be able to explain the pH scale and find pH from the H_3O^+ concentration.

5. What is a buffer?

THE GOAL: Be able to explain how a buffer maintains pH and how the bicarbonate buffer functions in the body.

6. How is the acid or base concentration of a solution determined?

THE GOAL: Be able to explain how a titration procedure works and use the results of a titration to calculate acid or base concentration in a solution.

A cids! The word evokes images of dangerous, corrosive liquids that eat away everything they touch. Although a few well-known substances such as sulfuric acid (H_2SO_4) do indeed fit this description, most acids are relatively harmless. In fact, many acids, such as ascorbic acid (vitamin C), are necessary for life.

10.1 Acids and Bases in Aqueous Solution

Let us take a moment to review what we said about acids and bases in Sections 4.11 and 6.10 before going on to a more systematic study:

- An acid is a substance that produces hydrogen ions, H^+, when dissolved in water.

- A base is a substance that produces hydroxide ions, OH^-, when dissolved in water.

- The neutralization reaction of an acid with a base yields water plus a *salt*, an ionic compound composed of the cation from the base and the anion from the acid.

The above definitions of acids and bases were proposed in 1887 by the Swedish chemist Svante Arrhenius and are useful for many purposes. The definitions are limited, however, because they refer only to reactions that take place in aqueous solution. (We will see shortly how the definitions can be broadened.) Another issue is that the H^+ ion is so reactive it does not exist in water. Instead, H^+ reacts with H_2O to give the **hydronium ion**, H_3O^+, as mentioned in Section 4.11. When gaseous HCl dissolves in water, for instance, H_3O^+ and Cl^- are formed. As described in Section 5.8, electrostatic potential maps show that the hydrogen of HCl is positively polarized and electron-poor (blue), whereas the oxygen of water is negatively polarized and electron-rich (red):

Hydronium ion The H_3O^+ ion, formed when an acid reacts with water.

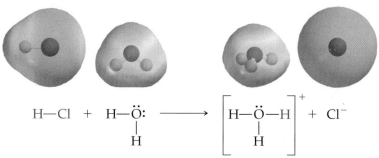

Thus, the Arrhenius definition is updated to acknowledge that an acid yields H_3O^+ in water rather than H^+. In practice, however, the notations H_3O^+ and $H^+(aq)$ are often used interchangeably.

The Arrhenius definition of a base is correct as far as it goes, but it is important to realize that the OH^- ions "produced" by the base can come from either of two sources. Metal hydroxides, such as NaOH, KOH, and $Ba(OH)_2$, are ionic compounds that already contain OH^- ions and merely release those ions when they dissolve in water. Ammonia, however, is not ionic and contains no OH^- ions in its structure. Nonetheless, ammonia is a base because it undergoes a reaction with water when it dissolves, producing NH_4^+ and OH^- ions:

This OH^- ion comes from NaOH.

$$NaOH(s) \xrightarrow[\text{in } H_2O]{\text{Dissolve}} Na^+(aq) + OH^-(aq)$$

This OH^- ion comes from H_2O.

$$H-\overset{\cdot\cdot}{\underset{H}{N}}-H(g) + H_2O(l) \rightleftharpoons H-\overset{H}{\underset{H}{N^{\pm}}}-H(aq) + OH^-(aq)$$

The reaction of ammonia with water is a reversible process (Section 7.7) whose equilibrium strongly favors unreacted ammonia. (∞, p. 198) Nevertheless, *some* OH^- ions are produced, so NH_3 is a base.

10.2 Some Common Acids and Bases

Acids and bases are present in a variety of foods and consumer products. Acids generally have a sour taste, and nearly every sour food contains an acid: Lemons, oranges, and grapefruit contain citric acid, for instance, and sour milk contains lactic acid. Bases are not so obvious in foods, but most of us have them stored under the kitchen or bathroom sink. Bases are present in many household cleaning agents, from perfumed toilet soap, to ammonia-based window cleaners, to the substance you put down the drain to dissolve hair, grease, and other materials that clog it.

Some of the most common acids and bases are listed below. It is a good idea at this point to learn their names and formulas, because we will refer to them often.

- **Sulfuric acid, H_2SO_4,** is probably the most important raw material in the chemical and pharmaceutical industries, and is manufactured in greater quantity worldwide than any other industrial chemical. Over 45 million tons are prepared in the United States annually for use in many hundreds of industrial processes, including the preparation of phosphate fertilizers. Its most common consumer use is as the acid found in automobile batteries. As anyone who has splashed battery acid on their skin or clothing knows, sulfuric acid is highly corrosive and can cause painful burns.

- **Hydrochloric acid, HCl,** or *muriatic acid* as it was historically known, has many industrial applications, including its use in metal cleaning and in the manufacture of high-fructose corn syrup. Aqueous HCl is also present as "stomach acid" in the digestive systems of most mammals.

- **Phosphoric acid, H_3PO_4,** is used in vast quantities in the manufacture of phosphate fertilizers. In addition, it is also used as an additive in foods and toothpastes. The tart taste of many soft drinks is due to the presence of phosphoric acid.

- **Nitric acid, HNO_3,** is a strong oxidizing agent that is used for many purposes, including the manufacture of ammonium nitrate fertilizer and military explosives. When spilled on the skin, it leaves a characteristic yellow coloration because of its reaction with skin proteins.

- **Acetic acid, CH_3CO_2H,** is the primary organic constituent of vinegar. It also occurs in all living cells and is used in many industrial processes such as the preparation of solvents, lacquers, and coatings.

▲ Hydrochloric acid, also known as muriatic acid, has many industrial applications.

- **Sodium hydroxide, NaOH,** also called *caustic soda* or *lye*, is the most commonly used of all bases. Industrially, it is used in the production of aluminum from its ore, in the production of glass, and in the manufacture of soap from animal fat. Concentrated solutions of NaOH can cause severe burns if allowed to sit on the skin for long. Drain cleaners often contain NaOH because it reacts with the fats and proteins found in grease and hair.

- **Calcium hydroxide, Ca(OH)$_2$,** or *slaked lime*, is made industrially by treating lime (CaO) with water. It has many applications, including its use in mortars and cements. An aqueous solution of Ca(OH)$_2$ is often called *limewater*.

- **Magnesium hydroxide, Mg(OH)$_2$,** or *milk of magnesia*, is an additive in foods, toothpaste, and many over-the-counter medications. Antacids such as Rolaids, Mylanta, and Maalox, for instance, all contain magnesium hydroxide.

- **Ammonia, NH$_3$,** is used primarily as a fertilizer, but it also has many other industrial applications including the manufacture of pharmaceuticals and explosives. A dilute solution of ammonia is frequently used around the house as a glass cleaner.

▲ Soap is manufactured by the reaction of vegetable oils and animal fats with the bases NaOH and KOH.

10.3 The Brønsted–Lowry Definition of Acids and Bases

The Arrhenius definition of acids and bases discussed in Section 10.1 applies only to reactions that take place in aqueous solution. A far more general definition was proposed in 1923 by the Danish chemist Johannes Brønsted and the English chemist Thomas Lowry. A **Brønsted–Lowry acid** is any substance that is able to give a hydrogen ion, H$^+$, to another molecule or ion. A hydrogen *atom* consists of a proton and an electron, so a hydrogen *ion*, H$^+$, is simply a proton. Thus, we often refer to acids as *proton donors*. The reaction need not occur in water, and a Brønsted–Lowry acid need not give appreciable concentrations of H$_3$O$^+$ ions in water.

Different acids can supply different numbers of H$^+$ ions, as we saw in Section 4.11. (⊂⊃, p. 98) Acids with one proton to donate, such as HCl and HNO$_3$, are called *monoprotic acids*; H$_2$SO$_4$ is a *diprotic acid* because it has two protons to donate, and H$_3$PO$_4$ is a *triprotic acid* because it has three protons to donate. Notice that the acidic H atoms (that is, the H atoms that are donated as protons) are bonded to electronegative atoms, such as chlorine or oxygen.

Brønsted–Lowry acid A substance that can donate a hydrogen ion, H$^+$, to another molecule or ion.

H—Cl

Hydrochloric acid
(monoprotic)

Nitric acid
(monoprotic)

Sulfuric acid
(diprotic)

Phosphoric acid
(triprotic)

Acetic acid (CH$_3$CO$_2$H), an example of an organic acid, actually has a total of 4 hydrogens, but only the one bonded to the electronegative oxygen is positively polarized and therefore acidic. The 3 hydrogens bonded to carbon are not acidic. Most organic acids are similar in that they contain many hydrogen atoms, but only the one in the —CO$_2$H group (blue in the electrostatic potential map) is acidic:

This hydrogen is acidic.

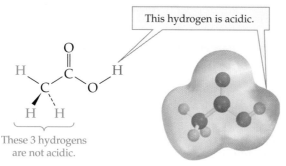

These 3 hydrogens are not acidic.

Brønsted–Lowry base A substance that can accept H$^+$ from an acid.

Whereas a Brønsted–Lowry acid is a substance that *donates* H$^+$ ions, a **Brønsted–Lowry base** is a substance that *accepts* H$^+$ from an acid. The reaction need not occur in water, and the Brønsted–Lowry base need not give appreciable concentrations of OH$^-$ ions in water. Gaseous NH$_3$, for example, acts as a base to accept H$^+$ from gaseous HCl and yield the ionic solid NH$_4$$^+Cl^-$:

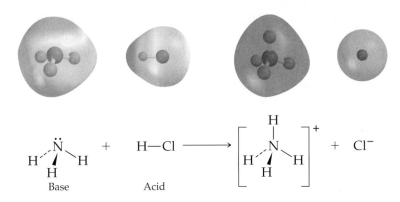

Base   Acid

Putting the acid and base definitions together, *an acid–base reaction is one in which a proton is transferred*. The general reaction between proton-donor acids and proton-acceptor bases can be represented as

Electrons on base form bond with H$^+$ from acid.

$$B: + H-A \rightleftharpoons B\overset{+}{-}H + A^-$$

$$B:^- + H-A \rightleftharpoons B-H + A^-$$

where the abbreviation HA represents a Brønsted–Lowry acid and B: or B:$^-$ represents a Brønsted–Lowry base. Notice in these acid–base reactions that both electrons in the product B—H bond come from the base, as indicated by the curved arrow flowing from the electron pair of the base to the hydrogen atom of the acid. Thus, the B—H bond that forms is a coordinate covalent bond (Section 5.4). (⊂⊃, p. 115) In fact, a Brønsted–Lowry base *must* have such a lone pair of electrons; without them, it could not accept H$^+$ from an acid.

A base can be either neutral (B:) or negatively charged (B:$^-$). If the base is neutral, then the product has a positive charge (BH$^+$) after H$^+$ has added. Ammonia is an example:

Adding an H$^+$ creates positive charge.

$$H-N: + H-A \rightleftharpoons H-\overset{+}{N}-H + :A^-$$

Ammonia   Ammonium ion
(a neutral base, B:)

If the base is negatively charged, then the product is neutral (BH). Hydroxide ion is an example:

$$H-\ddot{O}:^- + H-A \rightleftharpoons H-\ddot{O}-H + :A^-$$

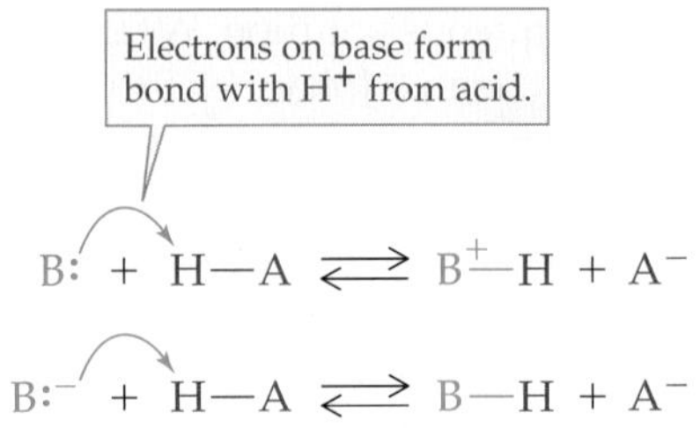

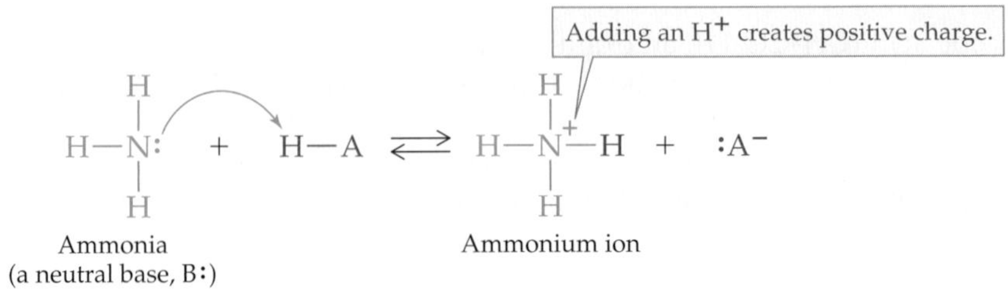

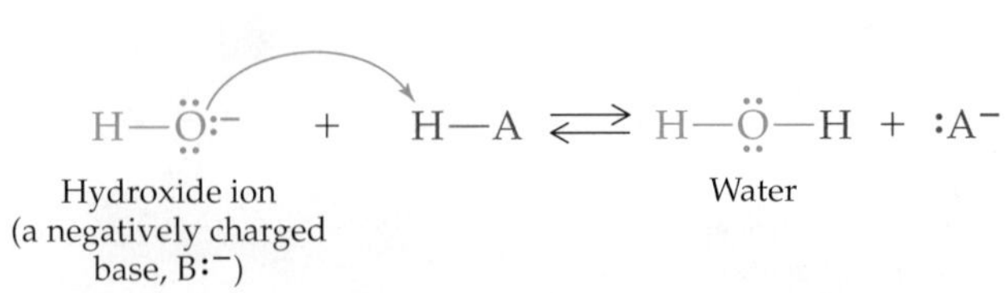

Hydroxide ion   Water
(a negatively charged
base, B:$^-$)

An important consequence of the Brønsted–Lowry definitions is that the *products* of an acid–base reaction can also behave as acids and bases. Many acid–base reactions are reversible (Section 7.8), although in some cases the equilibrium constant for the reaction is quite large. (⊂⊃, p. 200) For example, suppose we have as a forward reaction an acid HA donating a proton to a base B to produce A^-. This product A^- is a base because it can act as a proton acceptor in the reverse reaction. At the same time, the product BH^+ acts as an acid because it donates a proton in the reverse reaction:

$$\boxed{\text{Double arrow indicates reversible reaction.}}$$

$$\underset{\text{Base}}{B:} \; + \; \underset{\text{Acid}}{H\!-\!A} \; \rightleftarrows \; \underset{\text{Base}}{:A^-} \; + \; \underset{\text{Acid}}{\overset{+}{B}\!-\!H}$$

Conjugate acid–base pair

Pairs of chemical species such as B, BH^+ and HA, A^- are called **conjugate acid–base pairs**. They are species that are found on opposite sides of a chemical reaction whose formulas differ by only one H^+. Thus, the product anion A^- is the **conjugate base** of the reactant acid HA, and HA is the **conjugate acid** of the base A^-. Similarly, the reactant B is the conjugate base of the product acid BH^+, and BH^+ is the conjugate acid of the base B. The number of protons in a conjugate acid–base pair is always one greater than the number of protons in the base of the pair. To give some examples, acetic acid and acetate ion, the hydronium ion and water, and the ammonium ion and ammonia all make conjugate acid–base pairs:

Conjugate acid–base pair Two substances whose formulas differ by only a hydrogen ion, H^+.

Conjugate base The substance formed by loss of H^+ from an acid.

Conjugate acid The substance formed by addition of H^+ to a base.

$$\left. \begin{array}{l} \text{Conjugate} \\ \text{acids} \end{array} \right\{ \quad \begin{array}{l} CH_3\overset{\overset{O}{\|}}{C}OH \rightleftarrows H^+ + CH_3\overset{\overset{O}{\|}}{C}O^- \\ H_3O^+ \rightleftarrows H^+ + H_2O \\ NH_4{}^+ \rightleftarrows H^+ + NH_3 \end{array} \quad \left\} \begin{array}{l} \text{Conjugate} \\ \text{bases} \end{array} \right.$$

WORKED EXAMPLE   **10.1** Acids and Bases: Identifying Brønsted–Lowry Acids and Bases

Identify each of the following as a Brønsted–Lowry acid or base:

(a) $PO_4{}^{3-}$
(b) $HClO_4$
(c) CN^-

ANALYSIS A Brønsted–Lowry acid must have a hydrogen that it can donate as H^+, and a Brønsted–Lowry base must have an atom with a lone pair of electrons that can bond to H^+. Typically, a Brønsted–Lowry base is an anion derived by loss of H^+ from an acid.

SOLUTION

(a) The phosphate anion ($PO_4{}^{3-}$) is a Brønsted–Lowry base derived by loss of 3 H^+ ions from phosphoric acid, H_3PO_4.
(b) Perchloric acid ($HClO_4$) is a Brønsted–Lowry acid because it can donate an H^+ ion.
(c) The cyanide ion (CN^-) is a Brønsted–Lowry base derived by removal of an H^+ ion from hydrogen cyanide, HCN.

WORKED EXAMPLE **10.2** Acids and Bases: Identifying Conjugate Acid–Base Pairs

Write formulas for

(a) The conjugate acid of the cyanide ion, CN^-

(b) The conjugate base of perchloric acid, $HClO_4$

ANALYSIS A conjugate acid is formed by adding H^+ to a base; a conjugate base is formed by removing H^+ from an acid.

SOLUTION

(a) HCN is the conjugate acid of CN^-.

(b) ClO_4^- is the conjugate base of $HClO_4$.

PROBLEM 10.1

Which of the following would you expect to be Brønsted–Lowry acids?

(a) HCO_2H (b) H_2S (c) $SnCl_2$

PROBLEM 10.2

Which of the following would you expect to be Brønsted–Lowry bases?

(a) SO_3^{2-} (b) Ag^+ (c) F^-

PROBLEM 10.3

Write formulas for:

(a) The conjugate acid of HS^- (b) The conjugate acid of PO_4^{3-}

(c) The conjugate base of H_2CO_3 (d) The conjugate base of NH_4^+

◯━ KEY CONCEPT PROBLEM 10.4

For the reaction shown here, identify the Brønsted–Lowry acids, bases, and conjugate acid–base pairs.

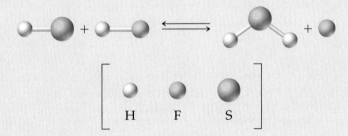

10.4 Water as Both an Acid and a Base

Water is neither an acid nor a base in the Arrhenius sense because it does not contain appreciable concentrations of either H_3O^+ or OH^-. In the Brønsted–Lowry sense, however, water can act as *both* an acid and a base. When in contact with a base, water reacts as a Brønsted–Lowry acid and *donates* a proton to the base. In its reaction with ammonia, for example, water donates H^+ to ammonia to form the ammonium ion:

$$NH_3 + H_2O \longrightarrow NH_4^+ + OH^-$$

Ammonia	Water	Ammonium ion	Hydroxide ion
(base)	(acid)	(acid)	(base)

When in contact with an acid, water reacts as a Brønsted–Lowry base and *accepts* H^+ from the acid. This, of course, is exactly what happens when an acid such as HCl dissolves in water, as discussed in Section 10.1.

Water uses two electrons
to form a bond to H^+.

$$H\!-\!\ddot{O}\!: \ + \ H\!-\!Cl \ \longrightarrow \ H\!-\!\overset{..\,+}{O}\!-\!H \ + \ Cl^-$$

Water	(An acid)	Hydronium ion
(A base)		

Substances like water, which can react as either an acid or a base depending on the circumstances, are said to be **amphoteric** (am-pho-**tare**-ic). When water acts as an acid, it donates H^+ and becomes OH^-; when it acts as a base, it accepts H^+ and becomes H_3O^+.

Amphoteric Describing a substance that can react as either an acid or a base.

PROBLEM 10.5

Is water an acid or a base in the following reactions?

(a) $H_3PO_4(aq) + H_2O(l) \longrightarrow H_2PO_4^-(aq) + H_3O^+(aq)$

(b) $F^-(aq) + H_2O(l) \longrightarrow HF(aq) + OH^-(aq)$

(c) $NH_4^+(aq) + H_2O(aq) \longrightarrow NH_3(aq) + H_3O^+(aq)$

10.5 Acid and Base Strength

Some acids and bases, such as sulfuric acid (H_2SO_4), hydrochloric acid (HCl), or sodium hydroxide (NaOH), are highly corrosive. They react readily and, in contact with skin, can cause serious burns. Other acids and bases are not nearly as reactive. Acetic acid (CH_3COOH, the major component in vinegar) and phosphoric acid (H_3PO_4) are found in many food products. Why are some acids and bases relatively "safe," while others must be handled with extreme caution? The answer lies in how easily they produce the active ions for an acid (H^+) or a base (OH^-).

As indicated in Table 10.1, acids differ in their ability to give up a proton. The six acids at the top of the table are **strong acids**, meaning that they give up a proton easily and are essentially 100% **dissociated**, or split apart into ions, in water. Those remaining are **weak acids**, meaning that they give up a proton with difficulty and are substantially less than 100% dissociated in water. In a similar way, the bases at the top of the table are **weak bases** because they have little affinity for a proton, and the bases at the bottom of the table are **strong bases** because they grab and hold a proton tightly.

Note that diprotic acids, such as sulfuric acid, undergo two stepwise dissociations in water. The first dissociation yields HSO_4^- and occurs to the extent of nearly 100%, so H_2SO_4 is a strong acid. The second dissociation yields SO_4^{2-} and takes place to a much lesser extent because separation of a positively charged H^+ from the negatively charged HSO_4^- anion is difficult. Thus, HSO_4^- is a weak acid:

$$H_2SO_4(l) + H_2O(l) \longrightarrow H_3O^+(aq) + HSO_4^-(aq)$$

$$HSO_4^-(aq) + H_2O(l) \rightleftharpoons H_3O^+(aq) + SO_4^{2-}(aq)$$

Strong acid An acid that gives up H^+ easily and is essentially 100% dissociated in water.

Dissociation The splitting apart of an acid in water to give H^+ and an anion.

Weak acid An acid that gives up H^+ with difficulty and is less than 100% dissociated in water.

Weak base A base that has only a slight affinity for H^+ and holds it weakly.

Strong base A base that has a high affinity for H^+ and holds it tightly.

APPLICATION ▶   GERD—Too Much Acid or Not Enough?

Strong acids are very caustic substances that can dissolve even metals, and no one would think of ingesting them. However, the major component of the gastric juices secreted in the stomach is hydrochloric acid—a strong acid—and the acidic environment in the stomach is vital to good health and nutrition.

Stomach acid is essential for the digestion of proteins and for the absorption of certain micronutrients, such as calcium, magnesium, iron, and vitamin B_{12}. It also creates a sterile environment in the gut by killing yeast and bacteria that may be ingested. If these gastric juices leak up into the esophagus, the tube through which food and drink enter the stomach, they can cause the burning sensation in the chest or throat known as either heartburn or acid indigestion. Persistent irritation of the esophagus is known as gastroesophageal reflux disease (GERD) and, if untreated, can lead to more serious health problems.

Hydrogen ions and chloride ions are secreted separately from the cytoplasm of cells lining the stomach and then combine to form HCl that is usually close to 0.10 M. The HCl is then released into the stomach cavity, where the concentration is diluted to about 0.01–0.001 M. Unlike the esophagus, the stomach is coated by a thick mucus layer that protects the stomach wall from damage by this caustic solution.

Those who suffer from acid indigestion can obtain relief using over-the-counter antacids, such as Tums or Rolaids (see Section 10.14, p. 320). Chronic conditions such as GERD, however, are often treated with prescription medications. GERD can be treated by two classes of drugs. Proton-pump inhibitors (PPI), such as Prevacid and Prilosec, prevent the production the H^+ ions in the parietal cells, while H2-receptor blockers (Tagamet, Zantac, and Pepcid) prevent the release of stomach acid into the lumen. Both drugs effectively decrease the production of stomach acid to ease the symptoms of GERD.

Ironically, GERD can also be caused by not having enough stomach acid—a condition known as *hypochlorhydria*. The valve that controls the release of stomach contents to the small intestine is triggered by acidity. If this valve fails to open because the stomach is not acidic enough, the contents of the stomach can be churned up into the esophagus.

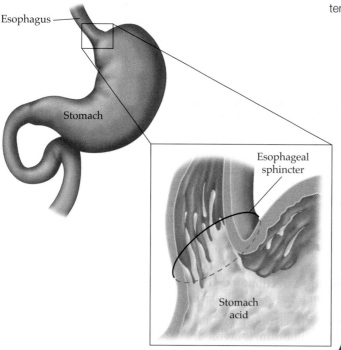

▲ The burning sensation and other symptoms associated with GERD are caused by the reflux of the acidic contents of the stomach into the esophagus.

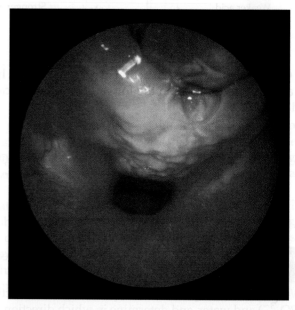

▲ If not treated, GERD can cause ulcers and scarring of esophageal tissue.

See Additional Problem 10.96 at the end of the chapter.

PROBLEM 10.6

Use Table 10.1 to identify the stronger acid in the following pairs:

(a) H_2O or NH_4^+
(b) H_2SO_4 or CH_3CO_2H
(c) HCN or H_2CO_3

PROBLEM 10.7

Use Table 10.1 to identify the stronger base in the following pairs:

(a) F^- or Br^- (b) OH^- or HCO_3^-

PROBLEM 10.8

Write a balanced equation for the proton-transfer reaction between a hydrogen phosphate ion and a hydroxide ion. Identify each acid–base pair, and determine in which direction the equilibrium is favored.

KEY CONCEPT PROBLEM 10.9

From this electrostatic potential map of the amino acid alanine, identify the most acidic hydrogens in the molecule:

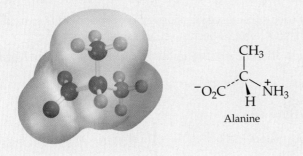

Alanine

10.6 Acid Dissociation Constants

The reaction of a weak acid with water, like any chemical equilibrium, can be described by an equilibrium equation (Section 7.8), where square brackets indicate the concentrations of the enclosed species in molarity (moles per liter). (⬭, p. 200)

For the reaction $HA(aq) + H_2O(l) \rightleftharpoons H_3O^+(aq) + A^-(aq)$

We have $$K = \frac{[H_3O^+][A^-]}{[HA][H_2O]}$$

Because water is a solvent as well as a participant for the reaction, its concentration is essentially constant and has no effect on the equilibrium. Therefore, we usually put the equilibrium constant K and the water concentration $[H_2O]$ together to make a new constant called the **acid dissociation constant, K_a**. The acid dissociation constant is simply the hydronium ion concentration $[H_3O^+]$ times the conjugate base concentration $[A^-]$ divided by the undissociated acid concentration $[HA]$:

Acid dissociation constant $K_a = K[H_2O] = \dfrac{[H_3O^+][A^-]}{[HA]}$

For a strong acid, the H_3O^+ and A^- concentrations are much larger than the HA concentration, so K_a is very large. In fact, the K_a values for strong acids such as HCl are so large that it is difficult and not very useful to measure them. For a weak acid, however, the H_3O^+ and A^- concentrations are smaller than the HA concentration, so K_a is small. Table 10.2 gives K_a values for some common acids and illustrates several important points:

- Strong acids have K_a values much greater than 1 because dissociation is favored.
- Weak acids have K_a values much less than 1 because dissociation is not favored.

TABLE 10.2 Some Acid Dissociation Constants, K_a, at 25 °C

ACID	K_a	ACID	K_a
Hydrofluoric acid (HF)	3.5×10^{-4}	*Polyprotic acids*	
Hydrocyanic acid (HCN)	4.9×10^{-10}	Sulfuric acid	
Ammonium ion (NH_4^+)	5.6×10^{-10}	H_2SO_4	Large
		HSO_4^-	1.2×10^{-2}
Organic acids		Phosphoric acid	
Formic acid (HCOOH)	1.8×10^{-4}	H_3PO_4	7.5×10^{-3}
Acetic acid (CH_3COOH)	1.8×10^{-5}	$H_2PO_4^-$	6.2×10^{-8}
Propanoic acid	1.3×10^{-5}	HPO_4^{2-}	2.2×10^{-13}
(CH_3CH_2COOH)		Carbonic acid	
Ascorbic acid (vitamin C)	7.9×10^{-5}	H_2CO_3	4.3×10^{-7}
		HCO_3^-	5.6×10^{-11}

- Donation of each successive H^+ from a polyprotic acid is more difficult than the one before it, so K_a values become successively lower.
- Most organic acids, which contain the $-CO_2H$ group, have K_a values near 10^{-5}.

PROBLEM 10.10

Benzoic acid has $K_a = 6.5 \times 10^{-5}$, and citric acid has $K_a = 7.2 \times 10^{-4}$. Which of the two is the stronger acid?

10.7 Dissociation of Water

We saw previously that water is amphoteric – it can act as an acid when a base is present and as a base when an acid is present. What about when no other acids or bases are present, however? In this case, one water molecule acts as an acid while another water molecule acts as a base, reacting to form the hydronium and hydroxide ions:

$$H_2O(l) + H_2O(l) \rightleftharpoons H_3O^+(aq) + OH^-(aq)$$

Because each dissociation reaction yields one H_3O^+ ion and one OH^- ion, the concentrations of the two ions are identical. At 25 °C, the concentration of each is 1.00×10^{-7} M. We can write the equilibrium constant expression for the dissociation of water as

$$K = \frac{[H_3O^+][OH^-]}{[H_2O][H_2O]}$$

and

$$K_a = K[H_2O] = \frac{[H_3O^+][OH^-]}{[H_2O]}$$

where $[H_3O^+] = [OH^-] = 1.00 \times 10^{-7}$ M   (at 25 °C)

As both a reactant and a solvent, the concentration of water is essentially constant. We can therefore put the acid dissociation constant K_a and the water concentration $[H_2O]$ together to make a new constant called the **ion-product constant for water (K_w)**, which is simply the H_3O^+ concentration times the OH^- concentration. At 25 °C, $K_w = 1.00 \times 10^{-14}$.

Ion-product constant for water $K_w = K_a[H_2O] = [H_3O^+][OH^-]$

$$= (1.00 \times 10^{-7})(1.00 \times 10^{-7})$$

$$= 1.00 \times 10^{-14} \quad \text{(at 25 °C)}$$

The importance of the equation $K_w = [H_3O^+][OH^-]$ is that it applies to all aqueous solutions, not just to pure water. Since the product of $[H_3O^+]$ times $[OH^-]$ is always constant for any solution, we can determine the concentration of one species if we know the concentration of the other. If an acid is present in solution, for instance, so that $[H_3O^+]$ is large, then $[OH^-]$ must be small. If a base is present in solution so that $[OH^-]$ is large, then $[H_3O^+]$ must be small. For example, for a 0.10 M HCl solution, we know that $[H_3O^+] = 0.10$ M because HCl is 100% dissociated. Thus, we can calculate that $[OH^-] = 1.0 \times 10^{-13}$ M:

Since $K_w \times [H_3O^+][OH^-] = 1.00 \times 10^{-14}$

we have $[OH^-] = \dfrac{K_w}{[H_3O^+]} = \dfrac{1.00 \times 10^{-14}}{0.10} = 1.0 \times 10^{-13}$ M

Similarly, for a 0.10 M NaOH solution, we know that $[OH^-] = 0.10$ M, so $[H_3O^+] = 1.0 \times 10^{-13}$ M:

$$[H_3O^+] = \frac{K_w}{[OH^-]} = \frac{1.00 \times 10^{-14}}{0.10} = 1.0 \times 10^{-13} \text{ M}$$

Solutions are identified as acidic, neutral, or basic (*alkaline*) according to the value of their H_3O^+ and OH^- concentrations:

Acidic solution: $[H_3O^+] > 10^{-7}$ M and $[OH^-] < 10^{-7}$ M

Neutral solution: $[H_3O^+] = 10^{-7}$ M and $[OH^-] = 10^{-7}$ M

Basic solution: $[H_3O^+] < 10^{-7}$ M and $[OH^-] > 10^{-7}$ M

WORKED EXAMPLE **10.4** Water Dissociation Constant: Using K_w to Calculate $[OH^-]$

Milk has an H_3O^+ concentration of 4.5×10^{-7} M. What is the value of $[OH^-]$? Is milk acidic, neutral, or basic?

ANALYSIS The OH^- concentration can be found by dividing K_w by $[H_3O^+]$. An acidic solution has $[H_3O^+] > 10^{-7}$ M, a neutral solution has $[H_3O^+] = 10^{-7}$ M, and a basic solution has $[H_3O^+] < 10^{-7}$ M.

BALLPARK ESTIMATE Since the H_3O^+ concentration is slightly *greater* than 10^{-7} M, the OH^- concentration must be slightly *less* than 10^{-7} M, on the order of 10^{-8}.

SOLUTION

$$[OH^-] = \frac{K_w}{[H_3O^+]} = \frac{1.00 \times 10^{-14}}{4.5 \times 10^{-7}} = 2.2 \times 10^{-8} \text{ M}$$

Milk is slightly acidic because its H_3O^+ concentration is slightly larger than 1×10^{-7} M.

BALLPARK CHECK The OH^- concentration is of the same order of magnitude as our estimate.

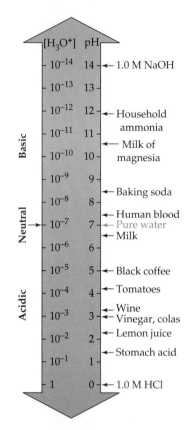

▲ **FIGURE 10.1 The pH scale and the pH values of some common substances.** A low pH corresponds to a strongly acidic solution, a high pH corresponds to a strongly basic solution, and a pH of 7 corresponds to a neutral solution.

p function The negative common logarithm of some variable, $pX = -\log(X)$.

pH A measure of the acid strength of a solution; the negative common logarithm of the H_3O^+ concentration.

▲ Adding only a teaspoonful of concentrated (6 M) hydrochloric acid lowers the pH of this pool from 7 to 6. Lowering the pH from 7 to 1 would take 400 gallons.

PROBLEM 10.11

Identify the following solutions as either acidic or basic. What is the value of $[OH^-]$ in each?

(a) Beer, $[H_3O^+] = 3.2 \times 10^{-5}$ M

(b) Household ammonia, $[H_3O^+] = 3.1 \times 10^{-12}$ M

10.8 Measuring Acidity in Aqueous Solution: pH

In many fields, from medicine to chemistry to winemaking, it is necessary to know the exact concentration of H_3O^+ or OH^- in a solution. If, for example, the H_3O^+ concentration in blood varies only slightly from a value of 4.0×10^{-8} M, death can result.

Although correct, it is nevertheless awkward to refer to low concentrations of H_3O^+ using molarity. If you were asked which concentration is higher, 9.0×10^{-8} M or 3.5×10^{-7} M, you would probably have to stop and think for a moment before answering. Fortunately, there is an easier way to express and compare H_3O^+ concentrations—the *pH scale*.

The pH of an aqueous solution is a number, usually between 0 and 14, that indicates the H_3O^+ concentration of the solution. A pH smaller than 7 corresponds to an acidic solution, a pH larger than 7 corresponds to a basic solution, and a pH of exactly 7 corresponds to a neutral solution. The pH scale and pH values of some common substances are shown in Figure 10.1

Mathematically, a **p function** is defined as the negative common logarithm of some variable. The **pH** of a solution, therefore, is the negative common logarithm of the H_3O^+ concentration:

$$\mathbf{pH} = -\log[H^+] \quad (or[H_3O^+])$$

If you have studied logarithms, you may remember that the common logarithm of a number is the power to which 10 must be raised to equal the number. The pH definition can therefore be restated as

$$[H_3O^+] = 10^{-pH}$$

For example, in neutral water at 25 °C, where $[H_3O^+] = 1 \times 10^{-7}$ M, the pH is 7; in a strong acid solution where $[H_3O^+] = 1 \times 10^{-1}$ M, the pH is 1; and in a strong base solution where $[H_3O^+] = 1 \times 10^{-14}$ M, the pH is 14:

Acidic solution: $\quad$ pH < 7, $\quad [H_3O^+] > 1 \times 10^{-7}$ M

Neutral solution: $\quad$ pH = 7, $\quad [H_3O^+] = 1 \times 10^{-7}$ M

Basic solution: $\quad$ pH > 7, $\quad [H_3O^+] < 1 \times 10^{-7}$ M

Keep in mind that the pH scale covers an enormous range of acidities because it is a *logarithmic* scale, which involves powers of 10 (Figure 10.2). A change of only 1 pH unit means a tenfold change in $[H_3O^+]$, a change of 2 pH units means a hundredfold change in $[H_3O^+]$, and a change of 12 pH units means a change of 10^{12} (a million) in $[H_3O^+]$.

To get a feel for the size of the quantities involved, think of a typical backyard swimming pool, which contains about 100,000 L of water. You would have to add only 0.10 mol of HCl (3.7 g) to lower the pH of the pool from 7.0 (neutral) to 6.0, but you would have to add 10,000 mol of HCl (370 kg!) to lower the pH of the pool from 7.0 to 1.0.

The logarithmic pH scale is a convenient way of reporting the relative acidity of solutions, but using logarithms can also be useful when calculating H_3O^+ and

OH$^-$ concentrations. Remember that the equilibrium between H$_3$O$^+$ and OH$^-$ in aqueous solutions is expressed by K_w, where

$$K_w = [H_3O^+][OH^-] = 1 \times 10^{-14} \quad \text{(at 25 °C)}$$

If we convert this equation to its negative logarithmic form, we obtain

$$-\log(K_w) = -\log(H_3O^+) - \log(OH^-)$$

$$-\log(1 \times 10^{-14}) = -\log(H_3O^+) - \log(OH^-)$$

$$or \quad 14.00 = pH + pOH$$

The logarithmic form of the K_w equation can simplify the calculation of solution pH from OH$^-$ concentration, as demonstrated in Worked Example 10.7.

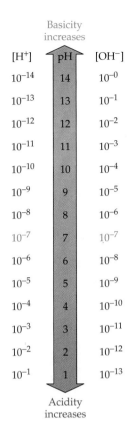

[H$^+$]	pH	[OH$^-$]
	Basicity increases	
10^{-14}	14	10^{-0}
10^{-13}	13	10^{-1}
10^{-12}	12	10^{-2}
10^{-11}	11	10^{-3}
10^{-10}	10	10^{-4}
10^{-9}	9	10^{-5}
10^{-8}	8	10^{-6}
10^{-7}	7	10^{-7}
10^{-6}	6	10^{-8}
10^{-5}	5	10^{-9}
10^{-4}	4	10^{-10}
10^{-3}	3	10^{-11}
10^{-2}	2	10^{-12}
10^{-1}	1	10^{-13}
	Acidity increases	

▲ **FIGURE 10.2 The relationship of the pH scale to H$^+$ and OH$^-$ concentrations.**

WORKED EXAMPLE **10.5** Measuring Acidity: Calculating pH from [H$_3$O$^+$]

The H$_3$O$^+$ concentration in coffee is about 1×10^{-5} M. What pH is this?

ANALYSIS The pH is the negative common logarithm of the H$_3$O$^+$ concentration: pH = $-\log[H_3O^+]$.

SOLUTION
Since the common logarithm of 1×10^{-5} M is -5, the pH is 5.0.

WORKED EXAMPLE **10.6** Measuring Acidity: Calculating [H$_3$O$^+$] from pH

Lemon juice has a pH of about 2. What [H$_3$O$^+$] is this?

ANALYSIS In this case, we are looking for the [H$_3$O$^+$], where [H$_3$O$^+$] = 10^{-pH}.

SOLUTION
Since pH = 2.0, [H$_3$O$^+$] = $10^{-2} = 1 \times 10^{-2}$ M.

WORKED EXAMPLE **10.7** Measuring Acidity: Using K_w to Calculate [H$_3$O$^+$] and pH

A cleaning solution is found to have [OH$^-$] = 1×10^{-3} M. What is the pH?

ANALYSIS To find pH, we must first find the value of [H$_3$O$^+$] by using the equation [H$_3$O$^+$] = K_w/[OH$^-$]. Alternatively, we can calculate the pOH of the solution and then use the logarithmic form of the K_w equation: pH = 14.00 − pOH.

SOLUTION
Rearranging the K_w equation, we have

$$[H_3O^+] = \frac{K_w}{[OH^-]} = \frac{1.00 \times 10^{-14}}{1 \times 10^{-3}} = 1 \times 10^{-11} \text{ M}$$

$$pH = -\log(1 \times 10^{-11}) = 11.0$$

Using the logarithmic form of the K_w equation, we have

$$pH = 14.0 - pOH = 14.0 - (-\log(OH^-))$$

$$pH = 14.0 - (-\log(1 \times 10^{-3}))$$

$$pH = 14.0 - 3.0 = 11.0$$

WORKED EXAMPLE   **10.8** Measuring Acidity: Calculating pH of Strong Acid Solutions

What is the pH of a 0.01 M solution of HCl?

ANALYSIS To find pH, we must first find the value of $[H_3O^+]$.

SOLUTION
Since HCl is a strong acid (Table 10.1), it is 100% dissociated, and the H_3O^+ concentration is the same as the HCl concentration: $[H_3O^+] = 0.01$ M, or 1×10^{-2} M, and pH = 2.0.

PROBLEM 10.12

Which solution has the higher H_3O^+ concentration, one with pH = 5 or one with pH = 9? Which has the higher OH^- concentration?

PROBLEM 10.13

Give the pH of solutions with the following concentrations:

(a) $[H_3O^+] = 1 \times 10^{-5}$ M

(b) $[OH^-] = 1 \times 10^{-9}$ M

PROBLEM 10.14

Give the hydronium ion concentrations of solutions with the following values of pH. Which of the solutions is most acidic? Which is most basic?

(a) pH 13.0   (b) pH 3.0   (c) pH 8.0

PROBLEM 10.15

What is the pH of a 1×10^{-4} M solution of HNO_3?

10.9 Working with pH

Converting between pH and H_3O^+ concentration is easy when the pH is a whole number, but how do you find the H_3O^+ concentration of blood, which has a pH of 7.4, or the pH of a solution with $[H_3O^+] = 4.6 \times 10^{-3}$ M? Sometimes it is sufficient to make an estimate. The pH of blood (7.4) is between 7 and 8, so the H_3O^+ concentration of blood must be between 1×10^{-7} and 1×10^{-8} M. To be exact about finding pH values, though, requires a calculator.

Converting from pH to $[H_3O^+]$ requires finding the *antilogarithm* of the negative pH, which is done on many calculators with an "INV" key and a "log" key. Converting from $[H_3O^+]$ to pH requires finding the logarithm, which is commonly done with a "log" key and an "expo" or "EE" key for entering exponents of 10. Consult your calculator instructions if you are not sure how to use these keys. Remember that the sign of the number given by the calculator must be changed from minus to plus to get the pH.

The H_3O^+ concentration in blood with pH = 7.4 is

$$[H_3O^+] = \text{antilog}(-7.4) = 4 \times 10^{-8} \text{ M}$$

The pH of a solution with $[H_3O^+] = 4.6 \times 10^{-3}$ M is

$$pH = -\log(4.6 \times 10^{-3}) = -(-2.34) = 2.34$$

A note about significant figures: An antilogarithm contains the same number of digits that the original number has to the right of the decimal point. A logarithm contains the same number of digits to the right of the decimal point that the original number has

$$antilog(-7.4) = 4 \times 10^{-8} \qquad \log(4.6 \times 10^{-3}) = -2.34$$

| 1 digit after decimal point | 1 digit | 2 digits | 2 digits after decimal point |

WORKED EXAMPLE **10.9** Working with pH: Converting a pH to $[H_3O^+]$

Soft drinks usually have a pH of approximately 3.1. What is the $[H_3O^+]$ concentration in a soft drink?

ANALYSIS To convert from a pH value to an $[H_3O^+]$ concentration requires using the equation $[H_3O^+] = 10^{-pH}$, which requires finding an antilogarithm on a calculator.

BALLPARK ESTIMATE Because the pH is between 3.0 and 4.0, the $[H_3O^+]$ must be between 1×10^{-3} and 1×10^{-4}. A pH of 3.1 is very close to 3.0, so the $[H_3O^+]$ must be just slightly below 1×10^{-3} M.

SOLUTION
Entering the negative pH on a calculator (−3.1) and pressing the "INV" and "log" keys gives the answer 7.943×10^{-4}, which must be rounded off to 8×10^{-4} since the pH has only one digit to the right of the decimal point.

BALLPARK CHECK The calculated $[H_3O^+]$ of 8×10^{-4} M is between 1×10^{-3} M and 1×10^{-4} M and, as we estimated, just slightly below 1×10^{-3} M. (Remember, 8×10^{-4} is 0.8×10^{-3}.)

WORKED EXAMPLE **10.10** Working with pH: Calculating pH for Strong Acid Solutions

What is the pH of a 0.0045 M solution of $HClO_4$?

ANALYSIS Finding pH requires first finding $[H_3O^+]$ and then using the equation $pH = -\log[H_3O^+]$. Since $HClO_4$ is a strong acid (see Table 10.1), it is 100% dissociated, and so the H_3O^+ concentration is the same as the $HClO_4$ concentration.

BALLPARK ESTIMATE Because $[H^+] = 4.5 \times 10^{-3}$ M is close to midway between 1×10^{-2} M and 1×10^{-3} M, the pH must be close to the midway point between 2.0 and 3.0. (Unfortunately, because the logarithm scale is not linear, trying to estimate the midway point is not a simple process.)

SOLUTION
$[H_3O^+] = 0.0045$ M $= 4.5 \times 10^{-3}$ M. Taking the negative logarithm gives pH = 2.35.

BALLPARK CHECK The calculated pH is consistent with our estimate.

WORKED EXAMPLE **10.11** Working with pH: Calculating pH for Strong Base Solutions

What is the pH of a 0.0032 M solution of NaOH?

ANALYSIS Since NaOH is a strong base, the OH^- concentration is the same as the NaOH concentration. Starting with the OH^- concentration, finding pH requires either using the K_w equation to find $[H_3O^+]$ or calculating pOH and then using the logarithmic form of the K_w equation.

BALLPARK ESTIMATE Because $[OH^-] = 3.2 \times 10^{-3}$ M is close to midway between 1×10^{-2} M and 1×10^{-3} M, the pOH must be close to the midway point between 2.0 and 3.0. Subtracting the pOH from 14 would therefore yield a pH between 11 and 12.

SOLUTION

$$[OH^-] = 0.0032 \text{ M} = 3.2 \times 10^{-3} \text{ M}$$

$$[H_3O^+] = \frac{K_w}{(3.2 \times 10^{-3})} = 3.1 \times 10^{-12} \text{ M}$$

Taking the negative logarithm gives pH $= -\log(3.1 \times 10^{-12}) = 11.51$. Alternatively, we can calculate pOH and subtract from 14.00 using the logarithmic form of the K_w equation. For $[OH^-] = 0.0032$ M,

$$pOH = -\log(3.2 \times 10^{-3}) = 2.49$$

$$pH = 14.00 - 2.49 = 11.51$$

Since the given OH^- concentration included two significant figures, the final pH includes two significant figures beyond the decimal point.

BALLPARK CHECK The calculated pH is consistent with our estimate.

PROBLEM 10.16

Identify the following solutions as acidic or basic, estimate $[H_3O^+]$ values for each, and rank them in order of increasing acidity:

(a) Saliva, pH = 6.5   (b) Pancreatic juice, pH = 7.9

(c) Orange juice, pH = 3.7   (d) Wine, pH = 3.5

PROBLEM 10.17

Find the pH of the following solutions:

(a) Seawater with $[H_3O^+] = 5.3 \times 10^{-9}$ M

(b) A urine sample with $[H_3O^+] = 8.9 \times 10^{-6}$ M

PROBLEM 10.18

What is the pH of a 0.0025 M solution of HCl?

10.10 Laboratory Determination of Acidity

Acid–base indicator A dye that changes color depending on the pH of a solution.

The pH of water is an important indicator of water quality in applications ranging from swimming pool and spa maintenance to municipal water treatment. There are several ways to measure the pH of a solution. The simplest but least accurate method is to use an **acid–base indicator**, a dye that changes color depending on

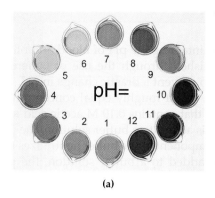
(a)

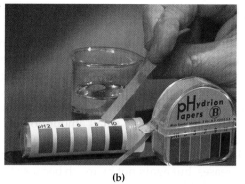
(b)

▲ **FIGURE 10.3   Finding pH.**   (a) The color of universal indicator in solutions of known pH from 1 to 12. (b) Testing pH with a paper strip. Comparing the color of the strip with the code on the package gives the approximate pH.

the pH of the solution. For example, the well-known dye *litmus* is red below pH 4.8 but blue above pH 7.8 and the indicator *phenolphthalein* (fee-nol-**thay**-lean) is colorless below pH 8.2 but red above pH 10. To make pH determination particularly easy, test kits are available that contain a mixture of indicators known as *universal indicator* to give approximate pH measurements in the range 2–10 (Figure 10.3a). Also available are rolls of "pH paper," which make it possible to determine pH simply by putting a drop of solution on the paper and comparing the color that appears to the color on a calibration chart (Figure 10.3b).

A much more accurate way to determine pH uses an electronic pH meter like the one shown in Figure 10.4. Electrodes are dipped into the solution, and the pH is read from the meter.

▲ **FIGURE 10.4   Using a pH meter to obtain an accurate reading of pH.** Is milk of magnesia acidic or basic?

APPLICATION ▶ pH of Body Fluids

Each fluid in our bodies has a pH range suited to its function, as shown in the accompanying table. The stability of cell membranes, the shapes of huge protein molecules that must be folded in certain ways to function, and the activities of enzymes are all dependent on appropriate H_3O^+ concentrations.

pH of Body Fluids

FLUID	pH
Blood plasma	7.4
Interstitial fluid	7.4
Cytosol	7.0
Saliva	5.8–7.1
Gastric juice	1.6–1.8
Pancreatic juice	7.5–8.8
Intestinal juice	6.3–8.0
Urine	4.6–8.0
Sweat	4.0–6.8

Blood plasma and the interstitial fluid surrounding cells, which together comprise one-third of body water, have a

slightly basic pH of 7.4. In fact, one of the functions of blood is to neutralize the acid by-products of cellular metabolism. The fluid within cells, called the *cytosol*, is slightly more acidic than the fluid outside, so a pH differential exists.

The strongly acidic gastric juice in the stomach has three important functions. First, gastric juice aids in the digestion of proteins by causing them to denature, or unfold. Second, it kills most of the bacteria we consume along with our food. Third, it converts the enzyme that breaks down proteins from an inactive form to the active form.

When the acidic mixture of partially digested food (*chyme*) leaves the stomach and enters the small intestine, it triggers secretion by the pancreas of an alkaline fluid containing bicarbonate ions, HCO_3^-. A principal function of this pancreatic juice and other intestinal fluids is to dilute and neutralize the hydrochloric acid carried along from the stomach.

Urine has a wide normal pH range, depending on the diet and recent activities. It is generally acidic, though, because one important function of urine is to eliminate a quantity of hydrogen ion equal to that produced by the body each day. Without this elimination, the body would soon be overwhelmed by acid.

See Additional Problem 10.97 at the end of the chapter.

As a result, the bicarbonate buffer system is intimately related to the elimination of CO_2, which is continuously produced in cells and transported to the lungs to be exhaled.

Because most CO_2 is present simply as the dissolved gas rather than as H_2CO_3, the acid dissociation constant for carbonic acid in blood can be written using $[CO_2]$:

$$K_a = \frac{[H_3O^+][HCO_3^-]}{[CO_2]}$$

which can be rearranged to

$$[H_3O^+] = K_a\frac{[CO_2]}{[HCO_3^-]}$$

An increase in $[CO_2]$ raises $[H_3O^+]$ and lowers pH.

A decrease in $[CO_2]$ lowers $[H_3O^+]$ and raises pH.

Converting this rearranged equation to the logarithmic form of the Henderson–Hasselbalch equation yields

$$pH = pK_a + \log\left(\frac{[HCO_3^-]}{[CO_2]}\right)$$

This rearranged equation shows that an increase in $[CO_2]$ makes the ratio of $[HCO_3^-]$ to $[CO_2]$ smaller, thereby decreasing the pH; that is, the blood becomes more acidic. Similarly, a decrease in $[CO_2]$ makes the ratio of $[HCO_3^-]$ to $[CO_2]$ larger, thereby increasing the pH; that is, the blood becomes more basic. At the normal blood pH of 7.4, the ratio $[HCO_3^-]/[CO_2]$ is about 20 to 1.

The relationships between the bicarbonate buffer system, the lungs, and the kidneys are shown in Figure 10.6. Under normal circumstances, the reactions shown in the figure are at equilibrium. Addition of excess acid (red arrows) causes formation of H_2CO_3 and results in lowering of H_3O^+ concentration. Removal of acid (blue arrows) causes formation of more H_3O^+ by dissociation of H_2CO_3. The maintenance of pH by this mechanism is supported by a reserve of bicarbonate ions in body fluids. Such a buffer can accommodate large additions of H_3O^+ before there is a significant change in the pH, a condition that meets the body's needs because excessive production of acid is a more common body condition than excessive loss of acid.

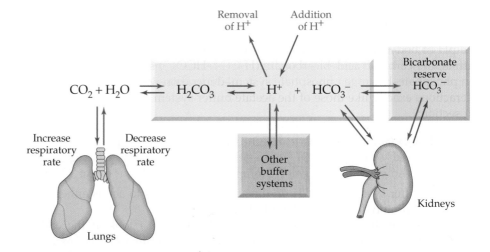

▶ **FIGURE 10.6 Relationships of the bicarbonate buffer system to the lungs and the kidneys.** The red and blue arrows show the responses to the stresses of increased or decreased respiratory rate and removal or addition of acid.

A change in the breathing rate provides a quick further adjustment in the bicarbonate buffer system. When the CO_2 concentration in the blood starts to rise, the breathing rate increases to remove CO_2, thereby decreasing the acid concentration (red arrows in Figure 10.6). When the CO_2 concentration in the blood starts to

APPLICATION ▶ Buffers in the Body: Acidosis and Alkalosis

A group of teenagers at a rock concert experience a collective fainting spell. A person taking high doses of aspirin for chronic pain appears disoriented and is having trouble breathing. An insulin-dependent diabetic patient complains of tiredness and stomach pains. An athlete who recently completed a highly strenuous workout suffers from muscle cramps and nausea. A patient on an HIV drug regimen experiences increasing weakness and numbness in the hands and feet. What do all these individuals have in common? They are all suffering from abnormal fluctuations in blood pH, resulting in conditions known as *acidosis* (pH < 7.35) or *alkalosis* (pH > 7.45).

The highly complex series of reactions and equilibria that take place throughout the body are very sensitive to pH—variations of even a few tenths of a pH unit can produce severe physiological symptoms. The carbonate–bicarbonate buffer system (Section 10.12) maintains the pH of blood serum at a fairly constant value of 7.4. The effective pH depends on the relative amounts of CO_2 and bicarbonate dissolved in the blood:

$$CO_2(aq) + H_2O(l)$$
$$\rightleftharpoons H_2CO_3(aq) \rightleftharpoons HCO_3^-(aq) + H_3O^+(aq)$$

Anything that significantly shifts the balance between dissolved CO_2 and HCO_3^- can raise or lower the pH. How does this happen, and how does the body compensate?

Respiratory acidosis can be caused by a decrease in respiration, which leads to a buildup of excess CO_2 in the blood and a corresponding decrease in pH. This could be caused by a blocked air passage due to inhaled food—removal of the blockage restores normal breathing and a return to the optimal pH. *Metabolic acidosis* results from an excess of other acids in the blood that reduce the bicarbonate concentration. High doses of aspirin (acetyl salicylic acid, Section 17.5), for example, increase the hydronium ion concentration and decrease the pH. Strenuous exercise generates excess lactate in the muscles, which is released into the bloodstream (Section 23.11). The liver converts lactate into glucose, which is the body's major source of energy; this process consumes bicarbonate ions, which decreases the pH. Some HIV drug therapies can damage cellular mitochondria (Section 21.3),

resulting in a buildup of lactic acid in the cells and blood stream. In the case of the diabetic patient, lack of insulin causes the body to start burning fat, which generates ketones and keto acids (Chapter 16), organic compounds that lower the blood pH.

The body attempts to correct acidosis by increasing the rate and depth of respiration—breathing faster "blows off" CO_2, shifting the CO_2–bicarbonate equilibrium to the left and lowering the pH. The net effect is rapid reversal of the acidosis. Although this may be sufficient for cases of respiratory acidosis, it provides only temporary relief for metabolic acidosis. A long-term solution depends on removal of excess acid by the kidneys, which can take several hours.

What about our teenage fans? In their excitement they have hyperventilated—their increased breathing rate has removed too much CO_2 from their blood and they are suffering from *respiratory alkalosis*. The body responds by "fainting" to decrease respiration and restore the CO_2 levels in the blood. When they regain consciousness, they will be ready to rock once again.

▲ Hyperventilation, the rapid breathing due to excitement or stress, removes CO_2 and increases blood pH resulting in respiratory alkalosis.

See Additional Problems 10.98 and 10.99 at the end of the chapter.

fall, the breathing rate decreases and acid concentration increases (blue arrows in Figure 10.6).

Additional backup to the bicarbonate buffer system is provided by the kidneys. Each day a quantity of acid equal to that produced in the body is excreted in the urine. In the process, the kidney returns HCO_3^- to the extracellular fluids, where it becomes part of the bicarbonate reserve.

◖▭◗ Looking Ahead

In Chapter 29, we will see how the regulation of blood pH by the bicarbonate buffer system is particularly important in preventing *acidosis* and *alkalosis*.   ◖▭◗

APPLICATION ▶ Acid Rain

As the water that evaporates from oceans and lakes condenses into raindrops, it dissolves small quantities of gases from the atmosphere. Under normal conditions, rain is slightly acidic, with a pH close to 5.6, because of atmospheric CO_2 that dissolves to form carbonic acid:

$$CO_2(aq) + H_2O(l) \rightleftharpoons H_2CO_3(aq) \rightleftharpoons HCO_3^-(aq) + H_3O^+(aq)$$

In recent decades, however, the acidity of rainwater in many industrialized areas of the world has increased by a factor of over 100, to a pH between 3 and 3.5.

The primary cause of this so-called *acid rain* is industrial and automotive pollution. Each year, large power plants and smelters pour millions of tons of sulfur dioxide (SO_2) gas into the atmosphere, where some is oxidized by air to produce sulfur trioxide (SO_3). Sulfur oxides then dissolve in rain to form dilute sulfurous acid (H_2SO_3) and sulfuric acid (H_2SO_4):

$$SO_2(g) + H_2O(l) \longrightarrow H_2SO_3(aq)$$
$$SO_3(g) + H_2O(l) \longrightarrow H_2SO_4(aq)$$

Nitrogen oxides produced by the high-temperature reaction of N_2 with O_2 in coal-burning plants and in automobile engines further contribute to the problem. Nitrogen dioxide (NO_2) dissolves in water to form dilute nitric acid (HNO_3) and nitric oxide (NO):

$$3\ NO_2(g) + H_2O(l) \longrightarrow 2\ HNO_3(aq) + NO(g)$$

Oxides of both sulfur and nitrogen have always been present in the atmosphere, produced by such natural sources as volcanoes and lightning bolts, but their amounts have increased dramatically over the last century because of industrialization. The result is a notable decrease in the pH of rainwater in more densely populated regions, including Europe and the eastern United States.

Many processes in nature require such a fine pH balance that they are dramatically upset by the shift that has occurred in the pH of rain. Some watersheds contain soils that have high "buffering capacity" and so are able to neutralize acidic compounds in acid rain (Section 10.11). Other areas, such as the northeastern United States and eastern Canada, where soil buffering capacity is poor, have experienced negative ecological effects. Acid rain releases aluminum salts from soil, and the ions then wash into streams. The low pH and increased aluminum levels are so toxic to fish and other organisms that many lakes and streams in these areas are devoid of aquatic life. Massive tree die-offs have occurred throughout central and eastern Europe as acid rain has lowered the pH of the soil and has leached nutrients from leaves.

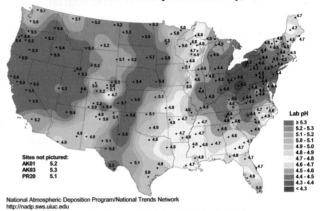

Hydrogen ion concentration as pH from measurements made at the Central Analytical Laboratory, 1996
Sites not pictured:
AK01 5.2
AK03 5.3
PR20 5.1
Lab pH
≥ 5.3
5.2 - 5.3
5.1 - 5.2
5.0 - 5.1
4.9 - 5.0
4.8 - 4.9
4.7 - 4.8
4.6 - 4.7
4.5 - 4.6
4.4 - 4.5
4.3 - 4.4
< 4.3
National Atmospheric Deposition Program/National Trends Network
http://nadp.sws.uiuc.edu

Hydrogen ion concentration as pH from measurements made at the Central Analytical Laboratory, 2006
Sites not pictured:
AK01 5.2
AK03 5.3
PR20 4.9
VI01 4.8
Lab pH
≥ 5.3
5.2 - 5.3
5.1 - 5.2
5.0 - 5.1
4.9 - 5.0
4.8 - 4.9
4.7 - 4.8
4.6 - 4.7
4.5 - 4.6
4.4 - 4.5
4.3 - 4.4
< 4.3
National Atmospheric Deposition Program/National Trends Network
http://nadp.sws.uiuc.edu

▲ These maps compare the average pH of precipitation in the United States in 1996 and in 2006. During this period, total acid deposition in much of the eastern United States decreased substantially.

Fortunately, acidic emissions in the United States have been greatly reduced in recent years as a result of the Clean Air Act Amendments of 1990. Industrial emissions of SO_2 and nitrogen oxides decreased by over 40% from 1990 to 2007, resulting in a decrease in acid rain depositions, particularly in the eastern United States and Canada (see accompanying figure). While significant reductions have been realized, most environmental scientists agree that additional reductions in these pollutant emissions are necessary to ensure the recovery of affected lakes and streams.

See Additional Problems 10.100 and 10.101 at the end of the chapter.

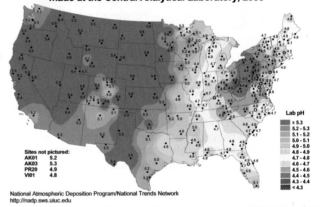

PROBLEM 10.29

How many milliliters of 0.150 M NaOH are required to neutralize 50.0 mL of 0.200 M H_2SO_4? The balanced neutralization reaction is:

$$H_2SO_4(aq) + 2\,NaOH(aq) \longrightarrow Na_2SO_4(aq) + 2\,H_2O(l).$$

PROBLEM 10.30

A 21.5 mL sample of a KOH solution of unknown concentration requires 16.1 mL of 0.150 M H_2SO_4 solution to reach the end point in a titration. What is the molarity of the KOH solution?

10.16 Acidity and Basicity of Salt Solutions

It is tempting to think of all salt solutions as neutral; after all, they come from the neutralization reaction between an acid and a base. In fact, salt solutions can be neutral, acidic, or basic, depending on the ions present, because some ions react with water to produce H_3O^+ and some ions react with water to produce OH^-. To predict the acidity of a salt solution, it is convenient to classify salts according to the acid and base from which they are formed in a neutralization reaction. The classification and some examples are given in Table 10.3.

TABLE 10.3 Acidity and Basicity of Salt Solutions

ANION DERIVED FROM ACID THAT IS:	CATION DERIVED FROM BASE THAT IS:	SOLUTION	EXAMPLE
Strong	Weak	Acidic	NH_4Cl, NH_4NO_3
Weak	Strong	Basic	$NaHCO_3$, KCH_3CO_2
Strong	Strong	Neutral	$NaCl$, KBr, $Ca(NO_3)_2$
Weak	Weak	More information needed	

The general rule for predicting the acidity or basicity of a salt solution is that the stronger partner from which the salt is formed dominates. That is, a salt formed from a strong acid and a weak base yields an acidic solution because the strong acid dominates; a salt formed from a weak acid and a strong base yields a basic solution because the base dominates; and a salt formed from a strong acid and a strong base yields a neutral solution because neither acid nor base dominates. Here are some examples.

Salt of Strong Acid + Weak Base $\longrightarrow$ Acidic Solution

A salt such as NH_4Cl, which can be formed by reaction of a strong acid (HCl) with a weak base (NH_3), yields an acidic solution. The Cl^- ion does not react with water, but the NH_4^+ ion is a weak acid that gives H_3O^+ ions:

$$NH_4^+(aq) + H_2O(l) \rightleftharpoons NH_3(aq) + H_3O^+(aq)$$

Salt of Weak Acid + Strong Base $\longrightarrow$ Basic Solution

A salt such as sodium bicarbonate, which can be formed by reaction of a weak acid (H_2CO_3) with a strong base (NaOH), yields a basic solution. The Na^+ ion does not react with water, but the HCO_3^- ion is a weak base that gives OH^- ions:

$$HCO_3^-(aq) + H_2O(l) \rightleftharpoons H_2CO_3(aq) + OH^-(aq)$$

10.75 Which system would you expect to be a better buffer: $HNO_3 + Na^+NO_3^-$, or $CH_3CO_2H + CH_3CO_2^-Na^+$? Explain.

10.76 The pH of a buffer solution containing 0.10 M acetic acid and 0.10 M sodium acetate is 4.74.

(a) Write the Henderson–Hasselbalch equation for this buffer.

(b) Write the equations for reaction of this buffer with a small amount of HNO_3 and with a small amount of NaOH.

10.77 Which of the following buffer systems would you use if you wanted to prepare a solution having a pH of approximately 9.5?

(a) 0.08 M $H_2PO_4^-$/0.12 M HPO_4^{2-}
(b) 0.08 M NH_4^+/0.12 M NH_3

10.78 What is the pH of a buffer system that contains 0.200 M hydrocyanic acid (HCN) and 0.150 M sodium cyanide (NaCN)? The pK_a of hydrocyanic acid is 9.31.

10.79 What is the pH of 1.00 L of the 0.200 M hydrocyanic acid–0.150 M cyanide ion buffer system described in Problem 10.78 after 0.020 mol of HCl is added? After 0.020 mol of NaOH is added?

10.80 What is the pH of a buffer system that contains 0.15 M NH_4^+ and 0.10 M NH_3? The pK_a of NH_4^+ is 9.25.

10.81 How many moles of NaOH must be added to 1.00 L of the solution described in Problem 10.80 to increase the pH to 9.25?

CONCENTRATIONS OF ACID AND BASE SOLUTIONS

10.82 What does it mean when we talk about acid *equivalents* and base *equivalents*?

10.83 How is normality defined as a means of expressing acid or base concentration?

10.84 Calculate the gram-equivalent for each of the following acids and bases.

(a) HNO_3 (b) H_3PO_4
(c) KOH   (d) $Mg(OH)_2$

10.85 What mass of each of the acids and bases in Problem 10.84 is needed to prepare 500 mL of 0.15 N solution?

10.86 How many milliliters of 0.0050 N KOH are required to neutralize 25 mL of 0.0050 N H_2SO_4? To neutralize 25 mL of 0.0050 N HCl?

10.87 What is the normality of a 0.12 M H_2SO_4 solution? Of a 0.12 M H_3PO_4 solution?

10.88 How many equivalents of an acid or base are in the following?

(a) 0.25 mol $Mg(OH)_2$
(b) 2.5 g $Mg(OH)_2$
(c) 15 g CH_3CO_2H

10.89 What mass of citric acid (triprotic, $C_6H_5O_7H_3$) contains 152 mEq of citric acid?

10.90 What are the molarity and the normality of a solution made by dissolving 5.0 g of $Ca(OH)_2$ in enough water to make 500.0 mL of solution?

10.91 What are the molarity and the normality of a solution made by dissolving 25 g of citric acid (triprotic, $C_6H_5O_7H_3$) in enough water to make 800 mL of solution?

10.92 Titration of a 12.0 mL solution of HCl requires 22.4 mL of 0.12 M NaOH. What is the molarity of the HCl solution?

10.93 What volume of 0.085 M HNO_3 is required to titrate 15.0 mL of 0.12 M $Ba(OH)_2$ solution?

10.94 Titration of a 10.0 mL solution of KOH requires 15.0 mL of 0.0250 M H_2SO_4 solution. What is the molarity of the KOH solution?

10.95 If 35.0 mL of a 0.100 N acid solution is needed to reach the end point in titration of 21.5 mL of a base solution, what is the normality of the base solution?

Applications

10.96 The concentration of HCl when released to the stomach cavity is diluted to between 0.01 and 0.001 M [*GERD— Too Much Acid or Not Enough? p. 302*]

(a) What is the pH range in the stomach cavity?
(b) Write a balanced equation for the neutralization of stomach acid by $NaHCO_3$.
(c) How many grams of $NaHCO_3$ are required to neutralize 15.0 mL of a solution having a pH of 1.8?

10.97 Which body fluid is most acidic? Which is most basic? [*pH of Body Fluids, p. 311*]

10.98 Metabolic acidosis is often treated by administering bicarbonate intravenously. Explain how this treatment can increase blood serum pH. [*Buffers in the Body: Acidosis and Alkalosis, p. 317*]

10.99 The normal $[HCO_3^-]/[CO_2]$ ratio in the blood is about 20 to 1 at a pH = 7.4. What is this ratio at pH = 7.3 (acidosis) and at pH = 7.5 (alkalosis)? [*Buffers in the Body: Acidosis and Alkalosis, p. 317*]

10.100 Rain typically has a pH of about 5.6. What is the H_3O^+ concentration in rain? [*Acid Rain, p. 324*]

10.101 Acid rain with a pH as low as 1.5 has been recorded in West Virginia. [*Acid Rain, p. 324*]

(a) What is the H_3O^+ concentration in this acid rain?
(b) How many grams of HNO_3 must be dissolved to make 25 L of solution that has a pH of 1.5?

General Questions and Problems

10.102 Alka-Seltzer, a drugstore antacid, contains a mixture of $NaHCO_3$, aspirin, and citric acid, $C_6H_5O_7H_3$. Why does Alka-Seltzer foam and bubble when dissolved in water? Which ingredient is the antacid?

10.103 How many milliliters of 0.50 M NaOH solution are required to titrate 40.0 mL of a 0.10 M H_2SO_4 solution to an end point?

10.104 Which solution contains more acid, 50 mL of a 0.20 N HCl solution or 50 mL of a 0.20 N acetic acid solution? Which has a higher hydronium ion concentration? Which has a lower pH?

10.105 One of the buffer systems used to control the pH of blood involves the equilibrium between $H_2PO_4^-$ and HPO_4^{2-}. The pK_a for $H_2PO_4^-$ is 7.21.

   (a) Write the Henderson–Hasselbalch equation for this buffer system.

   (b) What HPO_4^{2-} to $H_2PO_4^-$ ratio is needed to maintain the optimum blood pH of 7.40?

10.106 A 0.15 M solution of HCl is used to titrate 30.0 mL of a $Ca(OH)_2$ solution of unknown concentration. If 140 mL of HCl is required, what is the concentration (in molarity) of the $Ca(OH)_2$ solution?

10.107 Which of the following combinations produces an effective buffer solution? Assuming equal concentrations of each acid and its conjugate base, calculate the pH of each buffer solution.

   (a) NaF and HF
   (b) $HClO_4$ and $NaClO_4$
   (c) NH_4Cl and NH_3
   (d) KBr and HBr

10.108 One method of analyzing ammonium salts is to treat them with NaOH and then heat the solution to remove the NH_3 gas formed.

$$NH_4^+(aq) + OH^-(aq) \longrightarrow NH_3(g) + H_2O(l)$$

   (a) Label the Brønsted–Lowry acid–base pairs.

   (b) If 2.86 L of NH_3 at 60 °C and 755 mmHg is produced by the reaction of NH_4Cl, how many grams of NH_4Cl were in the original sample?

10.109 One method of reducing acid rain is *scrubbing* the combustion products before they are emitted from power plant smoke stacks. The process involves addition of an aqueous suspension of lime (CaO) to the combustion chamber and stack, where the lime reacts with SO_2 to give calcium sulfite ($CaSO_3$).

   (a) Write the balanced chemical equation for this reaction.

   (b) How much lime is needed to remove 1 kg of SO_2?

10.110 Sodium oxide, Na_2O, reacts with water to give NaOH.

   (a) Write a balanced equation for the reaction.

   (b) What is the pH of the solution prepared by allowing 1.55 g of Na_2O to react with 500.0 mL of water? Assume that there is no volume change.

   (c) How many milliliters of 0.0100 M HCl are needed to neutralize the NaOH solution prepared in (b)?

CHAPTER 11

Nuclear Chemistry

CONCEPTS TO REVIEW

Atomic Theory
(Section 3.1)

Elements and Atomic Number
(Section 3.2)

Isotopes
(Section 3.3)

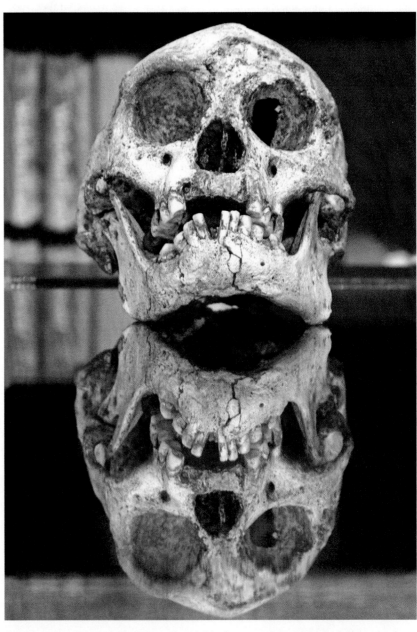

▲ The age of this skull, from a hominid discovered in 2004 in Indonesia, is estimated to be 18,000 years.

CONTENTS

CHAPTER GOALS

In this chapter we will answer the following questions about nuclear chemistry:

1. What is a nuclear reaction, and how are equations for nuclear reactions balanced?

THE GOAL: Be able to write and balance equations for nuclear reactions.

2. What are the different kinds of radioactivity?

THE GOAL: Be able to list the characteristics of three common kinds of radiation—α, β, and γ (alpha, beta, and gamma).

3. How are the rates of nuclear reactions expressed?

THE GOAL: Be able to explain half-life and calculate the quantity of a radioisotope remaining after a given number of half-lives.

4. What is ionizing radiation?

THE GOAL: Be able to describe the properties of the different types of ionizing radiation and their potential for harm to living tissue.

5. How is radioactivity measured?

THE GOAL: Be able to describe the common units for measuring radiation.

6. What is transmutation?

THE GOAL: Be able to explain nuclear bombardment and balance equations for nuclear bombardment reactions.

7. What are nuclear fission and nuclear fusion?

THE GOAL: Be able to explain nuclear fission and nuclear fusion.

I n all of the reactions we have discussed thus far, only the *bonds* between atoms have changed; the chemical identities of atoms themselves have remained unchanged. Anyone who reads the paper or watches television knows, however, that atoms *can* change, often resulting in the conversion of one element into another. Atomic weapons, nuclear energy, and radioactive radon gas in our homes are all topics of societal importance, and all involve *nuclear chemistry*—the study of the properties and reactions of atomic nuclei.

11.1 Nuclear Reactions

Recall from Section 3.2 that an atom is characterized by its *atomic number, Z,* and its *mass number, A*. (⬤▭ , p. 53) The atomic number, written below and to the left of the element symbol, gives the number of protons in the nucleus and identifies the element. The mass number, written above and to the left of the element symbol, gives the total number of **nucleons**, a general term for both protons (p) and neutrons (n). The most common isotope of carbon, for example, has 12 nucleons: 6 protons and 6 neutrons: $^{12}_{6}C$.

Nucleon A general term for both protons and neutrons.

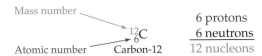

Atoms with identical atomic numbers but different mass numbers are called *isotopes* (Section 3.3), and the nucleus of a specific isotope is called a **nuclide**. (⬤▭ , p. 54) Thirteen isotopes of carbon are known—two occur commonly (^{12}C and ^{13}C) and one (^{14}C) is produced in small amounts in the upper atmosphere by the action of neutrons from cosmic rays on ^{14}N. The remaining ten carbon isotopes have been produced artificially. Only the two commonly occurring isotopes are stable indefinitely. The others undergo spontaneous **nuclear reactions**, which change their nuclei. Carbon-14, for example, slowly decomposes to give nitrogen-14 plus an electron, a process we can write as

Nuclide The nucleus of a specific isotope of an element.

Nuclear reaction A reaction that changes an atomic nucleus, usually causing the change of one element into another.

$$^{14}_{6}C \longrightarrow \; ^{14}_{7}N + \; ^{0}_{-1}e$$

The electron is often written as $^{0}_{-1}e$, where the superscript 0 indicates that the mass of an electron is essentially zero when compared with that of a proton or neutron, and the subscript -1 indicates that the charge is -1. (The subscript in this instance is not a true atomic number.)

Nuclear reactions, such as the spontaneous decay of ^{14}C, are distinguished from chemical reactions in several ways:

- A *nuclear* reaction involves a change in an atom's nucleus, usually producing a different element. A *chemical* reaction, by contrast, involves only a change in distribution of the outer-shell electrons around the atom and never changes the nucleus itself or produces a different element.

- Different isotopes of an element have essentially the same behavior in chemical reactions but often have completely different behavior in nuclear reactions.

- The rate of a nuclear reaction is unaffected by a change in temperature or pressure or by the addition of a catalyst.

- The nuclear reaction of an atom is essentially the same whether it is in a chemical compound or in an uncombined, elemental form.

- The energy change accompanying a nuclear reaction can be up to several million times greater than that accompanying a chemical reaction. The nuclear transformation of 1.0 g of uranium-235 releases 3.4×10^8 kcal, for example, whereas the chemical combustion of 1.0 g of methane releases only 12 kcal.

11.2 The Discovery and Nature of Radioactivity

The discovery of *radioactivity* dates to the year 1896 when the French physicist Henri Becquerel made a remarkable observation. While investigating the nature of phosphorescence—the luminous glow of some minerals and other substances that remains when the light is suddenly turned off—Becquerel happened to place a sample of a uranium-containing mineral on top of a photographic plate that had been wrapped in black paper and put in a drawer to protect it from sunlight. On developing the plate, Becquerel was surprised to find a silhouette of the mineral. He concluded that the mineral was producing some kind of unknown radiation, which passed through the paper and exposed the photographic plate.

Radioactivity The spontaneous emission of radiation from a nucleus.

Marie Sklodowska Curie and her husband, Pierre, took up the challenge and began a series of investigations into this new phenomenon, which they termed **radioactivity**. They found that the source of the radioactivity was the element uranium (U) and that two previously unknown elements, which they named polonium (Po) and radium (Ra), were also radioactive. For these achievements, Becquerel and the Curies shared the 1903 Nobel Prize in physics.

Further work on radioactivity by the English scientist Ernest Rutherford established that there were at least two types of radiation, which he named *alpha* (α) and *beta* (β) after the first two letters of the Greek alphabet. Shortly thereafter, a third type of radiation was found and named for the third Greek letter, *gamma* (γ).

Subsequent studies showed that when the three kinds of radiation are passed between two plates with opposite electrical charges, each is affected differently. Alpha radiation bends toward the negative plate and must therefore have a positive charge. Beta radiation, by contrast, bends toward the positive plate and must have a negative charge, whereas gamma radiation does not bend toward either plate and has no charge (Figure 11.1).

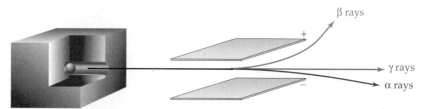

▲ **FIGURE 11.1   The effect of an electric field on α, β, and γ, radiation.** The radioactive source in the shielded box emits radiation, which passes between the two electrically charged plates. Alpha radiation is deflected toward the negative plate, β radiation is deflected toward the positive plate, and γ radiation is not deflected.

Another difference among the three kinds of radiation soon became apparent when it was discovered that alpha and beta radiations are composed of small particles with a measurable mass, whereas **gamma (γ) radiation** consists of high-energy electromagnetic waves and has no mass (see the Application "Atoms and Light" in Chapter 3). (◁▭▷, p. 72) Rutherford was able to show that a **beta (β) particle** is an electron (e⁻) and that an **alpha (α) particle** is simply a helium nucleus, He²⁺. (Recall that a helium *atom* consists of two protons, two neutrons, and two electrons. When the two electrons are removed, the remaining helium nucleus, or α particle, has only the two protons and two neutrons.)

Yet a third difference among the three kinds of radiation is their penetrating power. Because of their relatively large mass, α particles move slowly (up to about one-tenth the speed of light) and can be stopped by a few sheets of paper or by the top layer of skin. Beta particles, because they are much lighter, move at up to nine-tenths the speed of light and have about 100 times the penetrating power of α particles. A block of wood or heavy protective clothing is necessary to stop β radiation, which can otherwise penetrate the skin and cause burns and other damage. Gamma rays move at the speed of light (3.00×10^8 m/s) and have about 1000 times the penetrating power of α particles. A lead block several inches thick is needed to stop γ radiation, which can otherwise penetrate and damage the body's internal organs.

The characteristics of the three kinds of radiation are summarized in Table 11.1. Note that an α particle, even though it is an ion with a 2+ charge, is usually written using the symbol $^4_2$He without the charge. A β particle is usually written $^0_{-1}$e, as noted previously.

Gamma (γ) radiation Radioactivity consisting of high-energy light waves.

Beta (β) particle An electron (e⁻), emitted as radiation.

Alpha (α) particle A helium nucleus (He²⁺), emitted as α radiation.

TABLE 11.1 Characteristics of α, β, and γ Radiation

TYPE OF RADIATION	SYMBOL	CHARGE	COMPOSITION	MASS (AMU)	VELOCITY	RELATIVE PENETRATING POWER
Alpha	α, $^4_2$He	+2	Helium nucleus	4	Up to 10% speed of light	Low (1)
Beta	β, $^0_{-1}$e	−1	Electron	1/1823	Up to 90% speed of light	Medium (100)
Gamma	γ, $^0_0\gamma$	0	High-energy radiation	0	Speed of light (3.00×10^8 m/s)	High (1000)

11.3 Stable and Unstable Isotopes

Every element in the periodic table has at least one radioactive isotope, or **radioisotope**, and more than *3300* radioisotopes are known. Their radioactivity is the result of having unstable nuclei, although the exact causes of this instability are not fully understood. Radiation is emitted when an unstable radioactive nucleus, or **radionuclide**, spontaneously changes into a more stable one.

For elements in the first few rows of the periodic table, stability is associated with a roughly equal number of neutrons and protons (Figure 11.2). Hydrogen, for example, has stable $^1_1$H (protium) and $^2_1$H (deuterium) isotopes, but its $^3_1$H isotope (tritium) is radioactive. As elements get heavier, the number of neutrons relative to protons in stable nuclei increases. Lead-208 ($^{208}_{82}$Pb), for example, the most abundant stable isotope of lead, has 126 neutrons and 82 protons in its nuclei. Nevertheless, of the 35 known isotopes of lead, only 3 are stable whereas 32 are radioactive. In fact, there are only 264 stable isotopes among all the elements. All isotopes of elements with atomic numbers higher than that of bismuth (83) are radioactive.

Most of the more than 3300 known radioisotopes have been made in high-energy particle accelerators by reactions that will be described in Section 11.10. Such isotopes are called *artificial radioisotopes* because they are not found in nature. All isotopes of the transuranium elements (those heavier than uranium) are artificial. The much smaller number of radioactive isotopes found in the earth's crust, such as $^{238}_{92}$U, are called *natural radioisotopes*.

Aside from their radioactivity, different radioisotopes of the same element have the same chemical properties as stable isotopes, which accounts for their great

Radioisotope A radioactive isotope.

Radionuclide The nucleus of a radioactive isotope.

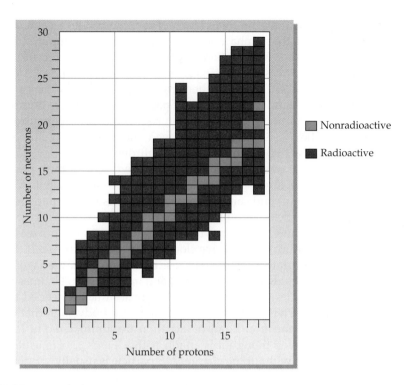

▲ FIGURE 11.2 **A plot of the numbers of neutrons and protons for known isotopes of the first 18 elements.** Stable (nonradioactive) isotopes of these elements have equal or nearly equal numbers of neutrons and protons.

usefulness as *tracers*. A chemical compound tagged with a radioactive atom undergoes exactly the same reactions as its nonradioactive counterpart. The difference is that the tagged compound can be located with a radiation detector and its whereabouts determined, as discussed in the Application "Body Imaging" on page 352.

11.4 Nuclear Decay

Think for a minute about the consequences of α and β radiation. If radioactivity involves the spontaneous emission of a small particle from an unstable atomic nucleus, then the nucleus itself must undergo a change. With that understanding of radioactivity came the startling discovery that atoms of one element can change into atoms of another element, something that had previously been thought impossible. The spontaneous emission of a particle from an unstable nucleus is called **nuclear decay**, or *radioactive decay*, and the resulting change of one element into another is called **transmutation**.

Nuclear decay The spontaneous emission of a particle from an unstable nucleus.

Transmutation The change of one element into another.

> **Nuclear decay:** Radioactive element $\longrightarrow$ New element + Emitted particle

We now look at what happens to a nucleus when nuclear decay occurs.

Alpha Emission

When an atom of uranium-238 ($^{238}_{92}U$) emits an α particle, the nucleus loses two protons and two neutrons. Because the number of protons in the nucleus has now changed from 92 to 90, the *identity* of the atom has changed from uranium to thorium. Furthermore, since the total number of nucleons has decreased by 4, uranium-238 has become thorium-234 ($^{234}_{90}Th$) (Figure 11.3).

Note that the equation for a nuclear reaction is not balanced in the usual chemical sense because the kinds of atoms are not the same on both sides of the arrow. Instead, we say that a nuclear equation is balanced when the number of nucleons is the same on both sides of the equation and when the sums of the charges on the nuclei plus any ejected subatomic particles (protons or electrons) are the same on

PROBLEM 11.4

Write nuclear equation

(a) ^3_1H (b)

Gamma Emission

Emission of γ rays, unlike
mass or atomic number b
waves. Although γ emissio
sion as a mechanism for th
rid of some extra energy.

Since γ emission affec
omitted from nuclear equa
penetrating power makes
tion for humans and also
Cobalt-60, for example, is
that kill cancerous tissue.

Positron Emission

In addition to α, β, and γ
decay process called *positro*
the nucleus into a neutron
be thought of as a "positiv
tive charge. This process ca

The result of positron emi
nucleus because a proton
number. Potassium-40, for
a nuclear reaction importa
sum of the two subscripts
equal to the subscript in th

19 protons
21 neutrons —
40 nucleons

Electron Capture

Electron capture, symboliz
inner-shell electron from t
ton into a neutron. The n
the atomic number decrea
mercury-197 into gold-197

80 protons
117 neutrons
197 nucleons

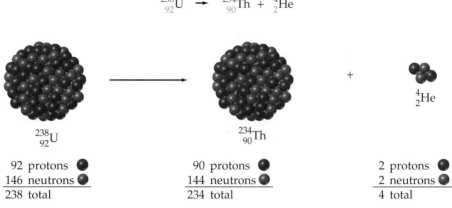

$$^{238}_{92}U \longrightarrow ^{234}_{90}Th + ^4_2He$$

$^{238}_{92}U$

92 protons ●
146 neutrons ●
238 total

$^{234}_{90}Th$

90 protons ●
144 neutrons ●
234 total

2 protons ●
2 neutrons ●
4 total

◀ **FIGURE 11.3 Alpha emission.**
Emission of an α particle from an
atom of uranium-238 produces an
atom of thorium-234.

both sides. In the decay of $^{238}_{92}U$ to give ^4_2He and $^{234}_{90}Th$, for example, there are 238
nucleons and 92 nuclear charges on both sides of the nuclear equation.

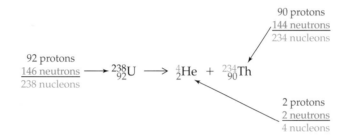

90 protons
144 neutrons
234 nucleons

92 protons
146 neutrons
238 nucleons

$$^{238}_{92}U \longrightarrow ^4_2He + ^{234}_{90}Th$$

2 protons
2 neutrons
4 nucleons

WORKED EXAMPLE   **11.1** Balancing Nuclear Reactions: Alpha Emission

Polonium-208 is one of the α emitters studied by Marie Curie. Write the equation for the α decay of polonium-208, and identify the element formed.

ANALYSIS Look up the atomic number of polonium (84) in the periodic table,
and write the known part of the nuclear equation, using the standard symbol
for polonium-208:

$$^{208}_{84}Po \longrightarrow ^4_2He + ?$$

Then calculate the mass number and atomic number of the product element,
and write the final equation.

SOLUTION
The mass number of the product is 208 − 4 = 204, and the atomic number is
84 − 2 = 82. A look at the periodic table identifies the element with atomic
number 82 as lead (Pb).

$$^{208}_{84}Po \longrightarrow ^4_2He + ^{204}_{82}Pb$$

Check your answer by making sure that the mass numbers and atomic numbers on the two sides of the equation are balanced:

Mass numbers: 208 = 4 + 204   Atomic numbers: 84 = 2 + 82

PROBLEM 11.1

High levels of radioactive radon-222 ($^{222}_{86}Rn$) have been found in many homes
built on radium-containing rock, leading to the possibility of health hazards.
What product results from α emission by radon-222?

APPLICATION ▶ Medical Uses of Radioactivity

The origins of nuclear medicine date from 1901 when the French physician Henri Danlos first used radium in the treatment of a tubercular skin lesion. Since that time, the use of radioactivity has become a crucial part of modern medical care, both diagnostic and therapeutic. Current nuclear techniques can be grouped into three classes: (1) in vivo procedures, (2) radiation therapy, and (3) imaging procedures. The first two are described here, and the third one is described on page 352 in the Application "Body Imaging."

In Vivo Procedures

In vivo studies—those that take place inside the body—are carried out to assess the functioning of a particular organ or body system. A *radiopharmaceutical* agent is administered, and its path in the body—whether absorbed, excreted, diluted, or concentrated—is determined by analysis of blood or urine samples.

Among the many in vivo procedures utilizing radioactive agents is a simple method for the determination of whole-blood volume by injecting a known quantity of red blood cells labeled with radioactive chromium-51. After a suitable interval to allow the labeled cells to be distributed evenly throughout the body, a blood sample is taken and blood volume is calculated by comparing the concentration of labeled cells in the blood with the quantity of labeled cells injected. This and similar procedures are known as *isotope dilution* and are described by

$$R_{sample} = R_{tracer}\left(\frac{W_{sample}}{W_{system} + W_{tracer}}\right)$$

where R_{sample} is the counting rate of the analyzed sample, R_{tracer} is the counting rate of the tracer added to the system, and W refers to either the mass or volume of the analyzed sample, added tracer, or total system as indicated.

Therapeutic Procedures

Therapeutic procedures—those in which radiation is purposely used as a weapon to kill diseased tissue—involve either external or internal sources of radiation. External radiation therapy for the treatment of cancer is often carried out with γ rays emanating from a cobalt-60 source. The highly radioactive source is shielded by a thick lead container and has a small opening directed toward the site of the tumor. By focusing the radiation beam on the tumor, the tumor receives the full exposure while exposure of surrounding parts of the body is minimized. Nevertheless, enough healthy tissue is affected so that most patients treated in this manner suffer the effects of radiation sickness.

Internal radiation therapy is a much more selective technique than external therapy. In the treatment of thyroid disease, for example, a radioactive substance such as iodine-131 is administered. This powerful β emitter is incorporated into the iodine-containing hormone thyroxine, which concentrates in the thyroid gland. Because β particles penetrate no farther than several millimeters, the localized ^{131}I produces

a high radiation dose that destroys only the surrounding diseased tissue. To treat some tumors, such as those in the female reproductive system, a radioactive source is placed physically close to the tumor for a specific amount of time.

Boron neutron-capture therapy (BNCT) is a relatively new technique in which boron-containing drugs are administered to a patient and concentrate in the tumor site. The tumor is then irradiated with a neutron beam from a nuclear reactor. The boron absorbs a neutron and undergoes transmutation to produce an alpha particle and a lithium nucleus. These highly energetic particles have very low penetrating power and can kill nearby tumor tissue while sparing the healthy surrounding tissue. Because one disadvantage of BNCT is the need for access to a nuclear reactor, this treatment is available only in limited locations.

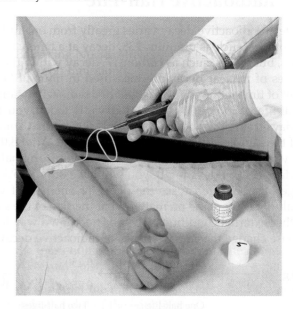

▲ A person's blood volume can be found by injecting a small amount of radioactive chromium-51 and measuring the dilution factor.

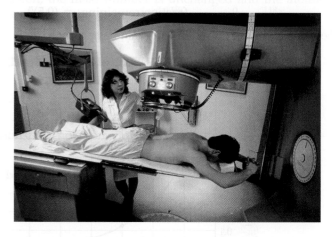

▲ T/B/W when new photo chosen.

See Additional Problems 11.70 and 11.71 at the end of the chapter.

The half-lives of some useful radioisotopes are given in Table 11.3. As you might expect, radioisotopes that are used internally for medical applications have fairly short half-lives so that they decay rapidly and do not remain in the body for prolonged periods.

TABLE 11.3 Half-Lives of Some Useful Radioisotopes

RADIOISOTOPE	SYMBOL	RADIATION	HALF-LIFE	USE
Tritium	$^{3}_{1}H$	β	12.33 years	Biochemical tracer
Carbon-14	$^{14}_{6}C$	β	5730 years	Archaeological dating
Sodium-24	$^{24}_{11}Na$	β	14.959 hours	Examining circulation
Phosphorus-32	$^{32}_{15}P$	β	14.262 days	Leukemia therapy
Potassium-40	$^{40}_{19}K$	β, β^{+}	1.277×10^{9} years	Geological dating
Cobalt-60	$^{60}_{27}Co$	β, γ	5.271 years	Cancer therapy
Arsenic-74	$^{74}_{33}As$	β^{+}	17.77 days	Locating brain tumors
Technetium-99m*	$^{99m}_{43}Tc$	γ	6.01 hours	Brain scans
Iodine-131	$^{131}_{53}I$	β	8.021 days	Thyroid therapy
Uranium-235	$^{235}_{92}U$	α, γ	7.038×10^{8} years	Nuclear reactors

*The m in technetium-99m stands for metastable, meaning that the nucleus undergoes γ emission but does not change its mass number or atomic number.

WORKED EXAMPLE **11.4** Nuclear Reactions: Half-Life

Phosphorus-32, a radioisotope used in leukemia therapy, has a half-life of about 14 days. Approximately what percent of a sample remains after 8 weeks?

ANALYSIS Determine how many half-lives have elapsed. For an integral number of half-lives, we can multiply the starting amount (100%) by 1/2 for each half-life that has elapsed.

SOLUTION
Since one half-life of $^{32}_{15}P$ is 14 days (2 weeks), 8 weeks represents four half-lives. The fraction that remains after 8 weeks is thus

Four half-lives

$$\text{Final Percentage} = 100\% \times (0.5)^4 = 100\% \times \left(\tfrac{1}{2} \times \tfrac{1}{2} \times \tfrac{1}{2} \times \tfrac{1}{2}\right)$$
$$= 100\% \times \tfrac{1}{16} = 6.25\%$$

WORKED EXAMPLE **11.5** Nuclear Reactions: Half-Life

As noted on page 341 and in Table 11.3, iodine-131 has a half-life of about 8 days. Approximately what fraction of a sample remains after 20 days?

ANALYSIS Determine how many half-lives have elapsed. For a non-integral number (i.e., fraction) of half-lives, use the equation below to determine the fraction of radioisotope remaining.

$$\text{fraction remaining} = (0.5)^n$$

BALLPARK ESTIMATE Since the half-life of iodine-131 is 8 days, an elapsed time of 20 days is 2.5 half-lives. The fraction remaining should be between 0.25 (fraction remaining after two half-lives) and 0.125 (fraction remaining after three half-lives). Since the relationship between the number of half-lives and fraction

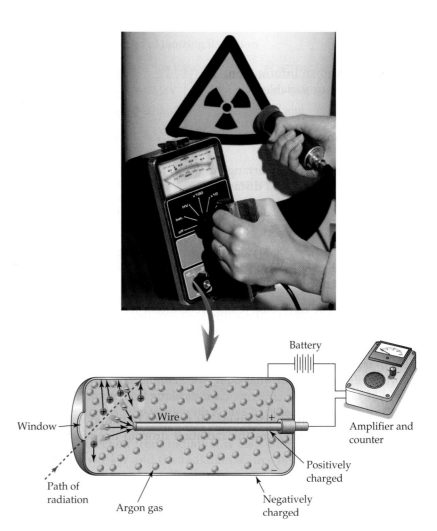

► **FIGURE 11.6 A Geiger counter for measuring radiation.** As radiation enters the tube through a thin window, it ionizes argon atoms and produces electrons that conduct a tiny electric current between the walls and the center electrode. The current flow then registers on the meter.

11.9 Measuring Radiation

Radiation intensity is expressed in different ways, depending on what characteristic of the radiation is measured (Table 11.5). Some units measure the number of nuclear decay events, while others measure exposure to radiation or the biological consequences of radiation.

TABLE 11.5 Common Units for Measuring Radiation

UNIT	QUANTITY MEASURED	DESCRIPTION
Curie (Ci)	Decay events	Amount of radiation equal to 3.7×10^{10} disintegrations per second
Roentgen (R)	Ionizing intensity	Amount of radiation producing 2.1×10^9 charges per cubic centimeter of dry air
Rad	Energy absorbed per gram of tissue	1 rad = 1 R
Rem	Tissue damage	Amount of radiation producing the same damage as 1 R of X rays
Sievert (Sv)	Tissue damage	1 Sv = 100 rem

The *curie* (Ci), the *millicurie* (mCi), and the *microcurie* (μCi) measure the number of radioactive disintegrations occurring each second in a sample. One curie is the decay rate of 1 g of radium, equal to 3.7×10^{10} disintegrations per second; 1 mCi = 0.001 Ci = 3.7×10^7 disintegrations per second; and 1 μCi = 0.000 001 Ci = 3.7×10^4 disintegrations per second.

APPLICATION ▶ Irradiated Food

The idea of irradiating food to kill harmful bacteria is not new; it goes back almost as far as the earliest studies on radiation. Not until the 1940s did serious work get under way, however, when U.S. Army scientists found that irradiation increased the shelf-life of ground beef. Nevertheless, widespread civilian use of the technique has been a long time in coming, spurred on in recent years by outbreaks of food poisoning that resulted in several deaths.

The principle of food irradiation is simple: Exposure of contaminated food to ionizing radiation—usually γ rays produced by cobalt-60 or cesium-137—destroys the genetic material of any bacteria or other organisms present, thereby killing them. Irradiation will not, however, kill viruses or prions (⚬═⚬, p. 584), the cause of mad-cow disease. The food itself undergoes little if any change when irradiated and does not itself become radioactive. The only real argument against food irradiation, in fact, is that it is *too* effective. Knowing that irradiation will kill nearly all harmful organisms, a food processor might be tempted to cut back on normal sanitary practices!

Food irradiation has been implemented to a much greater extent in Europe than in the United States. The largest marketers of irradiated food are Belgium, France, and the Netherlands, which irradiate between 10,000 and 20,000 tons of food per year. One of the major concerns in the United States is the possible generation of *radiolytic products*, compounds formed in food by exposure to ionizing radiation. The U.S. Food and Drug Administration, after studying the matter extensively, has declared that food irradiation is safe and that it does not appreciably alter the vitamin or other nutritional content of food. Spices, fruits, pork, and vegetables were

approved for irradiation in 1986, followed by poultry in 1990 and red meat, particularly ground beef, in 1997. In 2000, approval was extended to whole eggs and sprouting seeds. Should the food industry adopt irradiation of meat as its standard practice, such occurrences as the 1993 Seattle outbreak of *E. coli* poisoning caused by undercooked hamburgers will become a thing of the past.

▲ Irradiating food kills bacteria and extends shelf-life. The strawberries in these two containers were picked at the same time, but only the batch on the right was irradiated.

See Additional Problems 11.72 and 11.73 at the end of the chapter.

The dosage of a radioactive substance administered orally or intravenously is usually given in millicuries. To calculate the size of a dose, it is necessary to determine the decay rate of the isotope solution per milliliter. Because the emitter concentration is constantly decreasing as it decays, the activity must be measured immediately before administration. Suppose, for example, that a solution containing iodine-131 for a thyroid function study is found to have a decay rate of 0.020 mCi/mL and the dose administered is to be 0.050 mCi. The amount of the solution administered must be

$$\frac{0.05 \ \cancel{mCi}}{\text{Dose}} \times \frac{1 \ \text{mL} \ ^{131}\text{I solution}}{0.020 \ \cancel{mCi}} = 2.5 \ \text{mL} \ ^{131}\text{I solution/dose}$$

- **Roentgen** The *roentgen* (R) is a unit for measuring the ionizing intensity of γ or X radiation. In other words, the roentgen measures the capacity of the radiation for affecting matter. One roentgen is the amount of radiation that produces 2.1×10^9 units of charge in 1 cm^3 of dry air at atmospheric pressure. Each collision of ionizing radiation with an atom produces one ion, or one unit of charge.

- **Rad** The *rad* (radiation absorbed dose) is a unit for measuring the energy absorbed per gram of material exposed to a radiation source and is defined as the absorption of 1×10^{-5} J of energy per gram. The energy absorbed varies with the type of material irradiated and the type of radiation. For most purposes, though, the roentgen and the rad are so close that they can be considered identical when used for X rays and γ rays: 1 R = 1 rad.

- **Rem** The *rem* (roentgen equivalent for man) measures the amount of tissue damage caused by radiation, taking into account the differences in energy of different types of radiation. One rem is the amount of radiation that produces the same effect as 1 R of X rays.

  Rems are the preferred units for medical purposes because they measure equivalent doses of different kinds of radiation. For example, 1 rad of α radiation causes 20 times more tissue damage than 1 rad of γ rays, but 1 rem of α radiation and 1 rem of γ rays cause the same amount of damage. Thus, the rem takes both ionizing intensity and biological effect into account, whereas the rad deals only with intensity.

- **SI Units** In the SI system, the *becquerel* (Bq) is defined as one disintegration per second. The SI unit for energy absorbed is the *gray* (Gy; 1 Gy = 100 rad). For radiation dose, the SI unit is the *sievert* (Sv), which is equal to 100 rem.

The biological consequences of different radiation doses are given in Table 11.6. Although the effects seem fearful, the average radiation dose received annually by most people is only about 0.27 rem. About 80% of this *background radiation* comes from natural sources (rocks and cosmic rays); the remaining 20% comes from medical procedures such as X rays and from consumer products. The amount due to emissions from nuclear power plants and to fallout from testing of nuclear weapons in the 1950s is barely detectable.

TABLE 11.6 Biological Effects of Short-Term Radiation on Humans

DOSE (REM)	BIOLOGICAL EFFECTS
0–25	No detectable effects
25–100	Temporary decrease in white blood cell count
100–200	Nausea, vomiting, longer-term decrease in white blood cells
200–300	Vomiting, diarrhea, loss of appetite, listlessness
300–600	Vomiting, diarrhea, hemorrhaging, eventual death in some cases
Above 600	Eventual death in nearly all cases

▲ After the 1986 nuclear-reactor disaster at Chernobyl, security police in Ukraine limited access to the area within 30 km of the site. *(©Shirley Clive/Greenpeace International)*

PROBLEM 11.11

Radiation released during the 1986 Chernobyl nuclear power plant disaster is expected to increase the background radiation level worldwide by about 5 mrem. By how much will this increase the annual dose of the average person. Express your answer as a percentage.

PROBLEM 11.12

A solution of selenium-75, a radioisotope used in the diagnosis of pancreatic disease, is found just prior to administration to have an activity of 44 μCi/mL. How many milliliters should be administered intravenously for a dose of 175 μCi?

11.10 Artificial Transmutation

Artificial transmutation The change of one atom into another brought about by a nuclear bombardment reaction.

Very few of the approximately 3300 known radioisotopes occur naturally. Most are made from stable isotopes by **artificial transmutation**, the change of one atom into another brought about by nuclear bombardment reactions.

When an atom is bombarded with a high-energy particle, such as a proton, neutron, α particle, or even the nucleus of another element, an unstable nucleus is created in the collision. A nuclear change then occurs, and a different element is produced. For example, transmutation of ^{14}N to ^{14}C occurs in the upper atmosphere when neutrons produced by cosmic rays collide with atmospheric nitrogen. In the collision, a neutron dislodges a proton (^{1}H) from the nitrogen nucleus as the neutron and nucleus fuse together:

$$^{14}_{7}N + {}^{1}_{0}n \longrightarrow {}^{14}_{6}C + {}^{1}_{1}H$$

Artificial transmutation can lead to the synthesis of entirely new elements never before seen on earth. In fact, all the *transuranium elements*—those elements with atomic numbers greater than 92—have been produced by bombardment reactions. For example, plutonium-241 (^{241}Pu) can be made by bombardment of uranium-238 with α particles:

$$^{238}_{92}U + {}^{4}_{2}He \longrightarrow {}^{241}_{94}Pu + {}^{1}_{0}n$$

Plutonium-241 is itself radioactive, with a half-life of 14.35 years, decaying by β emission to yield americium-241, which in turn decays by α emission with a half-life of 432.2 years. (If the name *americium* sounds vaguely familiar, it is because this radioisotope is used in smoke detectors.)

$$^{241}_{94}Pu \longrightarrow {}^{241}_{95}Am + {}^{0}_{-1}e$$

Note that all the equations just given for artificial transmutations are balanced. The sum of the mass numbers and the sum of the charges are the same on both sides of each equation.

▲ Smoke detectors contain a small amount of americium-241. The α particles emitted by this radioisotope ionize the air within the detector, causing it to conduct a tiny electric current. When smoke enters the chamber, conductivity drops and an alarm is triggered.

WORKED EXAMPLE **11.7** Balancing Nuclear Reactions: Transmutation

Californium-246 is formed by bombardment of uranium-238 atoms. If four neutrons are also formed, what particle is used for the bombardment?

ANALYSIS First write an incomplete nuclear equation incorporating the known information:

$$^{238}_{92}U + ? \longrightarrow {}^{246}_{98}Cf + 4\,{}^{1}_{0}n$$

Then find the numbers of nucleons and charges necessary to balance the equation. In this instance, there are 238 nucleons on the left and $246 + 4 = 250$ nucleons on the right, so the bombarding particle must have $250 - 238 = 12$ nucleons. Furthermore, there are 92 nuclear charges on the left and 98 on the right, so the bombarding particle must have $98 - 92 = 6$ protons.

SOLUTION
The missing particle is $^{12}_{6}C$.

$$^{238}_{92}U + {}^{12}_{6}C \longrightarrow {}^{246}_{98}Cf + 4\,{}^{1}_{0}n$$

PROBLEM 11.13

What isotope results from α decay of the americium-241 in smoke detectors?

PROBLEM 11.14

The element berkelium, first prepared at the University of California at Berkeley in 1949, is made by α bombardment of $^{241}_{95}Am$. Two neutrons are also produced during the reaction. What isotope of berkelium results from this transmutation? Write a balanced nuclear equation.

APPLICATION ▶ Body Imaging

We are all familiar with the appearance of a standard X-ray image, produced when X rays pass through the body and the intensity of the radiation that exits is recorded on film. X-ray imaging is, however, only one of a host of noninvasive imaging techniques that are now in common use.

Among the most widely used imaging techniques are those that give diagnostic information about the health of various parts of the body by analyzing the distribution pattern of a radioactively tagged substance in the body. A radiopharmaceutical agent that is known to concentrate in a specific organ or other body part is injected into the body, and its distribution pattern is monitored by an external radiation detector such as a γ-ray camera. Depending on the medical condition, a diseased part might concentrate more of the radiopharmaceutical than normal and thus show up on the film as a radioactive hot spot against a cold background. Alternatively, the diseased part might concentrate less of the radiopharmaceutical than normal and thus show up as a cold spot on a hot background.

Among the radioisotopes most widely used for diagnostic imaging is technetium-99m, whose short half-life of only six hours minimizes the patient's exposure to radioactivity. Bone scans using this nuclide, such as that shown in the accompanying photograph, are an important tool in the diagnosis of cancer and other conditions.

Several other techniques now used in medical diagnosis are made possible by *tomography*, a technique in which computer processing allows production of images through "slices" of the body. In X-ray tomography, commonly known as *CAT* or *CT* scanning (computerized tomography), the X-ray source and an array of detectors move rapidly in a circle around a patient's body, collecting up to 90,000 readings. CT scans can detect structural abnormalities such as tumors without the use of radioactive materials.

Combining tomography with radioisotope imaging gives cross-sectional views of regions that concentrate a radioactive substance. One such technique, *positron emission tomography* (PET), utilizes radioisotopes that emit positrons and ultimately yield γ rays. Oxygen-15, nitrogen-13, carbon-11, and

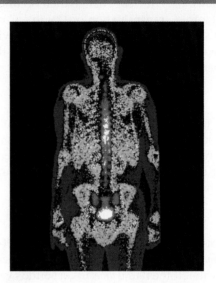

▲ A bone scan carried out with radioactive technetium-99m. Color has been added to help the visualization.

fluorine-18 are commonly used for PET because they can be readily incorporated into many physiologically active compounds. An ^{18}F-labeled glucose derivative, for instance, is useful for imaging brain regions that respond to various stimuli. The disadvantage of PET scans is that the necessary radioisotopes are so short-lived that they must be produced on-site immediately before use. The cost of PET is therefore high, because a hospital must install and maintain the necessary nuclear facility.

Magnetic resonance imaging (MRI) is a medical imaging technique that uses powerful magnetic and radio-frequency fields to interact with specific nuclei in the body (usually the nuclei of hydrogen atoms) to generate images in which the contrast between soft tissues is much better than that seen with CT. The original name for this technique was *nuclear* magnetic resonance imaging, but the *nuclear* was eliminated because in the public mind this word conjured up negative images of ionizing radiation. Ironically, MRI does not involve any nuclear radiation at all.

See Additional Problems 11.74 and 11.75 at the end of the chapter.

PROBLEM 11.15

Write a balanced nuclear equation for the reaction of argon-40 with a proton:

$$^{40}_{18}\text{Ar} + ^{1}_{1}\text{H} \longrightarrow ? + ^{1}_{0}\text{n}$$

11.11 Nuclear Fission and Nuclear Fusion

In the preceding section, we saw that particle bombardment of various elements causes artificial transmutation and results in the formation of new, usually heavier elements. Under very special conditions with a very few isotopes, however, different kinds of nuclear events occur. Certain very heavy nuclei can split apart, and certain very light nuclei can fuse together. The two resultant processes—**nuclear fission** for the fragmenting of heavy nuclei and **nuclear fusion** for the joining together of light nuclei—have changed the world since their discovery in the late 1930s and early 1940s.

The huge amounts of energy that accompany these nuclear processes are the result of mass-to-energy conversions and are predicted by Einstein's equation

$$E = mc^2$$

where E = energy, m = mass change associated with the nuclear reaction, and c = the speed of light (3.0×10^8 m/s). Based on this relationship, a mass change as small as 1 µg results in a release of 2.15×10^4 kcal of energy!

Nuclear Fission

Uranium-235 is the only naturally occurring isotope that undergoes nuclear fission. When this isotope is bombarded by a stream of relatively slow-moving neutrons, its nucleus splits to give isotopes of other elements. The split can take place in more than 400 ways, and more than 800 different fission products have been identified. One of the more frequently occurring pathways generates barium-142 and krypton-91, along with two additional neutrons plus the one neutron that initiated the fission:

$$^1_0\text{n} + ^{235}_{92}\text{U} \longrightarrow ^{142}_{56}\text{Ba} + ^{91}_{36}\text{Kr} + 3\,^1_0\text{n}$$

As indicated by the balanced nuclear equation above, *one* neutron is used to initiate fission of a ^{235}U nucleus, but *three* neutrons are released. Thus, a nuclear **chain reaction** can be started: 1 neutron initiates one fission that releases 3 neutrons. The 3 neutrons initiate three new fissions that release 9 neutrons. The 9 neutrons initiate nine fissions that release 27 neutrons, and so on at an ever faster pace (Figure 11.7). It is worth noting that the neutrons produced by fission reactions are highly energetic. They possess penetrating power greater than α and β particles, but less than γ rays. In a nuclear fission reactor, the neutrons must first be slowed down to allow them to react. If the sample size is small, many of the neutrons escape before initiating additional fission events, and the chain reaction stops. If a sufficient amount of ^{235}U is present, however—an amount called the **critical mass**—then the chain reaction becomes self-sustaining. Under high-pressure conditions that confine the ^{235}U to a small volume, the chain reaction occurs so rapidly that a nuclear explosion results. For ^{235}U, the critical mass is about 56 kg, although the amount can be reduced to approximately 15 kg by placing a coating of ^{238}U around the ^{235}U to reflect back some of the escaping neutrons.

An enormous quantity of heat is released during nuclear fission—the fission of just 1.0 g of uranium-235 produces 3.4×10^8 kcal, for instance. This heat can be used to convert water to steam, which can be harnessed to turn huge generators and produce electric power. The use of nuclear power is much more advanced in some countries than in others, with Lithuania and France leading the way by generating about 86% and 77%, respectively, of their electricity in nuclear plants. In the United States, only about 22% of the electricity is nuclear-generated.

Two major objections that have caused much public debate about nuclear power plants are safety and waste disposal. Although a nuclear explosion is not possible under the conditions that exist in a power plant, there is a serious potential radiation hazard should an accident rupture the containment vessel holding the nuclear fuel and release radioactive substances to the environment. Perhaps even more important is the problem posed by disposal of radioactive wastes from nuclear plants. Many of these wastes have such long half-lives that hundreds or even thousands of years must elapse before they will be safe for humans to approach. How to dispose of such hazardous materials safely is an unsolved problem.

Nuclear fission The fragmenting of heavy nuclei.

Nuclear fusion The joining together of light nuclei.

Chain reaction A reaction that, once started, is self-sustaining.

Critical mass The minimum amount of radioactive material needed to sustain a nuclear chain reaction.

▲ Energy from the fission of uranium-235 is used to produce steam and generate electricity in this nuclear power plant.

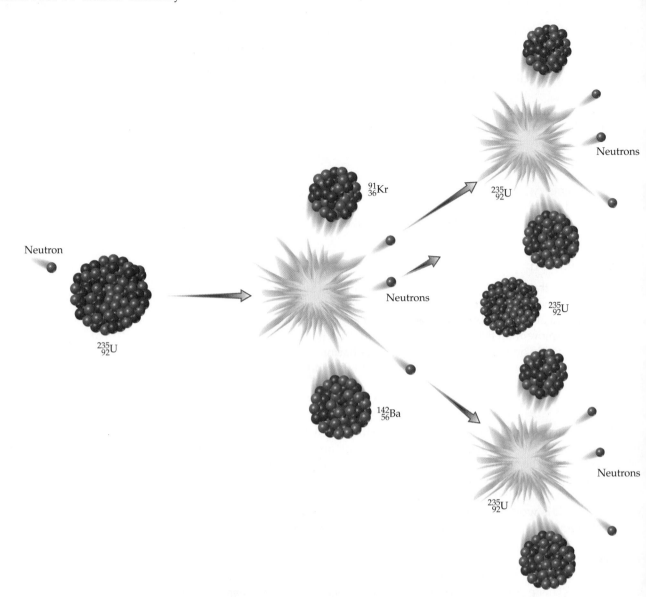

▲ **FIGURE 11.7 A chain reaction.** Each fission event produces additional neutrons that induce more fissions. The rate of the process increases at each stage. Such chain reactions usually lead to the formation of many different fission products in addition to the two indicated.

PROBLEM 11.16

What other isotope besides tellurium-137 is produced by nuclear fission of uranium-235?

$$^{235}_{92}\text{U} + {}^{1}_{0}\text{n} \longrightarrow {}^{137}_{52}\text{Te} + 2\,{}^{1}_{0}\text{n} + ?$$

Nuclear Fusion

Just as heavy nuclei such as ^{235}U release energy when they undergo *fission*, very light nuclei such as the isotopes of hydrogen release enormous amounts of energy when they undergo *fusion*. In fact, it is just such a fusion reaction of hydrogen nuclei to produce helium that powers our sun and other stars. Among the processes thought to occur in the sun are those in the following sequence leading to helium-4:

$$^{1}_{1}\text{H} + {}^{2}_{1}\text{H} \longrightarrow {}^{3}_{2}\text{He}$$

$$^{3}_{2}\text{He} + {}^{3}_{2}\text{He} \longrightarrow {}^{4}_{2}\text{He} + 2\,{}^{1}_{1}\text{H}$$

$$^{3}_{2}\text{He} + {}^{1}_{1}\text{H} \longrightarrow {}^{4}_{2}\text{He} + {}^{0}_{1}\text{e}$$

APPLICATION ▶ Archaeological Radiocarbon Dating

Biblical scrolls are found in a cave near the Dead Sea. Are they authentic? A mummy is discovered in an Egyptian tomb. How old is it? The burned bones of a man are dug up near Lubbock, Texas. How long ago did humans live on the North American continent? Using a technique called *radiocarbon dating*, archaeologists can answer these and many other questions. (The Dead Sea Scrolls are 1900 years old and authentic, the mummy is 3100 years old, and the human remains found in Texas are 9900 years old.)

Radiocarbon dating depends on the slow and constant production of radioactive carbon-14 atoms in the upper atmosphere by bombardment of nitrogen atoms with neutrons from cosmic rays. Carbon-14 atoms combine with oxygen to yield $^{14}CO_2$, which slowly mixes with ordinary $^{12}CO_2$ and is then taken up by plants during photosynthesis. When these plants are eaten by animals, carbon-14 enters the food chain and is distributed evenly throughout all living organisms.

As long as a plant or animal is living, a dynamic equilibrium is established in which the organism excretes or exhales the same amount of ^{14}C that it takes in. As a result, the ratio of ^{14}C to ^{12}C in the living organism is the same as that in the atmosphere—about 1 part in 10^{12}. When the plant or animal dies, however, it no longer takes in more ^{14}C. Thus, the $^{14}C/^{12}C$ ratio in the organism slowly decreases as ^{14}C undergoes radioactive decay. At 5730 years (one ^{14}C half-life) after the death of the organism, the $^{14}C/^{12}C$ ratio has decreased by a factor of 2; at 11,460 years after death, the $^{14}C/^{12}C$ ratio has decreased by a factor of 4; and so on.

By measuring the amount of ^{14}C remaining in the traces of any once-living organism, archaeologists can determine how long ago the organism died. Human hair from well-preserved remains, charcoal or wood fragments from once-living trees, and cotton or linen from once-living plants are all useful sources for radiocarbon dating. The accuracy of the technique lessens as a sample gets older and the amount of ^{14}C it contains diminishes, but artifacts with an age of 1000–20,000 years can be dated with reasonable accuracy.

▲ Radiocarbon dating has determined that these charcoal paintings in the Lascaux cave in France are approximately 15,000 years old.

See Additional Problems 11.76 and 11.77 at the end of the chapter.

Under the conditions found in stars, where the temperature is on the order of 2×10^7 K and pressures approach 10^5 atmospheres, nuclei are stripped of all their electrons and have enough kinetic energy that nuclear fusion readily occurs. The energy of our sun, and all the stars, comes from thermonuclear fusion reactions in their core that fuse hydrogen and other light elements transmuting them into heavier elements. On earth, however, the necessary conditions for nuclear fusion are not easily created. For more than 50 years scientists have been trying to create the necessary conditions for fusion in laboratory reactors, including the Tokamak Fusion Test Reactor (TFTR) at Princeton, New Jersey, and the Joint European Torus (JET) at Culham, England. Recent advances in reactor design have raised hopes that a commercial fusion reactor will be realized within the next 20 years.

If the dream becomes reality, controlled nuclear fusion can provide the ultimate cheap, clean power source. The fuel is deuterium (^2H), available in the oceans in limitless amounts, and there are few radioactive by-products.

▲ A researcher stands inside the D3D Tokamak nuclear fusion reactor at the General Atomics facility in San Diego, California.

SUMMARY: REVISITING THE CHAPTER GOALS

1. What is a nuclear reaction, and how are equations for nuclear reactions balanced? A *nuclear reaction* is one that changes an atomic nucleus, causing the change of one element into another. Loss of an α particle leads to a new atom whose atomic number is 2 less than

KEY WORDS

Alpha (α) particle, *p. 335*

Artificial transmutation, *p. 350*

that of the starting atom. Loss of a β particle leads to an atom whose atomic number is 1 greater than that of the starting atom:

$$\alpha \text{ emission: } {}^{238}_{92}\text{U} \longrightarrow {}^{234}_{90}\text{Th} + {}^{4}_{2}\text{He}$$

$$\beta \text{ emission: } {}^{131}_{53}\text{I} \longrightarrow {}^{131}_{54}\text{Xe} + {}^{0}_{-1}\text{e}$$

A nuclear reaction is balanced when the sum of the *nucleons* (protons and neutrons) is the same on both sides of the reaction arrow and when the sum of the charges on the nuclei plus any ejected subatomic particles is the same.

2. **What are the different kinds of radioactivity?** *Radioactivity* is the spontaneous emission of radiation from the nucleus of an unstable atom. The three major kinds of radiation are called *alpha* (α), *beta* (β), and gamma (γ). Alpha radiation consists of helium nuclei, small particles containing two protons and two neutrons (${}^{4}_{2}\text{He}$); β radiation consists of electrons (${}^{0}_{-1}\text{e}$); and γ radiation consists of high-energy light waves. Every element in the periodic table has at least one radioactive isotope, or *radioisotope*.

3. **How are the rates of nuclear reactions expressed?** The rate of a nuclear reaction is expressed in units of *half-life* ($t_{1/2}$), where one half-life is the amount of time necessary for one half of the radioactive sample to decay.

4. **What is ionizing radiation?** High-energy radiation of all types—α particles, β particles, γ rays, and X rays—is called *ionizing radiation*. When any of these kinds of radiation strikes an atom, it dislodges an electron and gives a reactive ion that can be lethal to living cells. Gamma rays and X rays are the most penetrating and most harmful types of external radiation; α and β particles are the most dangerous types of internal radiation because of their high energy and the resulting damage to surrounding tissue.

5. **How is radioactivity measured?** Radiation intensity is expressed in different ways according to the property being measured. The *curie* (Ci) measures the number of radioactive disintegrations per second in a sample; the *roentgen* (R) measures the ionizing ability of radiation; the *rad* measures the amount of radiation energy absorbed per gram of tissue; and the *rem* measures the amount of tissue damage caused by radiation. Radiation effects become noticeable with a human exposure of 25 rem and become lethal at an exposure above 600 rem.

6. **What is transmutation?** *Transmutation* is the change of one element into another brought about by a nuclear reaction. Most known radioisotopes do not occur naturally but are made by bombardment of an atom with a high-energy particle. In the ensuing collision between particle and atom, a nuclear change occurs and a new element is produced by *artificial transmutation*.

7. **What are nuclear fission and nuclear fusion?** With a very few isotopes, including ${}^{235}_{92}\text{U}$, the nucleus is split apart by neutron bombardment to give smaller fragments. A large amount of energy is released during this *nuclear fission*, leading to use of the reaction for generating electric power. *Nuclear fusion* results when small nuclei such as those of tritium (${}^{3}_{1}\text{H}$) and deuterium (${}^{2}_{1}\text{H}$) combine to give a heavier nucleus.

UNDERSTANDING KEY CONCEPTS

11.17 Magnesium-28 decays by β emission to give aluminum-28. If yellow spheres represent ${}^{28}_{12}\text{Mg}$ atoms and blue spheres represent ${}^{28}_{13}\text{Al}$ atoms, how many half-lives have passed in the following sample?

11.18 Write a balanced nuclear equation to represent the decay reaction described in Problem 11.17.

11.19 Refer to Figure 11.4 and then make a drawing similar to those in Problem 11.17 representing the decay of a sample of ${}^{28}_{12}\text{Mg}$ after approximately four half-lives have passed.

11.20 Write the symbol of the isotope represented by the following drawing. Blue spheres represent neutrons and red spheres represent protons.

11.21 Shown below is a portion of the decay series for plutonium-241 (${}^{241}_{94}\text{Pu}$). The series has two kinds of arrows: shorter arrows pointing right and longer arrows pointing left. Which arrow corresponds to an α emission, and which to a β emission? Explain.

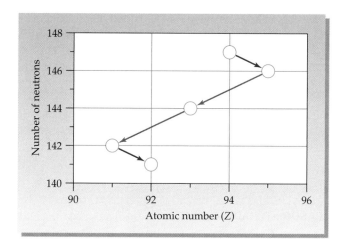

11.22 Identify and write the symbol for each nuclide in the decay series shown in Problem 11.21.

11.23 Identify the isotopes involved, and tell the type of decay process occurring in the following nuclear reaction:

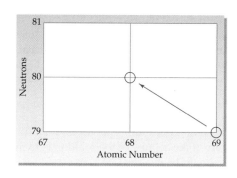

11.24 What is the half-life of the radionuclide that shows the following decay curve?

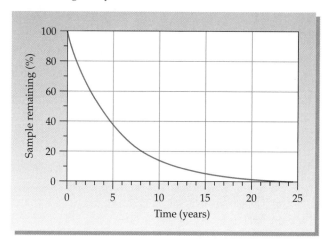

11.25 What is wrong with the following decay curve? Explain.

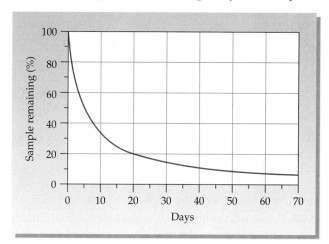

ADDITIONAL PROBLEMS

RADIOACTIVITY

11.26 What does it mean to say that a substance is radioactive?

11.27 Describe how α radiation, β radiation, γ radiation, positron emission, and electron capture differ.

11.28 List several ways in which a nuclear reaction differs from a chemical reaction.

11.29 What word is used to describe the change of one element into another?

11.30 What symbol is used for an α particle in a nuclear equation?

11.31 What symbol is used for a β particle in a nuclear equation? For a positron?

11.32 Which kind of radiation, α, β, or γ, has the highest penetrating power, and which has the lowest?

11.33 What happens when ionizing radiation strikes an atom in a chemical compound?

11.34 How does ionizing radiation lead to cell damage?

11.35 What are the main sources of background radiation?

11.36 How can a nucleus emit an electron during β decay when there are no electrons present in the nucleus to begin with?

11.37 What is the difference between an α particle and a helium atom?

NUCLEAR DECAY AND TRANSMUTATION

11.38 What does it mean to say that a nuclear equation is balanced?

11.39 What are transuranium elements, and how are they made?

11.40 What happens to the mass number and atomic number of an atom that emits an α particle? A β particle?

11.41 What happens to the mass number and atomic number of an atom that emits a γ ray? A positron?

11.42 How does nuclear fission differ from normal radioactive decay?

11.43 What characteristic of uranium-235 fission causes a chain reaction?

11.44 What products result from radioactive decay of the following β emitters?

(a) $^{35}_{16}S$ (b) $^{24}_{10}Ne$ (c) $^{90}_{38}Sr$

11.45 What products result from radioactive decay of the following α emitters?

    (a) $^{190}_{78}\text{Pt}$ **(b)** $^{208}_{87}\text{Fr}$ **(c)** $^{245}_{96}\text{Cm}$

11.46 Identify the starting radioisotopes needed to balance each of these nuclear reactions:

    (a) $? + {}^{4}_{2}\text{He} \rightarrow {}^{113}_{49}\text{In}$

    (b) $? + {}^{4}_{2}\text{He} \rightarrow {}^{13}_{7}\text{N} + {}^{1}_{0}\text{n}$

11.47 Identify the product radioisotope needed to balance each of these nuclear reactions:

    (a) $^{140}_{55}\text{Cs} \rightarrow ? + {}^{0}_{-1}\text{e}$

    (b) $^{248}_{96}\text{Cm} \rightarrow ? + {}^{4}_{2}\text{He}$

11.48 Balance the following equations for the nuclear fission of $^{235}_{92}\text{U}$:

    (a) $^{235}_{92}\text{U} + {}^{1}_{0}\text{n} \rightarrow {}^{160}_{62}\text{Sm} + {}^{72}_{30}\text{Zn} + ? \ {}^{1}_{0}\text{n}$

    (b) $^{235}_{92}\text{U} + {}^{1}_{0}\text{n} \rightarrow {}^{87}_{35}\text{Br} + ? + 3 \ {}^{1}_{0}\text{n}$

11.49 Complete and balance the following nuclear equations:

    (a) $^{126}_{50}\text{Sn} \rightarrow {}^{0}_{-1}\text{e} + ?$

    (b) $^{210}_{88}\text{Ra} \rightarrow {}^{4}_{2}\text{He} + ?$

    (c) $^{76}_{36}\text{Kr} + {}^{0}_{-1}\text{e} \rightarrow ?$

11.50 For centuries, alchemists dreamed of turning base metals into gold. The dream finally became reality when it was shown that mercury-198 can be converted into gold-198 on bombardment by neutrons. What small particle is produced in addition to gold-198? Write a balanced nuclear equation for the reaction.

11.51 Cobalt-60 (half-life = 5.3 years) is used to irradiate food, to treat cancer, and to disinfect surgical equipment. It is produced by irradiation of cobalt-59 in a nuclear reactor. It decays to nickel-60. Write nuclear equations for the formation and decay reactions of cobalt-60.

11.52 Bismuth-212 attaches readily to monoclonal antibodies and is used in the treatment of various cancers. It is formed after the parent isotope undergoes a decay series consisting of four α decays and one β decay. What is the parent isotope for this decay series?

11.53 Meitnerium-266 ($^{266}_{109}\text{Mt}$) was prepared in 1982 by bombardment of bismuth-209 atoms with iron-58. What other product must also have been formed? Write a balanced nuclear equation for the transformation.

HALF-LIFE

11.54 What does it mean when we say that strontium-90, a waste product of nuclear power plants, has a half-life of 28.8 years?

11.55 What percentage of the original mass remains in a radioactive sample after two half-lives have passed? After three half-lives? After 3.5 half-lives?

11.56 Selenium-75, a β emitter with a half-life of 120 days, is used medically for pancreas scans. Approximately how much selenium-75 would remain from a 0.050 g sample that has been stored for one year?

11.57 Approximately how long would it take a sample of selenium-75 to lose 99% of its radioactivity? (See Problem 11.56.)

11.58 The half-life of mercury-197 is 64.1 hours. If a patient undergoing a kidney scan is given 5.0 ng of mercury-197, how much will remain after 7 days? After 30 days?

11.59 Gold-198, a β emitter used to treat leukemia, has a half-life of 2.695 days. The standard dosage is about 1.0 mCi/kg body weight.

    (a) What is the product of the β emission of gold-198?

    (b) How long does it take a 30.0 mCi sample of gold-198 to decay so that only 3.75 mCi remains?

    (c) How many millicuries are required in a single dosage administered to a 70.0 kg adult?

MEASURING RADIOACTIVITY

11.60 Describe how a Geiger counter works.

11.61 Describe how a film badge works.

11.62 Describe how a scintillation counter works.

11.63 Why are rems the preferred units for measuring the health effects of radiation?

11.64 Approximately what amount (in rems) of short-term exposure to radiation produces noticeable effects in humans?

11.65 Match each unit in the left column with the property being measured in the right column:

    1. curie   **(a)** Ionizing intensity of radiation
    2. rem   **(b)** Amount of tissue damage
    3. rad   **(c)** Number of disintegrations per second
    4. roentgen   **(d)** Amount of radiation per gram of tissue

11.66 Technetium-99*m* is used for radioisotope-guided surgical biopsies of certain bone cancers. A patient must receive an injection of 28 mCi of technetium-99*m* 6–12 hours before surgery. If the activity of the solution is 15 mCi, what volume should be injected?

11.67 Sodium-24 is used to study the circulatory system and to treat chronic leukemia. It is administered in the form of saline (NaCl) solution, with a therapeutic dosage of 180 μCi/kg body weight. How many milliliters of a 6.5 mCi/mL solution are needed to treat a 68 kg adult?

11.68 A selenium-75 source is producing 300 rem at a distance of 2.0 m. What is its intensity at 25 m?

11.69 If a radiation source has an intensity of 650 rem at 1.0 m, what distance is needed to decrease the intensity of exposure to below 25 rem, the level at which no effects are detectable?

Applications

11.70 What are the three main classes of techniques used in nuclear medicine? Give an example of each. [*Medical Uses of Radioactivity, p. 342*]

11.71 A 2 mL solution containing 1.25 μCi/mL is injected into the blood stream of a patient. After dilution, a 1.00 mL sample is withdrawn and found to have an activity of 2.6×10^{-4} μCi. Calculate total blood volume. [*Medical Uses of Radioactivity, p. 342*]

11.72 What is the purpose of food irradiation, and how does it work? [*Irradiated Food, p. 349*]

11.73 What kind of radiation is used to treat food? [*Irradiated Food, p. 349*]

11.74 What are the advantages of CT and PET relative to conventional X rays? [*Body Imaging, p. 352*]

11.75 What advantages does MRI have over CT and PET imaging? [*Body Imaging, p. 352*]

11.76 Why is ^{14}C dating useful only for samples that contain material from objects that were once alive? [*Archaeological Radiocarbon Dating, p. 355*]

11.77 Some dried beans with a ^{14}C/^{12}C ratio one-eighth of the current value are found in an old cave. How old are the beans? [*Archaeological Radiocarbon Dating, p. 355*]

General Questions and Problems

11.78 Harmful chemical spills can often be cleaned up by treatment with another chemical. For example, a spill of H_2SO_4 might be neutralized by addition of $NaHCO_3$. Why is it that the harmful radioactive wastes from nuclear power plants cannot be cleaned up just as easily?

11.79 Why is a scintillation counter or Geiger counter more useful for determining the existence and source of a new radiation leak than a film badge?

11.80 Technetium-99*m*, used for brain scans and to monitor heart function, is formed by decay of molybdenum-99.
   (a) By what type of decay does ^{99}Mo produce ^{99m}Tc?
   (b) Molybdenum-99 is formed by neutron bombardment of a natural isotope. If one neutron is absorbed and there are no other by-products of this process, from what isotope is ^{99}Mo formed?

11.81 The half-life of technetium-99*m* (Problem 11.80) is 6.01 hours. If a sample with an initial activity of 15 μCi is injected into a patient, what is the activity in 24 hours, assuming that none of the sample is excreted?

11.82 Plutonium-238 is an α emitter used to power batteries for heart pacemakers.
   (a) Write the balanced nuclear equation for this emission.
   (b) Why is a pacemaker battery enclosed in a metal case before being inserted into the chest cavity?

11.83 Sodium-24, a beta-emitter used in diagnosing circulation problems, has a half-life of 15 hours.
   (a) Write the balanced nuclear equation for this emission.
   (b) What fraction of sodium-24 remains after 50 hours?

11.84 High levels of radioactive fallout after the 1986 accident at the Chernobyl nuclear power plant in what is now Ukraine resulted in numerous miscarriages and many instances of farm animals born with severe defects. Why are embryos and fetuses particularly susceptible to the effects of radiation?

11.85 One way to demonstrate the dose factor of ionizing radiation (penetrating distance $\times$ ionizing energy) is to think of radiation as cookies. Imagine that you have four cookies—an α cookie, a β cookie, a γ cookie, and a neutron cookie. Which one would you eat, which would you hold in your hand, which would you put in your pocket, and which would you throw away?

11.86 What are the main advantages of fusion relative to fission as an energy source? What are the drawbacks?

11.87 Write a balanced nuclear equation for
   (a) α emission of ^{162}Re and
   (b) β emission of ^{188}W.

11.88 Balance the following transmutation reactions:
   (a) $^{253}_{99}\text{Es} + ? \rightarrow ^{256}_{101}\text{Md} + ^{1}_{0}\text{n}$
   (b) $^{250}_{98}\text{Cf} + ^{11}_{5}\text{B} \rightarrow ? + 4\,^{1}_{0}\text{n}$

11.89 The most abundant isotope of uranium, ^{238}U, does not undergo fission. In a *breeder reactor*, however, a ^{238}U atom captures a neutron and emits two beta particles to make a fissionable isotope of plutonium, which can then be used as fuel in a nuclear reactor. Write the balanced nuclear equation.

11.90 Boron is used in *control rods* for nuclear reactors because it can absorb neutrons and emit α particles. Balance the equation
$$^{10}_{5}\text{B} + ^{1}_{0}\text{n} \longrightarrow ? + ^{4}_{2}\text{He}$$

11.91 Thorium-232 decays by a ten-step series, ultimately yielding lead-208. How many α particles and how many β particles are emitted?

11.92 Californium-246 is formed by bombardment of uranium-238 atoms. If four neutrons are formed as by-products, what particle is used for the bombardment?

CHAPTER 12

Introduction to Organic Chemistry: Alkanes

CONCEPTS TO REVIEW

Covalent Bonds
(Sections 5.1 and 5.2)

Multiple Covalent Bonds
(Section 5.3)

Drawing Lewis Structures
(Section 5.6)

VSEPR and Molecular Shapes
(Section 5.7)

Polar Covalent Bonds
(Section 5.8)

▲ The gasoline, kerosene, and other products of this petroleum refinery are primarily mixtures of simple organic compounds called alkanes.

CONTENTS

CHAPTER GOALS

In this and the next five chapters, we will look at the chemistry of organic compounds, beginning with answers to the following questions:

1. **What are the basic properties of organic compounds?**
   THE GOAL: Be able to identify organic compounds and the types of bonds contained in them.

2. **What are functional groups, and how are they used to classify organic molecules?**
   THE GOAL: Be able to classify organic molecules into families by functional group.

3. **What are isomers?**
   THE GOAL: Be able to recognize and draw constitutional isomers.

4. **How are organic molecules drawn?**
   THE GOAL: Be able to convert between structural formulas and condensed or line structures.

5. **What are alkanes and cycloalkanes, and how are they named?**
   THE GOAL: Be able to name an alkane or cycloalkane from its structure, or write the structure, given the name.

6. **What are the general properties and chemical reactions of alkanes?**
   THE GOAL: Be able to describe the physical properties of alkanes and the products formed in the combustion and halogenation reactions of alkanes.

As knowledge of chemistry slowly grew in the 1700s, mysterious differences were noted between compounds obtained from living sources and those obtained from minerals. It was found, for instance, that chemicals from living sources were often liquids or low-melting solids, whereas chemicals from mineral sources were usually high-melting solids. Furthermore, chemicals from living sources were generally more difficult to purify and work with than those from minerals. To express these differences, the term *organic chemistry* was introduced to mean the study of compounds from living organisms, and *inorganic chemistry* was used to refer to the study of compounds from minerals.

Today we know that there are no fundamental differences between organic and inorganic compounds: The same scientific principles are applicable to both. The only common characteristic of compounds from living sources is that they contain the element carbon as their primary component. Thus, organic chemistry is now defined as the study of carbon-based compounds.

Why is carbon special? The answer derives from its position in the periodic table. As a group 4A nonmetal, carbon atoms have the unique ability to form four strong covalent bonds. Also, unlike atoms of other elements, carbon atoms can readily form strong bonds with other carbon atoms to produce long chains and rings. As a result, only carbon is able to form such an immense array of compounds, from methane with one carbon atom to DNA with billions of carbons.

12.1 The Nature of Organic Molecules

Let us begin a study of **organic chemistry**—the chemistry of carbon compounds—by reviewing what we have seen in earlier chapters about the structures of organic molecules:

- **Carbon is tetravalent; it always forms four bonds** (Section 5.2). In methane, for example, carbon is connected to four hydrogen atoms:

Organic chemistry The study of carbon compounds.

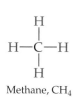

Methane, CH_4

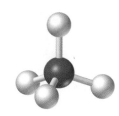

- **Organic molecules have covalent bonds** (Section 5.2). In ethane, for example, the bonds result from the sharing of two electrons, either between two C atoms or a C and a H atom:

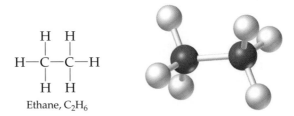

Ethane, C_2H_6

- **Organic molecules contain polar covalent bonds when carbon bonds to an electronegative element on the right side of the periodic table** (Section 5.8). In chloromethane, for example, the electronegative chlorine atom attracts electrons more strongly than carbon, resulting in polarization of the C—Cl bond so that carbon has a partial positive charge, $\delta+$, and chlorine has a partial negative charge, $\delta-$. In electrostatic potential maps (Section 5.8), the chlorine atom is therefore in the red region of the map and the carbon atom in the blue region:

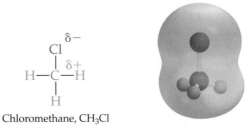

Chloromethane, CH_3Cl

- **Carbon forms multiple covalent bonds by sharing more than two electrons with a neighboring atom** (Section 5.3). In ethylene, for example, the two carbon atoms share four electrons in a double bond; in acetylene (also called ethyne), the two carbons share six electrons in a triple bond:

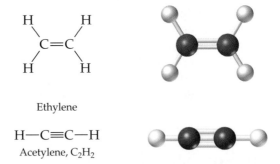

Ethylene

$$H—C≡C—H$$
Acetylene, C_2H_2

- **Organic molecules have specific three-dimensional shapes** (Section 5.7). When carbon is bonded to four atoms, as in methane, CH_4, the bonds are oriented toward the four corners of a regular tetrahedron with carbon in the center. Such three-dimensionality is commonly shown using normal lines for bonds in the plane of the page, dashed lines for bonds receding behind the page, and wedged lines for bonds coming out of the page:

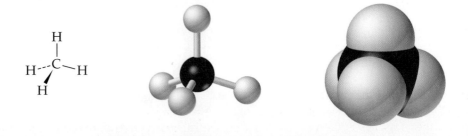

- **Organic molecules often contain hydrogen, nitrogen, and oxygen, in addition to carbon** (Section 5.6). Nitrogen can form single, double, and triple bonds to carbon; oxygen can form single and double bonds:

$$C-N \quad C-O \quad C-H$$
$$C=N \quad C=O$$
$$C\equiv N$$

Covalent bonding makes organic compounds quite different from the inorganic compounds we have been concentrating on up to this point. For example, inorganic compounds such as NaCl have high melting points and high boiling points because they consist of large numbers of oppositely charged ions held together by strong electrical attractions (Section 4.4). (, p. 84) Organic compounds, by contrast, consist of atoms joined by covalent bonds into individual molecules. Because the molecules are attracted to one another only by weak non-ionic intermolecular forces (Section 8.11), organic compounds generally have lower melting and boiling points than inorganic salts. (, p. 235) Because of their relatively low melting and boiling points, simple organic compounds are usually liquids at room temperature, and a few are gases.

Other important differences between organic and inorganic compounds include solubility and electrical conductivity. Whereas many inorganic compounds dissolve in water to yield solutions of ions that conduct electricity (Section 9.9), most organic compounds are insoluble in water, and almost all of those that are soluble do not conduct electricity. (, p. 275) Only small polar organic molecules, such as glucose and ethyl alcohol, or large molecules with many polar groups, such as some proteins, dissolve in water. This lack of water solubility for organic compounds has important practical consequences, varying from the difficulty in removing greasy dirt and cleaning up environmental oil spills to drug delivery.

◀ Oil spills can be a serious environmental problem because oil is insoluble in water.

Looking Ahead

The interior of a living cell is largely a water solution that contains many hundreds of different compounds. In later chapters, we will see how cells use membranes composed of water-insoluble organic molecules to enclose their watery interiors and to regulate the flow of substances across the cell boundary.

12.2 Families of Organic Molecules: Functional Groups

More than 18 *million* organic compounds are described in the scientific literature. Each of these 18 million compounds has unique physical properties, such as a melting point and a boiling point, each has unique chemical properties, and many of them have unique biological properties (both desired and undesired). How can we ever understand them all?

Chemists have learned through experience that organic compounds can be classified into families according to their structural features and that the chemical behavior of the members of a family is often predictable based on these specific grouping of atoms. Instead of 18 million compounds with seemingly random chemical reactivity, there are just a few general families of organic compounds whose chemistry falls into simple patterns.

Functional group An atom or group of atoms within a molecule that has a characteristic physical and chemical behavior.

The structural features that allow us to classify organic compounds into distinct chemical families are called **functional groups**. A functional group is an atom or group of atoms that has a characteristic physical and chemical behavior. Each functional group is always part of a larger molecule, and a molecule may have more than one class of functional group present, as we shall soon see. An important property of functional groups is that a given functional group *tends to undergo the same reactions in every molecule of which it is a part*. For example, the carbon–carbon double bond is a common functional group. Ethylene (C_2H_4), the simplest compound with a double bond, undergoes many chemical reactions similar to those of oleic acid ($C_{18}H_{34}O_2$), a much larger and more complex compound that also contains a double bond. Both, for example, react with hydrogen gas in the same manner, as shown in Figure 12.1. These identical reactions with hydrogen are typical: *The chemistry of an organic molecule is primarily determined by the functional groups it contains, not by its size and complexity.*

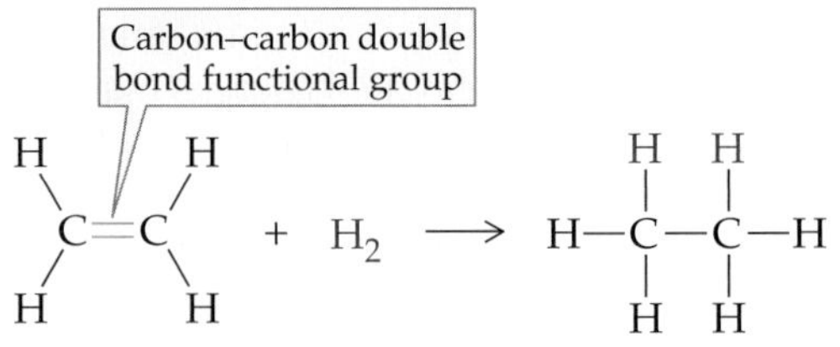

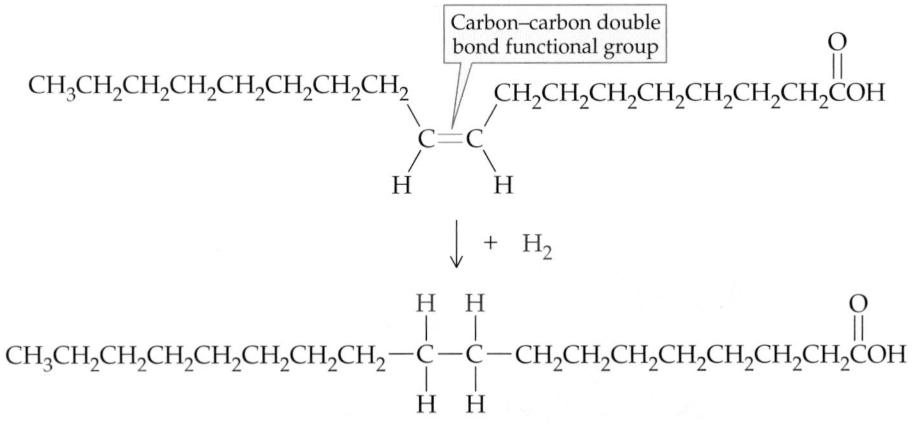

▶ FIGURE 12.1 The reactions of (a) ethylene and (b) oleic acid with hydrogen. The carbon–carbon double-bond functional group adds 2 hydrogen atoms in both cases, regardless of the complexity of the rest of the molecule.

Table 12.1 lists some of the most important families of organic molecules and their distinctive functional groups. Compounds that contain a $C=C$ double bond, for instance, are in the *alkene* family; compounds that have an $-OH$ group bound to a tetravalent carbon are in the *alcohol* family; and so on.

Much of the chemistry discussed in this and the next five chapters is the chemistry of the families listed in Table 12.1, so it is best to memorize the names and become familiar with their structures now. Note that they fall into three groups:

Hydrocarbon An organic compound that contains only carbon and hydrogen.

- The first four families in Table 12.1 are **hydrocarbons**, organic compounds that contain only carbon and hydrogen. *Alkanes* have only single bonds and contain no functional groups. As we will see, the absence of functional groups makes alkanes relatively unreactive. *Alkenes* contain a carbon–carbon double-bond functional group; *alkynes* contain a carbon–carbon triple-bond functional group; and *aromatic* compounds contain a six-membered ring of carbon atoms with three alternating double bonds.

- The next four families in Table 12.1 have functional groups that contain only single bonds and have a carbon atom bonded to an electronegative atom.

TABLE 12.1 Some Important Families of Organic Molecules

FAMILY NAME	FUNCTIONAL GROUP STRUCTURE*	SIMPLE EXAMPLE	NAME ENDING
Alkane	Contains only C—H and C—C single bonds	CH_3CH_3 Ethane	-ane
Alkene	C=C	H_2C=CH_2 Ethylene	-ene
Alkyne	—C≡C—	H—C≡C—H Acetylene (Ethyne)	-yne
Aromatic	C=C ring structure	Benzene	None
Alkyl halide	—C—X (X=F, Cl, Br, I)	CH_3—Cl Methyl chloride	None
Alcohol	—C—O—H	CH_3—OH Methyl alcohol (Methanol)	-ol
Ether	—C—O—C—	CH_3—O—CH_3 Dimethyl ether	None
Amine	—C—N	CH_3—NH_2 Methylamine	-amine
Aldehyde	—C—C—H (with =O)	CH_3—C(=O)—H Acetaldehyde (Ethanal)	-al
Ketone	—C—C—C— (with =O)	CH_3—C(=O)—CH_3 Acetone	-one
Carboxylic acid	—C—C—OH (with =O)	CH_3—C(=O)—OH Acetic acid	-ic acid
Anhydride	—C—C—O—C—C— (with two =O)	CH_3—C(=O)—O—C(=O)—CH_3 Acetic anhydride	None
Ester	—C—C—O—C— (with =O)	CH_3—C(=O)—O—CH_3 Methyl acetate	-ate
Amide	—C—C—NH_2, —C—C—N—H, —C—C—N— (with =O)	CH_3—C(=O)—NH_2 Acetamide	-amide

*The bonds whose connections are not specified are assumed to be attached to carbon or hydrogen atoms in the rest of the molecule.

Alkyl halides have a carbon–halogen bond; *alcohols* have a carbon–oxygen bond; *ethers* have two carbons bonded to the same oxygen; and *amines* have a carbon–nitrogen bond.

- The remaining families in Table 12.1 have functional groups that contain a carbon–oxygen double bond: *aldehydes, ketones, carboxylic acids, anhydrides, esters,* and *amides.*

WORKED EXAMPLE   **12.1** Molecular Structures: Identifying Functional Groups

To which family of organic compounds do the following compounds belong? Explain.

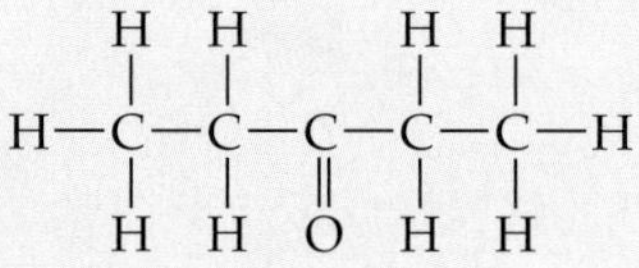

ANALYSIS Identify each functional group from the list in Table 12.1, and name the corresponding family to which the compound belongs.

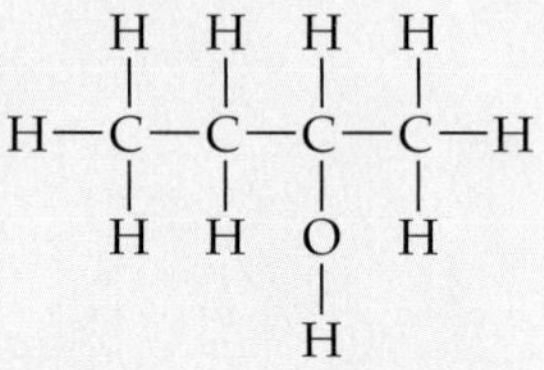

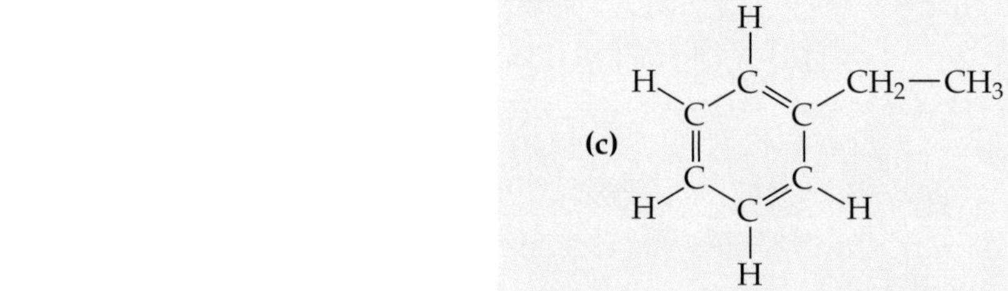

SOLUTION

(a) This compound contains only carbon and hydrogen atoms, so it is a *hydrocarbon*. There is a carbon–carbon double bond, so it is an *alkene*.

(b) The O—H group bonded to tetravalent carbon identifies this compound as an *alcohol*.

(c) This compound also contains only carbon and hydrogen atoms, which identifies it as a *hydrocarbon*. The six-membered carbon ring with alternating double bonds also identifies this compound as an *aromatic* hydrocarbon compound.

(d) The carbon–oxygen double bond in the middle of the carbon chain (as opposed to at either end of the chain) identifies this compound as a *ketone*.

WORKED EXAMPLE   **12.2** Molecular Structures: Drawing Functional Groups

Given the family of organic compounds to which the compound belongs, propose structures for compounds having the following chemical formulas.

(a) An amine having the formula C_2H_7N

(b) An alkyne having the formula C_3H_4

(c) An ether having the formula $C_4H_{10}O$

ANALYSIS Identify the functional group for each compound from Table 12.1. Once the atoms in this functional group are eliminated from the chemical formula, the remaining structure can be determined. (Remember that each carbon atom forms four bonds, nitrogen forms three bonds, oxygen forms two bonds, and hydrogen forms only one bond.)

SOLUTION

(a) Amines have a C—NH$_2$ group. Eliminating these atoms from the formula leaves 1 C atom and 5 H atoms. Since only the carbons are capable of forming more than one bond, the 2 C atoms must be bonded together. The remaining H atoms are then bonded to the carbons until each C has 4 bonds.

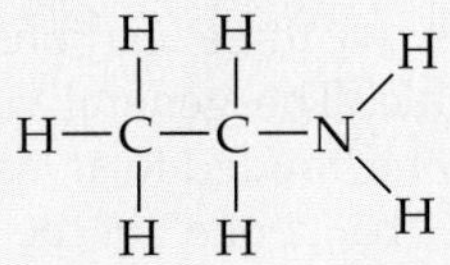

$$H-\underset{\underset{H}{|}}{\overset{\overset{H}{|}}{C}}-\underset{\underset{H}{|}}{\overset{\overset{H}{|}}{C}}-N\begin{smallmatrix}H\\ \\H\end{smallmatrix}$$

(b) The alkynes contain a C≡C bond. This leaves 1 C atom and 4 H atoms. Attach this C to one of the carbons in the triple bond, and then distribute the H atoms until each carbon has a full complement of four bonds.

$$H-\underset{\underset{H}{|}}{\overset{\overset{H}{|}}{C}}-C\equiv C-H$$

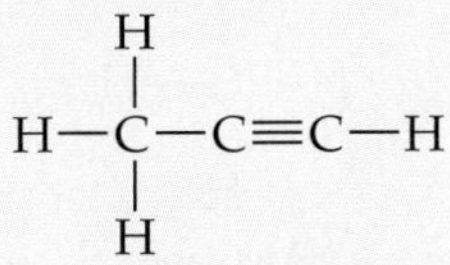

(c) The ethers contain a C—O—C group. Eliminating these atoms leaves 2 C atoms and 10 H atoms. The C atoms can be distributed on either end of the ether group, and the H atoms are then distributed until each carbon atom has a full complement of four bonds.

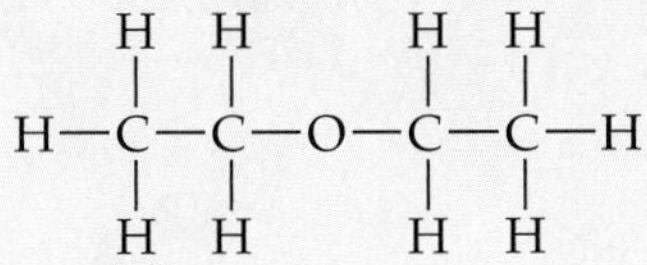

$$H-C-C-O-C-C-H \quad \text{or} \quad H-C-C-C-O-C-H$$

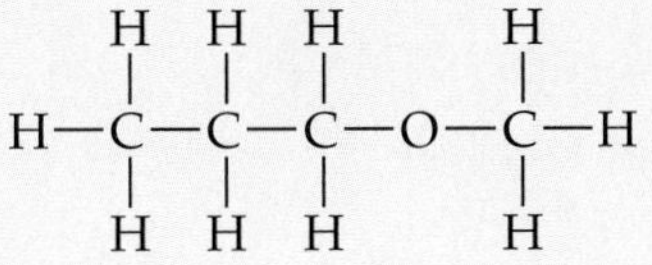

PROBLEM 12.1

Many organic compounds contain more than one functional group. Locate and identify the functional groups in (a) lactic acid, from sour milk; (b) methyl methacrylate, used in making Lucite and Plexiglas; and (c) phenylalanine, an amino acid found in proteins.

(a) 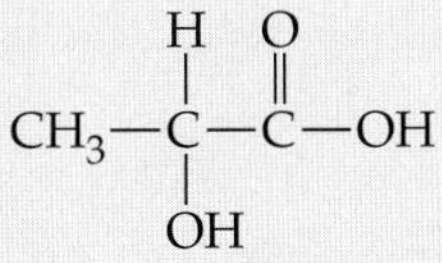 $CH_3-\overset{\overset{H}{|}}{\underset{\underset{OH}{|}}{C}}-\overset{\overset{O}{||}}{C}-OH$

(b) $CH_2=\overset{}{\underset{\underset{CH_3}{|}}{C}}-\overset{\overset{O}{||}}{C}-O-CH_3$

(c) (phenylalanine structure) $C-CH_2-\overset{\overset{H}{|}}{\underset{\underset{NH_2}{|}}{C}}-\overset{\overset{O}{||}}{C}-OH$

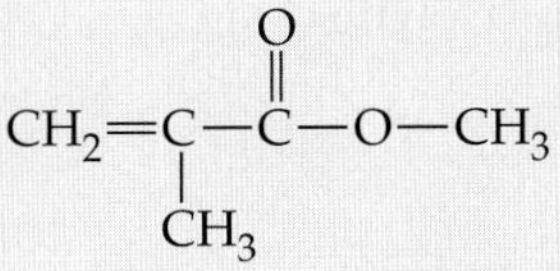

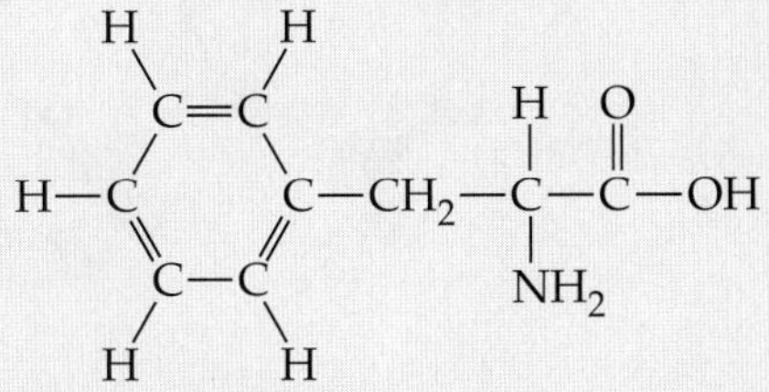

PROBLEM 12.2

Propose structures for molecules that fit the following descriptions:

(a) C_2H_4O containing an aldehyde functional group
(b) $C_3H_6O_2$ containing a carboxylic acid functional group

12.3 The Structure of Organic Molecules: Alkanes and Their Isomers

Alkane A hydrocarbon that has only single bonds.

Hydrocarbons that contain only single bonds belong to the family of organic molecules called **alkanes**. Imagine how one carbon and four hydrogens can combine, and you will realize there is only one possibility: methane, CH_4. Now imagine how two carbons and six hydrogens can combine—only ethane, CH_3CH_3, is possible. Likewise with the combination of three carbons with eight hydrogens—only propane, $CH_3CH_2CH_3$, is possible. The general rule for *all* hydrocarbons except methane is that each carbon *must* be bonded to at least one other carbon. The carbon atoms bond together to form the "backbone" of the compound, with the hydrogens on the periphery. The general formula for alkanes is C_nH_{2n+2}, where n is the number of carbons in the compound.

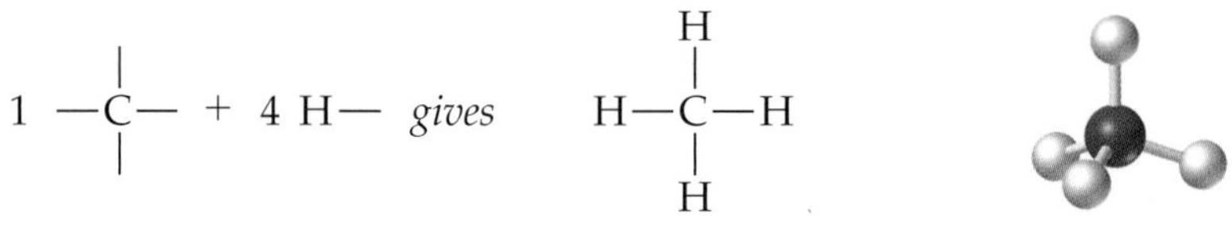

Methane

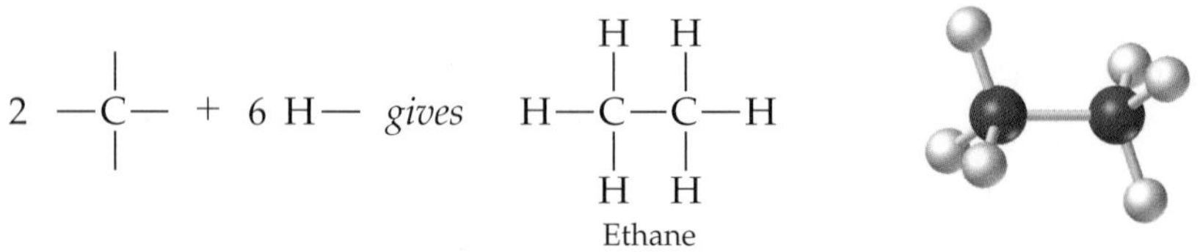

Ethane

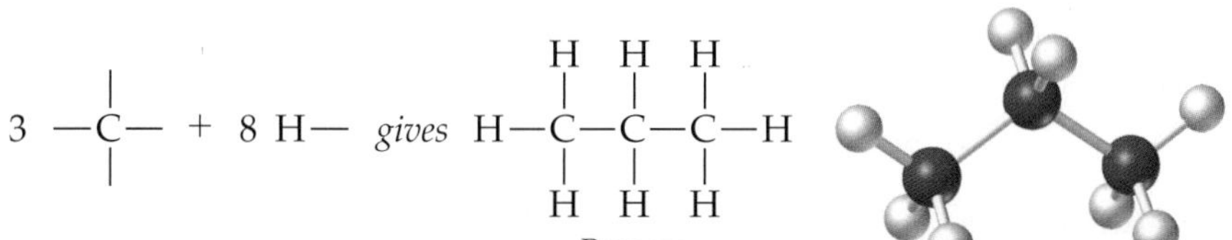

Propane

Isomers Compounds with the same molecular formula but different structures.

As larger numbers of carbons and hydrogens combine, the ability to form *isomers* arises. Compounds that have the same molecular formula but different structural formulas are called **isomers** of one another. For example, there are two ways in which molecules that have the formula C_4H_{10} can be formed: The four carbons can either be joined in a contiguous row or have a branched arrangement:

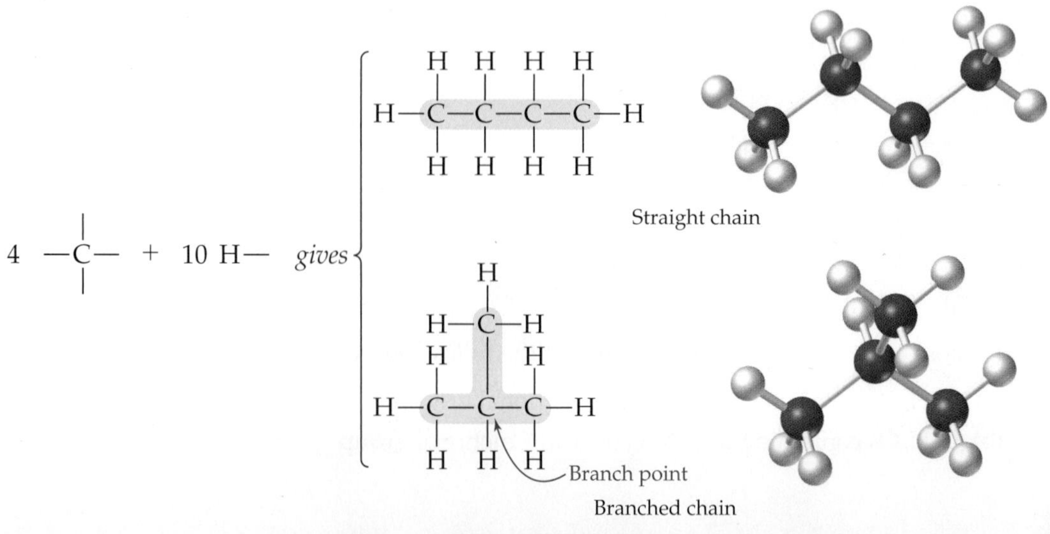

Straight chain

Branch point
Branched chain

The same is seen with the molecules that have the formula C_5H_{12}, for which three isomers are possible:

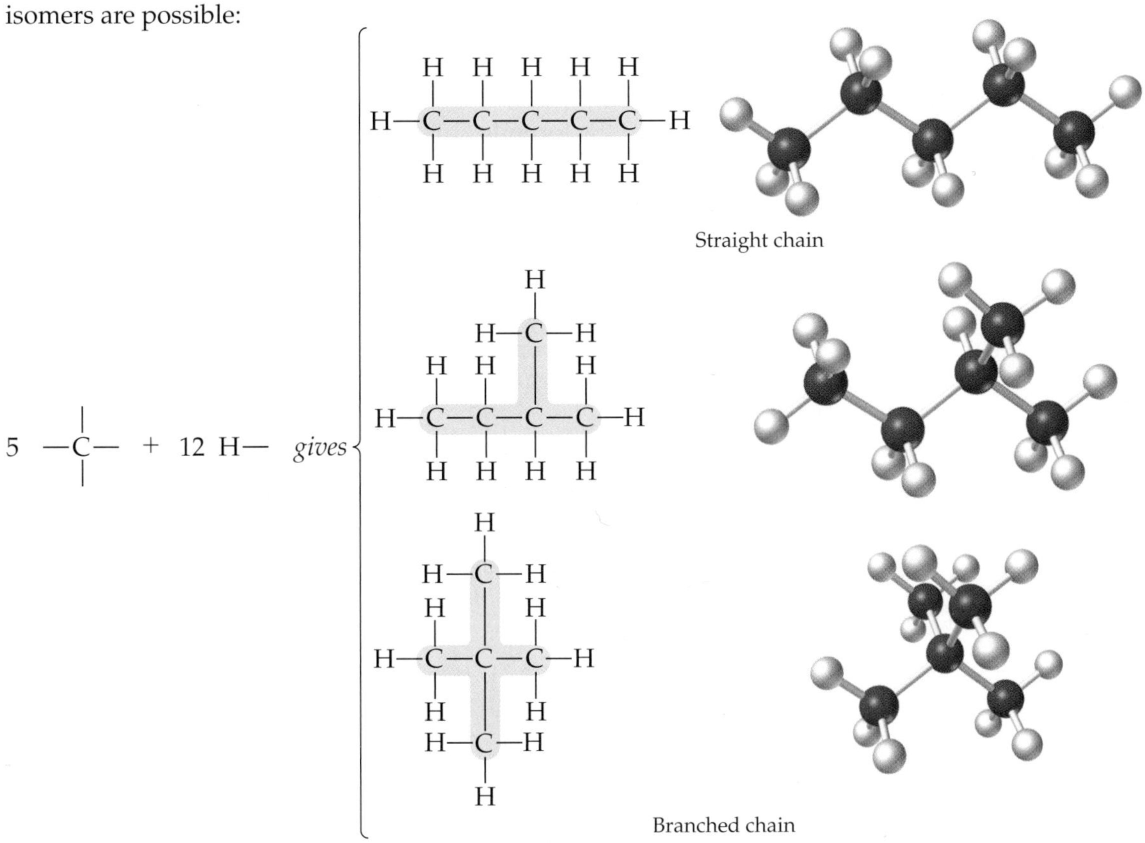

Straight chain

$$5 \ -\!\!\overset{|}{\underset{|}{C}}\!\!- \ + \ 12 \ H\!- \quad gives$$

Branched chain

Compounds with all their carbons connected in a continuous chain are called **straight-chain alkanes**; those with a branching connection of carbons are called **branched-chain alkanes**. Note that in a straight-chain alkane, you can draw a line through all the carbon atoms without lifting your pencil from the paper. In a branched-chain alkane, however, you must either lift your pencil from the paper or retrace your steps to draw a line through all the carbons.

The two isomers of C_4H_{10} and the three isomers of C_5H_{12} shown above are **constitutional isomers**—compounds with the same molecular formula but with different connections among their constituent atoms. Needless to say, the number of possible alkane isomers grows rapidly as the number of carbon atoms increases.

Constitutional isomers of a given molecular formula are chemically completely different from one another. They have different structures, different physical properties such as melting and boiling points, and potentially different physiological properties. For example, ethyl alcohol and dimethyl ether both have the formula C_2H_6O, but ethyl alcohol is a liquid with a boiling point of 78.5 °C and dimethyl ether is a gas with a boiling point of −23 °C (Table 12.2). Clearly, molecular formulas by

Straight-chain alkane An alkane that has all its carbons connected in a row.

Branched-chain alkane An alkane that has a branching connection of carbons.

Constitutional isomers Compounds with the same molecular formula but different connections among their atoms.

TABLE 12.2 Some Properties of Ethyl Alcohol and Dimethyl Ether

NAME AND MOLECULAR FORMULA	STRUCTURE	BOILING POINT	MELTING POINT	PHYSIOLOGICAL ACTIVITY
Ethyl alcohol C_2H_6O	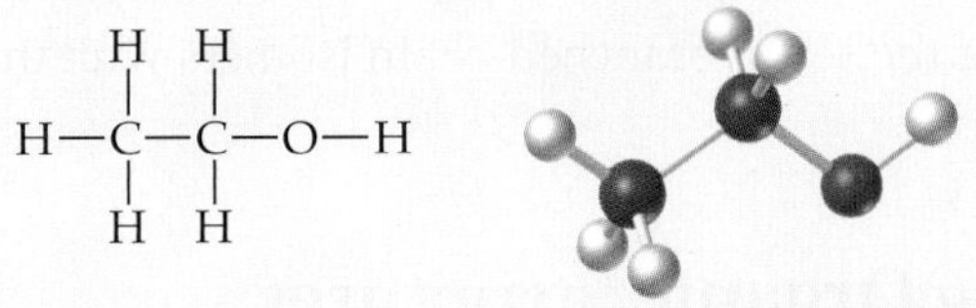	78.5 °C	− 117.3 °C	Central-nervous-system depressant
Dimethyl ether C_2H_6O	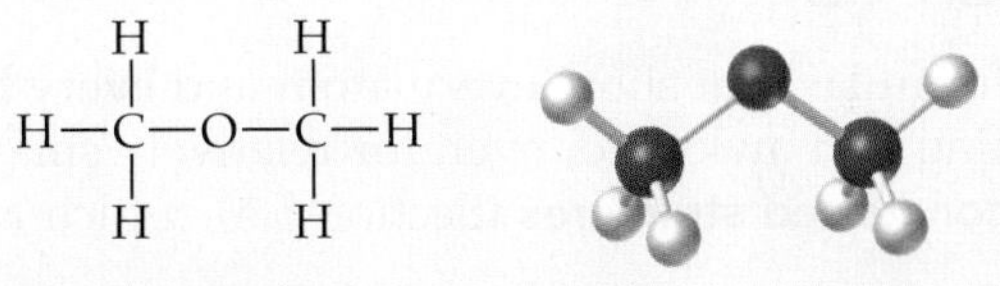	− 23 °C	− 138.5 °C	Nontoxic; anesthetic at high concentration

themselves are not very useful in organic chemistry; a knowledge of structure is also necessary.

WORKED EXAMPLE **12.3** Molecular Structures: Drawing Isomers

Draw all isomers that have the formula C_6H_{14}.

ANALYSIS Knowing that all the carbons must be bonded together to form the molecule, find all possible arrangements of the 6 carbon atoms. Begin with the isomer that has all 6 carbons in a straight chain, then draw the isomer that has 5 carbons in a straight chain, using the remaining carbon to form a branch, then repeat for the isomer having 4 carbons in a straight chain and 2 carbons in branches. Once each carbon backbone is drawn, arrange the hydrogens around the carbons to complete the structure. (Remember that each carbon can only have *four* bonds.)

SOLUTION

The straight-chain isomer contains all 6 carbons bonded to form a chain with no branches. The branched isomers are drawn by starting with either a 5-carbon chain or a 4-carbon chain, and adding the extra carbons as branches in the middle of the chain. Hydrogens are added until each carbon has a full complement of 4 bonds.

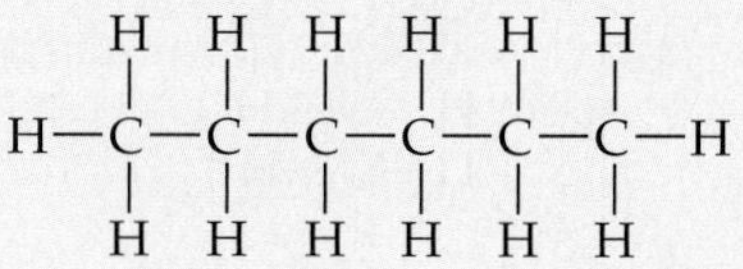

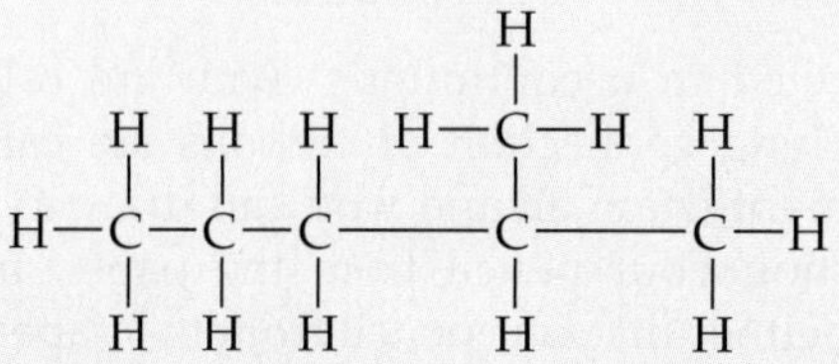

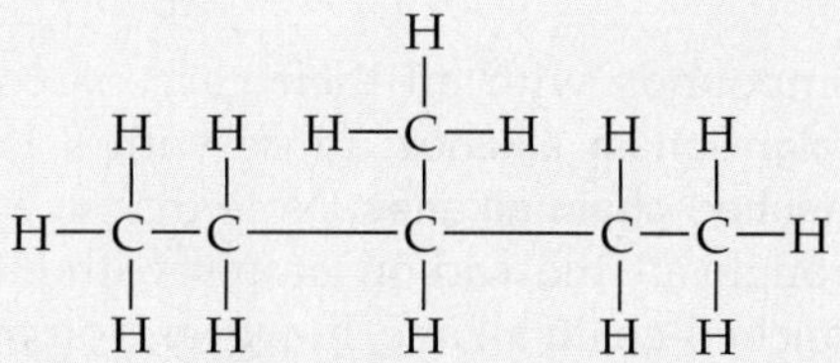

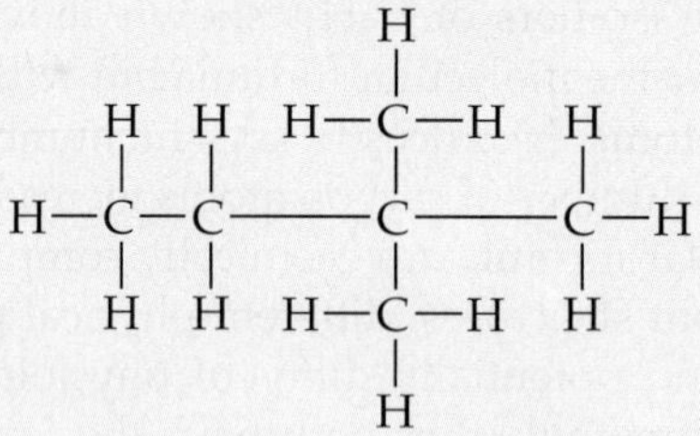

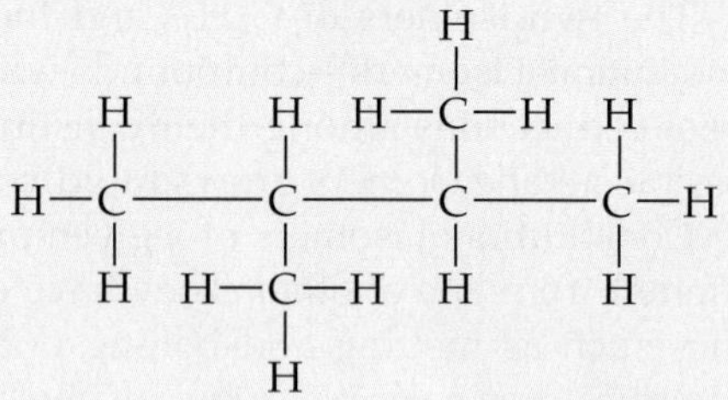

PROBLEM 12.3

Draw the straight-chain isomer with the formula C_7H_{16}.

PROBLEM 12.4

Draw any two of the seven branched-chain isomers with the formula C_7H_{16}.

12.4 Drawing Organic Structures

Condensed structure A shorthand way of drawing structures in which C—C and C—H bonds are understood rather than shown.

Drawing structural formulas that show every atom and every bond in a molecule is both time-consuming and awkward, even for relatively small molecules. Much easier is the use of **condensed structures** (Section 5.6), which are simpler but still show the essential information about which functional groups are present and how atoms are connected. (p. 118) In condensed structures, C—C and C—H single bonds are not shown; rather, they are "understood." If a carbon atom has 3 hydrogens bonded to it, we write CH_3; if the carbon has 2 hydrogens bonded to it, we write CH_2; and so on. For example, the 4-carbon, straight-chain alkane (butane) and its branched-chain isomer (2-methylpropane) can be written as the following condensed structures:

 = $CH_3CH_2CH_2CH_3$

Butane

Structural formula — Condensed formula

 =

2-Methylpropane

Structural formula — Condensed formula

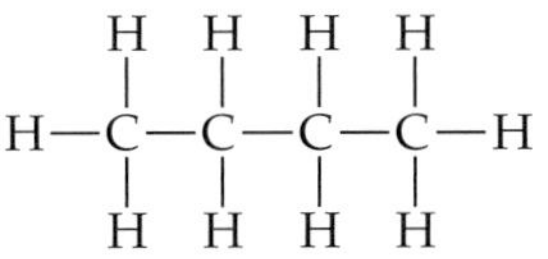

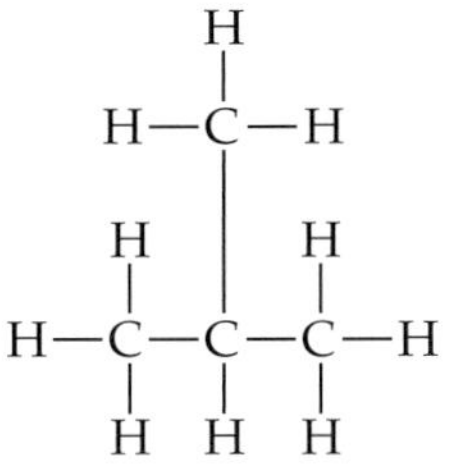

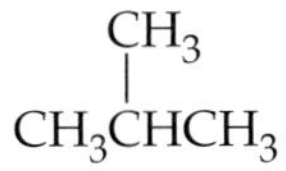

Note in these condensed structures for butane and 2-methylpropane that the horizontal bonds between carbons are not usually shown—the CH_3 and CH_2 units are simply placed next to one another—but that the vertical bond in 2-methylpropane *is* shown for clarity.

Occasionally, as a further simplification, not all the CH_2 groups (called **methylenes**) are shown. Instead, CH_2 is shown once in parentheses, with a subscript to the right of the) indicating the number of methylene units strung together. For example, the 6-carbon straight-chain alkane (hexane) can be written as

Methylene Another name for a CH_2 unit.

$$CH_3CH_2CH_2CH_2CH_2CH_3 = CH_3(CH_2)_4CH_3$$

WORKED EXAMPLE 12.4 Molecular Structures: Writing Condensed Structures

Write condensed structures for the isomers from Worked Example 12.3.

ANALYSIS Eliminate all horizontal bonds, substituting reduced formula components (CH_3, CH_2, and so on) for each carbon in the compound. Show vertical bonds to branching carbons for clarity.

SOLUTION

 ⟶ $CH_3CH_2CH_2CH_2CH_2CH_3$ or $CH_3(CH_2)_4CH_3$

 ⟶

 ⟶

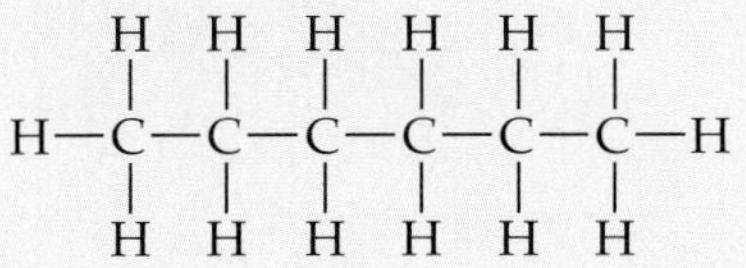

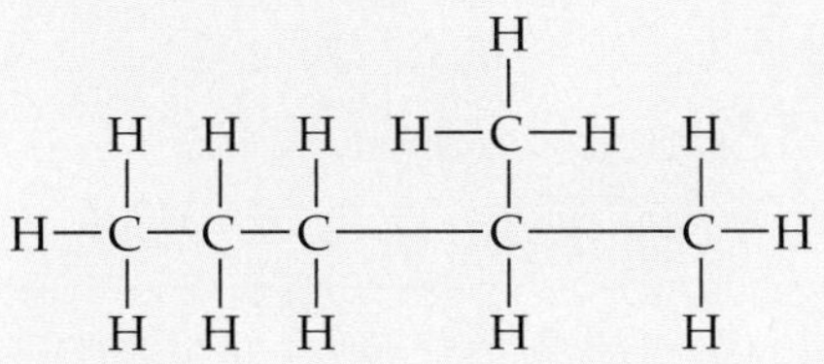

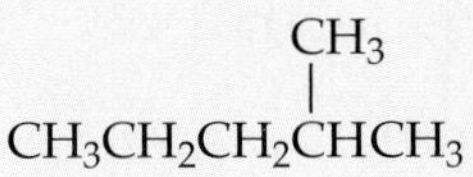

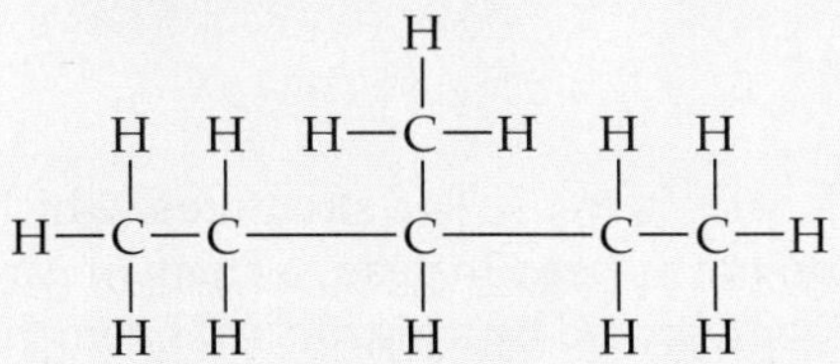

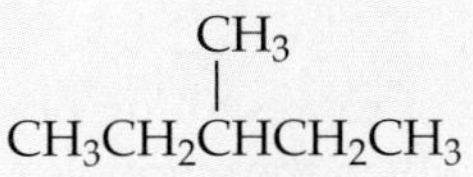

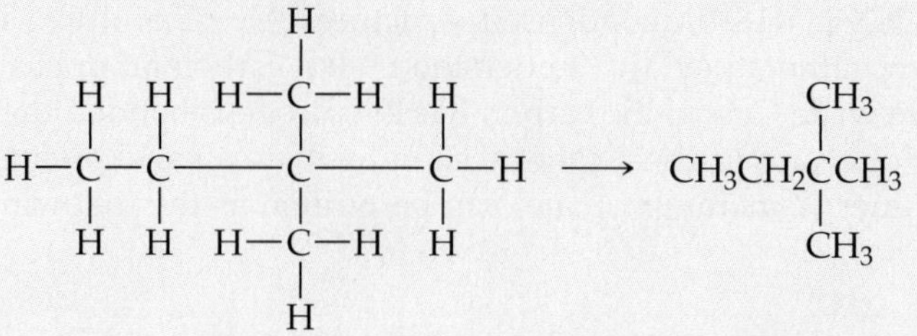

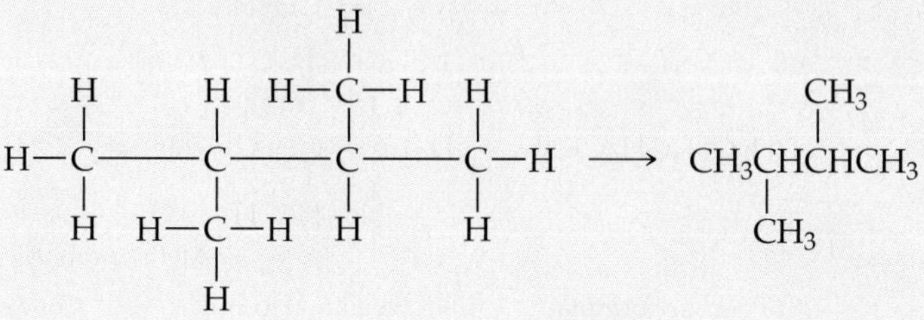

$$\text{(structure)} \longrightarrow \text{CH}_3\text{CH}_2\overset{\displaystyle \text{CH}_3}{\underset{\displaystyle \text{CH}_3}{\text{C}}}\text{CH}_3$$

$$\text{(structure)} \longrightarrow \text{CH}_3\overset{\displaystyle \text{CH}_3}{\text{CHCHCH}_3}\underset{\displaystyle \text{CH}_3}{}$$

PROBLEM 12.5

Draw the following three isomers of C_5H_{12} as condensed structures:

(a)

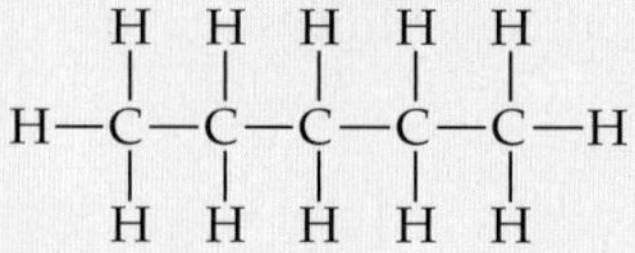

Pentane

(b)

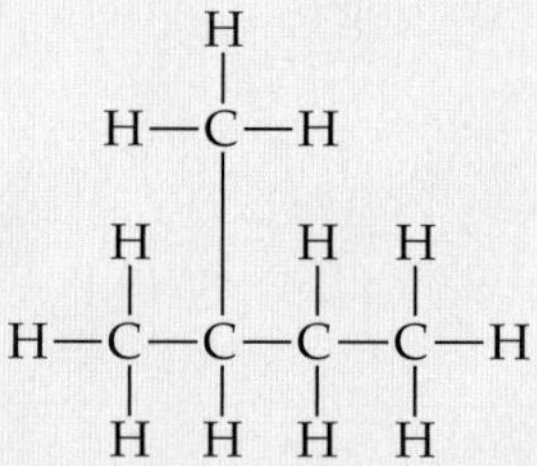

2-Methylbutane

(c)

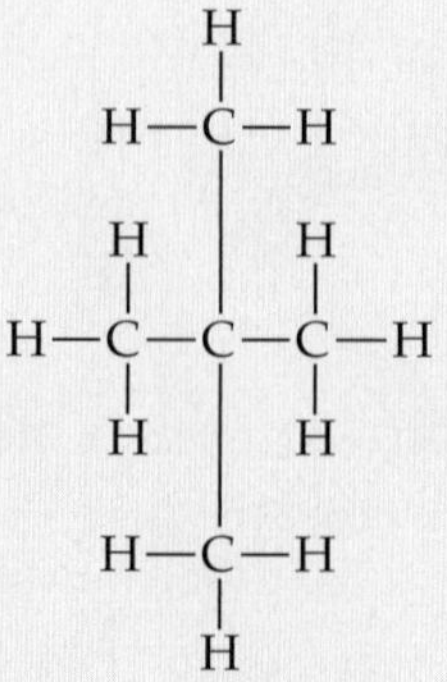

2,2-Dimethylpropane

Line structure A shorthand way of drawing structures in which carbon and hydrogen atoms are not shown. Instead, a carbon atom is understood to be wherever a line begins or ends and at every intersection of two lines, and hydrogens are understood to be wherever they are needed to have each carbon form four bonds.

Another way of representing organic molecules is to use **line structures**, which are structures in which the symbols C and H do not appear. Instead, a chain of carbon atoms and their associated hydrogens are represented by a zigzag arrangement of short lines, with any branches off the main chain represented by additional lines. The line structure for 2-methylbutane, for instance, is

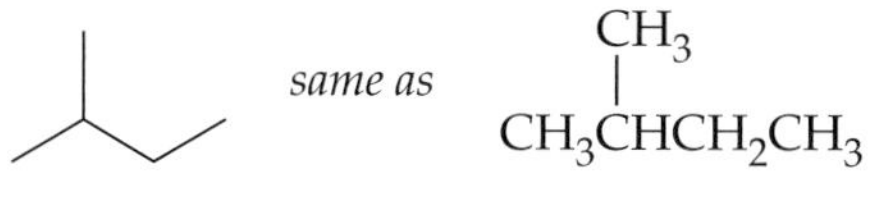

Line structures are a simple and quick way to represent organic molecules without the clutter arising from showing all carbons and hydrogens present. Chemists, biologists, pharmacists, doctors, and nurses all use line structures to conveniently convey to one another very complex organic structures. Another advantage is that a line structure gives a more realistic depiction of the angles seen in a carbon chain.

Drawing a molecule in this way is simple, provided one follows these guidelines:

1. Each carbon-carbon bond is represented by a line.

2. Anywhere a line ends or begins, as well as any vertex where two lines meet, represents a carbon atom.

3. Any atom other than another carbon or a hydrogen attached to a carbon must be shown.

4. Since a neutral carbon atom forms four bonds, all bonds not shown for any carbon are understood to be the number of carbon-hydrogen bonds needed to have the carbon form four bonds.

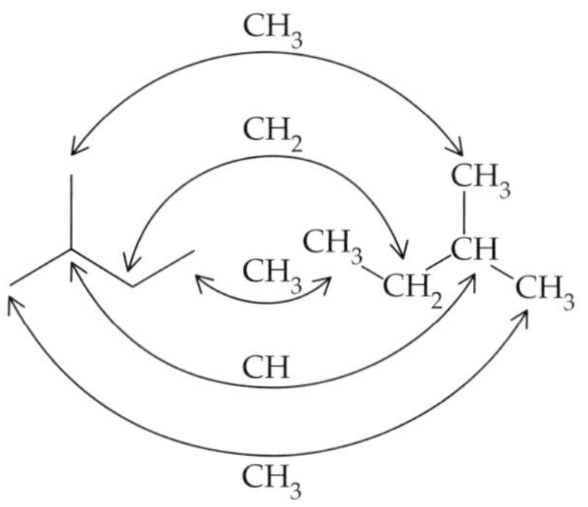

Converting line structures to structural formulas or to condensed structures is simply a matter of correctly interpreting each line ending and each intersection in a line structure. For example, the common pain reliever ibuprofen has the condensed and line structures

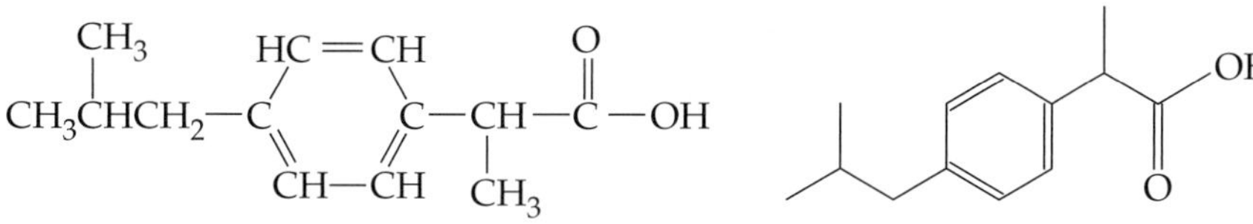

Finally, it is important to note that chemists and biochemists often use a mixture of structural formulas, condensed structures, and line structures to represent the molecules they study. As you progress through this textbook, you will see many complicated molecules represented in this way, so it is a good idea to get used to thinking interchangably in all three formats.

WORKED EXAMPLE **12.5** Molecular Structures: Converting Condensed Structures to Line Structures

Convert the following condensed structures to line structures:

(a) $CH_3CH_2CHCHCH_2CH_3$ with CH_3 above and CH_3 below

(b) $CH_3CHCH-C\ CH_2CH_3$ with OH and Cl above and CH_3 and CH_3 below

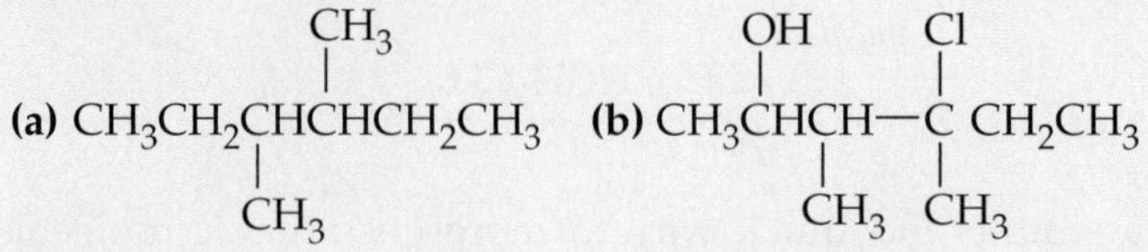

ANALYSIS Find the longest continuous chain of carbon atoms in the condensed structure. Begin the line structure by drawing a zigzag line in which the number of vertices plus line ends equals the number of carbon atoms in the chain. Show branches coming off the main chain by drawing vertical lines at the vertices as needed. Show all atoms that are not carbons or are not hydrogens attached to carbons.

SOLUTION

(a) Begin by drawing a zigzag line in which the total number of ends + vertices equals the number of carbons in the longest chain (here 6, with the carbons numbered for clarity):

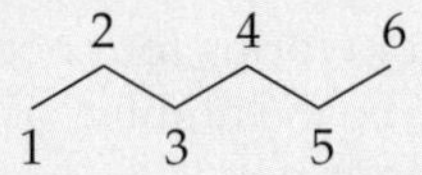

Looking at the condensed structure, you see CH_3 groups on carbons 3 and 4; these two methyl groups are represented by lines coming off those carbons in the line structure:

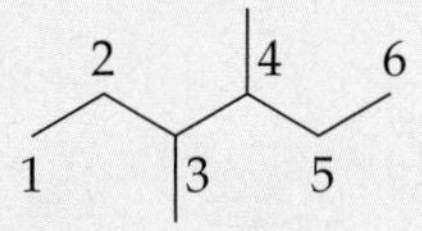

This is the complete line structure. Notice that the hydrogens are not shown, but understood. For example, carbon 4 has three bonds shown: one to carbon 3, one to carbon 5, and one to the branch methyl group; the fourth bond this carbon must have is understood to be to a hydrogen.

(b) Proceed as in (a), drawing a zigzag line for the longest chain of carbon atoms, which again contains 6 carbons. Next draw a line coming off each carbon bonded to a CH_3 group (carbons 3 and 4). Both the OH and the Cl groups must be shown to give the final structure:

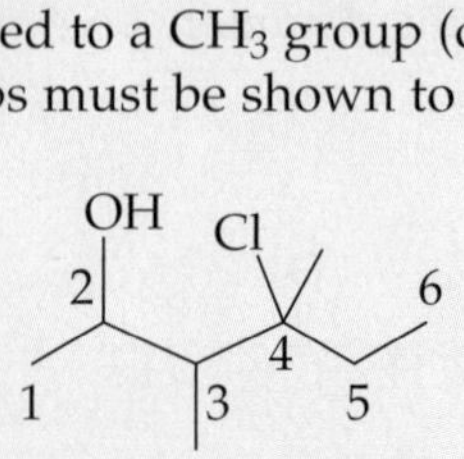

Note from this line structure than it does not matter in such a two-dimensional drawing what direction you show for a group that branches off the main chain, as long as it is attached to the correct carbon. This is true for condensed structures as well. Quite often the direction that a group is shown coming off a main chain of carbon atoms is chosen simply for aesthetic reasons.

WORKED EXAMPLE **12.6** Molecular Structures: Converting Line Structures to Condensed Structures

Convert the following line structures to condensed structures:

(a)

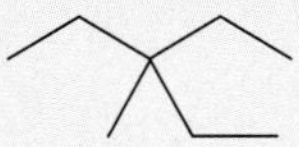

(b)

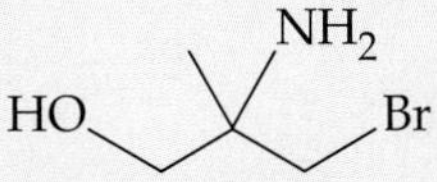

ANALYSIS Convert all vertices and line ends to carbons. Write in any noncarbon atoms and any hydrogens bonded to a noncarbon atom. Add hydrogens as needed so that each carbon has four groups attached. Remove lines connecting carbons except for branches.

SOLUTION

(a) Anywhere a line ends and anywhere two lines meet, write a C:

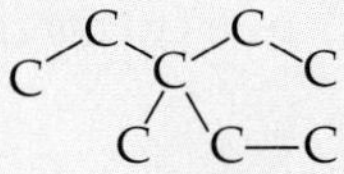

Because there are no atoms other than carbons and hydrogens in this molecule, the next step is to add hydrogens as needed to have four bonds for each carbon:

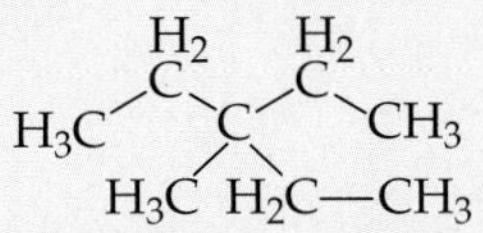

Finally, eliminate all lines except for branches to get the condensed structure:

$$CH_3CH_2 \overset{\overset{\textstyle CH_3}{|}}{\underset{\underset{\textstyle CH_2CH_3}{|}}{C}} CH_2CH_3$$

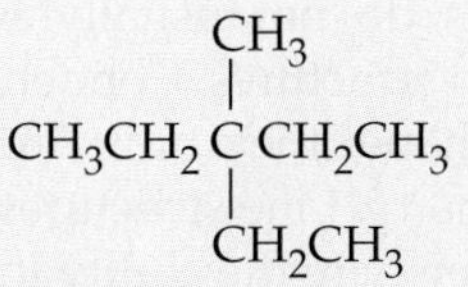

(b) Begin the condensed structure with a drawing showing a carbon at each line end and at each intersection of two lines:

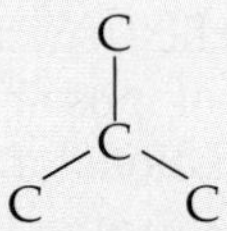

Next write in all the noncarbon atoms and the hydrogen bonded to the oxygen. Then add hydrogens so that each carbon forms four bonds:

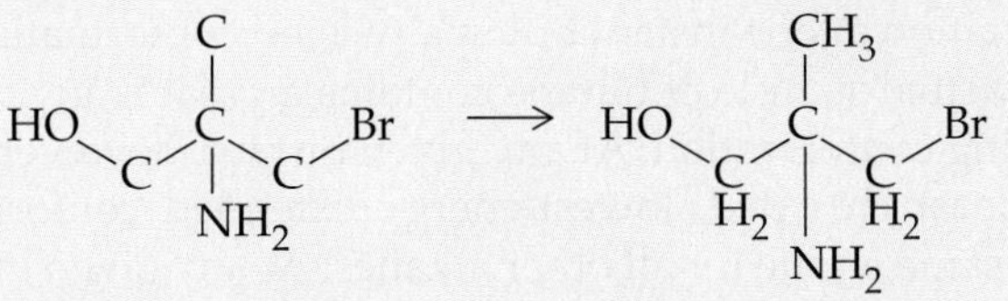

Eliminate all lines except for branches for the completed condensed structure:

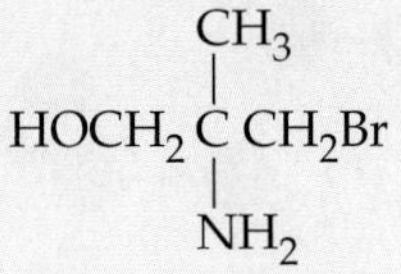

$$HOCH_2 \overset{\overset{\textstyle CH_3}{|}}{\underset{\underset{\textstyle NH_2}{|}}{C}} CH_2Br$$

PROBLEM 12.6

Convert the following condensed structures to line structures:

(a)

$$\underset{\underset{CH_2OH}{|}}{\overset{\overset{CH_2CH_3}{|}}{CH_3CH_2C}}-CH_2CH_2CH_3$$

(b)

$$\underset{\overset{}{CH_3CHCH_2CH_3}}{\overset{\overset{CH_2CH_3}{|}\quad\overset{CH_3}{|}}{CH_3CH\ CH\ CH_2CHCH_3}}$$

(c)

$$\underset{\underset{CH_3\ CHCH_2CH_3}{|\quad\quad|}}{\overset{\overset{Br}{|}\quad\quad\quad\quad\overset{Cl}{|}}{CH_3C}}-CHCH_2CH_2CHCH_2CH_3$$

PROBLEM 12.7

Convert the following line structures to condensed structures:

(a)

(b)

12.5 The Shapes of Organic Molecules

Every carbon atom in an alkane has its four bonds pointing toward the four corners of a tetrahedron, but chemists do not usually worry about three-dimensional shapes when writing condensed structures. Condensed structures do not imply any particular three-dimensional shape; they only indicate the connections between atoms without specifying geometry. Line structures do try to give some feeling for the shape of a molecule, but even here the ability to show three-dimensional shape is limited unless dashed and wedged lines are used for the bonds (page 125).

Butane, for example, has no one single shape because *rotation* takes place around carbon–carbon single bonds. The two parts of a molecule joined by a carbon–carbon single bond in a noncyclic structure are free to spin around the bond, giving rise to an infinite number of possible three-dimensional geometries, or **conformations**. The various conformations of a molecule such as butane are called **conformers** of one another. Conformers differ from one another as a result of rotation around carbon–carbon single bonds. Although the conformers of a given molecule have different three-dimensional shapes and different energies, the conformers cannot be separated from one another. A given butane molecule might be in its fully extended conformation at one instant but in a twisted conformation an instant later (Figure 12.2). An actual sample of butane contains a great many molecules that are constantly changing conformation. At any given instant, however, most of the molecules have the least crowded, lowest-energy extended conformation shown in Figure 12.2a. The same is true for all other alkanes: At any given instant, most molecules are in the least crowded conformation.

Conformation The specific three-dimensional arrangement of atoms in a molecule.

Conformer Molecular structures having identical connections between atoms; that is, they represent identical compounds.

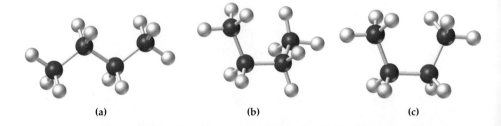

▶ **FIGURE 12.2 Some conformations of butane (there are many others as well).** The least crowded, extended conformation in (a) is the lowest-energy one.

(a)　　　　　(b)　　　　　(c)

As long as any two structures have identical connections between atoms, they are conformers of each other and represent the same compound, no matter how the structures are drawn. Sometimes you have to mentally rotate structures to see whether they are conformers or different molecules. To see that the following two structures represent conformers of the same compound rather than two isomers, picture one of them flipped right to left so that the red CH_3 groups are on the same side:

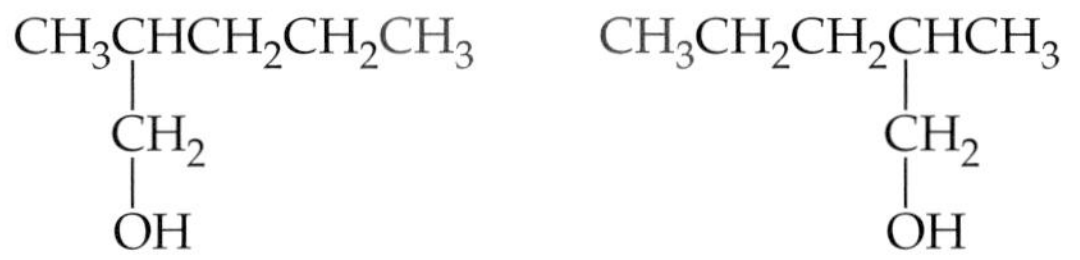

$$CH_3CHCH_2CH_2CH_3 \qquad CH_3CH_2CH_2CHCH_3$$
$$\qquad\ \ | \qquad\qquad\qquad\qquad\qquad\qquad | \quad$$
$$\qquad\ \ CH_2 \qquad\qquad\qquad\qquad\qquad\ CH_2$$
$$\qquad\ \ | \qquad\qquad\qquad\qquad\qquad\qquad | \quad$$
$$\qquad\ \ OH \qquad\qquad\qquad\qquad\qquad\ OH$$

Another way to determine whether two structures are conformers is to name each one using the IUPAC nomenclature rules (Section 12.6). If two structures have the same name, they are conformers of the same compound.

WORKED EXAMPLE   **12.7** Molecular Structures: Identifying Conformers

The following structures all have the formula C_7H_{16}. Which of them represent the same molecule?

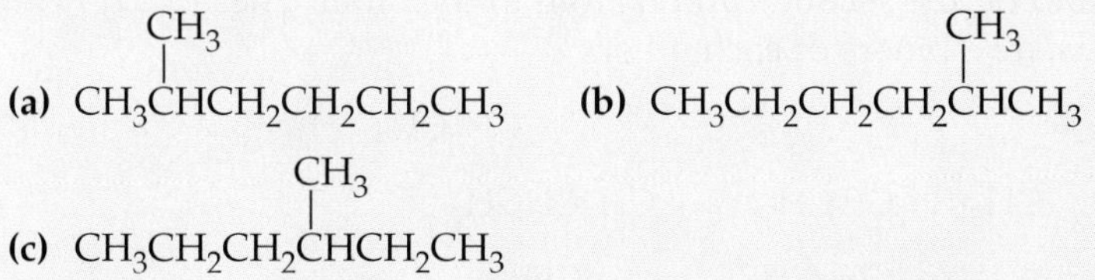

$$\qquad\ CH_3 \qquad\qquad\qquad\qquad\qquad\qquad\qquad\qquad\ CH_3$$
$$\qquad\ | \qquad\qquad\qquad\qquad\qquad\qquad\qquad\qquad\qquad | \ $$
(a) $CH_3CHCH_2CH_2CH_2CH_3$ (b) $CH_3CH_2CH_2CH_2CHCH_3$

$$\qquad\qquad\ CH_3$$
$$\qquad\qquad\ |$$
(c) $CH_3CH_2CH_2CHCH_2CH_3$

ANALYSIS Pay attention to the *connections* between atoms. Do not get confused by the apparent differences caused by writing a structure right to left versus left to right. Begin by identifying the longest chain of carbon atoms in the molecule.

SOLUTION
Molecule (a) has a straight chain of 6 carbons with a $—CH_3$ branch on the second carbon from the end. Molecule (b) also has a straight chain of 6 carbons with a $—CH_3$ branch on the second carbon from the end and is therefore identical to (a). That is, (a) and (b) are conformers of the same molecule. The only difference between (a) and (b) is that one is written "forward" and one is written "backward." Molecule (c), by contrast, has a straight chain of 6 carbons with a $—CH_3$ branch on the *third* carbon from the end and is therefore an isomer of (a) and (b).

WORKED EXAMPLE   **12.8** Molecular Structures: Identifying Conformers
and Isomers

Are the following pairs of compounds the same (conformers), isomers, or unrelated?

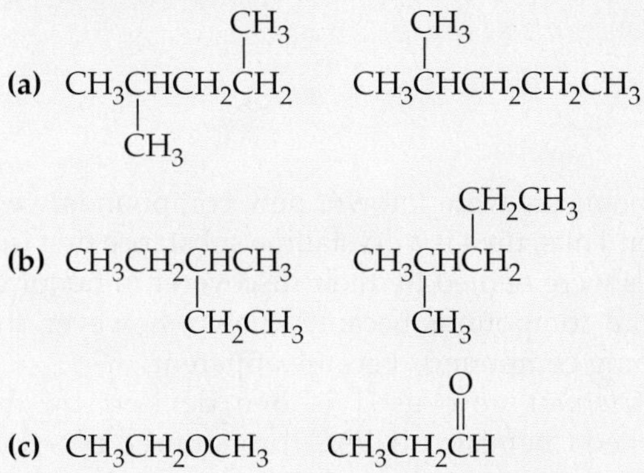

$$\qquad\qquad\ CH_3 \qquad\qquad\ CH_3$$
$$\qquad\qquad\ | \qquad\qquad\qquad\ |$$
(a) $CH_3CHCH_2CH_2 \qquad CH_3CHCH_2CH_2CH_3$
$$\qquad\ |$$
$$\qquad\ CH_3$$

$$\qquad\qquad\qquad\qquad\qquad\ CH_2CH_3$$
$$\qquad\qquad\qquad\qquad\qquad\ |$$
(b) $CH_3CH_2CHCH_3 \qquad CH_3CHCH_2$
$$\qquad\qquad\ | \qquad\qquad\qquad\qquad |$$
$$\qquad\qquad\ CH_2CH_3 \qquad\qquad\quad CH_3$$

$$\qquad\qquad\qquad\qquad\qquad\qquad O$$
$$\qquad\qquad\qquad\qquad\qquad\qquad \|$$
(c) $CH_3CH_2OCH_3 \qquad CH_3CH_2CH$

ANALYSIS First compare molecular formulas to see if the compounds are related, and then look at the structures to see if they are the same compound or isomers. Find the longest continuous carbon chain in each, and then compare the locations of the substituents connected to the longest chain.

SOLUTION

(a) Both compounds have the same molecular formula (C_6H_{14}) so they are related. Since the $-CH_3$ group is on the second carbon from the end of a 5-carbon chain in both cases, these structures represent the same compound and are conformers of each other.

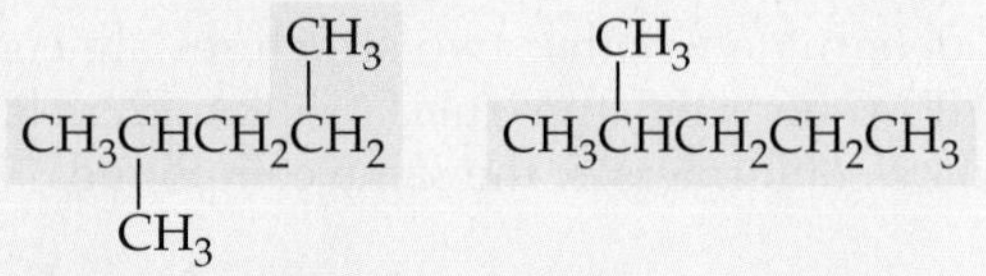

$$\underset{\underset{\displaystyle CH_3}{|}}{\overset{\overset{\displaystyle CH_3}{|}}{CH_3CHCH_2CH_2}} \qquad \overset{\overset{\displaystyle CH_3}{|}}{CH_3CHCH_2CH_2CH_3}$$

(b) Both compounds have the same molecular formula (C_6H_{14}) and the longest chain in each is 5 carbon atoms. A comparison shows, however, that the $-CH_3$ group is on the middle carbon atom in one structure and on the second carbon atom in the other. These compounds are isomers of each other.

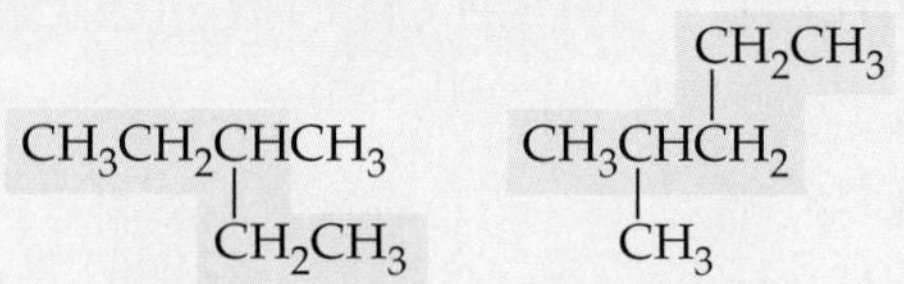

$$\underset{\underset{\displaystyle CH_2CH_3}{|}}{CH_3CH_2CHCH_3} \qquad \underset{\underset{\displaystyle CH_3}{|}}{\overset{\overset{\displaystyle CH_2CH_3}{|}}{CH_3CHCH_2}}$$

(c) These compounds have different formulas (C_3H_8O and C_3H_6O), so they are unrelated; they are neither conformers nor isomers of each other.

PROBLEM 12.8

Which of the following structures are conformers?

(a) 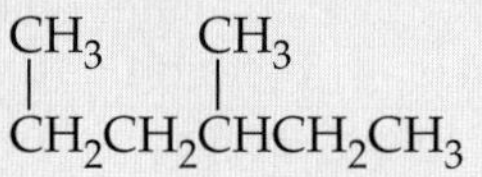 $\underset{}{\overset{\overset{\displaystyle CH_3}{|}\quad\overset{\displaystyle CH_3}{|}}{CH_2CH_2CHCH_2CH_3}}$
(b) 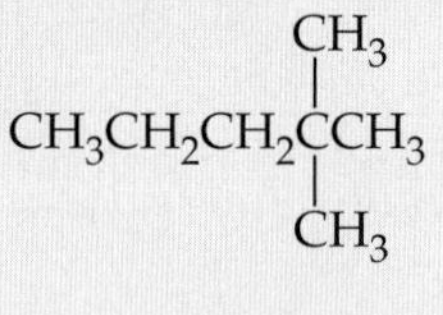 $\underset{\underset{\displaystyle CH_3}{|}}{\overset{\overset{\displaystyle CH_3}{|}}{CH_3CH_2CH_2CCH_3}}$

(c) 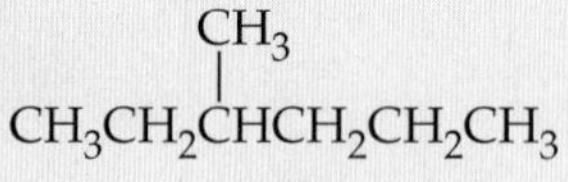 $\overset{\overset{\displaystyle CH_3}{|}}{CH_3CH_2CHCH_2CH_2CH_3}$

PROBLEM 12.9

There are 18 isomers with the formula C_8H_{18}. Draw condensed structures for as many as you can and then convert those condensed structures to line structures.

12.6 Naming Alkanes

When relatively few pure organic chemicals were known, new compounds were named at the whim of their discoverer. Thus, urea is a crystalline substance first isolated from urine, and the barbiturates were named by their discoverer in honor of his friend Barbara. As more and more compounds became known, however, the need for a systematic method of naming compounds became apparent.

The system of naming (*nomenclature*) now used is one devised by the International Union of Pure and Applied Chemistry, IUPAC (pronounced **eye**-you-pack). In the IUPAC system for organic compounds, a chemical name has three

APPLICATION ▶ Displaying Molecular Shapes

Molecular shapes are critical to the proper functioning of biological molecules. The tiniest difference in shape can cause two compounds to behave differently or to have different physiological effects in the body. It is therefore critical that chemists be able both to determine molecular shapes with great precision and to visualize these shapes in useful ways.

Three-dimensional shapes of molecules can be determined by *X-ray crystallography*, a technique that allows us to "see" molecules in a crystal using X-ray waves rather than light waves. The molecular "picture" obtained by X-ray crystallography looks at first like a series of regularly spaced dark spots against a lighter background. After computerized manipulation of the data, however, recognizable molecules can be drawn. Relatively small molecules like morphine are usually displayed in either a ball-and-stick format (a), which emphasizes the connections among atoms, or in a space-filling format (b), which emphasizes the overall shape. Chemists find this useful in designing new organic molecules that have specific biological properties that make the molecules useful as therapeutic agents.

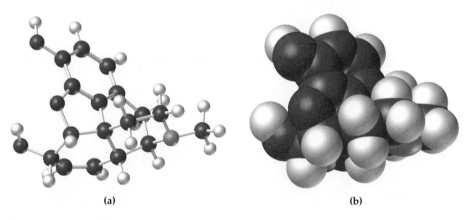

(a)   (b)

▲ This computer-generated model of morphine is displayed in both (a) ball-and-stick format and (b) space-filling format.

Enormous biological molecules like enzymes and other proteins are best displayed on computer terminals where their structures can be enlarged, rotated, and otherwise manipulated for the best view. An immunoglobulin molecule, for instance, is so large that little detail can be seen in ball-and-stick or space-filling views. Nevertheless, a cleft inside the molecule is visible if the model is rotated in just the right way.

See Additional Problem 12.64 at the end of the chapter.

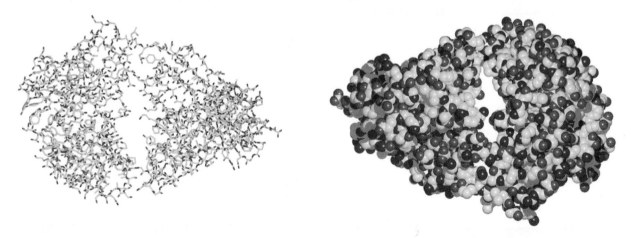

▲ Computer-generated models of an immunoglobulin, one of the antibodies in blood that protect us from harmful invaders such as bacteria and viruses.

parts: *prefix*, *parent*, and *suffix*. The prefix specifies the location of functional groups and other **substituents** in the molecule; the parent tells how many carbon atoms are present in the longest continuous chain; and the suffix identifies what family the molecule belongs to:

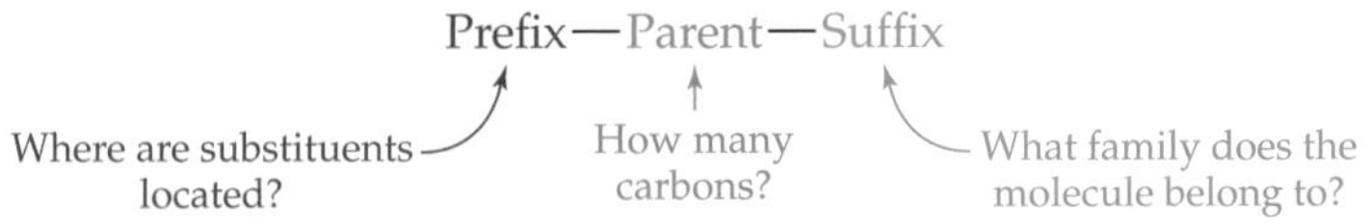

Substituent An atom or group of atoms attached to a parent compound.

$$\text{Prefix} \text{---} \text{Parent} \text{---} \text{Suffix}$$

Where are substituents located?　　How many carbons?　　What family does the molecule belong to?

Straight-chain alkanes are named by counting the number of carbon atoms and adding the family suffix *-ane*. With the exception of the first four compounds—*meth*ane, *eth*ane, *prop*ane, and *but*ane—whose parent names have historical origins, the alkanes are named from Greek numbers according to the number of carbons present (Table 12.3). Thus, *pent*ane is the 5-carbon alkane, *hex*ane is the 6-carbon alkane, and so on. The first ten alkane names are so common that they should be memorized.

TABLE 12.3　Names of Straight-Chain Alkanes

NUMBER OF CARBONS	STRUCTURE	NAME
1	CH_4	*Meth*ane
2	CH_3CH_3	*Eth*ane
3	$CH_3CH_2CH_3$	*Prop*ane
4	$CH_3CH_2CH_2CH_3$	*But*ane
5	$CH_3CH_2CH_2CH_2CH_3$	*Pent*ane
6	$CH_3CH_2CH_2CH_2CH_2CH_3$	*Hex*ane
7	$CH_3CH_2CH_2CH_2CH_2CH_2CH_3$	*Hept*ane
8	$CH_3CH_2CH_2CH_2CH_2CH_2CH_2CH_3$	*Oct*ane
9	$CH_3CH_2CH_2CH_2CH_2CH_2CH_2CH_2CH_3$	*Non*ane
10	$CH_3CH_2CH_2CH_2CH_2CH_2CH_2CH_2CH_2CH_3$	*Dec*ane

Alkyl group The part of an alkane that remains when a hydrogen atom is removed.

Methyl group The $—CH_3$ alkyl group.

Ethyl group The $—CH_2CH_3$ alkyl group.

Substituents such as $—CH_3$ and $—CH_2CH_3$ that branch off the main chain are called **alkyl groups**. An alkyl group can be thought of as the part of an alkane that remains when 1 hydrogen atom is removed to create an available bonding site. For example, removal of a hydrogen from methane gives the **methyl group,** $—CH_3$, and removal of a hydrogen from ethane gives the **ethyl group,** $—CH_2CH_3$. Notice that these alkyl groups are named simply by replacing the *-ane* ending of the parent alkane with an *-yl* ending:

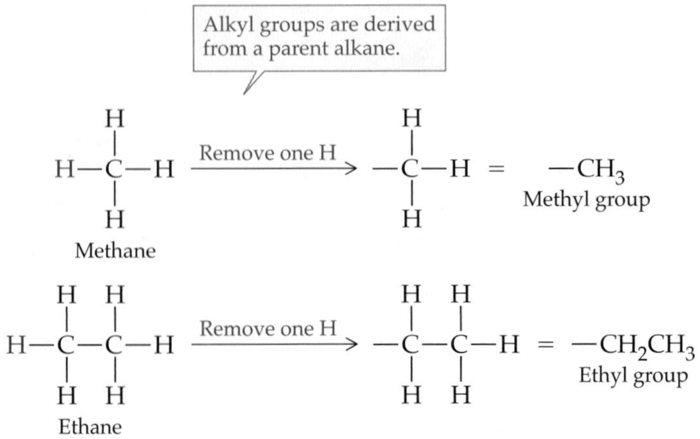

Alkyl groups are derived from a parent alkane.

Both methane and ethane have only one "kind" of hydrogen. It does not matter which of the 4 methane hydrogens is removed, so there is only one possible methyl group. Similarly, it does not matter which of the 6 equivalent ethane hydrogens is removed, so only one ethyl group is possible.

The situation is more complex for larger alkanes, which contain more than one kind of hydrogen. Propane, for example, has two different kinds of hydrogens. Removal of any one of the 6 hydrogens attached to an end carbon yields a straight-chain alkyl group called **propyl**, whereas removal of either one of the 2 hydrogens attached to the central carbon yields a branched-chain alkyl group called **isopropyl**:

Propyl group The straight-chain alkyl group $-CH_2CH_2CH_3$.

Isopropyl group The branched-chain alkyl group $-CH(CH_3)_2$.

Remove H from end carbon

$$-\overset{\overset{\displaystyle H}{|}}{C}-\overset{\overset{\displaystyle H}{|}}{C}-\overset{\overset{\displaystyle H}{|}}{C}-H \;=\; -CH_2CH_2CH_3$$

Propyl group (straight chain)

Propane

Remove H from inside carbon

$$H-\overset{\overset{\displaystyle H}{|}}{C}-\overset{\overset{\displaystyle H}{|}}{C}-\overset{\overset{\displaystyle H}{|}}{C}-H \;=\; CH_3\overset{|}{C}HCH_3 \;\; or \;\; (CH_3)_2CH-$$

Isopropyl group (branched chain)

It is important to realize that alkyl groups are not compounds but rather are simply partial structures that help us name compounds. The names of some common alkyl groups are listed in Table 12.4; you will want to memorize them.

TABLE 12.4 Some Common Alkyl Groups*

CH_3-	CH_3CH_2-	$CH_3CH_2CH_2-$	$CH_3\overset{\overset{\displaystyle CH_3}{|}}{C}H-$
Methyl	Ethyl	*n*-Propyl	Isopropyl
$CH_3CH_2CH_2CH_2-$	$CH_3\overset{|}{C}HCH_2CH_3$	$CH_3\overset{\overset{\displaystyle CH_3}{|}}{C}HCH_2-$	$CH_3\overset{\overset{\displaystyle CH_3}{|}}{\underset{\underset{\displaystyle CH_3}{|}}{C}}CH_3$
n-Butyl	*sec*-Butyl	Isobutyl	*tert*-Butyl

The red bond shows the connection to the rest of the molecule.

Notice that four butyl (four-carbon) groups are listed in Table 12.4: butyl, *sec*-butyl, isobutyl, and *tert*-butyl. The prefix *sec*- stands for *secondary*, and the prefix *tert*- stands for *tertiary*, referring to the number of other carbon atoms attached to the branch point. There are four possible substitution patterns, called *primary*, *secondary*, *tertiary*, and *quaternary*. A **primary (1°) carbon atom** has 1 other carbon attached to it (typically indicated as an —R group in the molecular structure), a **secondary (2°) carbon atom** has 2 other carbons attached, a **tertiary (3°) carbon atom** has 3 other carbons attached, and a **quaternary (4°) carbon atom** has 4 other carbons attached:

Primary (1°) carbon atom A carbon atom with 1 other carbon attached to it.

Secondary (2°) carbon atom A carbon atom with 2 other carbons attached to it.

Tertiary (3°) carbon atom A carbon atom with 3 other carbons attached to it.

Quaternary (4°) carbon atom A carbon atom with 4 other carbons attached to it.

$R-\overset{\overset{\displaystyle H}{|}}{\underset{\underset{\displaystyle H}{|}}{C}}-H$	$R-\overset{\overset{\displaystyle R}{|}}{\underset{\underset{\displaystyle H}{|}}{C}}-H$	$R-\overset{\overset{\displaystyle R}{|}}{\underset{\underset{\displaystyle R}{|}}{C}}-H$	$R-\overset{\overset{\displaystyle R}{|}}{\underset{\underset{\displaystyle R}{|}}{C}}-R$
Primary carbon (1°) has one other carbon attached.	*Secondary* carbon (2°) has two other carbons attached.	*Tertiary* carbon (3°) has three other carbons attached.	*Quaternary* carbon (4°) has four other carbons attached.

The symbol **R** *is used here and in later chapters as a general abbreviation for any organic substituent.* You should think of it as representing the **R**est of the molecule, which we are not bothering to specify. The R is used to allow you to focus on a particular structural feature of a molecule without the "clutter" of the other atoms in the molecule detracting from it. The R might represent a methyl, ethyl, or propyl group, or any of a vast number of other possibilities. For example, the generalized formula R—OH for an alcohol might refer to an alcohol as simple as CH_3OH or CH_3CH_2OH or one as complicated as cholesterol.

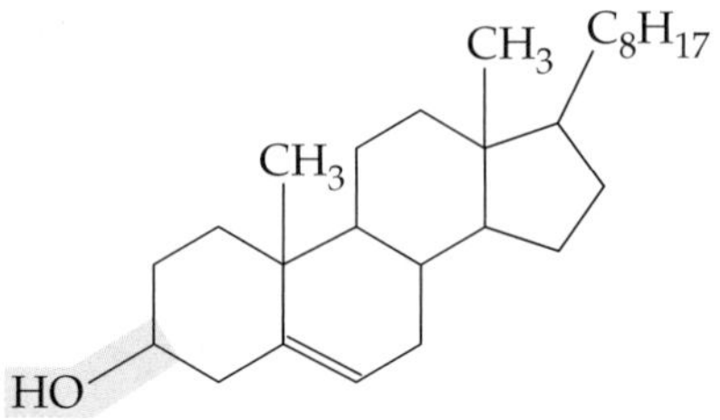

Branched-chain alkanes can be named by following four steps:

STEP 1: Name the main chain. Find the longest continuous chain of carbons, and name the chain according to the number of carbon atoms it contains. The longest chain may not be immediately obvious because it is not always written on one line; you may have to "turn corners" to find it.

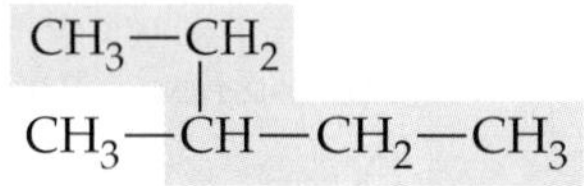

$$CH_3—CH_2$$
$$|$$
$$CH_3—CH—CH_2—CH_3$$

Name as a substituted pentane, not as a substituted butane, because the *longest* chain has five carbons.

STEP 2: Number the carbon atoms in the main chain, beginning at the end nearer the first branch point:

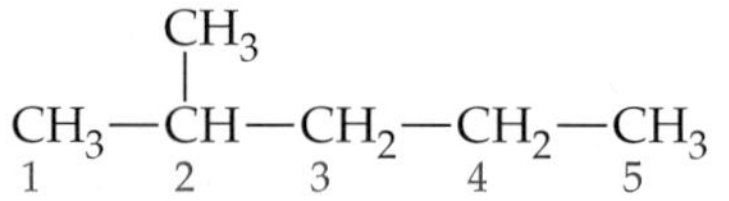

$$\underset{1}{CH_3}—\underset{2}{\overset{\overset{\displaystyle CH_3}{|}}{CH}}—\underset{3}{CH_2}—\underset{4}{CH_2}—\underset{5}{CH_3}$$

The first (and only) branch occurs at C2 if we start numbering from the left, but would occur at C4 if we started from the right by mistake.

STEP 3: Identify the branching substituents, and number each according to its point of attachment to the main chain:

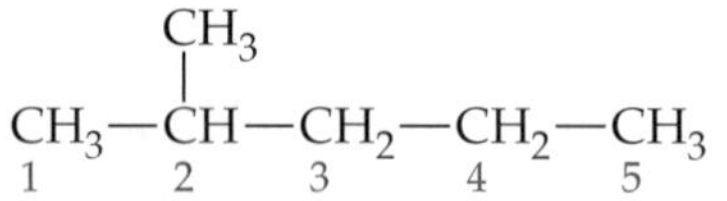

$$\underset{1}{CH_3}—\underset{2}{\overset{\overset{\displaystyle CH_3}{|}}{CH}}—\underset{3}{CH_2}—\underset{4}{CH_2}—\underset{5}{CH_3}$$

The main chain is a pentane. There is one —CH_3 substituent group connected to C2 of the chain.

If there are two substituents on the same carbon, assign the same number to both. There must always be as many numbers in the name as there are substituents.

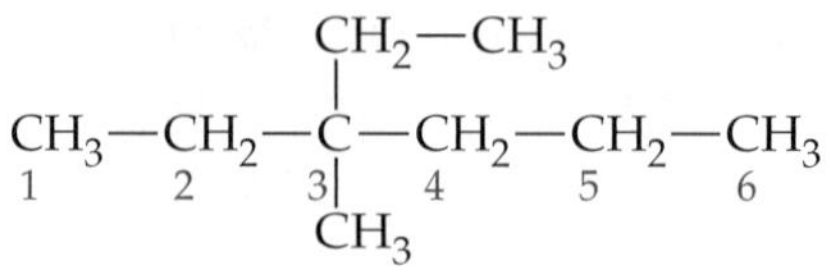

$$\underset{1}{CH_3}—\underset{2}{CH_2}—\underset{3}{\overset{\overset{\displaystyle CH_2—CH_3}{|}}{\underset{\underset{\displaystyle CH_3}{|}}{C}}}—\underset{4}{CH_2}—\underset{5}{CH_2}—\underset{6}{CH_3}$$

The main chain is a hexane. There are two substituents, a —CH_3 and a —CH_2CH_3, both connected to C3 of the chain.

STEP 4: Write the name as a single word, using hyphens to separate the numbers from the different prefixes and commas to separate numbers if necessary. If two or more different substituent groups are present, cite them in alphabetical order. If two or more identical substituents are present, use one of the prefixes *di-*, *tri-*, *tetra-*, and so forth, but do not use these prefixes for alphabetizing purposes.

$$CH_3-\overset{\overset{\displaystyle CH_3}{|}}{\underset{2}{CH}}-\underset{3}{CH_2}-\underset{4}{CH_2}-\underset{5}{CH_3}$$
$$\underset{1}{}$$

2-Methylpentane (a five-carbon main chain with a 2-methyl substituent)

$$\underset{1}{CH_3}-\underset{2}{CH_2}-\overset{\overset{\displaystyle CH_2-CH_3}{|}}{\underset{3}{C}}-\underset{4}{CH_2}-\underset{5}{CH_2}-\underset{6}{CH_3}$$
$$\underset{\displaystyle CH_3}{|}$$

3-Ethyl-3-methylhexane (a six-carbon main chain with 3-ethyl and 3-methyl substituents cited alphabetically)

$$CH_3-\overset{\overset{\displaystyle \overset{2|}{CH_2}-\overset{1}{CH_3}}{}}{\underset{3|}{C}}-\underset{4}{CH_2}-\underset{5}{CH_2}-\underset{6}{CH_3}$$
$$\underset{\displaystyle CH_3}{|}$$

3,3-Dimethylhexane (a six-carbon main chain with two 3-methyl substitutents)

WORKED EXAMPLE **12.9** Naming Organic Compounds: Alkanes

What is the IUPAC name of the following alkane?

$$CH_3-\overset{\overset{\displaystyle CH_3}{|}}{CH}-CH_2-CH_2-\overset{\overset{\displaystyle CH_3}{|}}{CH}-CH_2-CH_3$$

ANALYSIS Follow the four steps outlined in the text.

SOLUTION

STEP 1: The longest continuous chain of carbon atoms is seven, so the main chain is a *hept*ane.

STEP 2: Number the main chain beginning at the end nearer the first branch:

$$\underset{1}{CH_3}-\overset{\overset{\displaystyle CH_3}{|}}{\underset{2}{CH}}-\underset{3}{CH_2}-\underset{4}{CH_2}-\overset{\overset{\displaystyle CH_3}{|}}{\underset{5}{CH}}-\underset{6}{CH_2}-\underset{7}{CH_3}$$

STEP 3: Identify and number the substituents (a 2-methyl and a 5-methyl in this case):

$$\underset{1}{CH_3}-\overset{\overset{\displaystyle CH_3}{|}}{\underset{2}{CH}}-\underset{3}{CH_2}-\underset{4}{CH_2}-\overset{\overset{\displaystyle CH_3}{|}}{\underset{5}{CH}}-\underset{6}{CH_2}-\underset{7}{CH_3}$$

Substituents: 2-methyl, 5-methyl

STEP 4: Write the name as one word, using the prefix *di-* because there are two methyl groups. Separate the two numbers by a comma, and use a hyphen between the numbers and the word.

Name: 2, 5-Dimethylheptane

WORKED EXAMPLE **12.10** Molecular Structure: Identifying 1°, 2°, 3°, and 4° Carbons

Identify each carbon atom in the following molecule as primary, secondary, tertiary, or quaternary.

$$CH_3\overset{\overset{\displaystyle CH_3}{|}}{CH}CH_2CH_2\overset{\overset{\displaystyle CH_3}{|}}{\underset{\underset{\displaystyle CH_3}{|}}{C}}CH_3$$

ANALYSIS Look at each carbon atom in the molecule, count the number of other carbon atoms attached, and make the assignment accordingly: primary (1 carbon attached); secondary (2 carbons attached); tertiary (3 carbons attached); quaternary (4 carbons attached).

SOLUTION

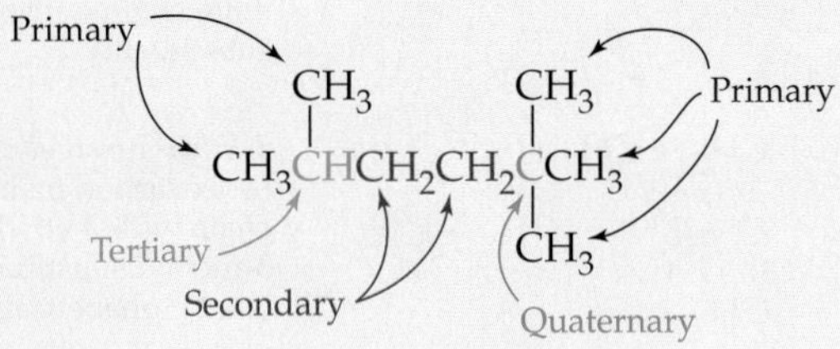

Primary

$$\underset{\substack{\text{Tertiary} \\ \text{Secondary}}}{\text{CH}_3\text{CHCH}_2\text{CH}_2\text{CCH}_3}$$

Primary

CH₃   CH₃

CH₃

Quaternary

WORKED EXAMPLE   **12.11** Molecular Structures: Drawing Condensed Structures from Names

Draw condensed structures corresponding to the following IUPAC names:

(a) 2,3-Dimethylpentane

(b) 3-Ethylheptane

ANALYSIS Starting with the parent chain, add the named alkyl substituent groups to the appropriately numbered carbon atom(s).

SOLUTION

(a) The parent chain has 5 carbons (*pent*ane), with two methyl groups (—CH₃) attached to the second and third carbon in the chain:

$$\underset{\substack{1 \quad 2 \quad 3 \quad 4 \quad 5}}{\text{CH}_3\text{CH CH CH}_2\text{CH}_3}$$

CH₃CH₃

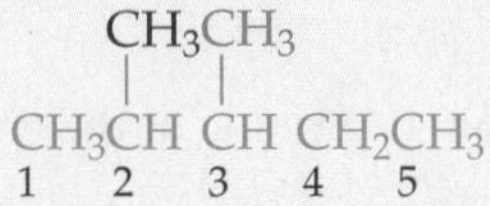

(b) The parent chain has 7 carbons (*hept*ane), with one ethyl group (—CH₂CH₃) attached to the third carbon in the chain:

$$\underset{\substack{1 \quad 2 \quad 3 \quad 4 \quad 5 \quad 6 \quad 7}}{\text{CH}_3\text{CH}_2\text{CH CH}_2\text{CH}_2\text{CH}_2\text{CH}_3}$$

CH₂CH₃

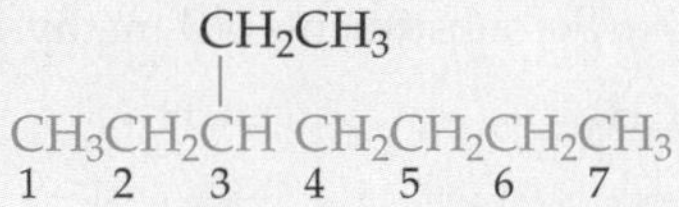

PROBLEM 12.10

What are the IUPAC names of the following alkanes?

(a) 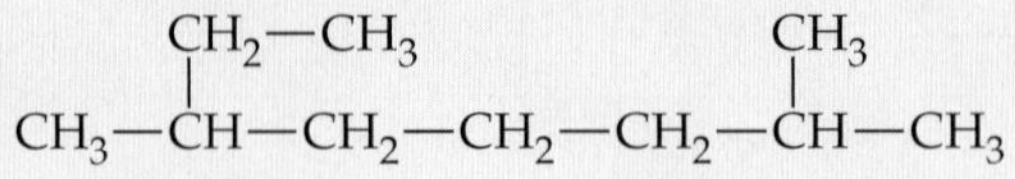 CH₃—CH—CH₂—CH₂—CH₂—CH—CH₃
     with CH₂—CH₃ on C2 and CH₃ on C6

(b) 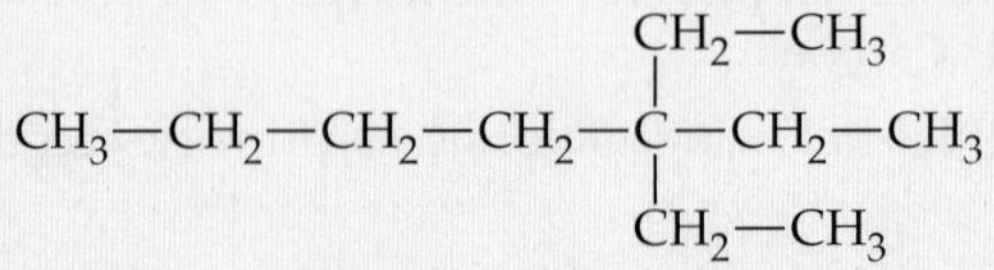 CH₃—CH₂—CH₂—CH₂—C—CH₂—CH₃
     with CH₂—CH₃ above and CH₂—CH₃ below the central C

PROBLEM 12.11

Draw both condensed and line structures corresponding to the following IUPAC names and label each carbon as primary, secondary, tertiary, or quaternary:

(a) 3-Methylhexane   (b) 3,4-Dimethyloctane

(c) 2,2,4-Trimethylpentane

PROBLEM 12.12

Draw and name alkanes that meet the following descriptions:

(a) An alkane with a tertiary carbon atom

(b) An alkane that has both a tertiary and a quaternary carbon atom

KEY CONCEPT PROBLEM 12.13

What are the IUPAC names of the following alkanes?

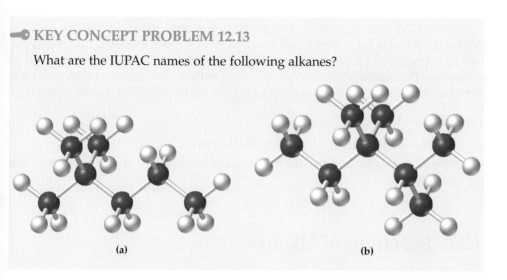

(a)   (b)

12.7 Properties of Alkanes

Alkanes contain only nonpolar C—C and C—H bonds, so the only intermolecular forces influencing them are weak London dispersion forces (Section 8.11). (⬭ , p. 235) The effect of these forces is shown in the regularity with which the melting and boiling points of straight-chain alkanes increase with molecular size (Figure 12.3). The first four alkanes—methane, ethane, propane, and butane—are gases at room temperature and pressure. Alkanes with 5–15 carbon atoms are liquids; those with 16 or more carbon atoms are generally low-melting, waxy solids.

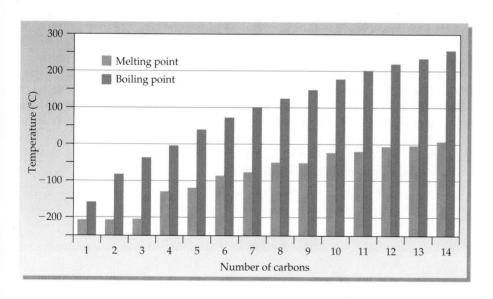

◀ **FIGURE 12.3** The boiling and melting points for the C_1–C_{14} straight-chain alkanes increase with molecular size.

In keeping with their low polarity, alkanes are insoluble in water but soluble in nonpolar organic solvents, including other alkanes (Section 9.2). (⬭ , p. 257) Because alkanes are generally less dense than water, they float on its surface.

▲ The waxy coating that makes these apples so shiny is a mixture of higher-molecular-weight alkanes.

Low-molecular-weight alkanes are volatile and must be handled with care because their vapors are flammable. Mixtures of alkane vapors and air can explode when ignited by a single spark.

The physiological effects of alkanes are limited. Methane, ethane, and propane gases are nontoxic, and the danger of inhaling them lies in potential suffocation due to lack of oxygen. Breathing the vapor of higher alkanes in large concentrations can induce loss of consciousness. There is also a danger in breathing droplets of liquid alkanes because they dissolve nonpolar substances in lung tissue and cause pneumonia-like symptoms.

Mineral oil, petroleum jelly, and paraffin wax are mixtures of higher alkanes. All are harmless to body tissue and are used in numerous food and medical applications. Mineral oil passes through the body unchanged and is sometimes used as a laxative. Petroleum jelly (sold as Vaseline) softens, lubricates, and protects the skin. Paraffin wax is used in candle making, on surfboards, and in home canning.

Properties of Alkanes

- Odorless or mild odor; colorless; tasteless; nontoxic
- Nonpolar; insoluble in water but soluble in nonpolar organic solvents; less dense than water
- Flammable; otherwise not very reactive

12.8 Reactions of Alkanes

Alkanes do not react with acids, bases, or most other common laboratory *reagents* (a substance that causes a reaction to occur). Their only major reactions are with oxygen (combustion) and with halogens (halogenation).

Combustion

Combustion A chemical reaction that produces a flame, usually because of burning with oxygen.

The reaction of an alkane with oxygen occurs during **combustion**, an oxidation reaction that commonly takes place in a controlled manner in an engine or furnace (Section 7.3). ($\bigcirc\hspace{-6pt}\bigcirc\hspace{-6pt}\bigcirc$, p. 184) Carbon dioxide and water are the products of complete combustion of any hydrocarbon, and a large amount of heat is released (ΔH is a negative number). Some examples were given in Table 7.1.

$$CH_4(g) + 2\,O_2(g) \longrightarrow CO_2(g) + 2\,H_2O(l) \qquad \Delta H = -213 \text{ kcal/mol}$$

When hydrocarbon combustion is incomplete because of faulty engine or furnace performance, carbon monoxide and carbon-containing soot are among the products. Carbon monoxide is a highly toxic and dangerous substance, especially so because it has no odor and can easily go undetected (See the Application "CO and NO: Pollutants or Miracle Molecules?" in Chapter 5). Breathing air that contains as little as 2% CO for only one hour can cause respiratory and nervous system damage or death. The supply of oxygen to the brain is cut off by carbon monoxide because it binds strongly to blood hemoglobin at the site where oxygen is normally bound. By contrast with CO, CO_2 is nontoxic and causes no harm, except by suffocation when present in high concentration.

PROBLEM 12.14

Write a balanced equation for the complete combustion of ethane with oxygen.

Halogenation

The second notable reaction of alkanes is *halogenation*, the replacement of an alkane hydrogen by a chlorine or bromine in a process initiated by heat or light. Only one

H at a time is replaced; however, if allowed to react for a long enough time, all H's will be replaced with halogens. Complete chlorination of methane, for example, yields carbon tetrachloride:

$$CH_4 + 4\,Cl_2 \xrightarrow{\text{Heat or light}} CCl_4 + 4\,HCl$$

Although the above equation for the reaction of methane with chlorine is balanced, it does not fully represent what actually happens. In fact, this reaction, like many organic reactions, yields a mixture of products:

$$CH_4 + Cl_2 \longrightarrow CH_3Cl + HCl$$
$$\xrightarrow{Cl_2} CH_2Cl_2 + HCl$$
$$\xrightarrow{Cl_2} CHCl_3 + HCl$$
$$\xrightarrow{Cl_2} CCl_4 + HCl$$

CH_3Cl, chloromethane
CH_2Cl_2, dichloromethane
$CHCl_3$, chloroform
CCl_4, carbon tetrachloride

When we write the equation for an organic reaction, our attention is usually focused on converting a particular reactant into a desired product; any minor by-products and inorganic compounds (such as the HCl formed in the chlorination of methane) are often of little interest and are ignored. Thus, it is not always necessary to balance the equation for an organic reaction as long as the reactant, the major product, and any necessary reagents and conditions are shown. A chemist who plans to convert methane into bromomethane might therefore write the equation as

$$CH_4 \xrightarrow[\text{Light, heat}]{Br_2} CH_3Br$$

Like many equations for organic reactions, this equation is not balanced.

In using this convention, it is customary to put reactants and reagents above the arrow and conditions, solvents, and catalysts below the arrow.

PROBLEM 12.15

Write the structures of all possible products with 1 and 2 chlorine atoms that form in the reaction of propane with Cl_2.

12.9 Cycloalkanes

The organic compounds described thus far have all been open-chain, or *acyclic*, alkanes. **Cycloalkanes**, which contain rings of carbon atoms, are also well known and are widespread throughout nature. To form a closed ring requires an additional C—C bond and the loss of 2 H atoms; the general formula for cycloalkanes, therefore, is C_nH_{2n}, which, as we will find in the next chapter, is the same as that for alkenes. Compounds of all ring sizes from 3 through 30 and beyond have been prepared in the laboratory. The two simplest cycloalkanes—cyclopropane and cyclobutane—contain 3 and 4 carbon atoms, respectively:

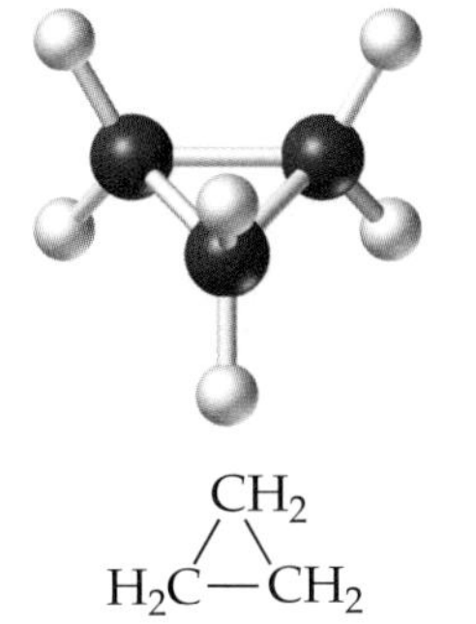

Cycloalkane An alkane that contains a ring of carbon atoms.

CH_2
/ \
H_2C—CH_2

Cyclopropane
(mp −128 °C, bp −33 °C)

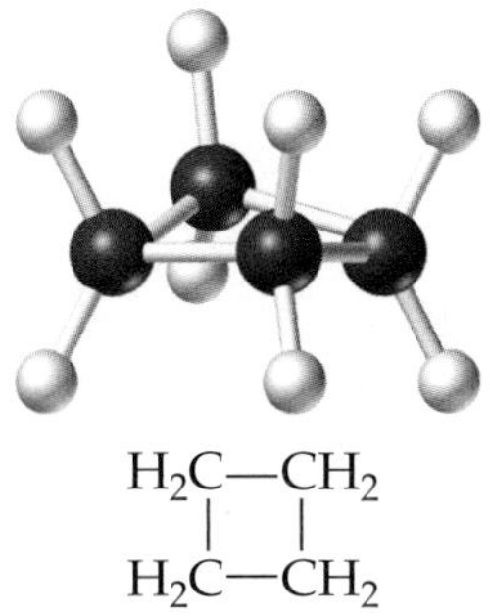

H_2C—CH_2
| |
H_2C—CH_2

Cyclobutane
(mp −50 °C, bp −12 °C)

APPLICATION ▶ Petroleum

Many alkanes occur naturally throughout plants and animals, but natural gas and petroleum deposits provide the world's most abundant supply. *Natural gas* consists chiefly of methane, along with smaller amounts of ethane, propane, and butane. *Petroleum* is a complex liquid mixture of hydrocarbons that must be separated, or *refined*, into different *fractions* before it can be used. The vast majority of petroleum products are used as fuels and lubricating oils in the transportation industry, but petroleum-based products are also found in plastics, medicines, food items, and a host of other products.

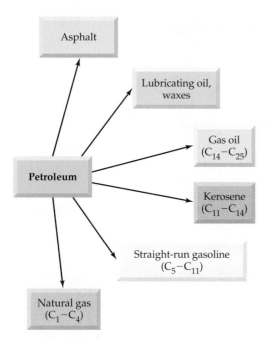

▲ The crude petroleum from this off-shore well is an enormously complex mixture of alkanes and other organic molecules.

Petroleum has been used throughout history in such diverse applications as a component in mortar and for coating walls and boat hulls. Native Americans used it in magic and paints, and often sold it to pioneers for medicinal uses (as Seneca oil or Genesee oil). The modern petroleum industry began in 1859 in Oil Creek, Pennsylvania, when American oil pioneer E. L. Drake drilled the first oil-producing well.

Petroleum refining begins with distillation to separate the crude oil into three main fractions according to boiling points: straight-run gasoline (bp 30–200 °C), kerosene (bp 175–300 °C), and gas oil (bp 275–400 °C). The residue is then further distilled under reduced pressure to recover lubricating oils, waxes, and asphalt. But distillation of petroleum is just the beginning of the process for making gasoline. It has long been known that straight-chain alkanes burn less smoothly in engines than do branched-chain alkanes, as measured by a compound's *octane number*. Heptane, a straight-chain alkane and particularly poor fuel, is assigned an octane rating of 0, whereas 2,2,4-trimethylpentane, a branched-chain alkane commonly known as isooctane, is given a rating of 100. Straight-run gasoline, with its high percentage of unbranched alkanes, is thus a poor fuel. Petroleum chemists, however, have devised methods to remedy the problem. One of these methods, called *catalytic cracking*, involves taking the kerosene fraction ($C_{11}–C_{14}$) and "cracking" it into smaller $C_3–C_5$ molecules at high temperature. These small hydrocarbons are then catalytically recombined to yield $C_7–C_{10}$ branched-chain molecules that are perfectly suited for use as automobile fuel.

In addition to the obvious fuel-based applications, petroleum is the source of paraffin wax (used in candy, candles, and polishes) and petroleum jelly (used in medical products and toiletries). Petroleum "feedstocks" are often converted into the basic chemical building blocks used to produce plastics, rubber, synthetic fibers, drugs, and detergents.

See Additional Problems 12.65 and 12.66 at the end of the chapter.

Note that if we flatten the rings in cyclopropane and cyclobutane, the C—C—C bond angles are 60° and 90°, respectively—values that are considerably compressed from the normal 109.5° tetrahedral value. As a result, these compounds are less stable and more reactive than other cycloalkanes. The five-membered (cyclopentane) ring has nearly ideal bond angles. So does the six-membered (cyclohexane) ring, which accomplishes this nearly ideal state by adopting a puckered, nonplanar shape called a *chair conformation*, further discussion of which, while important, is beyond the scope of this textbook. Both cyclopentane and cyclohexane rings are therefore stable, and many naturally occurring and biochemically active molecules contain such rings.

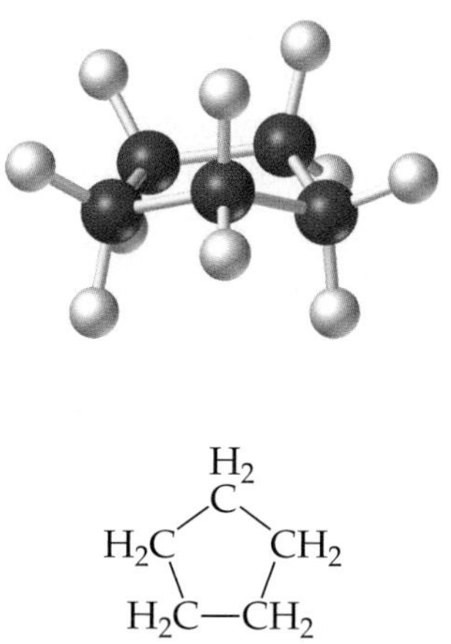

Cyclopentane—all bond angles are near 109°.

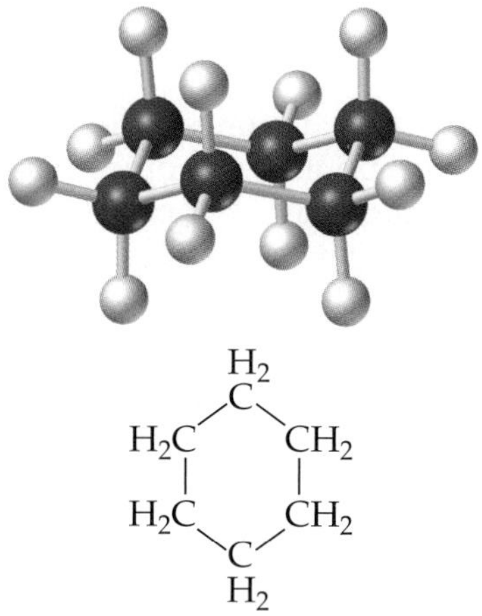

Cyclohexane—all bond angles are near 109.5°.

Cyclic and acyclic alkanes are similar in many of their properties. Cyclopropane and cyclobutane are gases, whereas larger cycloalkanes are liquids or solids. Like alkanes, cycloalkanes are nonpolar, insoluble in water, and flammable. Because of their cyclic structures, however, cycloalkane molecules are more rigid and less flexible than their open-chain counterparts. Rotation is not possible around the carbon–carbon bonds in cycloalkanes without breaking open the ring.

12.10 Drawing and Naming Cycloalkanes

Even condensed structures become awkward when we work with large molecules that contain rings. Thus, line structures are used almost exclusively in drawing cycloalkanes, with *polygons* used for the cyclic parts of the molecules. A triangle represents cyclopropane, a square represents cyclobutane, a pentagon represents cyclopentane, and so on.

Cyclopropane   Cyclobutane   Cyclopentane   Cyclohexane   Cycloheptane

Methylcyclohexane, for example, looks like this in a line structure:

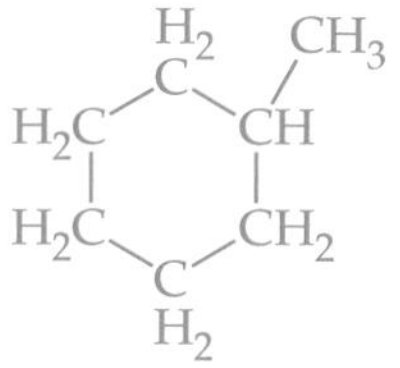

is the same as

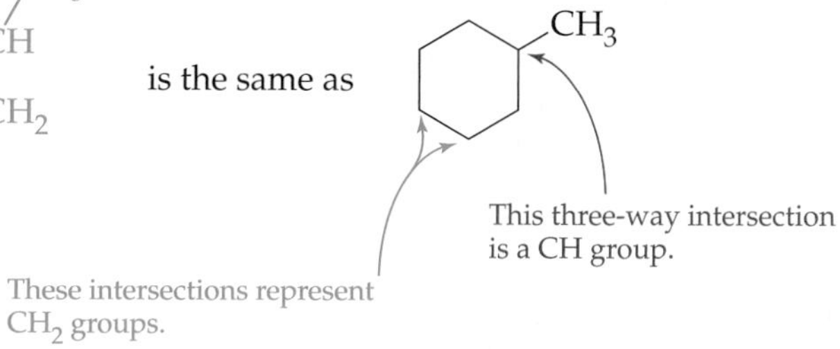

This three-way intersection is a CH group.

These intersections represent CH₂ groups.

Cycloalkanes are named by a straightforward extension of the rules for naming open-chain alkanes. In most cases, only two steps are needed:

STEP 1: Use the cycloalkane name as the parent. That is, compounds are named as alkyl-substituted cycloalkanes rather than as cycloalkyl-substituted alkanes. If there is only one substituent on the ring, it is not even necessary to assign a number because all ring positions are identical.

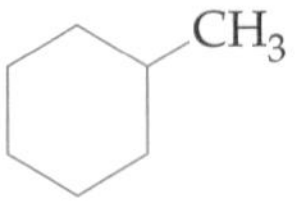

Parent compound: Cyclohexane
Name: Methylcyclohexane
(not cyclohexylmethane)

STEP 2: Identify and number the substituents. Start numbering at the group that has alphabetical priority, and proceed around the ring in the direction that gives the second substituent the lower possible number.

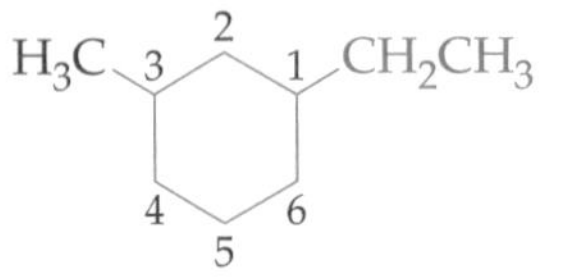

1-ethyl-3-methylcyclohexane
(not 1-ethyl-5-methylcyclohexane or
1-methyl-3-ethylcyclohexane or
1-methyl-5-ethylcyclohexane)

WORKED EXAMPLE 12.12 Naming Organic Compounds: Cycloalkanes

What is the IUPAC name of the following cycloalkane?

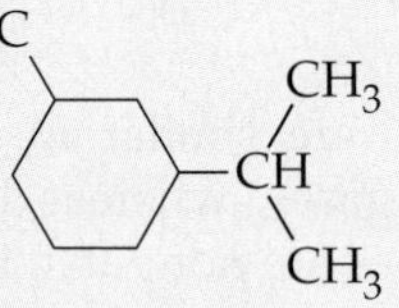

ANALYSIS First identify the parent cycloalkane, then add the positions and identity of any substituents.

SOLUTION

STEP 1: The parent cycloalkane contains 6 carbons (*hex*ane); hence, *cyclohexane*.

STEP 2: There are two substituents; a *methyl* (—CH_3) and an *isopropyl* (CH_3CHCH_3). Alphabetically, the isopropyl group is given priority (number 1); the methyl group is then found on the third carbon in the ring.

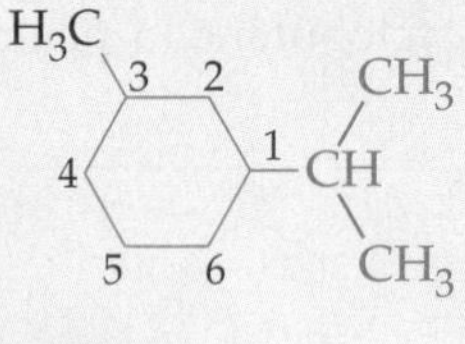

1-isopropyl-3-methylcyclohexane

WORKED EXAMPLE 12.13 Molecular Structures: Drawing Line Structures for Cycloalkanes

Draw a line structure for 1,4-dimethylcyclohexane.

ANALYSIS This structure consists of a 6-carbon ring with two methyl groups attached at positions 1 and 4. Draw a hexagon to represent a cyclohexane ring, and attach a —CH_3 group at an arbitrary position that becomes the first carbon in the chain, designated as C1. Then count around the ring to the fourth carbon (C4), and attach another —CH_3 group.

SOLUTION
Note that the second methyl group is written here as H_3C— because it is attached on the left side of the ring.

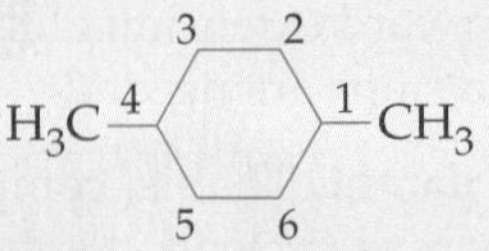

1,4-dimethylcyclohexane

PROBLEM 12.16

What are the IUPAC names of the following cycloalkanes?

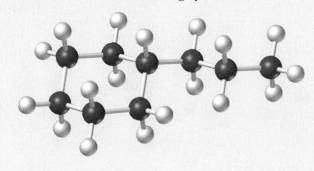

(a) H_3C—⬡—CH_2CH_3 **(b)** CH_3CH_2—⬠—$CH(CH_3)_2$

PROBLEM 12.17

Draw line structures that represent the following IUPAC names:

(a) 1,1-Diethylcyclohexane   **(b)** 1,3,5-Trimethylcycloheptane

◐ KEY CONCEPT PROBLEM 12.18

What is the IUPAC name of the following cycloalkane?

SUMMARY: REVISITING THE CHAPTER GOALS

1. **What are the basic properties of organic compounds?** Compounds made up primarily of carbon atoms are classified as organic. Many organic compounds contain carbon atoms that are joined in long chains by a combination of single (C—C), double (C=C), or triple (C≡C) bonds.

2. **What are functional groups, and how are they used to classify organic molecules?** Organic compounds can be classified into various families according to the functional groups they contain. A *functional group* is a part of a larger molecule and is composed of a group of atoms that has characteristic structure and chemical reactivity. A given functional group undergoes nearly the same chemical reactions in every molecule where it occurs. In this chapter we focused primarily on *alkanes*, hydrocarbon compounds that contain only single bonds between all C atoms.

3. **What are isomers?** *Isomers* are compounds that have the same formula but different structures. Isomers that differ in their connections among atoms are called *constitutional isomers*.

4. **How are organic molecules drawn?** Organic compounds can be represented by *structural formulas* in which all atoms and bonds are shown, by *condensed structures* in which not all bonds are drawn, or by *line structures* in which the carbon skeleton is represented by lines and the locations of C and H atoms are understood.

5. **What are alkanes and cycloalkanes, and how are they named?** Compounds that contain only carbon and hydrogen are called *hydrocarbons*, and hydrocarbons that have only single bonds are called *alkanes*. A *straight-chain alkane* has all its carbons connected in a row, a *branched-chain alkane* has a branching connection of atoms somewhere along its chain, and a *cycloalkane* has a ring of carbon atoms. Alkanes have the general formula C_nH_{2n+2}, whereas cycloalkanes have the formula C_nH_{2n}. Straight-chain alkanes are named by adding the family ending -ane to a parent; this tells how many carbon atoms are present. Branched-chain alkanes are named by using the longest continuous chain of carbon atoms for the parent and then identifying the *alkyl groups* present as branches off the main chain. The position of the substituent groups on the main chain are identified by numbering the carbons in the chain so that the substituents have the lowest number. Cycloalkanes are named by adding *cyclo-* as a prefix to the name of the alkane.

KEY WORDS

Alkane, *p. 368*

Alkyl group, *p. 380*

Branched-chain alkane, *p. 369*

Combustion, *p. 386*

Condensed structure, *p. 370*

Conformation, *p. 376*

Conformer, *p. 376*

Constitutional isomers, *p. 369*

Cycloalkane, *p. 387*

Ethyl group, *p. 380*

Functional group, *p. 364*

Hydrocarbon, *p. 364*

Isomers, *p. 368*

Isopropyl group, *p. 381*

Line structure, *p. 372*

Methyl group, *p. 380*

Methylene group, *p. 371*

Organic chemistry, *p. 361*

Primary (1°) carbon atom, *p. 381*

Propyl group, *p. 381*

Quaternary (4°) carbon atom, *p. 381*

Secondary (2°) carbon atom, *p. 381*

Straight-chain alkane, *p. 369*

Substituent, *p. 380*

Tertiary (3°) carbon atom, *p. 381*

6. What are the general properties and chemical reactions of alkanes?   Alkanes are generally soluble only in nonpolar organic solvents, have weak intermolecular forces, and are nontoxic. Their principal chemical reactions are *combustion*, a reaction with oxygen that gives carbon dioxide and water, and *halogenation*, a reaction in which hydrogen atoms are replaced by chlorine or bromine.

SUMMARY OF REACTIONS

1. Combustion of an alkane with oxygen (Section 12.8):

$$CH_4 + 2\,O_2 \longrightarrow CO_2 + 2\,H_2O$$

2. Halogenation of an alkane to yield an alkyl halide (Section 12.8):

$$CH_4 + Cl_2 \longrightarrow CH_3Cl + HCl$$

UNDERSTANDING KEY CONCEPTS

12.19 How many hydrogen atoms are needed to complete the hydrocarbon formulas for the following carbon backbones?

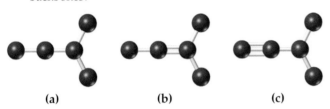

(a)   (b)   (c)

12.20 Convert the following models into condensed structures (gray = C; ivory = H; red = O):

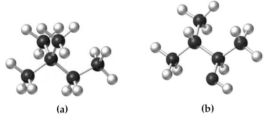

(a)   (b)

12.21 Convert the following models into line drawings (gray = C; ivory = H; red = O; blue = N):

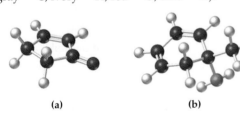

(a)   (b)

12.22 Identify the functional groups in the following compounds:

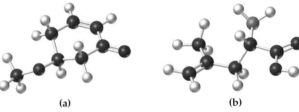

(a)   (b)

12.23 Give systematic names for the following alkanes:

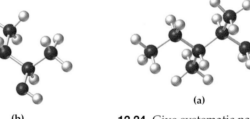

(a)   (b)

12.24 Give systematic names for the following cycloalkanes:

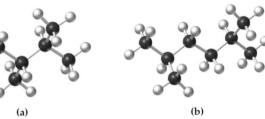

(a)   (b)

12.25 The following two compounds are isomers, even though both can be named 1,3-dimethylcyclopentane. What is the difference between them?

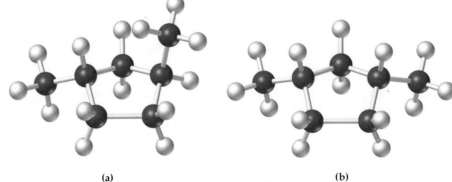

(a)   (b)

ADDITIONAL PROBLEMS

ORGANIC MOLECULES AND FUNCTIONAL GROUPS

12.26 What characteristics of carbon make possible the existence of so many different organic compounds?

12.27 What are functional groups, and why are they important?

12.28 Why are most organic compounds nonconducting and insoluble in water?

12.29 If you were given two unlabeled bottles, one containing hexane and one containing water, how could you tell them apart?

12.30 What is meant by the term *polar covalent bond*? Give an example of such a bond.

12.31 Give examples of compounds that are members of the following families:

(a) Alcohol   (b) Amine

(c) Carboxylic acid   (d) Ether

12.32 Locate and identify the functional groups in the following molecules ($-SO_2N-$ is a sulfanilamide):

(a)

Viagra

(b)

Aspirin

12.33 Identify the functional groups in the following molecules:

(a)

Vitamin A

(b)

Ambien

12.34 Propose structures for molecules that fit the following descriptions:

(a) A ketone with the formula $C_5H_{10}O$

(b) An ester with the formula $C_6H_{12}O_2$

(c) A compound with the formula $C_2H_5NO_2$ that is both an amine and a carboxylic acid

12.35 Propose structures for molecules that fit the following descriptions:

(a) An amide with the formula C_4H_9NO

(b) An aldehyde that has a ring of carbons, $C_6H_{10}O$

(c) An aromatic compound that is also an ether, $C_8H_{10}O$

ALKANES AND ISOMERS

12.36 What requirement must be met for two compounds to be isomers?

12.37 If one compound has the formula C_5H_{10} and another has the formula C_4H_{10}, are the two compounds isomers? Explain.

12.38 What is the difference between a secondary carbon and a tertiary carbon? Between a primary carbon and a quaternary carbon?

12.39 Why is it not possible for a compound to have a *quintary* carbon (five R groups attached to C)?

12.40 Give examples of compounds that meet the following descriptions:

(a) An alkane with two tertiary carbons

(b) A cycloalkane with only secondary carbons

12.41 Give examples of compounds that meet the following descriptions:

(a) A branched-chain alkane with only primary and quaternary carbons

(b) A cycloalkane with three substituents

12.42 There are three isomers with the formula C_3H_8O. Draw the condensed structure and the line structure for each isomer.

12.43 Write condensed structures for the following molecular formulas. (You may have to use rings and/or multiple bonds in some instances.)

(a) C_2H_7N

(b) C_4H_8 (Write the line structure as well.)

(c) C_2H_4O

(d) CH_2O_2 (Write the line structure as well.)

12.44 How many isomers can you write that fit the following descriptions?

(a) Alcohols with formula $C_4H_{10}O$

(b) Amines with formula C_3H_9N

(c) Ketones with formula $C_5H_{10}O$

12.45 How many isomers can you write that fit the following descriptions?

(a) Aldehydes with formula $C_5H_{10}O$

(b) Esters with formula $C_4H_8O_2$

(c) Carboxylic acids with formula $C_4H_8O_2$

12.46 Which of the following pairs of structures are identical, which are isomers, and which are unrelated?

(a) $CH_3CH_2CH_3$ and
$$CH_3$$
$$|$$
$$CH_2CH_3$$

(b) CH_3-N-CH_3 and CH_3CH_2-N-H
          $|$ $|$
          H   H

(c) $CH_3CH_2CH_2-O-CH_3$ and

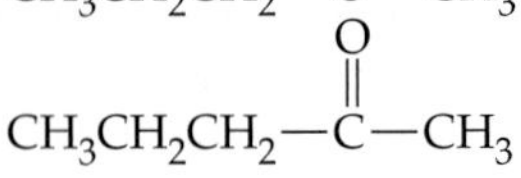

$$CH_3CH_2CH_2-\overset{\overset{\displaystyle O}{\|}}{C}-CH_3$$

(d) 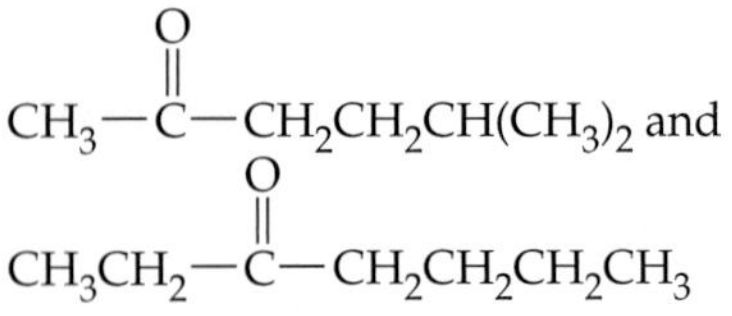 $CH_3-\overset{\overset{\displaystyle O}{\|}}{C}-CH_2CH_2CH(CH_3)_2$ and

$$CH_3CH_2-\overset{\overset{\displaystyle O}{\|}}{C}-CH_2CH_2CH_2CH_3$$

(e) $CH_3CH=CHCH_2CH_2-O-H$ and

$$CH_3CH_2\overset{\overset{\displaystyle}{\underset{\underset{\displaystyle CH_3}{|}}{C}}}H-\overset{\overset{\displaystyle O}{\|}}{C}-H$$

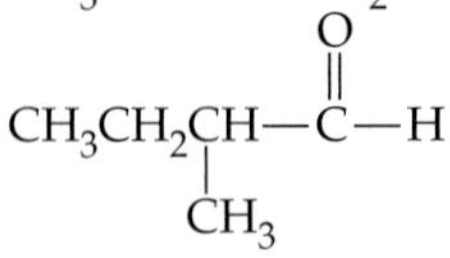

12.47 Which structure(s) in each group represent the same compound, and which represent isomers?

(a) 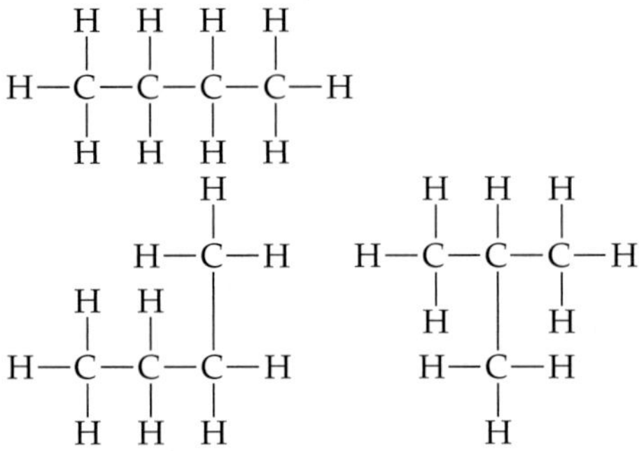
$$\begin{array}{cccccc} & H & H & H & H \\ & | & | & | & | \\ H-&C-&C-&C-&C-&H \\ & | & | & | & | \\ & H & H & H & H \end{array}$$

$$\begin{array}{c} H \\ | \\ H-C-H \\ | \end{array}$$
$$\begin{array}{ccc} H & H & H \\ | & | & | \\ H-C-&C-&C-H \\ | & | & | \\ H-\overset{\overset{\displaystyle H}{|}}{C}-\overset{\overset{\displaystyle H}{|}}{C}-\overset{\overset{\displaystyle H}{|}}{C}-H \\ | & | & | \\ H & H & H \end{array}$$

$$\begin{array}{ccc} & H & \\ H & | & H \\ | & C & | \\ H-C-&C-&C-H \\ | & | & | \\ H & \overset{\overset{\displaystyle H}{|}}{C} & H \\ & | & \\ & H & \end{array}$$

(b) 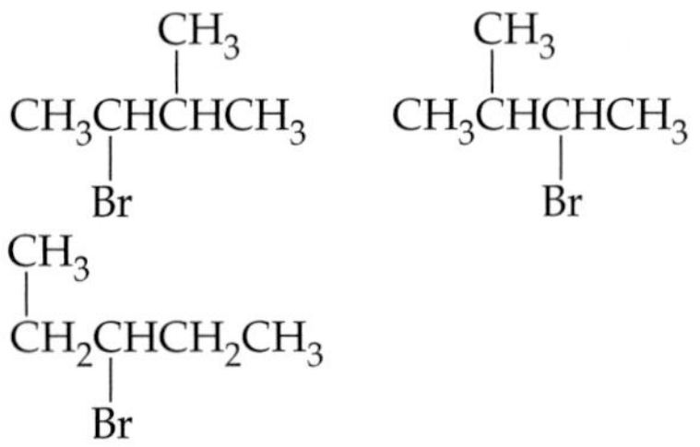
$$\underset{\underset{\displaystyle Br}{|}}{CH_3CHCHCH_3}\;\overset{\overset{\displaystyle CH_3}{|}}{}\qquad \underset{\underset{\displaystyle Br}{|}}{CH_3CHCHCH_3}\;\overset{\overset{\displaystyle CH_3}{|}}{}$$

$$\overset{\overset{\displaystyle CH_3}{|}}{\underset{\underset{\displaystyle Br}{|}}{CH_2CHCH_2CH_3}}$$

12.48 What is wrong with the following structures?

(a) $CH_3=CHCH_2CH_2OH$

(b) 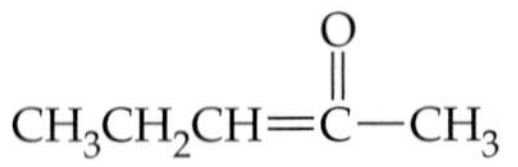 $CH_3CH_2CH=\overset{\overset{\displaystyle O}{\|}}{C}-CH_3$

(c) $CH_2CH_2CH_2C\equiv\underset{\underset{\displaystyle}{}}{\overset{\overset{\displaystyle CH_3}{|}}{C}}CH_3$

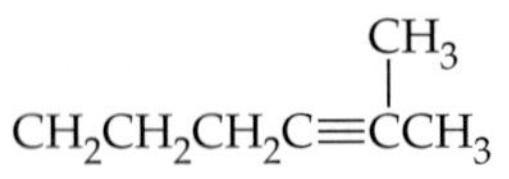

12.49 There are two things wrong with the following structure. What are they?

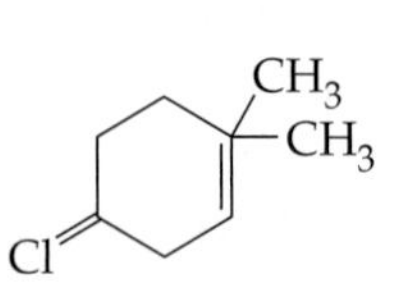

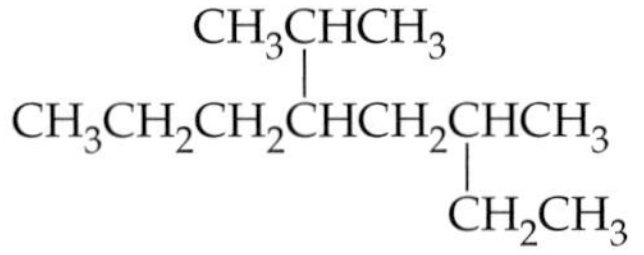

ALKANE NOMENCLATURE

12.50 What are the IUPAC names of the following alkanes?

(a) 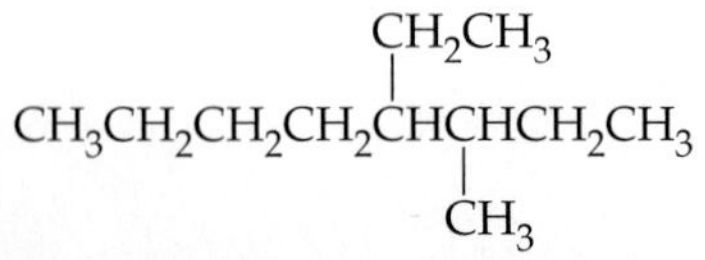 $CH_3CH_2CH_2CH_2\overset{\overset{\displaystyle CH_2CH_3}{|}}{C}HCHCH_2CH_3$ with $\underset{\underset{\displaystyle CH_3}{|}}{}$

(b) $CH_3CH_2CH_2\overset{\overset{\displaystyle CH_3CHCH_3}{|}}{C}HCH_2CHCH_3$ with $\underset{\underset{\displaystyle CH_2CH_3}{|}}{}$

(c) $CH_3\overset{\overset{\displaystyle CH_3}{|}}{C}CH_2CH_2CH_2\overset{\overset{\displaystyle CH_3}{|}}{C}HCH_3$ with $\underset{\underset{\displaystyle CH_3}{|}}{}$

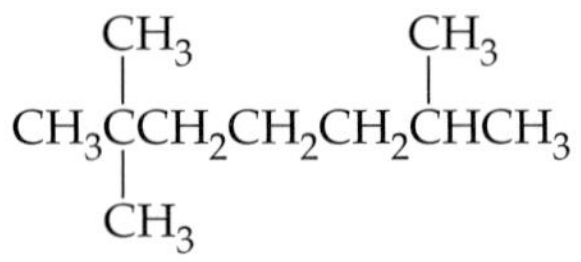

(d) 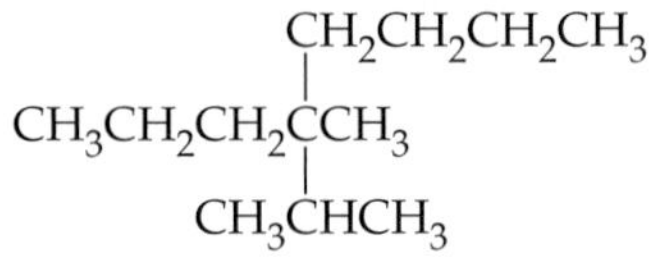 $CH_3CH_2CH_2\overset{\overset{\displaystyle CH_2CH_2CH_2CH_3}{|}}{C}CH_3$ with $\underset{\underset{\displaystyle CH_3CHCH_3}{|}}{}$

(e) 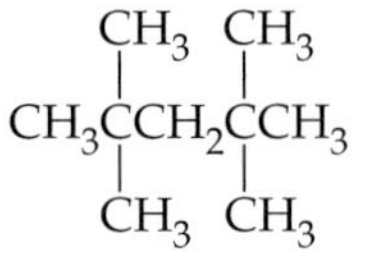 $CH_3\overset{\overset{\displaystyle CH_3}{|}}{C}CH_2\overset{\overset{\displaystyle CH_3}{|}}{C}CH_3$ with $\underset{\underset{\displaystyle CH_3}{|}}{}\;\underset{\underset{\displaystyle CH_3}{|}}{}$

(f) 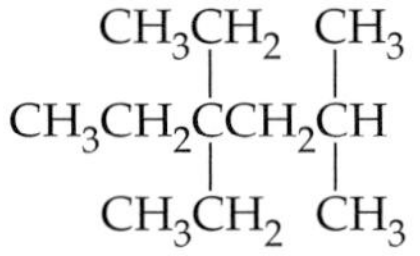 $CH_3CH_2\overset{\overset{\displaystyle CH_3CH_2}{|}}{C}CH_2\overset{\overset{\displaystyle CH_3}{|}}{C}H$ with $\underset{\underset{\displaystyle CH_3CH_2}{|}}{}\;\underset{\underset{\displaystyle CH_3}{|}}{}$

(g) 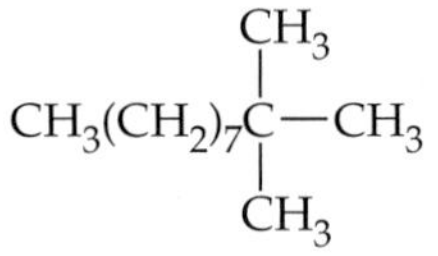 $CH_3(CH_2)_7\overset{\overset{\displaystyle CH_3}{|}}{\underset{\underset{\displaystyle CH_3}{|}}{C}}-CH_3$

12.51 Give IUPAC names for the five isomers with the formula C_6H_{14}.

12.52 Write condensed structures for the following compounds:
(a) 4-*tert*-Butyl-3,3,5-trimethylheptane
(b) 2,4-Dimethylpentane
(c) 4,4-Diethyl-3-methyloctane
(d) 3-Isopropyl-2,3,6,7-tetramethylnonane
(e) 3-Isobutyl-1-isopropyl-5-methylcycloheptane
(f) 1,1,3-Trimethylcyclopentane

12.53 Draw structures that correspond to the following IUPAC names:
(a) 1,1-Dimethylcyclopropane
(b) 1,2,3,4-Tetramethylcyclopentane
(c) 4-*tert*-Butyl-1,1-dimethylcyclohexane
(d) Cycloheptane
(e) 1,3,5-Triisopropylcyclohexane
(f) 1,3,5,7-Tetramethylcyclooctane

12.54 Name the following cycloalkanes:

(a)

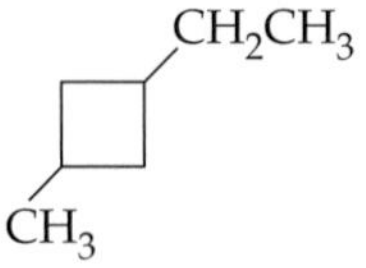

(b)

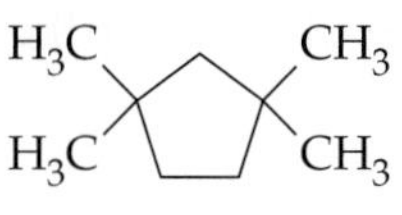

(c)

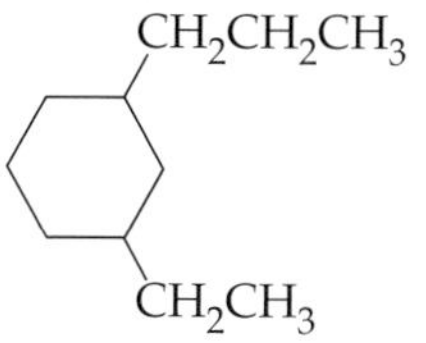

$CH_2CH_2CH_3$

CH_2CH_3

(d)

CH_3

CH_3

CH_3 —$CH_2CH_2CH_2CH_3$

CH_3

CH_3

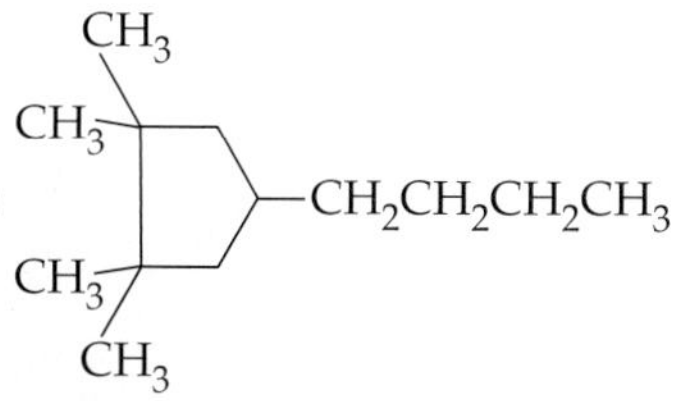

12.55 Name the following cycloalkanes:

(a)

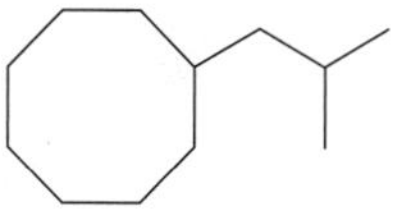

(b)

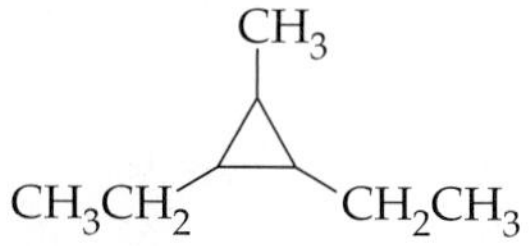

CH_3

CH_3CH_2 CH_2CH_3

(c)

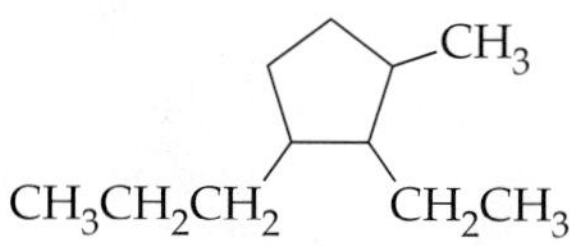

CH_3

$CH_3CH_2CH_2$ CH_2CH_3

12.56 The following names are incorrect. Tell what is wrong with each, and provide the correct names.

(a)

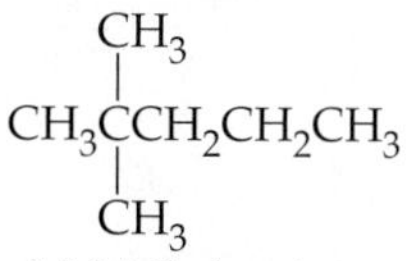

CH_3

$CH_3CCH_2CH_2CH_3$

CH_3

2,2-Methylpentane

(b)

CH_3 CH_3

CH—CH_2—CH

CH_3 CH_3

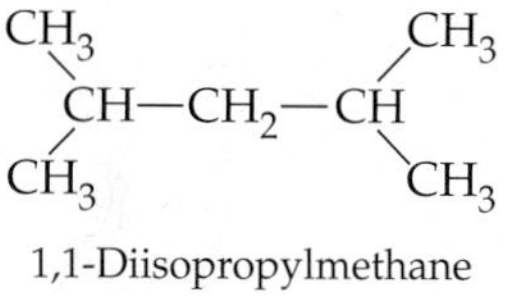

1,1-Diisopropylmethane

(c)

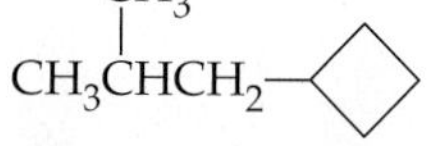

CH_3

CH_3CHCH_2—◇

1-Cyclobutyl-2-methylpropane

12.57 The following names are incorrect. Write the structural formula that agrees with the apparent name, and then write the correct name of the compound.

(a) 2-Ethylbutane
(b) 2-Isopropyl-2-methylpentane
(c) 5-Ethyl-1,1-methylcyclopentane
(d) 3-Ethyl-3,5,5-trimethylhexane
(e) 1,2-Dimethyl-4-ethylcyclohexane
(f) 2,4-Diethylpentane
(g) 5,5,6,6-Methyl-7,7-ethyldecane

12.58 Draw structures and give IUPAC names for the nine isomers of C_7H_{16}.

12.59 Draw the structural formulas and name all cyclic isomers with the formula C_6H_{12}.

REACTIONS OF ALKANES

12.60 Propane, commonly known as LP gas, burns in air to yield CO_2 and H_2O. Write a balanced equation for the reaction.

12.61 Write a balanced equation for the combustion of isooctane, C_8H_{16}, a component of gasoline.

12.62 Write the formulas of the three singly chlorinated isomers formed when 2,2-dimethylbutane reacts with Cl_2 in the presence of light.

12.63 Write the formulas of the seven doubly brominated isomers formed when 2,2-dimethylbutane reacts with Br_2 in the presence of light.

Applications

12.64 Why is it important to know the shape of a molecule? [*Displaying Molecular Shapes, p. 379*]

12.65 How does petroleum differ from natural gas? [*Petroleum, p. 388*]

12.66 What types of hydrocarbons burn most efficiently in an automobile engine? [*Petroleum, p. 388*]

General Questions and Problems

12.67 Identify the functional groups in the following molecules:

(a) Testosterone, a male sex hormone

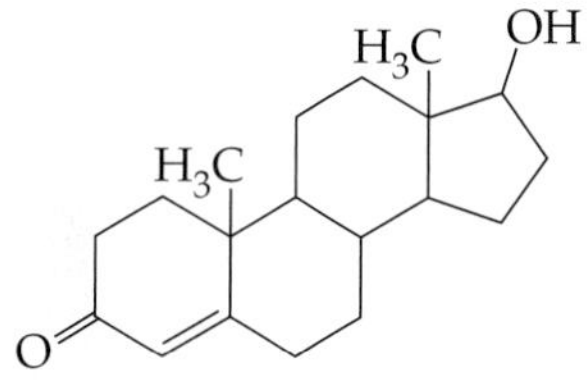

H_3C OH

H_3C

O

(b) Aspartame, an artificial sweetener

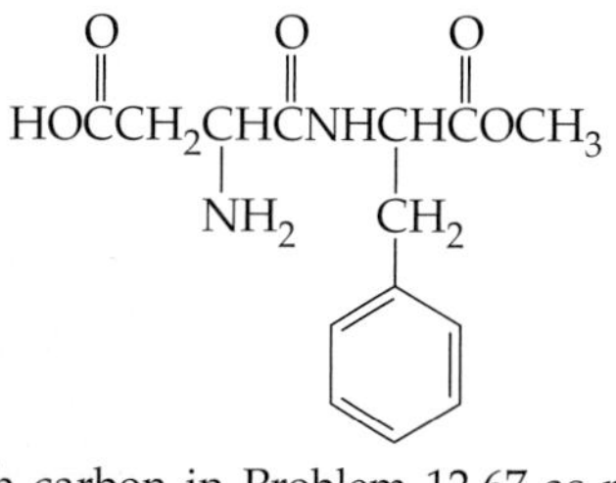

O   O   O

$HOCCH_2CHCNHCHCOCH_3$

NH_2 CH_2

12.68 Label each carbon in Problem 12.67 as primary, secondary, tertiary, or quaternary.

12.69 If someone reported the preparation of a compound with the formula C_3H_9 most chemists would be skeptical. Why?

12.70 Most lipsticks are about 70% castor oil and wax. Why is lipstick more easily removed with petroleum jelly than with water?

12.71 When cyclopentane is exposed to Br_2 in the presence of light, reaction occurs. Write the formulas of:

(a) All possible monobromination products
(b) All possible dibromination products

12.72 Which do you think has a higher boiling point, pentane or neopentane (2,2-dimethylpropane)? Why?

12.73 Propose structures for the following:

(a) An aldehyde, C_4H_8O
(b) An iodo-substituted alkene, C_5H_9I
(c) A cycloalkane, C_7H_{14}
(d) A diene (dialkene), C_5H_8

CHAPTER 13

Alkenes, Alkynes, and Aromatic Compounds

CONCEPTS TO REVIEW

VSEPR and Molecular Shapes
(Section 5.7)

The Shapes of Organic
Molecules
(Section 12.5)

Naming Alkanes
(Section 12.6)

▲ Flamingos owe their color to alkene pigments in their diet. Without these compounds, their feathers eventually turn white.

CONTENTS

CHAPTER GOALS

In this chapter, we will answer the following questions:

1. What are alkenes, alkynes, and aromatic compounds?

THE GOAL: Be able to recognize the functional groups in these three families of unsaturated organic compounds and give examples of each.

2. How are alkenes, alkynes, and aromatic compounds named?

THE GOAL: Be able to name an alkene, alkyne, or simple aromatic compound from its structure, or write the structure, given the name.

3. What are cis–trans isomers?

THE GOAL: Be able to identify cis–trans isomers of alkenes and predict their occurrence.

4. What are the categories of organic reactions?

THE GOAL: Be able to recognize and describe addition, elimination, substitution, and rearrangement reactions.

5. What are the typical reactions of alkenes, alkynes, and aromatic compounds?

THE GOAL: Be able to predict the products of reactions of alkenes, alkynes, and aromatic compounds.

6. How do organic reactions take place?

THE GOAL: Be able to show how addition reactions occur.

I n this and the remaining four chapters on organic chemistry, we examine some families of organic compounds whose functional groups give them characteristic properties. Compounds in the three families described in this chapter all contain carbon–carbon multiple bonds. *Alkenes*, such as ethylene, contain a double-bond functional group; *alkynes*, such as acetylene, contain a triple-bond functional group; and *aromatic compounds*, such as benzene, contain a six-membered ring of carbon atoms usually pictured as having three alternating double bonds with properties different from those of a typical alkene. All three functional groups are widespread in nature and are found in many biologically important molecules.

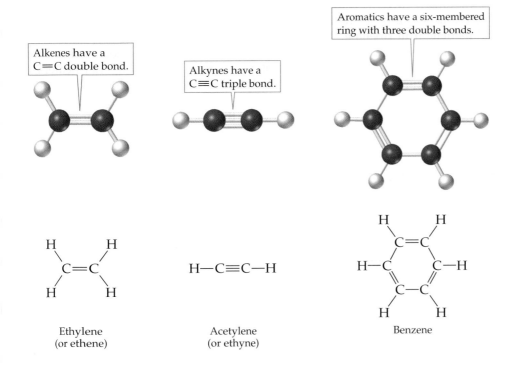

Alkenes have a C=C double bond.

Alkynes have a C≡C triple bond.

Aromatics have a six-membered ring with three double bonds.

Ethylene (or ethene)

Acetylene (or ethyne)

Benzene

13.1 Alkenes and Alkynes

Alkanes, introduced in Chapter 12, are often referred to as **saturated** because each carbon atom in an alkane forms four single bonds. Because this is the maximum number of bonds a carbon can form, no more atoms can be added to the alkane

Saturated A molecule whose carbon atoms bond to the maximum number of hydrogen atoms.

397

APPLICATION ▶ Polymer Applications—Currency

Polymers exhibit a wide range of properties, depending on both their chemical structure and how they are processed. What typically distinguishes polymeric materials from natural products, however, is their durability. Their resistance to degradation makes polymers attractive for applications including construction materials, storage containers, and food packaging. But did you ever think that the dollar bills in your wallet may someday be made from man-made polymers? This is already the case in many parts of the world, and the use of polymer-based currency is being investigated by more countries including the United States.

The first polymer-based banknotes were issued in 1988 in Australia. Since then, 17 other countries have adopted polymer-based currencies, including Brazil, Indonesia, Romania, Thailand, Vietnam, and Zambia. Made from biaxially oriented polypropylene (BOPP), polymer currency exhibits enhanced durability with lifetimes typically four times greater than paper currency of the same denomination. In addition, polymer banknotes can incorporate security features not available to paper currency. Many of the additional security features cannot be reproduced by photocopying or scanning, making counterfeiting more difficult.

The BOPP substrate is produced by simultaneously stretching the extruded polymer in two directions (called the transverse and machined directions), after which the film is heat-set to maintain the biaxial orientation. The BOPP substrate is then processed through the following steps:

- Opacifying—applying ink to each side of the note. In many cases, one area is intentionally left clear for the creation of a unique security feature called an optically variable device (OVD), a mark that changes colors when viewed at different angles.

- Sheeting—the substrate is cut into sheets prior to the printing process.

- Printing—the characteristic images and features are printed on the substrate using a variety of printing processes, including traditional offset, intaglio, and letterpress printing.

- Overcoating—a coating of protective varnish is added.

In addition to enhanced durability, the polymer currency is more resistant to folding and tearing, resists soiling, and is easier to machine process, which leads to greater handling efficiency. It is also 100% recyclable. Unlike paper currency,

▲ The first polymer banknote was released in 1988 to commemorate Australia's Bicentenary. Note the OVD in the upper right-hand corner.

▲ BOPP being produced using the "bubble" process, in which a thick-walled tube of extruded polypropylene is stretched in one direction (transverse) by applying air pressure, while simultaneously pulling down on the tube to stretch in the machined direction.

which is typically burned or placed in a landfill, the polymer currency can be shredded and reused.

See Additional Problem 13.72 at the end of the chapter.

13.9 Aromatic Compounds and the Structure of Benzene

In the early days of organic chemistry, the word *aromatic* was used to describe many fragrant substances from fruits, trees, and other natural sources. It was soon realized, however, that substances grouped as aromatic behave differently from most other organic compounds. Today, chemists use the term **aromatic** to refer to the class of compounds that contain benzene-like rings.

Benzene, the simplest aromatic compound, is a flat, symmetrical molecule with the molecular formula C_6H_6. It is often represented as cyclohexatriene, a six-membered carbon ring with three double bonds. Though useful, the problem with this representation is that it gives the wrong impression about benzene's chemical reactivity and bonding. Because benzene appears to have three double bonds, you might expect it to react with H_2, Br_2, HCl, and H_2O to give the same kinds of addition products that alkenes do. But this expectation is wrong. Benzene and other aromatic compounds are much less reactive than alkenes and do not normally undergo addition reactions.

Aromatic The class of compounds containing benzene-like rings.

▲ The odor of cherries is due to benzaldehyde, an aromatic compound.

Benzene's relative lack of chemical reactivity is a consequence of its structure. If you were to draw a six-membered ring with alternating single and double bonds, where would you place the double bonds? There are two equivalent possibilities (Figure 13.3b), neither of which is fully correct by itself. Experimental evidence shows that all six carbon–carbon bonds in benzene are identical, so a picture with three double bonds and three single bonds cannot be correct.

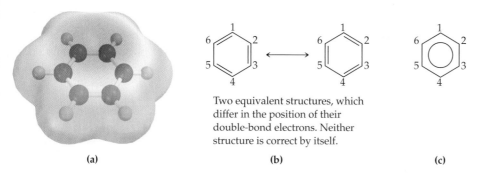

(a)   (b)   (c)

▲ **FIGURE 13.3   Some representations of benzene.**   (a) An electrostatic potential map shows the equivalency of the carbon–carbon bonds. Benzene is usually represented by the two equivalent structures in (b) or by the single structure in (c).

The properties of benzene are best explained by assuming that its true structure is an *average* of the two equivalent conventional structures. Rather than being held between specific pairs of atoms, the double-bond electrons are instead free to move over the entire ring. Each carbon–carbon bond is thus intermediate between a single bond and a double bond. The name **resonance** is given to this phenomenon where the true structure of a molecule is an average among two or more possible conventional structures, and a special double-headed arrow (⟷) is used to show the resonance relationship.

Resonance The phenomenon where the true structure of a molecule is an average among two or more conventional structures.

Because the real structure of benzene is intermediate between the two forms shown in Figure 13.3b, it is difficult to represent benzene with the standard conventions using lines for covalent bonds. Thus, we sometimes represent the double bonds as a circle inside the six-membered ring, as shown in Figure 13.3c. It is more common, though, to draw the ring with three double bonds, with the understanding that it is an aromatic ring with equivalent bonding all around. It is this convention that we use in this book.

Simple aromatic hydrocarbons like benzene are nonpolar, insoluble in water, volatile, and flammable. Unlike alkanes and alkenes, however, several aromatic hydrocarbons are toxic. Benzene itself has been implicated as a cause of leukemia, and the dimethyl-substituted benzenes are central nervous system depressants.

Everything we have said about the structure and stability of the benzene ring also applies to the ring when it has substituents, such as in the bacteriocidal agent hexachlorophene and the flavoring ingredient vanillin:

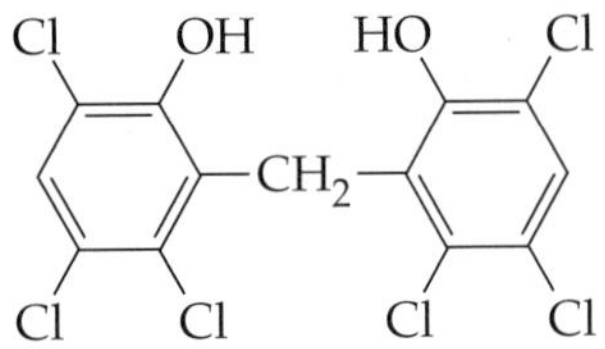

Hexachlorophene
(a germicide)

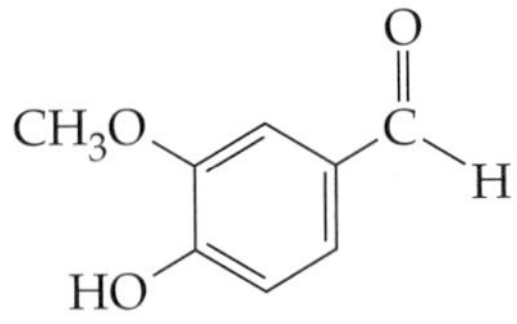

Vanillin
(vanilla flavoring)

The benzene ring is also present in many biomolecules and retains its characteristic properties in these compounds as well. In addition, aromaticity is not limited to rings that contain only carbon. For example, many compounds classified as aromatics have one or more nitrogen atoms in the ring. Pyridine, indole, and adenine are three examples:

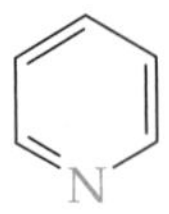

Pyridine 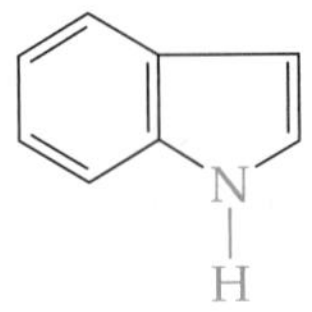   Indole 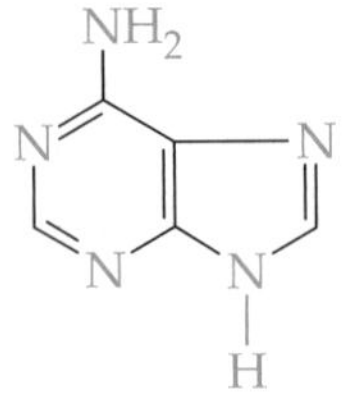   Adenine

These and all other compounds that contain a substituted benzene ring, or a similarly stable six-membered ring in which double-bond electrons are equally shared around the ring, are classified as aromatic compounds.

APPLICATION ▶ Polycyclic Aromatic Hydrocarbons and Cancer

The definition of the term *aromatic* can be extended beyond simple monocyclic (one-ring) compounds to include *polycyclic* aromatic compounds—substances that have two or more benzene-like rings joined together by a common bond. Naphthalene, familiar for its use in mothballs, is the simplest and best-known polycyclic aromatic compound.

In addition to naphthalene, there are many polycyclic aromatic compounds that are more complex. Benz[a]pyrene, for example, contains five benzene-like rings joined together; ordinary graphite (the "lead" in pencils) consists of enormous two-dimensional sheets of benzene-like rings stacked one on top of the other.

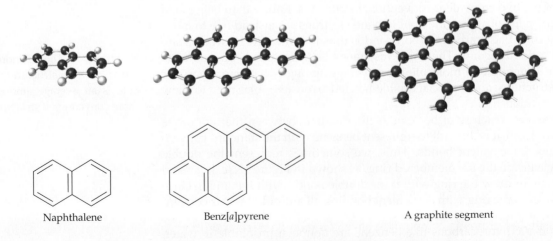

Naphthalene   Benz[*a*]pyrene   A graphite segment

Perhaps the most notorious polycyclic aromatic hydro-carbon is benz[*a*]pyrene, one of the carcinogenic (cancer-causing) substances found in chimney soot, cigarette smoke, and charcoal-broiled meat. Exposure to even a tiny amount is sufficient to induce a skin tumor in susceptible mice.

After benz[*a*]pyrene is taken into the body by eating or inhaling, the body attempts to rid itself of the foreign substance by converting it into a water-soluble metabolite called a *diol epoxide*, which can be excreted. Unfortunately, the diol epoxide metabolite reacts with and binds to cellular DNA, thereby altering the DNA and leading to mutations or cancer.

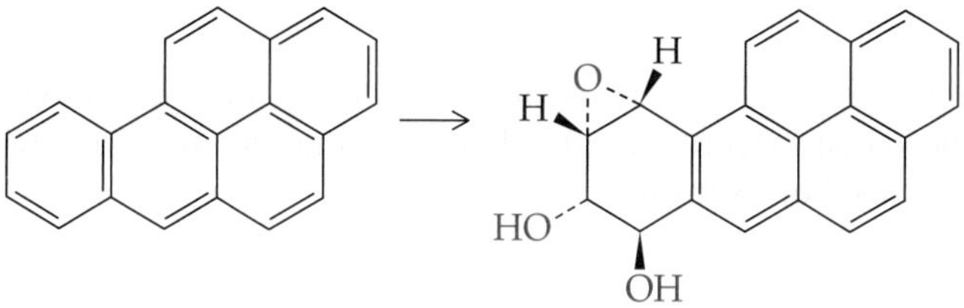

Benz[*a*]pyrene   A diol epoxide

Even benzene can cause certain types of cancer on prolonged exposure, so breathing the fumes of benzene and other volatile aromatic compounds in the laboratory should be avoided.

See Additional Problems 13.73 and 13.74 at the end of the chapter.

13.10 Naming Aromatic Compounds

Substituted benzenes are named using -*benzene* as the parent. Thus, C_6H_5Br is bromobenzene, $C_6H_5CH_2CH_3$ is ethylbenzene, and so on. No number is needed for monosubstituted benzenes because all the ring positions are identical.

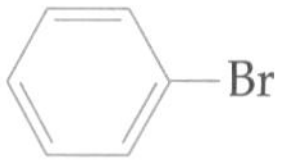

Br CH_2CH_3 NO_2

Bromobenzene    Ethylbenzene 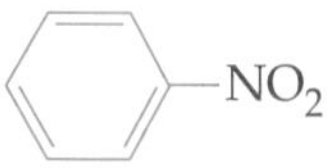   Nitrobenzene

When a benzene has more than one substituent present the positions of those substituents are indicated by numbers, just as in naming cycloalkanes. Disubstituted benzenes are unique in that the relational descriptors *o-* (*ortho*), *m-* (*meta*), and *p-* (*para*) may be used in place of 1,2-, 1,3-, and 1,4-, respectively. The terms *ortho-*, *meta-* or *para-* (or their single letter equivalents) are then used as prefixes:

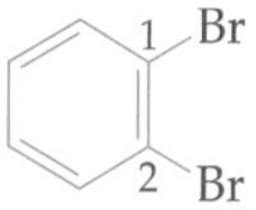

1,2-Dibromobenzene   3-Chloronitrobenzene   1,4-Dimethylbenzene
*ortho-*Dibromobenzene   *meta-*Chloronitrobenzene   *para-*Dimethylbenzene
*o-*Dibromobenzene   *m-*Chloronitrobenzene   *p-*Dimethylbenzene

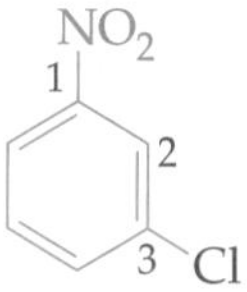

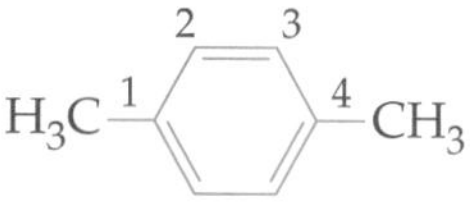

While any one of these three nomenclature schemes are acceptable, we will almost exclusively use *o-*, *m-*, and *p-* in naming these compounds.

Many substituted aromatic compounds have common names in addition to their systematic names. For example, methylbenzene is familiarly known as *toluene*,

KINDS OF REACTIONS

13.52 What is the difference between a substitution reaction and an addition reaction?

13.53 Give an example of an addition reaction.

13.54 If 2-methyl-2-pentene were somehow converted into 1-hexene, what kind of reaction would that be?

13.55 If bromocyclohexane were somehow converted into cyclohexene, what kind of reaction would that be?

13.56 Identify the type of reaction for the following:

(a) 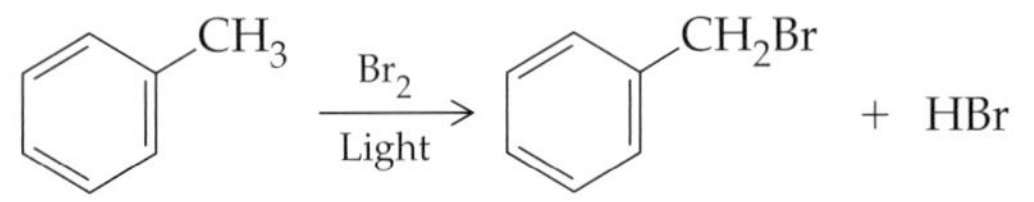 + HBr

(b)

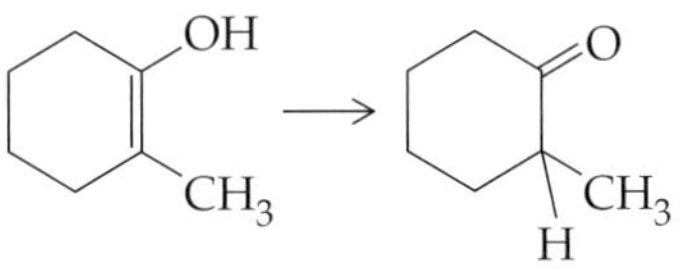

13.57 Identify the type of reaction for the following:

(a) $CH_3CHCH_2CH_2CH_2Br$ + NaCN $\longrightarrow$ (with CH_3 substituent)

$CH_3CHCH_2CH_2CH_2C\equiv N$ + NaBr (with CH_3 substituent)

(b) $2\,CH_3-\overset{O}{\underset{||}{C}}-H \xrightarrow{NaOH} CH_3-\overset{O-H}{\underset{H}{\underset{|}{C}}}-CH_2-\overset{O}{\underset{||}{C}}-H$

REACTIONS OF ALKENES AND ALKYNES

13.58 Write equations for the reaction of 1,2-dimethylcyclohexene with the following:

(a) H_2 and Pd catalyst   (b) Br_2
(c) HBr   (d) H_2O and H_2SO_4 catalyst

13.59 Write equations for the reaction of 1-methylcyclohexene with the reagents shown in Problem 13.58.

13.60 What alkene could you use to make the following products? Draw the structure of the alkene, and tell what other reagent is also required for the reaction to occur.

(a) $CH_3CHCHCCH_3$ (with Cl Cl CH_3 substituents)   (b) $CH_3CH_2CH_3$

(c) $CH_3CHCH_2CH_3$ (with Br substituent)   (d)

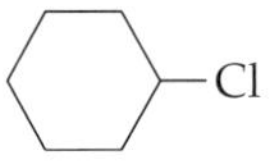

(e)

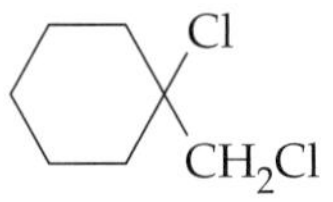

13.61 2,2-Dibromo-3-methylpentane can be prepared by an addition reaction of excess HBr with an alkyne. Draw the structure of the alkyne, name it, and write the reaction.

13.62 Draw the carbocation formed as an intermediate when HCl adds to styrene (phenylethylene).

13.63 4-Methyl-1-pentyne reacts with HBr in a 1:1 molar ratio to yield an addition product, $C_6H_{11}Br$. Draw the structures

of two possible products. Assuming that Markovnikov's rule is followed, predict which of the two structures you drew is formed, and draw the carbocation involved as an intermediate.

13.64 Polyvinylpyrrolidone (PVP) is often used in hair sprays to hold hair in place. Draw a few units of the PVP polymer. The vinylpyrrolidone monomer unit has the structure

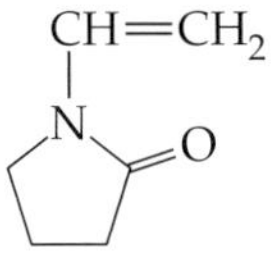

13.65 Saran, used as a plastic wrap for foods, is a polymer with the following structure. What is the monomer unit of Saran?

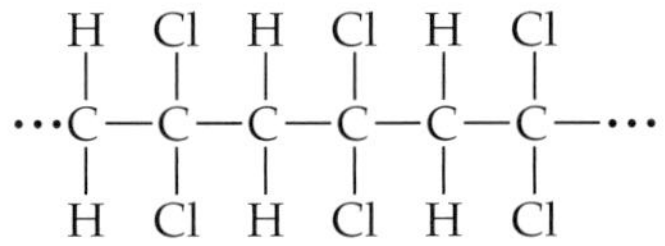

REACTIONS OF AROMATIC COMPOUNDS

13.66 Under ordinary conditions, benzene reacts with only one of the following reagents. Which of the four is it, and what is the structure of the product?

(a) H_2 and Pd catalyst
(b) Br_2 and iron catalyst
(c) HBr
(d) H_2O and H_2SO_4 catalyst

13.67 Write equations for the reaction of p-dichlorobenzene with the following:

(a) Br_2 and Fe catalyst
(b) HNO_3 and H_2SO_4 catalyst
(c) H_2SO_4 and SO_3
(d) Cl_2 and Fe catalyst

13.68 Aromatic compounds do not normally react with hydrogen in the presence of a palladium catalyst. If very high pressures (200 atm) and high temperatures are used, however, one aromatic molecule, toluene, adds three molecules of H_2 to give an addition product. What is a likely structure for the product?

13.69 The explosive trinitrotoluene, or TNT, is made by carrying out three successive nitration reactions on toluene. If these nitrations take place in the ortho and para positions relative to the methyl group, what is the structure of TNT?

Applications

13.70 What is the difference in the purpose of the rod cells and the cone cells in the eye? [*The Chemistry of Vision, p. 406*]

13.71 Describe the isomerization that occurs when light strikes the rhodopsin in the eye. [*The Chemistry of Vision, p. 406*]

13.72 The structure of polypropylene is similar to polyethylene, but has methyl groups ($-CH_3$) attached to the carbon-chain backbone. The methyl groups can be placed on the same side of the carbon chain (*isotactic*) or alternating on opposite sides of the backbone (*syndiotactic*). Draw structures for both forms of polypropylene (*Polymer Applications—Currency, p. 420*)

13.73 What is a polycyclic aromatic hydrocarbon? [*Polycyclic Aromatic Hydrocarbons and Cancer*, p. 422]

13.74 How does benz[*a*]pyrene cause cancer? [*Polycyclic Aromatic Hydrocarbons and Cancer*, p. 422]

13.75 Naphthalene is a white solid. Does it absorb light in the visible or in the ultraviolet range? [*Why We See Color*, p. 428]

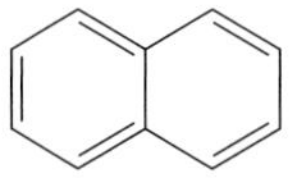

Naphthalene

13.76 Tetrabromofluorescein is a purple dye often used in lipsticks. If the dye is purple, what color does it absorb? [*Why We See Color*, p. 428]

General Questions and Problems

13.77 Why do you suppose small-ring cycloalkenes like cyclohexene do not exist as cis–trans isomers, whereas large ring cycloalkenes like cyclodecene *do* show isomerism?

13.78 Salicylic acid (*o*-hydroxybenzoic acid) is used as starting material to prepare aspirin. Draw the structure of salicylic acid.

13.79 "Superglue" is an alkene polymer made from the monomer unit

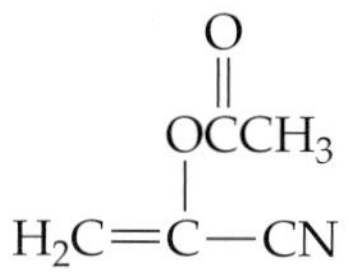

Draw a representative segment of the structure of superglue.

13.80 The following names are incorrect by IUPAC rules. Draw the structures represented by the following names, and write their correct names.

(a) 2-Methyl-4-hexene
(b) 1,3-Dimethyl-1-hexyne
(c) 2-Isopropyl-1-propene
(d) 1,4,6-Trinitrobenzene
(e) 1,2-Dimethyl-3-cyclohexene
(f) 3-Methyl-2,4-pentadiene

13.81 Assume that you have two unlabeled bottles, one with cyclohexane and one with cyclohexene. How could you tell them apart by carrying out chemical reactions?

13.82 Assume you have two unlabeled bottles, one with cyclohexene and one with benzene. How could you tell them apart by carrying out chemical reactions?

13.83 The compound *p*-dichlorobenzene has been used as an insecticide. Draw its structure.

13.84 Menthene, a compound found in mint plants, has the formula $C_{10}H_{18}$ and the IUPAC name 1-isopropyl-4-methylcyclohexene. What is the structure of menthene?

13.85 Cinnamaldehyde, the pleasant-smelling substance found in cinnamon oil, has the structure

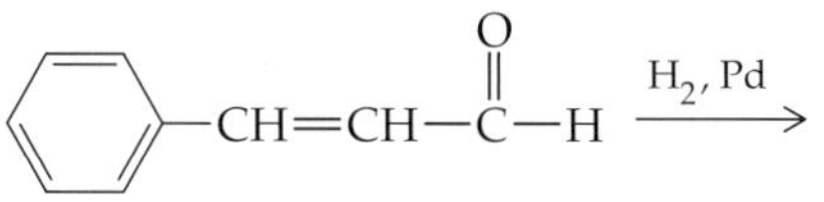

What product would you expect to obtain from reaction of cinnamaldehyde with hydrogen and a palladium catalyst?

13.86 Predict the products of the following reactions:

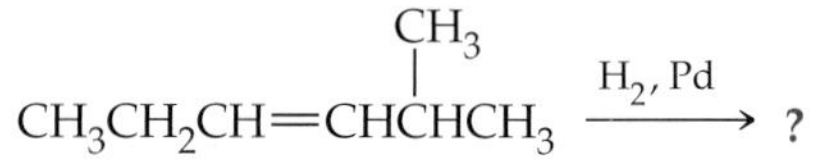

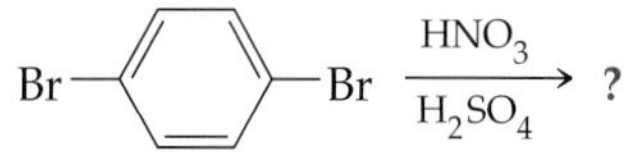

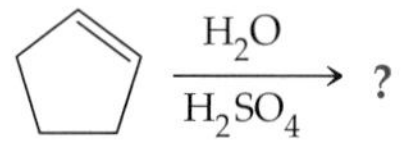

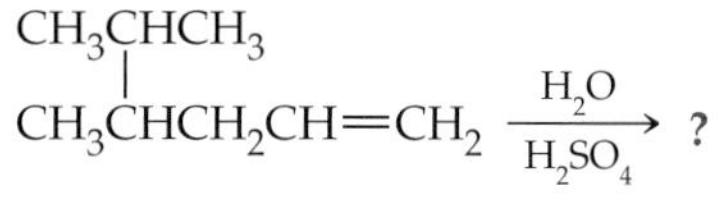

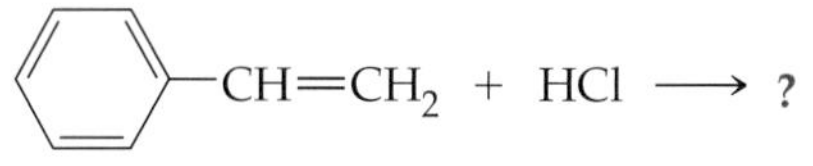

13.87 Two products are possible when 2-pentene is treated with HBr. Write the structures of the possible products, and explain why they are made in about equal amounts.

13.88 Benzene is a liquid at room temperature, but naphthalene, another aromatic compound (Problem 13.75), is a solid. Account for this difference in physical properties.

13.89 Ocimene, a compound isolated from the herb basil, has the IUPAC name 3,7-dimethyl-1,3-6-octatriene.

(a) Draw its structure.
(b) Draw the structure of the compound formed if enough HBr is added to react with all the double bonds in ocimene.

13.90 Describe how you could prepare the following compound from an alkene. Draw the formula of the alkene, name it, and list the inorganic reactants needed for the conversion.

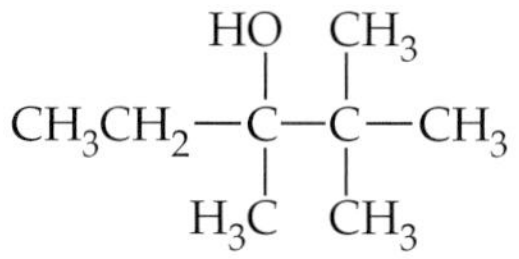

13.91 Which of the following compounds are capable of cis–trans isomerism?

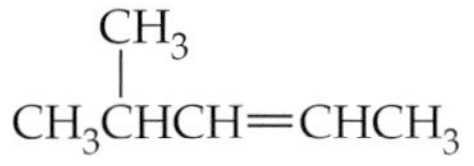

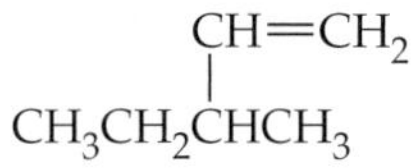

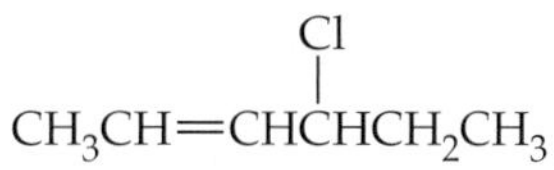

CHAPTER 14

Some Compounds with Oxygen, Sulfur, or a Halogen

CONCEPTS TO REVIEW

Oxidation and Reduction
(Section 6.11)

Hydrogen Bonds
(Section 8.11)

Acid Dissociation Constants
(Sections 10.6–10.7)

Naming Alkanes
(Section 12.6)

▲ Corn is a rich source of many important chemicals, most of which contain oxygen.

CONTENTS

APPENDIX A
Scientific Notation

What Is Scientific Notation?

The numbers that you encounter in chemistry are often either very large or very small. For example, there are about 33,000,000,000,000,000,000,000 H_2O molecules in 1.0 mL of water, and the distance between the H and O atoms in an H_2O molecule is 0.000 000 000 095 7 m. These quantities are more conveniently written in *scientific notation* as 3.3×10^{22} molecules and 9.57×10^{-11} m, respectively. In scientific notation (also known as *exponential notation*), a quantity is represented as a number between 1 and 10 multiplied by a power of 10. In this kind of expression, the small raised number to the right of the 10 is the exponent.

NUMBER	EXPONENTIAL FORM	EXPONENT
1,000,000	1×10^6	6
100,000	1×10^5	5
10,000	1×10^4	4
1,000	1×10^3	3
100	1×10^2	2
10	1×10^1	1
1		
0.1	1×10^{-1}	−1
0.01	1×10^{-2}	−2
0.001	1×10^{-3}	−3
0.000 1	1×10^{-4}	−4
0.000 01	1×10^{-5}	−5
0.000 001	1×10^{-6}	−6
0.000 000 1	1×10^{-7}	−7

Numbers greater than 1 have *positive* exponents, which tell how many times a number must be *multiplied* by 10 to obtain the correct value. For example, the expression 5.2×10^3 means that 5.2 must be multiplied by 10 three times:

$$5.2 \times 10^3 = 5.2 \times 10 \times 10 \times 10 = 5.2 \times 1000 = 5200$$

Note that doing this means moving the decimal point three places to the right:

$$5200.$$
$$123$$

The value of a positive exponent indicates *how many places to the right the decimal point must be moved* to give the correct number in ordinary decimal notation.

Numbers less than 1 have *negative exponents*, which tell how many times a number must be *divided* by 10 (or multiplied by one-tenth) to obtain the correct value. Thus, the expression 3.7×10^{-2} means that 3.7 must be divided by 10 two times:

$$3.7 \times 10^{-2} = \frac{3.7}{10 \times 10} = \frac{3.7}{100} = 0.037$$

Note that doing this means moving the decimal point two places to the left:

$$0.037$$
$$21$$

The value of a negative exponent indicates *how may places to the left the decimal point must be moved* to give the correct number in ordinary decimal notation.

Representing Numbers in Scientific Notation

How do you convert a number from ordinary notation to scientific notation? If the number is greater than or equal to 10, shift the decimal point to the *left* by n places until you obtain a number between 1 and 10. Then, multiply the result by 10^n. For example, the number 8137.6 is written in scientific notation as 8.1376×10^3:

Number of places decimal point was shifted to the left

$$8137.6 = 8.1376 \times 10^3$$

Shift decimal point to the left by 3 places to get a number between 1 and 10

When you shift the decimal point to the left by three places, you are in effect dividing the number by $10 \times 10 \times 10 = 1000 = 10^3$. Therefore, you must multiply the result by 10^3 so that the value of the number is unchanged.

To convert a number less than 1 to scientific notation, shift the decimal point to the *right* by n places until you obtain a number between 1 and 10. Then, multiply the result by 10^{-n}. For example, the number 0.012 is written in scientific notation as 1.2×10^{-2}:

Number of places decimal point was shifted to the right

$$0.012 = 1.2 \times 10^{-2}$$

Shift decimal point to the right by 2 places to get a number between 1 and 10

When you shift the decimal point to the right by two places, you are in effect multiplying the number by $10 \times 10 = 100 = 10^2$. Therefore, you must multiply the result by 10^{-2} so that the value of the number is unchanged. ($10^2 \times 10^{-2} = 10^0 = 1$.)

The following table gives some additional examples. To convert from scientific notation to ordinary notation, simply reverse the preceding process. Thus, to write the number 5.84×10^4 in ordinary notation, drop the factor of 10^4 and move the decimal point 4 places to the *right* ($5.84 \times 10^4 = 58{,}400$). To write the number 3.5×10^{-1} in ordinary notation, drop the factor of 10^{-1} and move the decimal point 1 place to the *left* ($3.5 \times 10^{-1} = 0.35$). Note that you don't need scientific notation for numbers between 1 and 10 because $10^0 = 1$.

NUMBER	SCIENTIFIC NOTATION
58,400	5.84×10^4
0.35	3.5×10^{-1}
7.296	$7.296 \times 10^0 = 7.296 \times 1$

Mathematical Operations with Scientific Notation

Addition and Subtraction in Scientific Notation

To add or subtract two numbers expressed in scientific notation, both numbers must have the same exponent. Thus, to add 7.16×10^3 and 1.32×10^2, first write the latter number as 0.132×10^3 and then add:

$$\begin{array}{r} 7.16 \ \times 10^3 \\ +0.132 \times 10^3 \\ \hline 7.29 \ \times 10^3 \end{array}$$

The answer has three significant figures. (Significant figures are discussed in Section 2.4.) Alternatively, you can write the first number as 71.6×10^2 and then add:

$$\begin{array}{r} 71.6 \ \times 10^2 \\ + \ 1.32 \times 10^2 \\ \hline 72.9 \ \times 10^2 = 7.29 \times 10^3 \end{array}$$

Subtraction of these two numbers is carried out in the same manner.

$$\begin{array}{rcl} \begin{array}{r} 7.16 \ \times 10^3 \\ -0.132 \times 10^3 \\ \hline 7.03 \ \times 10^3 \end{array} & \text{or} & \begin{array}{r} 71.6 \ \times 10^2 \\ - \ 1.32 \times 10^2 \\ \hline 70.3 \ \times 10^2 = 7.03 \times 10^3 \end{array} \end{array}$$

Multiplication in Scientific Notation

To multiply two numbers expressed in scientific notation, multiply the factors in front of the powers of 10 and then add the exponents. For example,

$$(2.5 \times 10^4)(4.7 \times 10^7) = (2.5)(4.7) \times 10^{4+7} = 12 \times 10^{11} = 1.2 \times 10^{12}$$

$$(3.46 \times 10^5)(2.2 \times 10^{-2}) = (3.46)(2.2) \times 10^{5+(-2)} = 7.6 \times 10^3$$

Both answers have two significant figures.

Division in Scientific Notation

To divide two numbers expressed in scientific notation, divide the factors in front of the powers of 10 and then subtract the exponent in the denominator from the exponent in the numerator. For example,

$$\frac{3 \times 10^6}{7.2 \times 10^2} = \frac{3}{7.2} \times 10^{6-2} = 0.4 \times 10^4 = 4 \times 10^3 \quad \text{(1 significant figure)}$$

$$\frac{7.50 \times 10^{-5}}{2.5 \times 10^{-7}} = \frac{7.50}{2.5} \times 10^{-5-(-7)} = 3.0 \times 10^2 \quad \text{(2 significant figures)}$$

Scientific Notation and Electronic Calculators

With a scientific calculator you can carry out calculations in scientific notation. You should consult the instruction manual for your particular calculator to learn how to enter and manipulate numbers expressed in an exponential format. On most calculators, you enter the number $A \times 10^n$ by (i) entering the number A, (ii) pressing a key labeled EXP or EE, and (iii) entering the exponent n. If the exponent is negative, you press a key labeled $+/-$ before entering the value of n. (Note that you do not enter the number 10.) The calculator displays the number $A \times 10^n$ with the number A on the left followed by some space and then the exponent n. For example,

$$4.625 \times 10^2 \text{ is displayed as } 4.625\ 02$$

To add, subtract, multiply, or divide exponential numbers, use the same sequence of keystrokes as you would in working with ordinary numbers. When you add or subtract on a calculator, the numbers need not have the same exponent; the calculator automatically takes account of the different exponents. Remember, though, that the calculator often gives more digits in the answer than the allowed number of significant figures. It's sometimes helpful to outline the calculation on paper, as in the preceding examples, to keep track of the number of significant figures.

PROBLEM A.1

Perform the following calculations, expressing the results in scientific notation with the correct number of significant figures. (You don't need a calculator for these.)

(a) $(1.50 \times 10^4) + (5.04 \times 10^3)$

(b) $(2.5 \times 10^{-2}) - (5.0 \times 10^{-3})$

(c) $(6.3 \times 10^{15}) \times (10.1 \times 10^3)$

(d) $(2.5 \times 10^{-3}) \times (3.2 \times 10^{-4})$

(e) $(8.4 \times 10^4) \div (3.0 \times 10^6)$

(f) $(5.530 \times 10^{-2}) \div (2.5 \times 10^{-5})$

ANSWERS

(a) 2.00×10^4	**(b)** 2.0×10^{-2}	**(c)** 6.4×10^{19}
(d) 8.0×10^{-7}	**(e)** 2.8×10^{-2}	**(f)** 2.2×10^3

PROBLEM A.2

Perform the following calculations, expressing the results in scientific notation with the correct number of significant figures. (Use a calculator for these.)

(a) $(9.72 \times 10^{-1}) + (3.4823 \times 10^2)$

(b) $(3.772 \times 10^3) - (2.891 \times 10^4)$

(c) $(1.956 \times 10^3) \div (6.02 \times 10^{23})$

(d) $3.2811 \times (9.45 \times 10^{21})$

(e) $(1.0015 \times 10^3) \div (5.202 \times 10^{-9})$

(f) $(6.56 \times 10^{-6}) \times (9.238 \times 10^{-4})$

ANSWERS

(a) 3.4920×10^2	**(b)** -2.514×10^4	**(c)** 3.25×10^{-21}
(d) 3.10×10^{22}	**(e)** 1.925×10^{11}	**(f)** 6.06×10^{-9}

APPENDIX B
Conversion Factors

Length   SI Unit: Meter (m)

1 meter = 0.001 kilometer (km)

= 100 centimeters (cm)

= 1.0936 yards (yd)

1 centimeter = 10 millimeters (mm)

= 0.3937 inch (in.)

1 nanometer = 1×10^{-9} meter

1 Angstrom (Å) = 1×10^{-10} meter

1 inch = 2.54 centimeters

1 mile = 1.6094 kilometers

Volume   SI Unit: Cubic meter (m³)

1 cubic meter = 1000 liters (L)

1 liter = 1000 cubic centimeters (cm³)

= 1000 milliliters (mL)

= 1.056710 quarts (qt)

1 cubic inch = 16.4 cubic centimeters

Temperature   SI Unit: Kelvin (K)

0 K = −273.15 °C

= −459.67 °F

°F = (9/5) °C + 32°; °F = (1.8 × °C) + 32°

°C = (5/9)(°F − 32°); °C = $\dfrac{(°F - 32°)}{1.8}$

K = °C + 273.15°

Mass   SI Unit: Kilogram (kg)

1 kilogram = 1000 grams (g)

= 2.205 pounds (lb)

1 gram = 1000 milligrams (mg)

= 0.03527 ounce (oz)

1 pound = 453.6 grams

1 atomic mass unit = 1.66054×10^{-24} gram

Pressure   SI Unit: Pascal (Pa)

1 pascal = 9.869×10^{-6} atmosphere

1 atmosphere = 101,325 pascals

= 760 mmHg (Torr)

= 14.70 lb/in²

Energy   SI Unit: Joule (J)

1 joule = 0.23901 calorie (cal)

1 calorie = 4.184 joules

1 Calorie (nutritional unit) = 1000 calories

= 1 kcal

Glossary

1,4 Link A glycosidic link between the hemiacetal hydroxyl group at C1 of one sugar and the hydroxyl group at C4 of another sugar.

Acetal A compound that has two ether-like —OR groups bonded to the same carbon atom.

Acetyl coenzyme A (acetyl-SCoA) Acetyl-substituted coenzyme A—the common intermediate that carries acetyl groups into the citric acid cycle.

Acetyl group A $CH_3C=O$ group.

Achiral The opposite of chiral; having no right- or left-handedness and no nonsuperimposable mirror images.

Acid A substance that provides H^+ ions in water.

Acid dissociation constant (K_a) The equilibrium constant for the dissociation of an acid (HA), equal to $[H^+][A^-]/[HA]$

Acidosis The abnormal condition associated with a blood plasma pH below 7.35; may be respiratory or metabolic.

Acid–base indicator A dye that changes color depending on the pH of a solution.

Activation (of an enzyme) Any process that initiates or increases the action of an enzyme.

Activation energy (E_{act}) The amount of energy necessary for reactants to surmount the energy barrier to reaction; affects reaction rate.

Active site A pocket in an enzyme with the specific shape and chemical makeup necessary to bind a substrate.

Active transport Movement of substances across a cell membrane with the assistance of energy (for example, from ATP).

Actual Yield The amount of product actually formed in a reaction.

Acyl group An $RC=O$ group.

Addition reaction A general reaction type in which a substance X—Y adds to the multiple bond of an unsaturated reactant to yield a saturated product that has only single bonds.

Addition reaction, aldehydes and ketones Addition of an alcohol or other compound to the carbon–oxygen double bond to give a carbon–oxygen single bond.

Adenosine triphosphate (ATP) The principal energy-carrying molecule; removal of a phosphoryl group to give ADP releases free energy.

Aerobic In the presence of oxygen.

Agonist A substance that interacts with a receptor to cause or prolong the receptor's normal biochemical response.

Alcohol A compound that has an —OH group bonded to a saturated, alkane-like carbon atom, R—OH.

Alcoholic fermentation The anaerobic breakdown of glucose to ethanol plus carbon dioxide by the action of yeast enzymes.

Aldehyde A compound that has a carbonyl group bonded to one carbon and one hydrogen, RCHO.

Aldose A monosaccharide that contains an aldehyde carbonyl group.

Alkali metal An element in group 1A of the periodic table.

Alkaline earth metal An element in group 2A of the periodic table.

Alkaloid A naturally occurring nitrogen-containing compound isolated from a plant; usually basic, bitter, and poisonous.

Alkalosis The abnormal condition associated with a blood plasma pH above 7.45; may be respiratory or metabolic.

Alkane A hydrocarbon that has only single bonds.

Alkene A hydrocarbon that contains a carbon–carbon double bond.

Alkoxide ion The anion resulting from deprotonation of an alcohol, RO^-.

Alkoxy group An —OR group.

Alkyl group The part of an alkane that remains when a hydrogen atom is removed.

Alkyl halide A compound that has an alkyl group bonded to a halogen atom, R—X.

Alkyne A hydrocarbon that contains a carbon–carbon triple bond.

Allosteric control An interaction in which the binding of a regulator at one site on a protein affects the protein's ability to bind another molecule at a different site.

Allosteric enzyme An enzyme whose activity is controlled by the binding of an activator or inhibitor at a location other than the active site.

Alpha (α) particle A helium nucleus (He^{2+}), emitted as α-radiation.

Alpha- (α-) amino acid An amino acid in which the amino group is bonded to the carbon atom next to the —COOH group.

Alpha- (α-) helix Secondary protein structure in which a protein chain forms a right-handed coil stabilized by hydrogen bonds between peptide groups along its backbone.

Amide A compound that has a carbonyl group bonded to a carbon atom and a nitrogen atom group, $RCONR'_2$, where the R' groups may be alkyl groups or hydrogen atoms.

Amine A compound that has one or more organic groups bonded to nitrogen; primary, RNH_2; secondary, R_2NH; or tertiary, R_3N.

Amino acid A molecule that contains both an amino group and a carboxylic acid functional group.

Amino acid pool The entire collection of free amino acids in the body.

Amino group The —NH_2 functional group.

Amino-terminal (N-terminal) amino acid The amino acid with the free —NH_3^+ group at the end of a protein.

Ammonium ion A positive ion formed by addition of hydrogen to ammonia or an amine (may be primary, secondary, or tertiary).

Ammonium salt An ionic compound composed of an ammonium cation and an anion; an amine salt.

Amorphous solid A solid whose particles do not have an orderly arrangement.

Amphoteric Describing a substance that can react as either an acid or a base.

Anabolism Metabolic reactions that build larger biological molecules from smaller pieces.

Anaerobic In the absence of oxygen.

Anion A negatively charged ion.

Anomeric carbon atom The hemiacetal C atom in a cyclic sugar; the C atom bonded to an —OH group and an O in the ring.

Anomers Cyclic sugars that differ only in positions of substituents at the hemiacetal carbon (the anomeric carbon); the α form has the —OH on the opposite side from the —CH_2OH; the β form has the —OH on the same side as the —CH_2OH.

Antagonist A substance that blocks or inhibits the normal biochemical response of a receptor.

Antibody (immunoglobulin) Glycoprotein molecule that identifies antigens.

Anticodon A sequence of three ribonucleotides on tRNA that recognizes the complementary sequence (the codon) on mRNA.

Antigen A substance foreign to the body that triggers the immune response.

Antioxidant A substance that prevents oxidation by reacting with an oxidizing agent.

Aqueous solution A solution in which water is the solvent.

Aromatic The class of compounds containing benzene-like rings.

Artificial transmutation The change of one atom into another brought about by a nuclear bombardment reaction.

Atom The smallest and simplest particle of an element.

Atomic mass unit (amu) A convenient unit for describing the mass of an atom; 1 amu = 1/12 the mass of a carbon-12 atom.

Atomic number (Z) The number of protons in an atom.

Atomic theory A set of assumptions proposed by English scientist John Dalton to explain the chemical behavior of matter.

Atomic weight The weighted average mass of an element's atoms.

ATP synthase The enzyme complex in the inner mitochondrial membrane at which hydrogen ions cross the membrane and ATP is synthesized from ADP.

Autoimmune disease Disorder in which the immune system identifies normal body components as antigens and produces antibodies to them.

Avogadro's law Equal volumes of gases at the same temperature and pressure contain equal numbers of molecules (V/n = constant, or $V_1/n_1 = V_2/n_2$).

Avogadro's number (N_A) The number of units in 1 mole of anything; 6.02×10^{23}.

Balanced equation Describing a chemical equation in which the numbers and kinds of atoms are the same on both sides of the reaction arrow.

Base A substance that provides OH^- ions in water.

Base pairing The pairing of bases connected by hydrogen bonding (G-C and A-T), as in the DNA double helix.

Beta- (β-) Oxidation pathway A repetitive series of biochemical reactions that degrades fatty acids to acetyl-SCoA by removing carbon atoms two at a time.

Beta (β) particle An electron (e^-), emitted as β radiation.

Beta- (β-) Sheet Secondary protein structure in which adjacent protein chains either in the same molecule or in different molecules are held in place by hydrogen bonds along the backbones.

Bile acids Steroid acids derived from cholesterol that are secreted in bile.

Bile Fluid secreted by the liver and released into the small intestine from the gallbladder during digestion; contains bile acids, bicarbonate ion, and other electrolytes.

Binary compound A compound formed by combination of two different elements.

Blood clot A network of fibrin fibers and trapped blood cells that forms at the site of blood loss.

Blood plasma Liquid portion of the blood: an extracellular fluid.

Blood serum Fluid portion of blood remaining after clotting has occurred.

Boiling point (bp) The temperature at which liquid and gas are in equilibrium.

Bond angle The angle formed by three adjacent atoms in a molecule.

Bond dissociation energy The amount of energy that must be supplied to break a bond and separate the atoms in an isolated gaseous molecule.

Bond length The optimum distance between nuclei in a covalent bond.

Boyle's law The pressure of a gas at constant temperature is inversely proportional to its volume (PV = constant, or $P_1V_1 = P_2V_2$).

Branched-chain alkane An alkane that has a branching connection of carbons.

Brønsted–Lowry acid A substance that can donate a hydrogen ion, H^+, to another molecule or ion.

Brønsted–Lowry base A substance that can accept H^+ from an acid.

Buffer A combination of substances that act together to prevent a drastic change in pH; usually a weak acid and its conjugate base.

Carbohydrate A member of a large class of naturally occurring polyhydroxy ketones and aldehydes.

Carbonyl compound Any compound that contains a carbonyl group $C=O$.

Carbonyl group A functional group that has a carbon atom joined to an oxygen atom by a double bond, $C=O$.

Carbonyl-group substitution reaction A reaction in which a new group replaces (substitutes for) a group attached to a carbonyl-group carbon in an acyl group.

Carboxyl group The —COOH functional group.

Carboxyl-terminal (C-terminal) amino acid The amino acid with the free —COO$^-$ group at the end of a protein.

Carboxylate anion The anion that results from ionization of a carboxylic acid, RCOO$^-$.

Carboxylic acid A compound that has a carbonyl group bonded to a carbon atom and an —OH group, RCOOH.

Carboxylic acid salt An ionic compound containing a carboxylic anion and a cation.

Catabolism Metabolic reaction pathways that break down food molecules and release biochemical energy.

Catalyst A substance that speeds up the rate of a chemical reaction but is itself unchanged.

Cation A positively charged ion.

Centromeres The central regions of chromosomes.

Chain reaction A reaction that, once started, is self-sustaining.

Change of state The conversion of a substance from one state to another—for example, from a liquid to a gas.

Charles's law The volume of a gas at constant pressure is directly proportional to its Kelvin temperature (V/T = constant, or $V_1/T_1 = V_2/T_2$).

Chemical change A change in the chemical makeup of a substance.

Chemical compound A pure substance that can be broken down into simpler substances by chemical reactions.

Chemical equation An expression in which symbols and formulas are used to represent a chemical reaction.

Chemical equilibrium A state in which the rates of forward and reverse reactions are the same.

Chemical formula A notation for a chemical compound using element symbols and subscripts to show how many atoms of each element are present.

Chemical reaction A process in which the identity and composition of one or more substances are changed.

Chemistry The study of the nature, properties, and transformations of matter.

Chiral carbon atom (chirality center) A carbon atom bonded to four different groups.

Chiral Having right- or left-handedness; able to have two different mirror-image forms.

Chromosome A complex of proteins and DNA; visible during cell division.

Cis-trans isomers Alkenes that have the same connections between atoms but differ in their three-dimensional structures because of the way that groups are attached to different sides of the double bond. The cis isomer has hydrogen atoms on the same side of the double bond; the trans isomer has them on opposite sides.

Citric acid cycle The series of biochemical reactions that breaks down acetyl groups to produce energy carried by reduced coenzymes and carbon dioxide.

Clones Identical copies of organisms, cells, or DNA segments from a single ancestor.

Codon A sequence of three ribonucleotides in the messenger RNA chain that codes for a specific amino acid; also the three nucleotide sequence (a stop codon) that stops translation.

Coefficient A number placed in front of a formula to balance a chemical equation.

Coenzyme An organic molecule that acts as an enzyme cofactor.

Cofactor A nonprotein part of an enzyme that is essential to the enzyme's catalytic activity; a metal ion or a coenzyme.

Colligative property A property of a solution that depends only on the number of dissolved particles, not on their chemical identity.

Colloid A homogeneous mixture that contains particles that range in diameter from 2 to 500 nm.

Combined gas law The product of the pressure and volume of a gas is proportional to its temperature (PV/T = constant, or $P_1V_1/T_1 = P_2V_2/T_2$).

Combustion A chemical reaction that produces a flame, usually because of burning with oxygen.

Competititve (enzyme) inhibition Enzyme regulation in which an inhibitor competes with a substrate for binding to the enzyme active site.

Concentration A measure of the amount of a given substance in a mixture.

Concentration gradient A difference in concentration within the same system.

Condensed structure A shorthand way of drawing structures in which C—C and C—H bonds are understood rather than shown.

Conformation The specific three-dimensional arrangement of atoms in a molecule at a given instant.

Conformers Molecular structures having identical connections between atoms.

Conjugate acid The substance formed by addition of H^+ to a base.

Conjugate acid–base pair Two substances whose formulas differ by only a hydrogen ion, H^+.

Conjugate base The substance formed by loss of H^+ from an acid.

Conjugated protein A protein that incorporates one or more non-amino acid units in its structure.

Constitutional isomers Compounds with the same molecular formula but different connections among their atoms.

Conversion factor An expression of the relationship between two units.

Coordinate covalent bond The covalent bond that forms when both electrons are donated by the same atom.

Cosmic rays A mixture of high-energy particles—primarily of protons and various atomic nuclei—that shower the earth from outer space.

Covalent bond A bond formed by sharing electrons between atoms.

Critical mass The minimum amount of radioactive material needed to sustain a nuclear chain reaction.

Crystalline solid A solid whose atoms, molecules, or ions are rigidly held in an ordered arrangement.

Cycloalkane An alkane that contains a ring of carbon atoms.

Cycloalkene A cyclic hydrocarbon that contains a double bond.

Cytoplasm The region between the cell membrane and the nuclear membrane in a eukaryotic cell.

Cytosol The fluid part of the cytoplasm surrounding the organelles within a cell.

d-Block element A transition metal element that results from the filling of d orbitals.

D-Sugar Monosaccharide with the —OH group on the chiral carbon atom farthest from the carbonyl group pointing to the right in a Fischer projection.

Dalton's law The total pressure exerted by a mixture of gases is equal to the sum of the partial pressures exerted by each individual gas.

Decay series A sequential series of nuclear disintegrations leading from a heavy radioisotope to a nonradioactive product.

Degree of unsaturation The number of carbon–carbon double bonds in a molecule.

Dehydration The loss of water from an alcohol to yield an alkene.

Denaturation The loss of secondary, tertiary, or quaternary protein structure due to disruption of noncovalent interactions and/or disulfide bonds that leaves peptide bond and primary structure intact.

Density The physical property that relates the mass of an object to its volume; mass per unit volume.

Deoxyribonucleotide A nucleotide containing 2-deoxy-D-ribose.

Diabetes mellitus A chronic condition due to either insufficient insulin or failure of insulin to activate crossing of cell membranes by glucose.

Diastereomers Stereoisomers that are not mirror images of each other.

Digestion A general term for the breakdown of food into small molecules.

Dilution factor The ratio of the initial and final solution volumes (V_1/V_2).

Dipole–dipole force The attractive force between positive and negative ends of polar molecules.

Disaccharide A carbohydrate composed of two monosaccharides.

Dissociation The splitting apart of an acid in water to give H^+ and an anion.

Disulfide A compound that contains a sulfur–sulfur bond, RS–SR.

Disulfide bond (in protein) An S–S bond formed between two cysteine side chains; can join two peptide chains together or cause a loop in a peptide chain.

DNA (deoxyribonucleic acid) The nucleic acid that stores genetic information; a polymer of deoxyribonucleotides.

Double bond A covalent bond formed by sharing two electron pairs.

Double helix Two strands coiled around each other in a screwlike fashion; in most organisms the two polynucleotides of DNA form a double helix.

Drug Any substance that alters body function when it is introduced from an external source.

Eicosanoid A lipid derived from a 20-carbon unsaturated carboxylic acid.

Electrolyte A substance that produces ions and therefore conducts electricity when dissolved in water.

Electron A negatively charged subatomic particle.

Electron affinity The energy released on adding an electron to a single atom in the gaseous state.

Electron capture A process in which the nucleus captures an inner-shell electron from the surrounding electron cloud, thereby converting a proton into a neutron.

Electron configuration The specific arrangement of electrons in an atom's shells and subshells.

Electron shell A grouping of electrons in an atom according to energy.

Electron subshell A grouping of electrons in a shell according to the shape of the region of space they occupy.

Electron-dot symbol An atomic symbol with dots placed around it to indicate the number of valence electrons.

Electron-transport chain The series of biochemical reactions that passes electrons from reduced coenzymes to oxygen and is coupled to ATP formation.

Electronegativity The ability of an atom to attract electrons in a covalent bond.

Element A fundamental substance that can't be broken down chemically into any simpler substance.

Elimination reaction A general reaction type in which a saturated reactant yields an unsaturated product by losing groups from two adjacent carbon atoms.

Enantiomers, optical isomers The two mirror-image forms of a chiral molecule.

Endergonic A nonspontaneous reaction or process that absorbs free energy and has a positive ΔG.

Endocrine system A system of specialized cells, tissues, and ductless glands that excretes hormones and shares with the nervous system the responsibility for maintaining constant internal body conditions and responding to changes in the environment.

Endothermic A process or reaction that absorbs heat and has a positive ΔH.

Energy The capacity to do work or supply heat.

Enthalpy A measure of the amount of energy associated with substances involved in a reaction.

Enthalpy change (ΔH) An alternative name for heat of reaction.

Entropy (S) The amount of disorder in a system.

Enzyme A protein or other molecule that acts as a catalyst for a biological reaction.

Equilibrium constant (K) Value of the equilibrium constant expression for a given reaction.

Equivalent For ions, the amount equal to 1 mol of charge.

Equivalent of acid Amount of an acid that contains 1 mole of H^+ ions.

Equivalent of base Amount of base that contains 1 mole of OH^- ions.

Erythrocytes Red blood cells; transporters of blood gases.

Essential amino acid An amino acid that cannot be synthesized by the body and thus must be obtained in the diet.

Ester A compound that has a carbonyl group bonded to a carbon atom and an —OR' group, RCOOR'.

Esterification The reaction between an alcohol and a carboxylic acid to yield an ester plus water.

Ether A compound that has an oxygen atom bonded to two organic groups, R—O—R.

Ethyl group The —CH_2CH_3 alkyl group.

Exergonic A spontaneous reaction or process that releases free energy and has a negative ΔG.

Exon A nucleotide sequence in DNA that is part of a gene and codes for part of a protein.

Exothermic A process or reaction that releases heat and has a negative ΔH.

Extracellular fluid Fluid outside cells.

***f*-Block element** An inner transition metal element that results from the filling of f orbitals.

Facilitated diffusion Passive transport across a cell membrane with the assistance of a protein that changes shape.

Factor–label method A problem-solving procedure in which equations are set up so that unwanted units cancel and only the desired units remain.

Fat A mixture of triacylglycerols that is solid because it contains a high proportion of saturated fatty acids.

Fatty acid A long-chain carboxylic acid; those in animal fats and vegetable oils often have 12–22 carbon atoms.

Feedback control Regulation of an enzyme's activity by the product of a reaction later in a pathway.

Fermentation The production of energy under anaerobic conditions.

Fibrin Insoluble protein that forms the fiber framework of a blood clot.

Fibrous protein A tough, insoluble protein whose protein chains form fibers or sheets.

Filtration (kidney) Filtration of blood plasma through a glomerulus and into a kidney nephron.

Fischer projection Structure that represents chiral carbon atoms as the intersections of two lines, with the horizontal lines representing bonds pointing out of the page and the vertical lines representing bonds pointing behind the page. For sugars, the aldehyde or ketone is at the top.

Formula unit The formula that identifies the smallest neutral unit of a compound.

Formula weight The sum of the atomic weights of the atoms in one formula unit of any compound.

Free radical An atom or molecule with an unpaired electron.

Free-energy change (ΔG) The criterion for spontaneous change (negative ΔG; $\Delta G = \Delta H - T\,\Delta S$).

Functional group An atom or group of atoms within a molecule that has a characteristic structure and chemical behavior.

Gamma (γ) radiation Radioactivity consisting of high-energy light waves.

Gas A substance that has neither a definite volume nor a definite shape.

Gas constant (R) The constant R in the ideal gas law, $PV = nRT$.

Gas laws A series of laws that predict the influence of pressure (P), volume (V), and temperature (T) on any gas or mixture of gases.

Gay-Lussac's law For a fixed amount of gas at a constant voume, pressure is directly proportional to the Kelvin temperature (P/T = constant, or $P_1/T_1 = P_2/T_2$).

Gene Segment of DNA that directs the synthesis of a single polypeptide.

Genetic (enzyme) control Regulation of enzyme activity by control of the synthesis of enzymes.

Genetic code The sequence of nucleotides, coded in triplets (codons) in mRNA, that determines the sequence of amino acids in protein synthesis.

Genome All of the genetic material in the chromosomes of an organism; its size is given as the number of base pairs.

Genomics The study of whole sets of genes and their functions.

Globular protein A water–soluble protein whose chain is folded in a compact shape with hydrophilic groups on the outside.

Glomerular filtrate Fluid that enters the nephron from the glomerulus; filtered blood plasma.

Gluconeogenesis The biochemical pathway for the synthesis of glucose from non-carbohydrates, such as lactate, amino acids, or glycerol.

Glycerophospholipid (phosphoglyceride) A lipid in which glycerol is linked by ester bonds to two fatty acids and one phosphate, which is in turn linked by another ester bond to an amino alcohol (or other alcohol).

Glycogenesis The biochemical pathway for synthesis of glycogen.

Glycogenolysis The biochemical pathway for breakdown of glycogen to free glucose.

Glycol A dialcohol, or diol having the two –OH groups on adjacent carbons.

Glycolipid A lipid with a fatty acid bonded to the $C2-NH_2$ and a sugar bonded to the $C1-OH$ group of sphingosine.

Glycolysis The biochemical pathway that breaks down a molecule of glucose into two molecules of pyruvate plus energy.

Glycoprotein A protein that contains a short carbohydrate chain.

Glycoside A cyclic acetal formed by reaction of a monosaccharide with an alcohol, accompanied by loss of H_2O.

Glycosidic bond Bond between the anomeric carbon atom of a monosaccharide and an —OR group.

Gram-equivalent For ions, the molar mass of the ion divided by the ionic charge.

Group One of the 18 vertical columns of elements in the periodic table.

Guanosine diphosphate (GDP) An energy-carrying molecule that can gain or lose a phosphoryl group to transfer energy.

Guanosine triphosphate (GTP) An energy-carrying molecule similar to ATP; removal of a phosphoryl group to give GDP releases free energy.

Half-life ($t_{1/2}$) The amount of time required for one-half of a radioactive sample to decay.

Halogen An element in group 7A of the periodic table.

Halogenation (alkene) The addition of Cl_2 or Br_2 to a multiple bond to give a 1,2-dihalide product.

Halogenation (aromatic) The substitution of a halogen group (—X) for a hydrogen on an aromatic ring.

Heat The kinetic energy transferred from a hotter object to a colder object when the two are in contact.

Heat of fusion The quantity of heat required to completely melt a substance once it has reached its melting point.

Heat of reaction (ΔH) The amount of heat absorbed or released in a reaction.

Heat of vaporization The quantity of heat needed to completely vaporize a liquid once it has reached its boiling point.

Hemiacetal A compound with both an alcohol-like —OH group and an ether-like —OR group bonded to the same carbon atom.

Hemostasis The stopping of bleeding.

Henderson-Hasselbalch equation The logarithmic form of the K_a equation for a weak acid, used in applications involving buffer solutions.

Henry's law The solubility of a gas in a liquid is directly proportional to its partial pressure over the liquid at constant temperature.

Heterocycle A ring that contains nitrogen or some other atom in addition to carbon.

Heterogeneous mixture A nonuniform mixture that has regions of different composition.

Heterogeneous nuclear RNA The initially synthesized mRNA strand containing both introns and exons.

Homogeneous mixture A uniform mixture that has the same composition throughout.

Hormone A chemical messenger secreted by cells of the endocrine system and transported through the bloodstream to target cells with appropriate receptors where it elicits a response.

Hydration The addition of water to a multiple bond to give an alcohol product.

Hydrocarbon An organic compound that contains only carbon and hydrogen.

Hydrogen bond The attraction between a hydrogen atom bonded to an electronegative O, N, or F atom and another nearby electronegative O, N, or F atom.

Hydrogenation The addition of H_2 to a multiple bond to give a saturated product.

Hydrohalogenation The addition of HCl or HBr to a multiple bond to give an alkyl halide product.

Hydrolysis A reaction in which a bond or bonds are broken and the H— and —OH of water add to the atoms of the broken bond or bonds.

Hydronium ion The H_3O^+ ion, formed when an acid reacts with water.

Hydrophilic Water-loving; a hydrophilic substance dissolves in water.

Hydrophobic Water-fearing; a hydrophobic substance does not dissolve in water.

Hygroscopic Having the ability to pull water molecules from the surrounding atmosphere.

Hyperglycemia Higher-than-normal blood glucose concentration.

Hypertonic Having an osmolarity greater than the surrounding blood plasma or cells.

Hypoglycemia Lower-than-normal blood glucose concentration.

Hypotonic Having an osmolarity less than the surrounding blood plasma or cells.

Ideal gas A gas that obeys all the assumptions of the kinetic–molecular theory.

Ideal gas law A general expression relating pressure, volume, temperature, and amount for an ideal gas: $PV = nRT$.

Immune response Defense mechanism of the immune system dependent on the recognition of specific antigens, including viruses, bacteria, toxic substances, and infected cells; either cell-mediated or antibody-mediated.

Induced-fit model A model of enzyme action in which the enzyme has a flexible active site that changes shape to best fit the substrate and catalyze the reaction.

Inflammation Result of the inflammatory response: includes swelling, redness, warmth, and pain.

Inflammatory response A nonspecific defense mechanism triggered by antigens or tissue damage.

Inhibition (of an enzyme) Any process that slows or stops the action of an enzyme.

Inner transition metal element An element in one of the 14 groups shown separately at the bottom of the periodic table.

Intermolecular force A force that acts between molecules and holds molecules close to one another in liquids and solids.

Interstitial fluid Fluid surrounding cells: an extracellular fluid.

Intracellular fluid Fluid inside cells.

Intron A portion of DNA between coding regions of a gene (exons); is transcribed and then removed from final messenger RNA.

Ion An electrically charged atom or group of atoms.

Ion-product constant for water (K_w) The product of the H_3O^+ and OH^- molar concentrations in water or any aqueous solution ($K_w = [H_3O^+][OH^-] = 1.00 \times 10^{-14}$).

Ionic bond The electrical attractions between ions of opposite charge in a crystal.

Ionic compound A compound that contains ionic bonds.

Ionic equation An equation in which ions are explicitly shown.

Ionic solid A crystalline solid held together by ionic bonds.

Ionization energy The energy required to remove one electron from a single atom in the gaseous state.

Ionizing radiation A general name for high-energy radiation of all kinds.

Irreversible (enzyme) inhibition Enzyme deactivation in which an inhibitor forms covalent bonds to the active site, permanently blocking it.

Isoelectric point (pI) The pH at which a sample of an amino acid has equal number of + and − charges.

Isomers Compounds with the same molecular formula but different structures.

Isopropyl group The branched-chain alkyl group $-CH(CH_3)_2$.

Isotonic Having the same osmolarity.

Isotopes Atoms with identical atomic numbers but different mass numbers.

Ketoacidosis Lowered blood pH due to accumulation of ketone bodies.

Ketogenesis The synthesis of ketone bodies from acetyl-SCoA.

Ketone A compound that has a carbonyl group bonded to two carbons in organic groups that can be the same or different, $R_2C=O$, RCOR'.

Ketone bodies Compounds produced in the liver that can be used as fuel by muscle and brain tissue; 3-hydroxybutyrate, acetoacetate, and acetone.

Ketose A monosaccharide that contains a ketone carbonyl group.

Kinetic energy The energy of an object in motion.

Kinetic–molecular theory (KMT) of gases A group of assumptions that explain the behavior of gases.

L-Sugar Monosaccharide with the —OH group on the chiral carbon atom farthest from the carbonyl group pointing to the left in a Fischer projection.

Law of conservation of energy Energy can be neither created nor destroyed in any physical or chemical change.

Law of conservation of mass Matter can be neither created nor destroyed in any physical or chemical change.

Le Châtelier's principle When a stress is applied to a system in equilibrium, the equilibrium shifts to relieve the stress.

Lewis base A compound containing an unshared pair of electrons.

Lewis structure A molecular representation that shows both the connections among atoms and the locations of lone-pair valence electrons.

Limiting reagent The reactant that runs out first in a chemical reaction.

Line structure A shorthand way of drawing structures in which atoms aren't shown; instead, a carbon atom is understood to be at every intersection of lines, and hydrogens are filled in mentally.

Lipid A naturally occurring molecule from a plant or animal that is soluble in nonpolar organic solvents.

Lipid bilayer The basic structural unit of cell membranes; composed of two parallel sheets of membrane lipid molecules arranged tail to tail.

Lipogenesis The biochemical pathway for synthesis of fatty acids from acetyl-SCoA.

Lipoprotein A lipid–protein complex that transports lipids.

Liposome A spherical structure in which a lipid bilayer surrounds a water droplet.

Liquid A substance that has a definite volume but that changes shape to fit its container.

London dispersion force The short-lived attractive force due to the constant motion of electrons within molecules.

Lone pair A pair of electrons that is not used for bonding.

Main group element An element in one of the two groups on the left or the six groups on the right of the periodic table.

Markovnikov's rule In the addition of HX to an alkene, the H becomes attached to the carbon that already has the most H's, and the X becomes attached to the carbon that has fewer H's.

Mass A measure of the amount of matter in an object.

Mass number (A) The total number of protons and neutrons in an atom.

Matter The physical material that makes up the universe; anything that has mass and occupies space.

Melting point (mp) The temperature at which solid and liquid are in equilibrium.

Messenger RNA (mRNA) The RNA that carries the code transcribed from DNA and directs protein synthesis.

Metal A malleable element with a lustrous appearance that is a good conductor of heat and electricity.

Metalloid An element whose properties are intermediate between those of a metal and a nonmetal.

Methyl group The $-CH_3$ alkyl group.

Methylene Another name for a CH_2 unit.

Micelle A spherical cluster formed by the aggregation of soap or detergent molecules so that their hydrophobic ends are in the center and their hydrophilic ends are on the surface.

Miscible Mutually soluble in all proportions.

Mitochondrial matrix The space surrounded by the inner membrane of a mitochondrion.

Mitochondrion (plural, mitochondria) An egg-shaped organelle where small molecules are broken down to provide the energy for an organism.

Mixture A blend of two or more substances, each of which retains its chemical identity.

Mobilization (of triacylglycerols) Hydrolysis of triacylglycerols in adipose tissue and release of fatty acids into the bloodstream.

Molar mass The mass in grams of one mole of a substance, numerically equal to the molecular weight.

Molarity (M) Concentration expressed as the number of moles of solute per liter of solution.

Mole The amount of a substance corresponding to 6.02×10^{23} units.

Molecular compound A compound that consists of molecules rather than ions.

Molecular formula A formula that shows the numbers and kinds of atoms in one molecule of a compound.

Molecular weight The sum of the atomic weights of the atoms in a molecule.

Molecule A group of atoms held together by covalent bonds.

Monomer A small molecule that is used to prepare a polymer.

Monosaccharide (simple sugar) A carbohydrate with 3–7 carbon atoms.

Mutagen A substance that causes mutations.

Mutarotation Change in rotation of plane-polarized light resulting from the equilibrium between cyclic anomers and the open-chain form of a sugar.

Mutation An error in base sequence that is carried along in DNA replication.

n-propyl group The straight-chain alkyl group $-CH_2CH_2CH_3$.

Native protein A protein with the shape (secondary, tertiary, and quaternary structure) in which it exists naturally in living organisms.

Net ionic equation An equation that does not include spectator ions.

Neurotransmitter A chemical messenger that travels between a neuron and a neighboring neuron or other target cell to transmit a nerve impulse.

Neutralization reaction The reaction of an acid with a base.

Neutron An electrically neutral subatomic particle.

Nitration The substitution of a nitro group ($-NO_2$) for a hydrogen on an aromatic ring.

Noble gas An element in group 8A of the periodic table.

Noncompetitive (enzyme) inhibition Enzyme regulation in which an inhibitor binds to an enzyme elsewhere than at the active site, thereby changing the shape of the enzyme's active site and reducing its efficiency.

Noncovalent forces Forces of attraction other than covalent bonds that can act between molecules or within molecules.

Nonelectrolyte A substance that does not produce ions when dissolved in water.

Nonessential amino acid One of eleven amino acids that are synthesized in the body and are therefore not necessary in the diet.

Nonmetal An element that is a poor conductor of heat and electricity.

Normal boiling point The boiling point at a pressure of exactly 1 atmosphere.

Normality (N) A measure of acid (or base) concentration expressed as the number of acid (or base) equivalents per liter of solution.

Nuclear decay The spontaneous emission of a particle from an unstable nucleus.

Nuclear fission The fragmenting of heavy nuclei.

Nuclear fusion The joining together of light nuclei.

Nuclear reaction A reaction that changes an atomic nucleus, usually causing the change of one element into another.

Nucleic acid A polymer of nucleotides.

Nucleon A general term for both protons and neutrons.

Nucleoside A five-carbon sugar bonded to a cyclic amine base; like a nucleotide but missing the phosphate group.

Nucleotide A five-carbon sugar bonded to a cyclic amine base and one phosphate group (a nucleoside monophosphate); monomer for nucleic acids.

Nucleus The dense, central core of an atom that contains protons and neutrons.

Nuclide The nucleus of a specific isotope of an element.

Octet rule Main-group elements tend to undergo reactions that leave them with 8 valence electrons.

Oil A mixture of triacylglycerols that is liquid because it contains a high proportion of unsaturated fatty acids.

Orbital A region of space within an atom where an electron in a given subshell can be found.

Organic chemistry The study of carbon compounds.

Osmolarity (osmol) The sum of the molarities of all dissolved particles in a solution.

Osmosis The passage of solvent through a semipermeable membrane separating two solutions of different concentration.

Osmotic pressure The amount of external pressure applied to the more concentrated solution to halt the passage of solvent molecules across a semipermeable membrane.

Oxidation The loss of one or more electrons by an atom.

Oxidation number A number that indicates whether an atom is neutral, electron-rich, or electron-poor.

Oxidation–Reduction, or Redox, reaction A reaction in which electrons are transferred from one atom to another.

Oxidative deamination Conversion of an amino acid $-NH_2$ group to an α-keto group, with removal of NH_4^+.

Oxidative phosphorylation The synthesis of ATP from ADP using energy released in the electron-transport chain.

Oxidizing agent A reactant that causes an oxidation by taking electrons from or increasing the oxidation number of another reactant.

p-Block element A main group element that results from the filling of p orbitals.

Partial pressure The pressure exerted by a gas in a mixture.

Parts per billion (ppb) Number of parts per one billion (10^9) parts.

Parts per million (ppm) Number of parts per one million (10^6) parts.

Passive transport Movement of a substance across a cell membrane without the use of energy, from a region of higher concentration to a region of lower concentration.

Pentose phosphate pathway The biochemical pathway that produces ribose (a pentose), NADPH, and other sugar phosphates from glucose; an alternative to glycolysis.

Peptide bond An amide bond that links two amino acids together.

Percent yield The percent of the theoretical yield actually obtained from a chemical reaction.

Period One of the 7 horizontal rows of elements in the periodic table.

Periodic table A table of the elements in order of increasing atomic number and grouped according to their chemical similarities.

pH A measure of the acid strength of a solution; the negative common logarithm of the H_3O^+ concentration.

Phenol A compound that has an —OH group bonded directly to an aromatic, benzene-like ring, Ar—OH.

Phenyl The C_6H_5— group.

Phosphate ester A compound formed by reaction of an alcohol with phosphoric acid; may be a monoester, $ROPO_3H_2$; a diester, $(RO)_2PO_3H$; or a triester, $(RO)_3PO$; also may be a di- or triphosphate.

Phospholipid A lipid that has an ester link between phosphoric acid and an alcohol (glycerol or sphingosine).

Phosphoryl group The $—PO_3^{2-}$ group in organic phosphates.

Phosphorylation Transfer of a phosphoryl group, $—PO_3^{2-}$, between organic molecules.

Physical change A change that does not affect the chemical makeup of a substance or object.

Physical quantity A physical property that can be measured.

Polar covalent bond A bond in which the electrons are attracted more strongly by one atom than by the other.

Polyatomic ion An ion that is composed of more than one atom.

Polymer A large molecule formed by the repetitive bonding together of many smaller molecules.

Polymorphism A variation in DNA sequence within a population.

Polysaccharide (complex carbohydrate) A carbohydrate that is a polymer of monosaccharides.

Polyunsaturated fatty acid A long-chain fatty acid that has two or more carbon–carbon double bonds.

Positron A "positive electron," which has the same mass as an electron but a positive charge.

Potential energy Energy that is stored because of position, composition, or shape.

Precipitate An insoluble solid that forms in solution during a chemical reaction.

Pressure The force per unit area pushing against a surface.

Primary carbon atom A carbon atom with one other carbon attached to it.

Primary protein structure The sequence in which amino acids are linked by peptide bonds in a protein.

Product A substance that is formed in a chemical reaction and is written on the right side of the reaction arrow in a chemical equation.

Property A characteristic useful for identifying a substance or object.

Protein A large biological molecule made of many amino acids linked together through amide (peptide) bonds.

Proton A positively charged subatomic particle.

Pure substance A substance that has uniform chemical composition throughout.

Quaternary ammonium ion A positive ion with four organic groups bonded to the nitrogen atom.

Quaternary ammonium salt An ionic compound composed of a quaternary ammonium ion and an anion.

Quaternary carbon atom A carbon atom with four other carbons attached to it.

Quaternary protein structure The way in which two or more protein chains aggregate to form large, ordered structures.

Radioactivity The spontaneous emission of radiation from a nucleus.

Radioisotope A radioactive isotope.

Radionuclide The nucleus of a radioactive isotope.

Reabsorption (kidney) Movement of solutes out of filtrate in a kidney tubule.

Reactant A substance that undergoes change in a chemical reaction and is written on the left side of the reaction arrow in a chemical equation.

Reaction mechanism A description of the individual steps by which old bonds are broken and new bonds are formed in a reaction.

Reaction rate A measure of how rapidly a reaction occurs.

Rearrangement reaction A general reaction type in which a molecule undergoes bond reorganization to yield an isomer.

Receptor A molecule or portion of a molecule with which a hormone, neurotransmitter, or other biochemically active molecule interacts to initiate a response in a target cell.

Recombinant DNA DNA that contains segments from two different species.

Reducing agent A reactant that causes a reduction by giving up electrons or increasing the oxidation number of another reactant.

Reducing sugar A carbohydrate that reacts in basic solution with a mild oxidizing agent.

Reduction The gain of one or more electrons by an atom.

Reductive deamination Conversion of an α-keto acid to an amino acid by reaction with NH_4^+.

Regular tetrahedron A geometric figure with four identical triangular faces.

Replication The process by which copies of DNA are made when a cell divides.

Residue (amino acid) An amino acid unit in a polypeptide.

Resonance The phenomenon where the true structure of a molecule is an average among two or more conventional structures.

Reversible reaction A reaction that can go in either the forward direction or the reverse direction, from products to reactants or reactants to products.

Ribonucleotide A nucleotide containing D-ribose.

Ribosomal RNA (rRNA) The RNA that is complexed with proteins in ribosomes.

Ribosome The structure in the cell where protein synthesis occurs; composed of protein and rRNA.

RNA (ribonucleic acids) The nucleic acids (messenger, transfer, and ribosomal) responsible for putting the genetic information to use in protein synthesis; polymers of ribonucleotides.

Rounding off A procedure used for deleting nonsignificant figures.

s-Block element A main group element that results from the filling of an s orbital.

Salt An ionic compound formed from reaction of an acid with a base.

Saponification The reaction of an ester with aqueous hydroxide ion to yield an alcohol and the metal salt of a carboxylic acid.

Saturated A molecule whose carbon atoms bond to the maximum number of hydrogen atoms.

Saturated fatty acid A long-chain carboxylic acid containing only carbon–carbon single bonds.

Saturated solution A solution that contains the maximum amount of dissolved solute at equilibrium.

Scientific Method Systematic process of observation, hypothesis, and experimentation to expand and refine a body of knowledge.

Scientific notation A number expressed as the product of a number between 1 and 10, times the number 10 raised to a power.

Second messenger Chemical messenger released inside a cell when a hydrophilic hormone or neurotransmitter interacts with a receptor on the cell surface.

Secondary carbon atom A carbon atom with two other carbons attached to it.

Secondary protein structure Regular and repeating structural patterns (for example, α-helix, β-sheet) created by hydrogen bonding between backbone atoms in neighboring segments of protein chains.

Secretion (kidney) Movement of solutes into filtrate in a kidney tubule.

SI units Units of measurement defined by the International System of Units.

Side chain (amino acid) The group bonded to the carbon next to the carboxyl group in an amino acid; different in different amino acids.

Significant figures The number of meaningful digits used to express a value.

Simple diffusion Passive transport by the random motion of diffusion through the cell membrane.

Simple protein A protein composed of only amino acid residues.

Single bond A covalent bond formed by sharing one electron pair.

Single nucleotide polymorphism Common single-base-pair variation in DNA.

Soap The mixture of salts of fatty acids formed on saponification of animal fat.

Solid A substance that has a definite shape and volume.

Solubility The maximum amount of a substance that will dissolve in a given amount of solvent at a specified temperature.

Solute A substance dissolved in a liquid.

Solution A homogeneous mixture that contains particles the size of a typical ion or small molecule.

Solvation The clustering of solvent molecules around a dissolved solute molecule or ion.

Solvent The liquid in which another substance is dissolved.

Specific gravity The density of a substance divided by the density of water at the same temperature.

Specific heat The amount of heat that will raise the temperature of 1 g of a substance by 1 °C.

Specificity (enzyme) The limitation of the activity of an enzyme to a specific substrate, specific reaction, or specific type of reaction.

Spectator ion An ion that appears unchanged on both sides of a reaction arrow.

Sphingolipid A lipid derived from the amino alcohol sphingosine.

Spontaneous process A process or reaction that, once started, proceeds on its own without any external influence.

Standard molar volume The volume of one mole of a gas at standard temperature and pressure (22.4 L).

Standard temperature and pressure (STP) Standard conditions for a gas, defined as 0 °C (273 K) and 1 atm (760 mmHg) pressure.

State of matter The physical state of a substance as a solid, a liquid, or a gas.

Stereoisomers Isomers that have the same molecular and structural formulas, but different spatial arrangements of their atoms.

Steroid A lipid whose structure is based on the following tetracyclic (four-ring) carbon skeleton:

Straight-chain alkane An alkane that has all its carbons connected in a row.

Strong acid An acid that gives up H^+ easily and is essentially 100% dissociated in water.

Strong base A base that has a high affinity for H^+ and holds it tightly.

Strong electrolyte A substance that ionizes completely when dissolved in water.

Structural formula A molecular representation that shows the connections among atoms by using lines to represent covalent bonds.

Subatomic particles Three kinds of fundamental particles from which atoms are made: protons, neutrons, and electrons.

Substituent An atom or group of atoms attached to a parent compound.

Substitution reaction A general reaction type in which an atom or group of atoms in a molecule is replaced by another atom or group of atoms.

Substrate A reactant in an enzyme catalyzed reaction.

Sulfonation The substitution of a sulfonic acid group ($-SO_3H$) for a hydrogen on an aromatic ring.

Supersaturated solution A solution that contains more than the maximum amount of dissolved solute; a nonequilibrium situation.

Synapse The place where the tip of a neuron and its target cell lie adjacent to each other.

Telomeres The ends of chromosomes; in humans, contain long series of repeating groups of nucleotides.

Temperature The measure of how hot or cold an object is.

Tertiary carbon atom A carbon atom with three other carbons attached to it.

Tertiary protein structure The way in which an entire protein chain is coiled and folded into its specific three-dimensional shape.

Theoretical yield The amount of product formed assuming complete reaction of the limiting reagent.

Thiol A compound that contains an $-SH$ group, $R-SH$.

Titration A procedure for determining the total acid or base concentration of a solution.

Transamination The interchange of the amino group of an amino acid and the keto group of an α-keto acid.

Transcription The process by which the information in DNA is read and used to synthesize RNA.

Transfer RNA (tRNA) The RNA that transports amino acids into position for protein synthesis.

Transition metal element An element in one of the 10 smaller groups near the middle of the periodic table.

Translation The process by which RNA directs protein synthesis.

Transmutation The change of one element into another.

Triacylglycerol (triglyceride) A triester of glycerol with three fatty acids.

Triple bond A covalent bond formed by sharing three electron pairs.

Turnover number The maximum number of substrate molecules acted upon by one molecule of enzyme per unit time.

Unit A defined quantity used as a standard of measurement.

Unsaturated A molecule that contains a carbon–carbon multiple bond, to which more hydrogen atoms can be added.

Unsaturated fatty acid A long-chain carboxylic acid containing one or more carbon–carbon double bonds.

Urea cycle The cyclic biochemical pathway that produces urea for excretion.

Valence electron An electron in the outermost, or valence, shell of an atom.

Valence shell The outermost electron shell of an atom.

Valence-shell electron-pair repulsion (VSEPR) model A method for predicting molecular shape by noting how many electron charge clouds surround atoms and assuming that the clouds orient as far away from one another as possible.

Vapor The gas molecules in equilibrium with a liquid.

Vapor pressure The partial pressure of gas molecules in equilibrium with a liquid.

Vitamin An organic molecule, essential in trace amounts that must be obtained in the diet because it is not synthesized in the body.

Volume/volume percent concentration [(v/v)%] Concentration expressed as the number of milliliters of solute dissolved in 100 mL of solution.

Wax A mixture of esters of long-chain carboxylic acids with long-chain alcohols.

Weak acid An acid that gives up H^+ with difficulty and is less than 100% dissociated in water.

Weak base A base that has only a slight affinity for H^+ and holds it weakly.

Weak electrolyte A substance that is only partly ionized in water.

Weight A measure of the gravitational force that the earth or other large body exerts on an object.

Weight/volume percent concentration [(w/v)%] Concentration expressed as the number of grams of solute per 100 mL of solution.

Whole blood Blood plasma plus blood cells.

X rays Electromagnetic radiation with an energy somewhat less than that of γ rays.

Zwitterion A neutral dipolar ion that has one + charge and one − charge.

Zymogen A compound that becomes an active enzyme after undergoing a chemical change.

Answers to Selected Problems

Short answers are given for in-chapter problems, *Understanding Key Concepts* problems, and even-numbered end-of-chapter problems. Explanations and full answers for all problems are provided in the accompanying *Study Guide and Solutions Manual*.

Chapter 1

1.1 all; natural: (a), (d); synthetic: (b), (c) **1.2** physical: (a), (d); chemical: (b), (c) **1.3** solid **1.4** mixture: (a), (d); pure: (b), (c) **1.5** physical: (a), (c); chemical: (b) **1.6** chemical change **1.7** (a) Na (b) Ti (c) Sr (d) Y (e) F (f) H **1.8** (a) uranium (b) calcium (c) neodymium (d) potassium (e) tungsten (f) tin **1.9** (a) 1 nitrogen atom, 3 hydrogen atoms (b) 1 sodium atom, 1 hydrogen atom, 1 carbon atom, 3 oxygen atoms (c) 8 carbon atoms, 18 hydrogen atoms (d) 6 carbon atoms, 8 hydrogen atoms, 6 oxygen atoms **1.10** (a) chromium (24) (b) potassium (19) (c) sulfur (16) (d) radon (86) **1.11** Metalloids are at the boundary between metals and nonmetals. **1.12** helium (He), neon (Ne), argon (Ar), krypton (Kr), xenon (Xe), radon (Rn) **1.13** copper (Cu), silver (Ag), gold (Au) **1.14** red: vanadium, metal; green: boron, metalloid; blue: bromine, nonmetal **1.15** Americium, a metal **1.16** Chemistry is the study of matter. **1.18** physical: (a), (c), (e); chemical (b), (d) **1.20** A gas has no definite shape or volume; a liquid has no definite shape but has a definite volume; a solid has a definite volume and a definite shape. **1.22** gas **1.24** mixture: (a), (b), (d), (f); pure: (c), (e) **1.26** element: (a); compound: (b), (c); mixture: (d), (e), (f) **1.28** (a) reactant: hydrogen peroxide; products: water, oxygen (b) compounds: hydrogen peroxide, water; element: oxygen **1.30** 117 elements; 90 occur naturally **1.32** Metals: lustrous, malleable, conductors of heat and electricity; nonmetals: gases or brittle solids, nonconductors; metalloids: properties intermediate between metals and nonmetals. **1.34** (a) Gd (b) Ge (c) Tc (d) As (e) Cd **1.36** (a) nitrogen (b) potassium (c) chlorine (d) calcium (e) phosphorus (f) manganese **1.38** Only the first letter of a chemical symbol is capitalized. **1.40** (a) Br (b) Mn (c) C (d) K **1.42** (a) A mixture doesn't have a chemical formula. (b) The symbol for nitrogen is N. **1.44** (a) magnesium, sulfur, oxygen (b) iron, bromine (c) cobalt, phosphorus (d) arsenic, hydrogen (e) calcium, chromium, oxygen **1.46** Carbon, hydrogen, nitrogen, oxygen; ten atoms **1.48** $C_{13}H_{18}O_2$ **1.50** (a) metal (b) nonmetal **1.52** 9 carbons, 8 hydrogens, 4 oxygens; 21 atoms **1.54** (a) A physical change doesn't alter chemical makeup; a chemical change alters a substance's chemical makeup. (b) Melting point is the temperature at which a change of state from solid to liquid occurs; boiling point is the temperature at which a change of state from liquid to gas occurs. (c) A reactant is a substance that undergoes change in a chemical reaction; a product is a substance formed as a result of a chemical reaction. (d) A metal is a lustrous malleable element that is a good conductor of heat and electricity; a nonmetal is an element that is a poor conductor. **1.56** compounds: (a), (c), (e); elements: (b), (d) **1.58** mixture **1.60** (a) Fe (b) Cu (c) Co (d) Mo (e) Cr (f) F (g) S **1.62** Elements 115,119: metals Element 117: metal or metalloid

Chapter 2

2.1 (a) deciliter (b) milligram (c) nanosecond (d) kilometer (e) microgram **2.2** (a) L (b) kg (c) nm (d) Mm **2.3** (a) 0.000 000 001 m (b) 0.1 g (c) 1000 m (d) 0.000 001 s (e) 0.000 000 001 g **2.4** (a) 3 (b) 4 (c) 5 (d) exact **2.5** 32.3 °C; three significant figures **2.6** (a) 5.8×10^{-2} g (b) 4.6792×10^4 m (c) 6.072×10^{-3} cm (d) 3.453×10^2 kg **2.7** (a) 48,850 mg (b) 0.000 008 3 m (c) 0.0400 m **2.8** (a) 6.3000×10^5 (b) 1.30×10^3 (c) 7.942×10^{11} **2.9** 2.78×10^{-10} m = 2.78×10^2 pm **2.10** (a) 2.30 g (b) 188.38 mL (c) 0.009 L (d) 1.000 kg **2.11** (a) 50.9 mL (b) 0.078 g (c) 11.9 m (d) 51 mg (e) 103 **2.12** (a) 1 L = 1000 mL; 1 mL = 0.001 L (b) 1 g = 0.03527 oz; 1 oz = 28.35 g (c) 1 L = 1.057 qt; 1 qt = 0.9464 L **2.13** (a) 454 g (b) 2.5 L (c) 105 qt **2.14** 795 mL **2.15** 7.36 m/s **2.16** (a) 3.4 kg (b) 120 mL **2.17** (a) 10.6 mg/kg (b) 36 mg/kg **2.18** 57.8 °C **2.19** −38.0 °F; 234.3 K **2.20** 7,700 cal

2.21 0.21 cal/g °C **2.22** float: ice, human fat, cork, balsa wood; sink: gold, table sugar, earth **2.23** 8.392 mL **2.24** 2.21 g/cm³ **2.25** more dense **2.26** (a) 34 mL (b) 2.7 cm; two significant figures **2.27** (no answer) **2.28** (a) 0.977 (b) three (c) less dense **2.29** The smaller cylinder is more precise because the gradations are smaller. **2.30** 3 1/8 in.; 8.0 cm **2.31** start: 0.11 mL stop: 0.25 mL volume: 0.14 mL **2.32** (a) Both are equally precise. (b) 355 mL **2.33** higher in chloroform **2.34** A physical quantity consists of a number and a unit. **2.36** mass (kg); volume (m³); length (m); temperature (K) **2.38** They are the same. **2.40** (a) centiliter (b) decimeter (c) millimeter (d) nanoliter (e) milligram (f) cubic meter (g) cubic centimeter **2.42** 10^9 pg, 3.5×10^4 pg **2.44** (a) 9.457×10^3 (b) 7×10^{-5} (c) 2.000×10^{10} (d) 1.2345×10^{-2} (e) 6.5238×10^2 **2.46** (a) 6 (b) 3 (c) 3 (d) 4 (e) 1–5 (f) 2–3 **2.48** (a) 7,926 mi, 7,900 mi, 7,926.38 mi (b) $7.926\,381 \times 10^3$ mi **2.50** (a) 12.1 g (b) 96.19 cm (c) 263 mL (d) 20.9 mg **2.52** (a) 0.3614 cg (b) 0.0120 ML (c) 0.0144 mm (d) 60.3 ng (e) 1.745 dL (f) 1.5×10^3 dm **2.54** (a) 97.8 kg (b) 0.133 mL (c) 0.46 ng (d) 2.99 Mm **2.56** (a) 62.1 mi/hr (b) 91.1 ft/s **2.58** 4×10^3 cells/in. **2.60** 10 g **2.62** 6×10^{10} cells **2.64** 37.0 °C, 310.2 K **2.66** 537 cal = 0.537 kcal **2.68** 0.092 cal/g·°C **2.70** Hg: 76 °C; Fe: 40.7 °C **2.72** 0.179 g/cm³ **2.74** 11.4 g/cm³ **2.76** 0.7856 g/mL; sp gr = 0.7856 **2.78** (a) 2.0×10^{-6} cm (b) 1.3×10^6 cells/in (c) 1 mL = 0.269 fluidram (d) 1 mL = 16 minim (e) 1 minim = 2.08×10^{-3} fluid ounce **2.80** −2 °C; 271 K **2.82** (a) BMI = 29 (b) BMI = 23.7 (c) BMI = 24.4; individual (a) **2.84** 3.12 in; 7.92 cm Discrepancies are due to rounding errors and changes in significant figures. **2.86** 177 °C **2.88** 3.9×10^{-2} g/dL iron, 8.3×10^{-3} g/dL calcium, 2.24×10^{-1} g/dL cholesterol **2.90** 7.8×10^6 mL/day **2.92** 0.13 g **2.94** 4.4 g; 0.0097 lb **2.96** 2200 mL **2.98** 2.2 tablespoons **2.100** iron **2.102** 4.99×10^{10} L **2.104** (a) 2×10^3 mg/L (b) 2×10^3 µg/mL (c) 2 g/L (d) 2×10^3 ng/µL **2.106** 34.1 °C **2.108** float

Chapter 3

3.1 14.0 amu **3.2** 4.99×10^{-8} g **3.3** 6.02×10^{23} atoms in all cases **3.4** When the mass in grams is numerically equal to the mass in amu, there are 6.02×10^{23} atoms. **3.5** (a) Re (b) Ca (c) Te **3.6** 27 protons, 27 electrons, 33 neutrons **3.7** technetium **3.8** The answers agree **3.9** $^{79}_{35}$Br, $^{81}_{35}$Br **3.10** (a) $^{11}_5$B (b) $^{56}_{26}$Fe (c) $^{37}_{17}$Cl **3.11** group 3A, period 3 **3.12** silver, calcium **3.13** Nitrogen (1), phosphorus (2), arsenic (3), antimony (4), bismuth (5) **3.14** Metals: titanium, scandium; nonmetals: selenium, argon; metalloids: tellurium, astatine **3.15** (a) nonmetal, main group (b) metal, main group (c) nonmetal, main group (d) metal, transition element **3.16** red = zinc, metal, period 4, group 2B; blue = oxygen, period 6, group 6A **3.17** 6, 2, 6 **3.18** 10, neon **3.19** 12, magnesium **3.20** (a) $1s^2\,2s^2\,2p^2$ (b) $1s^2\,2s^2\,2p^6\,3s^2\,3p^3$ (c) $1s^2\,2s^2\,2p^6\,3s^2\,3p^5$ (d) $1s^2\,2s^2\,2p^6\,3s^2\,3p^6\,4s^1$ **3.21** $1s^2\,2s^2\,2p^6\,3s^2\,3p^2$; $1s^2\,2s^2\,2p^6\,3s^2\,3p^6\,4s^2\,3d^{10}\,4p^6$ **3.22** $4p^3$, all are unpaired **3.23** gallium **3.24** (a) $1s^2\,2s^2\,2p^5$; [He] $2s^2\,2p^5$ (b) $1s^2\,2s^2\,2p^6\,3s^2\,3p^1$; [Ne] $3s^2\,3p^1$ (c) $1s^2\,2s^2\,2p^6\,3s^2\,3p^6\,4s^2\,3d^{10}\,4p^3$; [Ne] $4s^2\,3d^{10}\,4p^6$ **3.25** group 2A **3.26** group 7A, $1s^2\,2s^2\,2p^6\,3s^2\,3p^5$ **3.27** group 6A, $ns^2\,np^4$ **3.28** $\cdot\ddot{X}\cdot$ **3.29** $\ddot{\underset{..}{R}n}\colon$ $\cdot\ddot{P}b\cdot$ $\colon\ddot{X}e\colon$ $\cdot Ra\cdot$ **3.30** (a) p orbital (b) s orbital

3.31

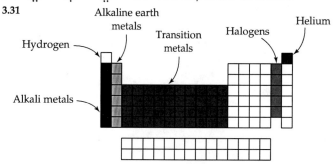

A-13

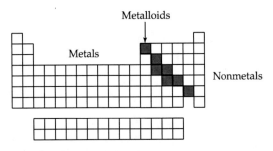

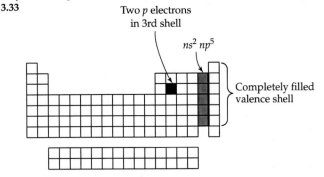

3.32 red: gas (fluorine); blue: atomic number 79 (gold); green: (calcium); beryllium, magnesium, strontium, barium, and radium are similar.

3.33

3.34 selenium **3.35** $1s^2\,2s^2\,2p^6\,3s^2\,3p^6\,4s^2\,3d^{10}\,4p^3$ **3.36** Matter is composed of atoms. Atoms of different elements differ. Compounds consist of different atoms combined in specific proportions. Atoms do not change in chemical reactions. **3.38 (a)** 3.4702×10^{-22} g **(b)** 2.1801×10^{-22} g **(c)** 6.6465×10^{-24} g **3.40** 14.01 g **3.42** 6.022×10^{23} atoms **3.44** protons (+ charge, 1 amu); neutrons (no charge, 1 amu); electrons (− charge, 0.0005 amu). **3.46 (a)** potassium **(b)** tin **(c)** zinc **3.48** 18, 20, 22 **3.50 (a)** and **(c)** **3.52 (a)** F-19 **(b)** Ne-19 **(c)** F-21 **(d)** Mg-21 **3.54 (a)** $^{14}_{6}$C **(b)** $^{39}_{19}$K **(c)** $^{20}_{10}$Ne **3.56** $^{12}_{6}$C—six neutrons $^{13}_{6}$C—seven neutrons $^{14}_{6}$C—eight neutrons **3.58** 63.55 amu **3.60** Eight electrons are needed to fill the 3s and 3p subshells. **3.62** Am, metal **3.64 (a, b)** transition metals **(c)** 3d **3.66 (a)** Rb: (i), (v), (vii) **(b)** W: (i), (iv) **(c)** Ge: (iii), (v) **(d)** Kr: (ii), (v), (vi) **3.68** selenium **3.70** sodium, potassium, rubidium, cesium, francium **3.72** 2 **3.74** 2, 8, 18 **3.76** 3, 4, 4 **3.78** 10, neon **3.80 (a)** two paired, two unpaired **(b)** four paired, one unpaired **(c)** two unpaired **3.82** 2, 1, 2, 0, 3, 4 **3.84** 2 **3.86** beryllium, 2s; arsenic, 4p **3.88 (a)** 8 **(b)** 4 **(c)** 2 **(d)** 1 **(e)** 3 **(f)** 7 **3.90** A scanning tunneling microscope has much higher resolution. **3.92** H, He **3.94 (a)** ultraviolet **(b)** gamma waves **(c)** X rays **3.96** He, Ne, Ar, Kr, Xe, Rn **3.98** Tellurium atoms have more neutrons than iodine atoms. **3.100** 1 (2 e), 2 (8 e), 3 (18 e), 4 (32 e), 5 (18 e), 6 (4 e) **3.102** 79.90 amu **3.104** carbon weighs more **3.106** 12 g **3.108** Sr, metal, group 2A, period 5, 38 protons **3.110** 2, 8, 18, 10, 2; metal **3.112 (a)** The 4s subshell fills before 3d. **(b)** The 2s subshell fills before 2p. **(c)** Silicon has 14 electrons: $1s^2\,2s^2\,2p^6\,3s^2\,3p^2$. **(d)** The 3s electrons have opposite spins. **3.114** An electron will fill or half-fill a d subshell instead of filling an s subshell of a higher shell.

Chapter 4

4.1 Mg^{2+} is a cation **4.2** S^{2-} is an anion **4.3** O^{2-} is an anion **4.4** less than Kr, but higher than most other elements **4.5 (a)** B **(b)** Ca **(c)** Sc **4.6 (a)** H **(b)** S **(c)** Cr **4.7** Potassium ($1s^2\,2s^2\,2p^6\,3s^2\,3p^6\,4s^1$) can gain the argon configuration by losing 1 electron. **4.8** Aluminum can lose 3 electrons to form Al^{3+}. **4.9** X: would be a 2A metal and would lose electrons; ·Ÿ· would be a 6A nonmetal and would gain electrons.

$$X: \;+\; \cdot\ddot{Y}\cdot \;\longrightarrow\; X^{2+} \;+\; :\ddot{Y}:^{2-}$$

4.10 cation **4.11 (b)**

4.12 (a) $Se + 2e^- \rightarrow Se^{2-}$ **(b)** $Ba \rightarrow Ba^{2+} + 2e^-$ **(c)** $Br + e^- \rightarrow Br^-$ **4.13 (a)** copper(II) ion **(b)** fluoride ion **(c)** magnesium ion **(d)** sulfide ion **4.14 (a)** Ag^+ **(b)** Fe^{2+} **(c)** Cu^+ **(d)** Te^{2-} **4.15** Na^+, sodium ion; K^+, potassium ion; Ca^{2+}, calcium ion; Cl^-, chloride ion **4.16 (a)** nitrate ion **(b)** cyanide ion **(c)** hydroxide ion **(d)** hydrogen phosphate ion **4.17 (a)** HCO_3^- **(b)** NH_4^+ **(c)** PO_4^{3-} **(d)** MnO_4^- **4.18 (a)** AgI **(b)** Ag_2O

(c) Ag_3PO_4 **4.19 (a)** Na_2SO_4 **(b)** $FeSO_4$ **(c)** $Cr_2(SO_4)_3$ **4.20** $(NH_4)_2CO_3$ **4.21** $Al_2(SO_4)_3$, $Al(CH_3CO_2)_3$ **4.22** blue: K_2S; red: $BaBr_2$ green: Al_2O_3 **4.23** Calcium ion = Ca^{2+}; nitride ion = N^{3-}; calcium nitride formula = Ca_3N_2 **4.24** $BaSO_4$ **4.25** silver(I) sulfide **4.26 (a)** tin(IV) oxide **(b)** calcium cyanide **(c)** sodium carbonate **(d)** copper(I) sulfate **(e)** barium hydroxide **(f)** iron(II) nitrate **4.27 (a)** Li_3PO_4 **(b)** $CuCO_3$ **(c)** $Al_2(SO_3)_3$ **(d)** CuF **(e)** $Fe_2(SO_4)_3$ **(f)** NH_4Cl **4.28** Cr_2O_3 chromium (III) oxide **4.29** Acids: **(a)**, **(d)**; bases **(b)**, **(c)** **4.30 (a)** HCl **(b)** H_2SO_4

4.31

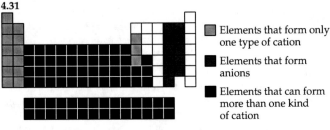

Elements that form only one type of cation

Elements that form anions

Elements that can form more than one kind of cation

All of the other elements form neither anions nor cations readily.

4.32

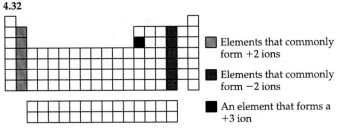

Elements that commonly form +2 ions

Elements that commonly form −2 ions

An element that forms a +3 ion

4.33 (a) O^{2-} **(b)** Na^+ **(c)** Ca **4.34 (a)** sodium atom (larger) **(b)** Na^+ ion (smaller) **4.35 (a)** chlorine atom (smaller) **(b)** Cl^- anion (larger) **4.36** red: MgO; blue: LiCl; green: $AlBr_3$ **4.37 (a)** ZnS **(b)** $PbBr_2$ **(c)** CrF_3 **(d)** Al_2O_3 **4.38 (a)** ·Be· **(b)** :Ne: **(c)** ·Sr· **(d)** ·Al· **4.40 (a)** $Ca \rightarrow Ca^{2+} + 2e^-$ **(b)** $Au \rightarrow Au^+ + e^-$ **(c)** $F + e^- \rightarrow F^-$ **(d)** $Cr \rightarrow Cr^{3+} + 3e^-$ **4.42** true: **(d)**; false: **(a)**, **(b)**, **(c)** **4.44** Main group atoms undergo reactions that leave them with a noble gas electron configuration. **4.46** −2 **4.48 (a)** Sr **(b)** Br **4.50 (a)** $1s^2\,2s^2\,2p^6\,3s^2\,3p^6\,4s^2\,3d^{10}\,4p^6$ **(b)** $1s^2\,2s^2\,2p^6\,3s^2\,3p^6\,4s^2\,3d^{10}\,4p^6$ **(c)** $1s^2\,2s^2\,2p^6\,3s^2\,3p^6$ **(d)** $1s^2\,2s^2\,2p^6\,3s^2\,3p^6\,4s^2\,3d^{10}\,4p^6\,5s^2\,4d^{10}\,5p^6$ **(e)** $1s^2\,2s^2\,2p^6$ **4.52 (a)** O **(b)** Li **(c)** Zn **(d)** N **4.54** none **4.56** Cr^{2+}: $1s^2\,2s^2\,2p^6\,3s^2\,3p^6\,3d^4$; Cr^{3+}: $1s^2\,2s^2\,2p^6\,3s^2\,3p^6\,3d^3$ **4.58** greater **4.60 (a)** sulfide ion **(b)** tin(II) ion **(c)** strontium ion **(d)** magnesium ion **(e)** gold(I) ion **4.62 (a)** Se^{2-} **(b)** O^{2-} **(c)** Ag^+ **4.64 (a)** OH^- **(b)** HSO_4^- **(c)** $CH_3CO_2^-$ **(d)** MnO_4^- **(e)** OCl^- **(f)** NO_3^- **(g)** CO_3^{2-} **(h)** $Cr_2O_7^{2-}$ **4.66 (a)** $Al(NO_3)_3$ **(b)** $AgNO_3$ **(c)** $Zn(NO_3)_2$ **(d)** $Ba(NO_3)_2$ **4.68 (a)** $Al_2(SO_4)_3$ **(b)** Ag_2SO_4 **(c)** $ZnSO_4$ **(d)** $BaSO_4$

4.70

	S^{2-}	Cl^-	PO_4^{3-}	CO_3^{2-}
copper(II)	CuS	$CuCl_2$	$Cu_3(PO_4)_2$	$CuCO_3$
Ca^{2+}	CaS	$CaCl_2$	$Ca_3(PO_4)_2$	$CaCO_3$
NH_4^+	$(NH_4)_2S$	NH_4Cl	$(NH_4)_3PO_4$	$(NH_4)_2CO_3$
ferric ion	Fe_2S_3	$FeCl_3$	$FePO_4$	$Fe_2(CO_3)_3$

4.72 copper(II) sulfide, copper(II) chloride, copper(II) phosphate, copper(II) carbonate; calcium sulfide, calcium chloride, calcium phosphate, calcium carbonate; ammonium sulfide, ammonium chloride, ammonium phosphate, ammonium carbonate; iron(III) sulfide, iron(III) chloride, iron(III) phosphate, iron(III) carbonate **4.74 (a)** magnesium carbonate **(b)** calcium acetate **(c)** silver(I) cyanide **(d)** sodium dichromate **4.76** $Ca_3(PO_4)_2$ **4.78** An acid gives H^+ ions in water; a base gives OH^- ions. **4.80 (a)** $H_2CO_3 \rightarrow 2H^+ + CO_3^{2-}$ **(b)** $HCN \rightarrow H^+ + CN^-$ **(c)** $Mg(OH)_2 \rightarrow Mg^{2+} + 2OH^-$ **(d)** $KOH \rightarrow K^+ + OH^-$ **4.82** To a geologist, a mineral is a naturally occurring crystalline compound. To a nutritionist, a mineral is a metal ion essential for human health. **4.84** slight **4.86** Sodium protects against fluid loss and is necessary for muscle contraction and transmission of nerve impulses.

4.88 10 Ca^{2+}, 6 PO$_4{}^{3-}$, 2 OH$^-$ **4.90** H$^-$ has the helium configuration, 1s^2 **4.92** (a) CrO$_3$ (b) VCl$_5$ (c) MnO$_2$ (d) MoS$_2$ **4.94** (a) -1 (b) 3 gluconate ions per iron(III) **4.96** (a) Co(CN)$_2$ (b) UO$_3$ (c) SnSO$_4$ (d) MnO$_2$ (e) K$_3$PO$_4$ (f) Ca$_3$P$_2$ (g) LiHSO$_4$ (h) Al(OH)$_3$ **4.98** (a) metal (b) nonmetal (c) X$_2$Y$_3$ (d) X: group 3A; Y: group 6A

Chapter 5

5.1 :I̤:I̤:; xenon **5.2** (a) P 3, H 1 (b) Se 2, H 1 (c) H 1, Cl 1 (d) Si 4, F 1

5.3 PbCl$_4$ **5.4** (a) CH$_2$Cl$_2$ (b) BH$_3$ (c) NI$_3$ (d) SiCl$_4$

5.5

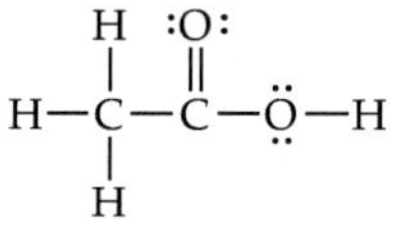

5.6

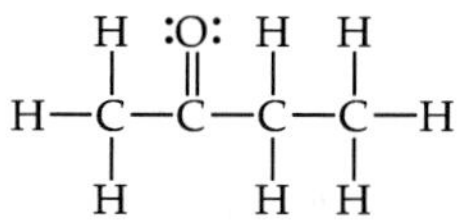

5.7

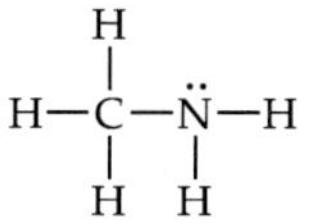

5.8 (a) 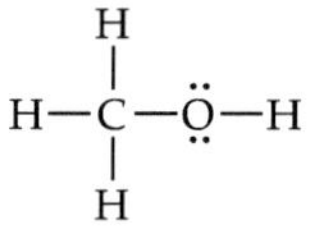 (b) 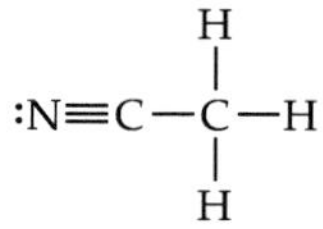 (c)

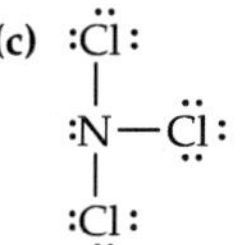

5.9 (a) 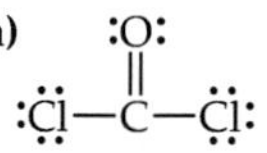 (b) 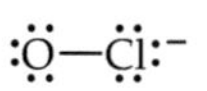 (c) 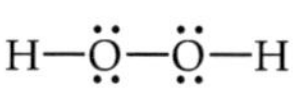 (d)

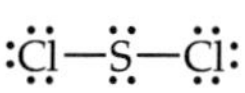

5.10

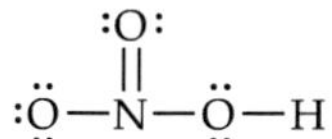

5.11 (a) C$_6$H$_{10}$O$_2$ (b)

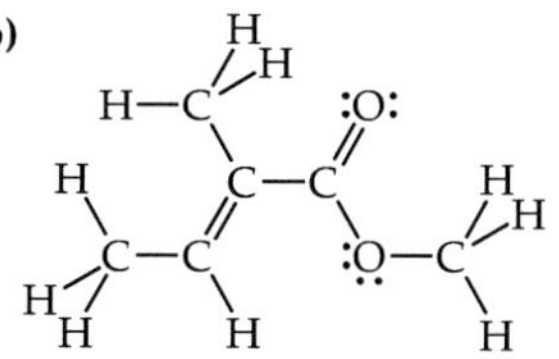

5.12 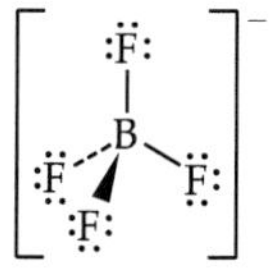 tetrahedral

5.13 chloroform: tetrahedral; dichloroethylene: planar **5.14** Both are tetrahedral. **5.15** Both are bent.

5.16

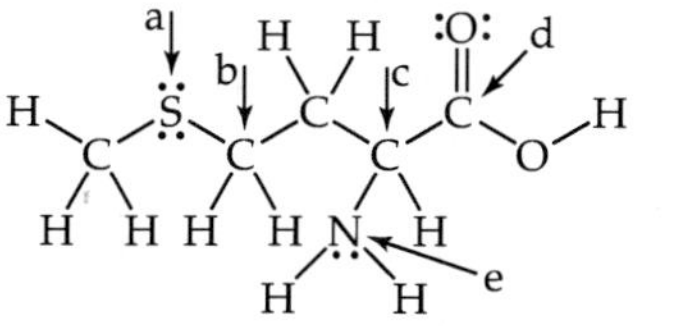

(a) bent
(b) tetrahedral
(c) tetrahedral
(d) planar triangular
(e) pyramidal

5.17 H < P < S < N < O **5.18** (a) polar covalent (b) ionic (c) covalent (d) polar covalent **5.19** (a) $^{\delta+}$S—F$^{\delta-}$ (b) $^{\delta+}$P—O$^{\delta-}$ (c) $^{\delta+}$As—Cl$^{\delta-}$

5.20

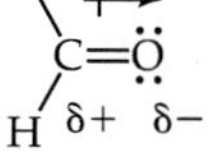

5.21 The carbons are tetrahedral; the oxygen is bent.

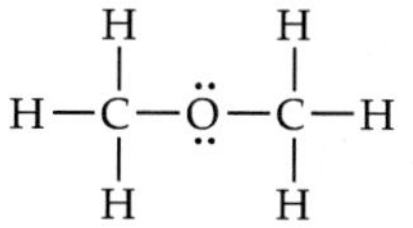

5.22

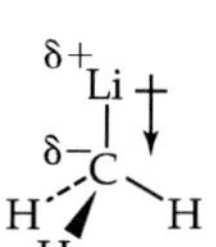

5.23 (a) disulfur dichloride (b) iodine chloride (c) iodine trichloride

5.24 (a) SeF$_4$ (b) P$_2$O$_5$ (c) BrF$_3$ **5.25** molecular solid **5.26** AlCl$_3$ is a covalent compound, and Al$_2$O$_3$ is ionic **5.27** (a) ionic (b) covalent **5.28** (a) **5.29** (a) tetrahedral (b) pyramidal (c) planar triangular **5.30** (c) is square planar **5.31** (a) C$_8$H$_9$NO$_2$
(b)

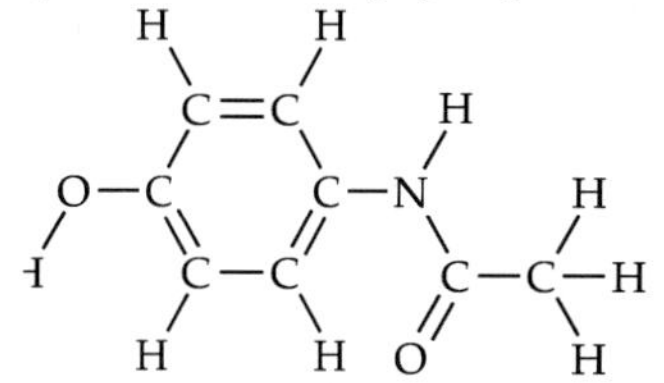

(c) All carbons are trigonal planar except the —CH$_3$ carbon. Nitrogen is pyramidal. **5.32**

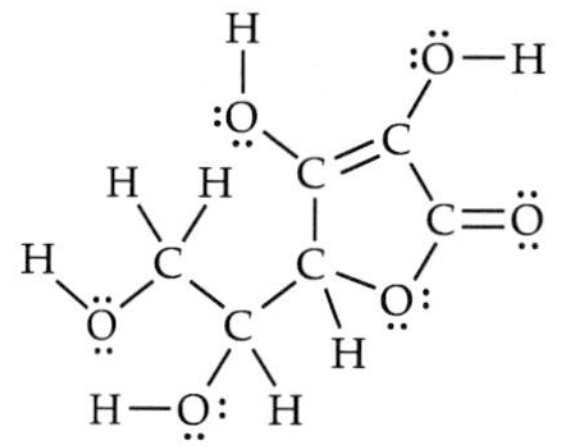

5.33 C$_{13}$H$_{10}$N$_2$O$_4$

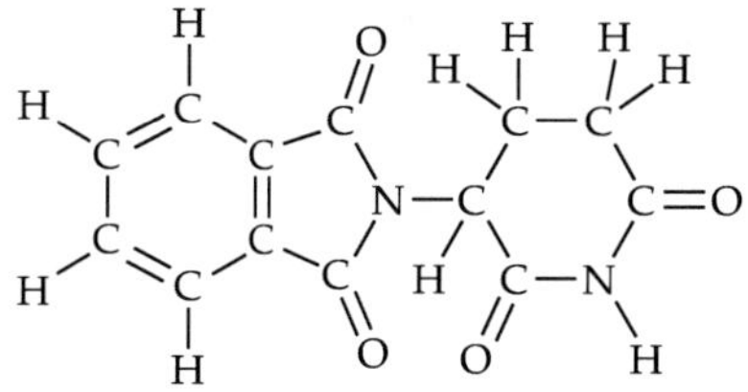

5.34

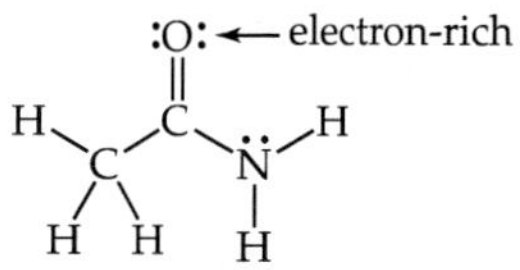

:O: ← electron-rich

5.36 In a coordinate covalent bond, both electrons in the bond come from the same atom. **5.38** covalent bonds: (a) (b); ionic bonds: (c) (d) (e) **5.40** two covalent bonds **5.42** (b), (c) **5.44** SnCl$_4$ **5.46** the N–O bond **5.48** (a) A molecular formula shows the numbers and kinds of atoms; a structural formula shows how the atoms are bonded to one another. (b) A structural formula shows the bonds between atoms; a condensed structure shows atoms but not bonds. (c) A lone pair of valence electrons is not shared in a bond; a shared pair of electrons is shared between two atoms. **5.50** (a) 10 (b) 10 (c) 24 (d) 20 **5.52** Too many hydrogens

5.54 (a) 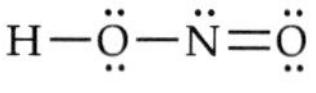 (b) 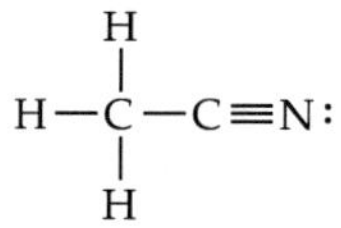 (c)

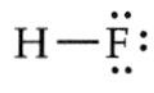

5.56 (a) CH$_3$CH$_2$CH$_3$ (b) H$_2$C=CHCH$_3$ (c) CH$_3$CH$_2$Cl
5.58 CH$_3$CO$_2$H

5.60 (a) 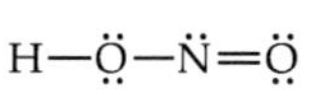 (b) 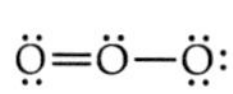 (c)

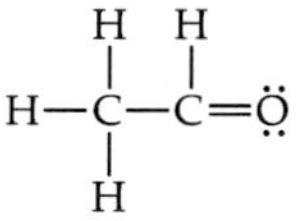

5.62 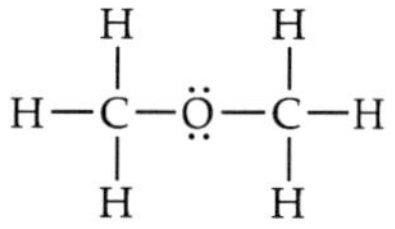 Dimethyl ether

5.64 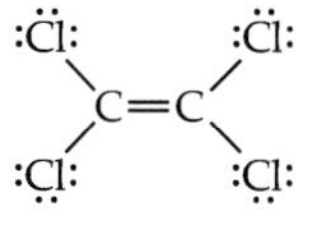 Tetrachloroethylene contains a double bond

5.66

$$H-\overset{\cdot\cdot}{N}-\overset{\cdot\cdot}{O}-H$$
$$\underset{|}{\overset{|}{H}}$$

5.68

(a) $\left[H-\overset{:\overset{\cdot\cdot}{O}:}{\underset{}{C}}-\overset{\cdot\cdot}{\underset{\cdot\cdot}{O}}: \right]^{-}$
(b) $\left[:\overset{\cdot\cdot}{\underset{\cdot\cdot}{O}}-\overset{:\overset{\cdot\cdot}{O}:}{\underset{}{C}}-\overset{\cdot\cdot}{\underset{\cdot\cdot}{O}}: \right]^{2-}$
(c) $\left[:\overset{\cdot\cdot}{\underset{\cdot\cdot}{O}}-\overset{:\overset{\cdot\cdot}{O}:}{\underset{}{S}}-\overset{\cdot\cdot}{\underset{\cdot\cdot}{O}}: \right]^{2-}$

(d) $\left[:\overset{\cdot\cdot}{\underset{\cdot\cdot}{S}}-C\equiv N: \right]^{-}$
(e) $\left[:\overset{\cdot\cdot}{\underset{\cdot\cdot}{O}}-\overset{\overset{:\overset{\cdot\cdot}{O}:}{|}}{\underset{\underset{:\overset{\cdot\cdot}{O}:}{}}{P}}-\overset{\cdot\cdot}{\underset{\cdot\cdot}{O}}: \right]^{3-}$
(f) $\left[:\overset{\cdot\cdot}{\underset{\cdot\cdot}{O}}-\overset{\cdot\cdot}{\underset{\cdot\cdot}{Cl}}-\overset{\cdot\cdot}{\underset{\cdot\cdot}{O}}: \right]^{-}$

5.70 tetrahedral; pyramidal; bent   **5.72** (a), (b) tetrahedral (c), (d) planar triangular (e) pyramidal   **5.74** All are planar triangular, except for the $-CH_3$ carbon, which is tetrahedral.   **5.76** It should have low electronegativity, like other alkali metals.   **5.78** $Cl > C > Cu > Ca > Cs$

5.80
(a) $\overset{\delta-}{O}-\overset{\delta+}{Br}$ (b) $\overset{\delta-}{N}-\overset{\delta+}{H}$ (c) $\overset{\delta+}{P}-\overset{\delta-}{O}$

(d) nonpolar   (e) $\overset{\delta-}{C}-\overset{\delta+}{Li}$

5.82 $PH_3 < HCl < H_2O < CF_4$

5.84 (a) $H-Cl$ polar   (b) $\underset{H}{\overset{\cdot\cdot}{P}} \nearrow$ polar   (c) polar   (d) nonpolar

5.86 S—H bonds are less polar because S is less electronegative than O.   **5.88** (a) silicon tetrachloride (b) sodium hydride (c) antimony pentafluoride (d) osmium tetroxide   **5.90** (a) SeO_2 (b) XeO_4 (c) N_2S_5 (d) P_3Se_4 **5.92** It relaxes arterial walls.   **5.94** Carbohydrates, DNA, and proteins are all polymers that occur in nature.   **5.96** no

5.98 (a)

(b) The $C=O$ carbons are planar triangular; the other carbons are tetrahedral.   (c) The $C=O$ bonds are polar.   **5.100** (a) C forms 4 bonds (b) N forms 3 bonds (c) S forms 2 bonds (d) could be correct   **5.102** (b) tetrahedral (c) contains a coordinate covalent bond (d) has 19 p and 18 e^-

$$\left[\underset{\underset{H}{|}}{\overset{\overset{H}{|}}{H-P-H}} \right]^{+}$$

5.104 (a) calcium chloride (b) tellurium dichloride (c) boron trifluoride (d) magnesium sulfate (e) potassium oxide (f) iron(III) fluoride (g) phosphorus trifluoride

5.106   **5.108**

5.110 (a)   (b)

Chapter 6
6.1 (a) Solid cobalt(II) chloride plus gaseous hydrogen fluoride gives solid cobalt(II) fluoride plus gaseous hydrogen chloride.   (b) Aqueous lead(II) nitrate plus aqueous potassium iodide gives solid lead(II) iodide plus aqueous potassium nitrate.   **6.2** balanced: (a), (c)   **6.3** $3 O_2 \rightarrow 2 O_3$ **6.4** (a) $Ca(OH)_2 + 2 HCl \rightarrow CaCl_2 + 2 H_2O$ (b) $4 Al + 3 O_2 \rightarrow 2 Al_2O_3$ (c) $2 CH_3CH_3 + 7 O_2 \rightarrow 4 CO_2 + 6 H_2O$ (d) $2 AgNO_3 + MgCl_2 \rightarrow 2 AgCl + Mg(NO_3)_2$ **6.5** $2 A + B_2 \rightarrow A_2B_2$ **6.6** (a) 206.0 amu (b) 232.0 amu   **6.7** 1.71×10^{21} molecules   **6.8** 0.15 g   **6.9** 111.0 amu **6.10** 0.217 mol; 4.6 g   **6.11** 5.00 g weighs more   **6.12** (a) $Ni + 2 HCl \rightarrow NiCl_2 + H_2$; 4.90 mol (b) 6.00 mol   **6.13** $6 CO_2 + 6 H_2O \rightarrow C_6H_{12}O_6 + 6 O_2$; 90.0 mol CO_2 **6.14** (a) 39.6 mol (b) 13.8 g   **6.15** 6.31 g WO_3; 0.165 g H_2 **6.16** 44.7 g; 57.0%   **6.17** 49.3 g   **6.18** A_2 **6.19** (a) precipitation (b) redox (c) acid–base neutralization   **6.20** Soluble: (b), (d); insoluble: (a), (c), (e)   **6.21** precipitation: (a), (b) **6.22** (a) $2 CsOH(aq) + H_2SO_4(aq) \rightarrow Cs_2SO_4(aq) + 2 H_2O(l)$ (b) $Ca(OH)_2(aq) + 2 CH_3CO_2H(aq) \rightarrow Ca(CH_3CO_2)_2(aq) + 2 H_2O(l)$ (c) $NaHCO_3(aq) + HBr(aq) \rightarrow NaBr(aq) + CO_2(g) + H_2O(l)$ **6.23** (a) oxidizing: Cu; reducing: Fe (b) oxidizing: Cl; reducing: Mg (c) oxidizing: Cr_2O_3; reducing: Al   **6.24** $2 K + Br_2 \rightarrow 2 KBr$; oxidizing: Br_2; reducing: K   **6.25** (a) V(III) (b) Sn(IV) (c) Cr(VI) (d) Cu(II) (e) Ni(II) **6.26** (a) not redox (b) Na oxidized from 0 to +1; H reduced from +1 to 0 (c) C oxidized from 0 to +4; O reduced from 0 to -2 (d) not redox (e) S oxidized from +4 to +6; Mn reduced from +7 to +2 **6.27** (a) $Zn(s) + Pb^{2+}(aq) \rightarrow Zn^{2+}(aq) + Pb(s)$ (b) $OH^-(aq) + H^+(aq) \rightarrow H_2O(l)$ (c) $2 Fe^{3+}(aq) + Sn^{2+}(aq) \rightarrow 2 Fe^{2+}(aq) + Sn^{4+}(aq)$ **6.28** (d)   **6.29** (c)   **6.30** reactants: (d); products: (c) **6.31** $C_5H_{11}NO_2S$; MW = 149.1 amu   **6.32** (a) $A_2 + 3 B \rightarrow 2 AB_3$ (b) 2 mol AB_3; 0.67 mol AB_3 **6.33** (a) box 1 (b) box 2 (c) box 3 **6.34** Ag_2CO_3 and $Ag_2Cr_2O_4$ are possible   **6.35** 22 g, 31 g   **6.36** In a balanced equation, the numbers and kinds of atoms are the same on both sides of the reaction arrow.   **6.38** (a) $SO_2(g) + H_2O(g) \rightarrow H_2SO_3(aq)$ (b) $2 K(s) + Br_2(l) \rightarrow 2 KBr(s)$ (c) $C_3H_8(g) + 5 O_2(g) \rightarrow 3 CO_2(g) + 4 H_2O(l)$ **6.40** (a) $2 C_2H_6(g) + 7 O_2(g) \rightarrow 4 CO_2(g) + 6 H_2O(g)$ (b) balanced   (c) $2 Mg(s) + O_2(g) \rightarrow 2 MgO(s)$ (d) $2 K(s) + 2 H_2O(l) \rightarrow 2 KOH(aq) + H_2(g)$ **6.42** (a) $Hg(NO_3)_2(aq) + 2 LiI(aq) \rightarrow 2 LiNO_3(aq) + HgI_2(s)$ (b) $I_2(s) + 5 Cl_2(g) \rightarrow 2 ICl_5(s)$ (c) $4 Al(s) + 3 O_2(g) \rightarrow 3 Al_2O_3(s)$ (d) $CuSO_4(aq) + 2 AgNO_3(aq) \rightarrow Ag_2SO_4(s) + Cu(NO_3)_2(aq)$ (e) $2 Mn(NO_3)_3(aq) + 3 Na_2S(aq) \rightarrow Mn_2S_3(s) + 6 NaNO_3(aq)$ (f) $4 NO_2(g) + O_2(g) \rightarrow 2 N_2O_5(g)$ (g) $P_4O_{10}(s) + 6 H_2O(l) \rightarrow 4 H_3PO_4(aq)$ **6.44** (a) $2 C_4H_{10}(g) + 13 O_2(g) \rightarrow 8 CO_2(g) + 10 H_2O(l)$ (b) $C_2H_6O(g) + 3 O_2(g) \rightarrow 2 CO_2(g) + 3 H_2O(l)$ (c) $2 C_8H_{18}(g) + 25 O_2(g) \rightarrow 16 CO_2(g) + 18 H_2O(l)$

6.46 molecular weight = sum of the weights of individual atoms in a molecule; formula weight = sum of weights of individual atoms in a formula unit; molar mass = mass in grams of 6.022×10^{23} molecules or formula units of any substance   **6.48** 5.25 mol ions   **6.50** 10.6 g uranium **6.52** (a) 1 mol (b) 1 mol (c) 2 mol   **6.54** 6.44×10^{-4} mol   **6.56** 284.5 g **6.58** (a) 0.0132 mol (b) 0.0536 mol (c) 0.0608 mol (d) 0.0129 mol **6.60** 0.27 g; 9.0×10^{20} molecules   **6.62** 1.4×10^{-3} mol; 0.18 g **6.64** (a) $C_4H_8O_2(l) + 2 H_2(g) \rightarrow 2 C_2H_6O(l)$ (b) 3.0 mol (c) 138 g (d) 12.5 g (e) 0.55 g   **6.66** (a) $N_2(g) + 3 H_2(g) \rightarrow 2 NH_3(g)$ (b) 0.471 mol (c) 16.1 g **6.68** (a) $Fe_2O_3(s) + 3 CO(g) \rightarrow 2 Fe(s) + 3 CO_2(g)$ (b) 1.59 g (c) 141 g **6.70** 158 kg   **6.72** (a) CO is limiting (b) 11.4 g (c) 83.8% **6.74** (a) $CH_4(g) + 2 Cl_2(g) \rightarrow CH_2Cl_2(l) + 2 HCl(g)$ (b) 444 g (c) 202 g **6.76** (a) redox (b) neutralization (c) precipitation (d) neutralization **6.78** (a) $Ba^{2+}(aq) + SO_4^{2-}(aq) \rightarrow BaSO_4(s)$ (b) $Zn(s) + 2 H^+(aq) \rightarrow Zn^{2+}(aq) + H_2(g)$ **6.80** $Ba(NO_3)_2$ **6.82** (a) $2 NaBr(aq) + Hg_2(NO_3)_2(aq) \rightarrow Hg_2Br_2(s) + 2 NaNO_3(aq)$ (d) $(NH_4)_2CO_3(aq) + CaCl_2(aq) \rightarrow CaCO_3(s) + 2 NH_4Cl(aq)$ (e) $2 KOH(aq) + MnBr_2(aq) \rightarrow Mn(OH)_2(s) + 2 KBr(aq)$ (f) $3 Na_2S(aq) + 2 Al(NO_3)_3(aq) \rightarrow Al_2S_3(s) + 6 NaNO_3(aq)$ **6.84** (a) $2 Au^{3+}(aq) + 3 Sn(s) \rightarrow 3 Sn^{2+}(aq) + 2 Au(s)$ (b) $2 I^-(aq) + Br_2(l) \rightarrow 2 Br^-(aq) + I_2(s)$ (c) $2 Ag^+(aq) + Fe(s) \rightarrow Fe^{2+}(aq) + 2 Ag(s)$ **6.86** Most easily oxidized: metals on left side; most easily reduced: groups 6A and 7A   **6.88** oxidation number increases: (b), (c) oxidation

number decreases **(a)**, **(d)** **6.90 (a)** Co: +3 **(b)** Fe: +2 **(c)** U: +6 **(d)** Cu: +2 **(e)** Ti: +4 **(f)** Sn: +2 **6.92 (a)** oxidized: S; reduced: O **(b)** oxidized: Na; reduced: Cl **(c)** oxidized: Zn; reduced: Cu **(d)** oxidized: Cl; reduced: F **6.94** $FeSO_4$; 151.9 g/mol; 91.8 mg Fe **6.96** Zn is the reducing agent, and Mn^{2+} is the oxidizing agent. **6.98** 132 kg Li_2O; not a redox reaction **6.100** 6×10^{13} molecules
6.102 (a) $C_{12}H_{22}O_{11}(s) \rightarrow 12\ C(s) + 11\ H_2O(l)$ **(b)** 25.3 g C **(c)** 8.94 g H_2O
6.104 (a) 6.40 g **(b)** 104 g
6.106 (a) $Al(OH)_3(aq) + 3\ HNO_3(aq) \rightarrow Al(NO_3)_3(aq) + 3\ H_2O(l)$
(b) $3\ AgNO_3(aq) + FeCl_3(aq) \rightarrow 3\ AgCl(s) + Fe(NO_3)_3(aq)$
(c) $(NH_4)_2Cr_2O_7(s) \rightarrow Cr_2O_3(s) + 4\ H_2O(g) + N_2(g)$
(d) $Mn_2(CO_3)_3(s) \rightarrow Mn_2O_3(s) + 3\ CO_2(g)$
6.108 (a) $2\ SO_2(g) + O_2(g) \rightarrow 2\ SO_3(g)$
(b) $SO_3(g) + H_2O(g) \rightarrow H_2SO_4(l)$ **(c)** SO_2: +4; SO_3, H_2SO_4: +6

Chapter 7

7.1 (a) endothermic **(b)** $\Delta H = +678$ kcal
(c) $C_6H_{12}O_6(aq) + 6\ O_2(g) \rightarrow 6\ CO_2(g) + 6\ H_2O(l) + 678$ kcal
7.2 (a) endothermic **(b)** 200 kcal **(c)** 74.2 kcal **7.3** 91 kcal
7.4 (a) increase **(b)** increase **(c)** decrease **7.5 (a)** no **(b)** increases **(c)** yes
7.6 (a) +0.06 kcal/mol; nonspontaneous **(b)** 0.00 kcal/mol; equilibrium **(c)** −0.05 kcal/mol; spontaneous **7.7 (a)** positive **(b)** spontaneous at all temperatures
7.8 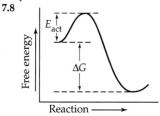 **7.9**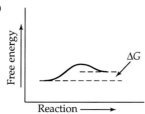

7.10 (a) rate increases **(b)** rate decreases **(c)** rate decreases

7.11 (a) $K = \dfrac{[NO_2]^2}{[N_2O_4]}$ **(b)** $K = \dfrac{[CH_3Cl][HCl]}{[CH_4][Cl_2]}$

(c) $K = \dfrac{[Br_2][F_2]^5}{[BrF_5]^2}$ **7.12 (a)** products favored **(b)** reactants favored

(c) products favored **7.13** $K = 29.0$ **7.14** The reaction forming CD has larger K. **7.15** reaction favored by high pressure and low temperature **7.16 (a)** favors reactants **(b)** favors product **(c)** favors product **7.17** ΔH is positive; ΔS is positive; ΔG is negative **7.18** ΔH is negative; ΔS is negative; ΔG is negative **7.19 (a)** $2\ A_2 + B_2 \rightarrow 2\ A_2B$ **(b)** ΔH is negative; ΔS is negative; ΔG is negative **7.20 (a)** blue curve represents faster reaction **(b)** red curve is spontaneous **7.21** red curve represents catalyzed reaction
7.22

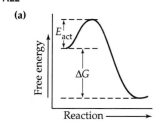

7.23 (a) positive **(b)** nonspontaneous at low temperature; spontaneous at high temperature **7.24** lower enthalpy for reactants
7.26 (a) positive **(b)** 43 kcal **(c)** 3.8 kcal
7.28 (a) $C_6H_{12}O_6 + 6\ O_2 \rightarrow 6\ CO_2 + 6\ H_2O$ **(b)** 1.0×10^3 kcal **(c)** 57 kcal
7.30 increased disorder: **(a)**; decreased disorder: **(b)**, **(c)**
7.32 A spontaneous process, once started, continues without external influence. **7.34** release or absorption of heat, and increase or decrease

in entropy **7.36** ΔH is usually larger than $T\Delta S$ **7.38 (a)** endothermic **(b)** increases **(c)** $T\Delta S$ is larger than ΔH
7.40 (a) $H_2(g) + Br_2(l) \rightarrow 2\ HBr(g)$ **(b)** increases **(c)** yes, because ΔH is negative and ΔS is positive **(d)** $\Delta G = -25.6$ kcal/mol
7.42 the amount of energy needed for reactants to surmount the barrier to reaction
7.44

(a) 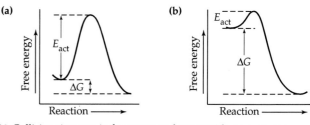 **(b)**

7.46 Collisions increase in frequency and occur with more energy.
7.48 A catalyst lowers the activation energy. **7.50 (a)** yes **(b)** reaction rate is slow **7.52** At equilibrium, the rates of forward and reverse reactions are equal. Amounts of reactants and products need not be equal.

7.54 (a) $K = \dfrac{[CO_2]^2}{[CO]^2[O_2]}$ **(b)** $K = \dfrac{[HCl]^2[C_2H_4Cl_2]}{[Cl_2]^2[C_2H_6]}$

(c) $K = \dfrac{[H_3O^+][F^-]}{[HF][H_2O]}$ **(d)** $K = \dfrac{[O_3]^2}{[O_2]^3}$ **7.56** $K = 7.2 \times 10^{-3}$

7.58 (a) 0.087 mol/L **(b)** 0.023 mol/L **7.60** more reactant
7.62 (a) endothermic **(b)** reactants are favored **(c)** (1) favors ozone; (2) favors ozone; (3) favors O_2; (4) no effect; (5) favors ozone
7.64 (a) decrease **(b)** no effect **(c)** increase **7.66** increase
7.68 (a) increase **(b)** decrease **(c)** no effect **(d)** decrease **7.70** fat
7.72 thyroid, hypothalamus **7.74** conversion of N_2 into chemically useful compounds; microorganisms and lightning
7.76 (a) $2\ C_2H_3OH(l) + 3\ O_2(g) \rightarrow 2\ CO_2(g) + 2\ H_2O(g)$
(b) negative **(c)** 35.5 kcal **(d)** 5.63 g **(e)** 5.60 kcal/mL
7.78 (a) $Fe_3O_4(s) + 4\ H_2(g) \rightarrow 3\ Fe(s) + 4\ H_2O(g)$ $\Delta H = +36$ kcal/mol **(b)** 12 kcal **(c)** 3.6 g H_2 **(d)** reactants **7.80** 450 g
7.82 (a) $4\ NH_3(g) + 5\ O_2(g) \rightarrow 4\ NO(g) + 6\ H_2O(g) +$ heat

(b) $K = \dfrac{[NO]^4[H_2O]^6}{[NH_3]^4[O_2]^5}$ **(c)** (1) favors reactants (2) favors reactants

(3) favors reactants (4) favors products **7.84 (a)** exergonic
(b) $\Delta G = -10$ kcal/mol **7.86** 1.91 kcal; exothermic

Chapter 8

8.1 (a) disfavored by ΔH; favored by ΔS **(b)** +0.02 kcal/mol
(c) $\Delta H = -9.72$ kcal/mol; $\Delta S = -26.1$ cal/(mol·K) **8.2** 0.29 atm; 4.3 psi; 29,000 Pa **8.3** 1000 mmHg **8.4** 450 L **8.5** 1.3 atm, 64 atm **8.6** 0.27 L; 0.88 L **8.7** 33 psi **8.8** 352 L **8.9** balloon **(a)**
8.10 4460 mol; 7.14×10^4 g CH_4; 1.96×10^5 g CO_2
8.11 5.0 atm **8.12** 1,100 mol; 4,400 g
8.13 **(a)** **(b)**

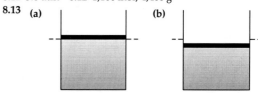

8.14 9.3 atm He; 0.19 atm O_2 **8.15** 75.4% N_2, 13.2% O_2, 5.3% CO_2, 6.2% H_2O **8.16** 35.0 mmHg **8.17 (c)** **8.18 (a)** decrease **(b)** increase
8.19 (a), **(c)** **8.20 (a)** London forces **(b)** hydrogen bonds, dipole–dipole forces, London forces **(c)** dipole–dipole forces, London forces
8.21 1.93 kcal, 14.3 kcal

8.22

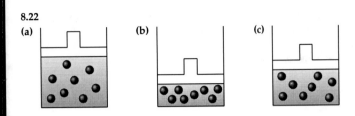

(a) volume increases by 50% (b) volume decreases by 50% (c) volume unchanged **8.23** (c) **8.24** (c)

8.25

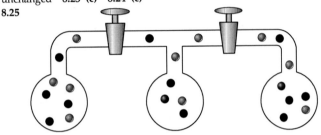

8.26

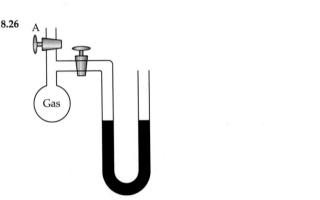

8.27 (a) 10 °C (b) 75 °C (c) 1.3 kcal/mol (d) 7.5 kcal/mol

8.28 (a)   (b)   (c)

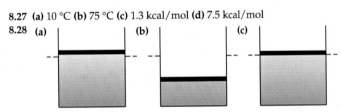

8.29 red = 300 mmHg; yellow = 100 mmHg; green = 200 mmHg
8.30 One atmosphere is equal to exactly 760 mmHg. **8.32** (1) A gas consists of tiny particles moving at random with no forces between them. (2) The amount of space occupied by the gas particles is small. (3) The average kinetic energy of the gas particles is proportional to the Kelvin temperature. (4) Collisions between particles are elastic.
8.34 (a) 760 mmHg (b) 1310 mmHg (c) 5.7×10^3 mmHg (d) 711 mmHg (e) 0.314 mmHg **8.36** 930 mmHg **8.38** V varies inversely with P when n and T are constant. **8.40** 101 mL **8.42** 1.75 L **8.44** V varies directly with T when n and P are constant. **8.46** 364 K = 91 °C
8.48 220 mL **8.50** P varies directly with T when n and V are constant.
8.52 1.2 atm **8.54** 493 K = 220 °C **8.56** 68.4 mL **8.58** (a) P increases by factor of 4 (b) P decreases by factor of 4 **8.60** 484 mL **8.62** Because gas particles are so far apart and have no interactions, their chemical identity does not matter. **8.64** 22.4 L **8.66** the same number of molecules; the O_2 sample weighs more **8.68** 11.8 g **8.70** 15 kg **8.72** $PV = nRT$
8.74 Cl_2 has fewer molecules but weighs more **8.76** 37 atm
8.78 2.2×10^4 mmHg **8.80** 22.3 L **8.82** the pressure contribution of one component in a mixture of gases **8.84** 93 mmHg **8.86** the partial pressure of the vapor above the liquid **8.88** Increased pressure raises a liquid's boiling point; decreased pressure lowers it. **8.90** (a) all molecules (b) molecules with polar covalent bonds (c) molecules with —OH or —NH bonds **8.92** Ethanol forms hydrogen bonds. **8.94** (a) 29.2 kcal (b) 173 kcal **8.96** Atoms in a crystalline solid have a regular, orderly

arrangement. **8.98** 4.82 kcal **8.100** Systolic pressure is the maximum pressure just after contraction; diastolic pressure is the minimum pressure at the end of the heart cycle. **8.102** Increase in atmospheric $[CO_2]$; increase in global temperatures **8.104** The supercritical state is intermediate in properties between liquid and gas. **8.106** As temperature increases, molecular collisions become more violent. **8.108** 0.13 mol; 4.0 L **8.110** 590 g/day **8.112** 0.92 g/L; less dense than air at STP
8.114 (a) 0.714 g/L (b) 1.96 g/L (c) 1.43 g/L
8.116 (a)   (b)

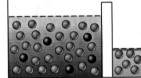

(c) Ethylene glycol forms hydrogen bonds.
8.118 (a) 492 °R (b) $R = 0.0455$ (L·atm)/(mol·°R)

Chapter 9
9.1 (a) heterogeneous mixture (b) homogeneous solution (c) homogeneous colloid (d) homogeneous solution **9.2** (c), (d)
9.3 $Na_2SO_4 \cdot 10H_2O$ **9.4** 322 g **9.5** 80 g/100 mL **9.6** 5.6 g/100 mL
9.7 6.8×10^{-5} g/100 mL **9.8** 0.925 M **9.9** (a) 0.061 mol (b) 0.67 mol
9.10 0.48 g **9.11** 0.39 g **9.12** 0.0086% (w/v) **9.13** 6.6% (w/v)
9.14 (a) 20 g (b) 1.2 g **9.15** Place 38 mL acetic acid in flask and dilute to 500.0 mL. **9.16** (a) 22 mL (b) 18 mL **9.17** 1.6 ppm **9.18** Pb: 0.015 ppm, 0.0015 mg; Cu: 1.3 ppm, 0.13 mg **9.19** 2.40 M **9.20** 39.1 mL
9.21 750 L **9.22** (a) 39.1 g; 39.1 mg (b) 79.9 g; 79.9 mg (c) 12.2 g; 12.2 mg (d) 48.0 g; 48.0 mg (e) 9.0 g; 9.0 mg (f) 31.7 g; 31.7 mg **9.23** 9.0 mg
9.24 102.0 °C **9.25** weak electrolyte **9.26** (a) red curve is pure solvent; green curve is solution (b) solvent bp = 62 °C; solution bp = 69 °C (c) 2 M
9.27 –1.9 °C **9.28** 3 ions/mol **9.29** (a) 0.70 osmol (b) 0.30 osmol
9.30 0.33 osmol
9.31

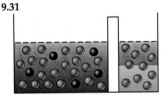

Before equilibrium   At equilibrium

9.32 HCl completely dissociates into ions; acetic acid dissociates only slightly. **9.33** HBr is completely dissociated; HF is not. **9.34** Upper red line: liquid; lower green line: gas **9.35** (a) **9.36** (d) **9.37** green curve is solution; red curve is solvent **9.38** homogeneous: mixing is uniform; heterogeneous: mixing is nonuniform **9.40** polarity **9.42** (b), (d)
9.44 15.3 g/100 mL **9.46** Concentrated solutions can be saturated or not; saturated solutions can be concentrated or not. **9.48** Molarity is the number of moles of solute per liter of solution. **9.50** Dissolve 45.0 mL of ethyl alcohol in water and dilute to 750.0 mL **9.52** Dissolve 1.5 g NaCl in water to a final volume of 250 mL. **9.54** (a) 7.7% (w/v) (b) 3.9% (w/v) **9.56** (a) 4.0 g (b) 15 g **9.58** 230 mL, 1600 mL **9.60** 10 ppm
9.62 (a) 0.425 M   (b) 1.53 M   (c) 1.03 M **9.64** 5.3 mL **9.66** 37 g
9.68 400 mL **9.70** 0.53 L **9.72** 600 mL **9.74** a substance that conducts electricity when dissolved in water **9.76** Ca^{2+} concentration is 0.0015 M **9.78** 40 mEq **9.80** 0.28 L **9.82** $Ba(OH)_2$ **9.84** 861 g
9.86 The inside of the cell has higher osmolarity than water, so water passes in and increases pressure. **9.88** (a) 0.20 M Na_2SO_4 (b) 3% (w/v) NaOH **9.90** 2.4 osmol **9.92** The body manufactures more hemoglobin. **9.94** Sports drinks contain electrolytes, carbohydrate, and vitamins. **9.96** (a) 6.84 mmHg (b) 1.9 g/100 mL **9.98** (a) 0.0067% (w/v) (b) 67 ppm (c) 0.000 40 M **9.100** 9.4 mL **9.102** NaCl: 0.147 M; KCl: 0.0040 M; $CaCl_2$: 0.0030 M **9.104** 0.00020 % (w/v) **9.106** 4.0 mL
9.108 (a) $CoCl_2 + 6 H_2O \rightarrow CoCl_2 \cdot 6H_2O$ (b) 1.13 g **9.110** (a) 1.36 mol particles (b) 2.53 °C

Chapter 10
10.1 (a), (b) **10.2** (a), (c) **10.3** (a) H_2S (b) HPO_4^{2-} (c) HCO_3^- (d) NH_3
10.4 acids: HF, H_2S; bases: HS^-, F^-; conjugate acid–base pairs: H_2S and

HS^-, HF and F^- **10.5 (a)** base **(b)** acid **(c)** base **10.6 (a)** NH_4^+
(b) H_2SO_4 **(c)** H_2CO_3 **10.7 (a)** F^- **(b)** OH^- **10.8** $HPO_4^{2-} + OH^- \rightleftharpoons$
$PO_4^{3-} + H_2O$; favored in forward direction **10.9** The $-NH_3^+$ hydrogens are most acidic **10.10** citric acid **10.11 (a)** acidic, $[OH^-] =$
3.1×10^{-10} M **(b)** basic, $[OH^-] = 3.2 \times 10^{-3}$ M **10.12** pH = 5 has
higher $[H^+]$; pH 9 has higher $[OH^-]$ **10.13 (a)** 5 **(b)** 5
10.14 (a) 1×10^{-13} M **(b)** 1×10^{-3} M **(c)** 1×10^{-8} M; **(b)** is most acidic;
(a) is most basic **10.15** pH = 4 **10.16 (a)** acidic, 3×10^{-7} M **(b)** most
basic, 1×10^{-8} M **(c)** acidic 2×10^{-4} M **(d)** most acidic, 3×10^{-4} M
10.17 (a) 8.28 **(b)** 5.05 **10.18** 2.60 **10.19** 3.38 **10.20** 9.45 **10.21** 9.13
10.22 (a) 0.079 Eq **(b)** 0.338 Eq **(c)** 0.14 Eq **10.23 (a)** 0.26 N **(b)** 1.13 N
(c) 0.47 N
10.24 $Al(OH)_3 + 3\,HCl \rightarrow AlCl_3 + 3\,H_2O$;
$Mg(OH)_2 + 2\,HCl \rightarrow MgCl_2 + 2\,H_2O$
10.25 (a) $2\,KHCO_3 + H_2SO_4 \rightarrow 2\,H_2O + 2\,CO_2 + K_2SO_4$
(b) $MgCO_3 + 2\,HNO_3 \rightarrow H_2O + CO_2 + Mg(NO_3)_2$
10.26 $H_2SO_4 + 2\,NH_3 \rightarrow (NH_4)_2SO_4$
10.27 $CH_3CH_2NH_2 + HCl \rightarrow CH_3CH_2NH_3^+\,Cl^-$
10.28 0.730 M **10.29** 133 mL **10.30** 0.225 M **10.31 (a)** neutral
(b) basic **(c)** basic **(d)** acidic
10.32 (a)

$$HCO_3^- + H_2O \longrightarrow CO_3^{2-} + H_3O^+$$

Acid   Base   Base   Acid

(b)

$$HCO_3^- + HF \longrightarrow H_2CO_3 + F^-$$

Base   Acid   Acid   Base

10.33 (a) box 2 **(b)** box 3 **(c)** box 1 **10.34** The O—H hydrogen in
each is most acidic; acetic acid **10.35 (a)** box 1 **(b)** box 2 **(c)** box 1
10.36 (a) box 3 **(b)** box 1 **10.37** 0.67 M **10.38** HBr dissociates into
ions **10.40** KOH dissociates into ions **10.42** A monoprotic acid can
donate one proton; a diprotic acid can donate two. **10.44 (a), (e)**
10.46 (a) acid **(b)** base **(c)** neither **(d)** acid **(e)** neither **(f)** acid
10.48 (a) CH_2ClCO_2H **(b)** $C_5H_5NH^+$ **(c)** $HSeO_4^-$ **(d)** $(CH_3)_3NH^+$
10.50 (a) $HCO_3^- + HCl \rightarrow H_2O + CO_2 + Cl^-$; $HCO_3^- + NaOH \rightarrow$
$H_2O + Na^+ + CO_3^{2-}$ **(b)** $H_2PO_4^- + HCl \rightarrow H_3PO_4 + Cl^-$;
$H_2PO_4^- + NaOH \rightarrow H_2O + Na^+ + HPO_4^{2-}$
10.52 $2\,HCl + CaCO_3 \rightarrow H_2O + CO_2 + CaCl_2$

10.54 $K_a = \dfrac{[H_3O^+][A^-]}{[HA]}$

10.56 $K_w = [H_3O^+][OH^-] = 1.0 \times 10^{-14}$
10.58 CH_3CO_2H is a weak acid and is only partially dissociated.

10.60
$$K_a = \frac{[H_2PO_4^{2-}][H_3O^+]}{[H_3PO_4]} \qquad K_a = \frac{[HPO_4^{2-}][H_3O^+]}{[H_2PO_4^-]} \qquad K_a = \frac{[PO_4^{3-}][H_3O^+]}{[HPO_4^{2-}]}$$

10.62 (a) OH^- **(b)** NO_2^- **(c)** OH^- **(d)** CN^- **(e)** HPO_4^{2-} **10.64** basic;
1.3×10^{-8} **10.66** 1×10^{-2} M **10.68** 1.0; 13.0 **10.70 (a)** 7.60 **(b)** 3.30
(c) 11.64 **10.72 (a)** 1×10^{-4} M; 1×10^{-10} M; **(b)** 1×10^{-11} M;
1×10^{-3} M **(c)** 1 M; 1×10^{-14} M **(d)** 4.2×10^{-2} M; 2.4×10^{-13} M
(e) 1.1×10^{-8} M; 9.1×10^{-7} M **10.74** A buffer contains a weak acid and
its anion. The acid neutralizes any added base, and the anion neutralizes
any added acid.

10.76 (a) $pH = pK_a + \log\dfrac{[CH_3CO_2^-]}{[CH_3CO_2H]} = 4.74 + \log\dfrac{[0.100]}{[0.100]} = 4.74$

(b) $CH_3CO_2^-\,Na^+ + H^+ \rightarrow CH_3CO_2H + Na^+$; $CH_3CO_2H + OH^- \rightarrow$
$CH_3CO_2^- + H_2O$ **10.78** 9.19 **10.80** 9.07 **10.82** An equivalent is the
formula weight in grams divided by the number of H_3O^+ or OH^- ions
produced. **10.84** 63.0 g; 32.7 g; 56.1 g; 29.3 g **10.86** 25 mL; 25 mL
10.88 (a) 0.50 Eq **(b)** 0.084 Eq **(c)** 0.25 Eq **10.90** 0.13 M; 0.26 N
10.92 0.22 M **10.94** 0.075 M **10.96 (a)** pH = 2 to 3
(b) $NaHCO_3 + HCl \rightarrow CO_2 + H_2O + NaCl^+$ **(c)** 20 mg

10.98 Intravenous bicarbonate neutralizes the hydrogen ions in the
blood and restores pH. **10.100** 2×10^{-6} M **10.102** Citric acid reacts
with sodium bicarbonate to release CO_2. **10.104** Both have the same
amount of acid; HCl has higher $[H_3O^+]$ and lower pH. **10.106** 0.35 M
10.108 (a) NH_4^+, acid; OH^-, base; NH_3, conjugate base; H_2O, conjugate
acid **(b)** 5.56 g **10.110 (a)** $Na_2O(aq) + H_2O(l) \rightarrow 2\,NaOH(aq)$ **(b)** 13.0
(c) 5000 mL

Chapter 11
11.1 $^{218}_{84}Po$ **11.2** $^{226}_{88}Ra$ **11.3** $^{14}_{6}C \rightarrow {}^{0}_{-1}e + {}^{14}_{7}N$
11.4 (a) $^{3}_{1}H \rightarrow {}^{0}_{-1}e + {}^{3}_{2}He$ **(b)** $^{210}_{82}Pb \rightarrow {}^{0}_{-1}e + {}^{210}_{83}Bi$ **(c)** $^{20}_{9}F \rightarrow {}^{0}_{-1}e + {}^{20}_{10}Ne$
11.5 (a) $^{38}_{20}Ca \rightarrow {}^{0}_{1}e + {}^{38}_{19}K$ **(b)** $^{118}_{54}Xe \rightarrow {}^{0}_{1}e + {}^{118}_{53}I$ **(c)** $^{79}_{37}Rb \rightarrow {}^{0}_{1}e + {}^{79}_{36}Kr$
11.6 (a) $^{62}_{30}Zn \rightarrow {}^{0}_{-1}e + {}^{62}_{29}Cu$ **(b)** $^{110}_{50}Sn + {}^{0}_{-1}e \rightarrow {}^{110}_{49}In$
(c) $^{81}_{36}Kr + {}^{0}_{-1}e \rightarrow {}^{81}_{35}Br$ **11.7** $^{120}_{49}In \rightarrow {}^{0}_{-1}e + {}^{120}_{50}Sn$ **11.8** 12%
11.9 3 days **11.10** 13 m **11.11** 2% **11.12** 4.0 mL **11.13** $^{237}_{93}Np$
11.14 $^{241}_{95}Am + {}^{4}_{2}He \rightarrow 2\,{}^{1}_{0}n + {}^{243}_{97}Bk$ **11.15** $^{40}_{18}Ar + {}^{1}_{1}H \rightarrow {}^{1}_{0}n + {}^{40}_{19}K$
11.16 $^{235}_{92}U + {}^{1}_{0}n \rightarrow 2\,{}^{1}_{0}n + {}^{137}_{52}Te + {}^{97}_{40}Zr$ **11.17** 2 half-lives
11.18 $^{28}_{12}Mg \rightarrow {}^{0}_{-1}e + {}^{28}_{13}Al$
11.19

○ Aluminum—28

○ Magnesium—28

11.20 $^{14}_{6}C$ **11.21** The shorter arrows represent β emission; longer arrows
represent α emission. **11.22** $^{241}_{94}Pu \rightarrow {}^{241}_{95}Am \rightarrow {}^{237}_{93}Np \rightarrow {}^{233}_{91}Pa \rightarrow {}^{233}_{92}U$
11.23 $^{148}_{69}Tm \rightarrow {}^{0}_{1}e + {}^{148}_{68}Er$ or $^{148}_{69}Tm + {}^{0}_{-1}e \rightarrow {}^{148}_{68}Er$ **11.24** 3.5 years
11.25 The curve doesn't represent nuclear decay. **11.26** It emits radiation. **11.28** A nuclear reaction changes the identity of the atoms, is
unaffected by temperature or catalysts, and often releases a large
amount of energy. A chemical reaction does not change the identity of
the atoms, is affected by temperature and catalysts, and involves relatively small energy changes. **11.30** $^{4}_{2}He$ **11.32** Gamma is highest and
alpha is lowest. **11.34** by breaking bonds in DNA **11.36** A neutron
decays to a proton and an electron. **11.38** The number of nucleons and
the number of charges is the same on both sides. **11.40** α emission: Z
decreases by 2 and A decreases by 4; β emission: Z increases by 1 and A
is unchanged **11.42** In fission, a nucleus fragments to smaller pieces.
11.44 (a) $^{35}_{17}Cl$ **(b)** $^{24}_{11}Na$ **(c)** $^{90}_{39}Y$ **11.46 (a)** $^{109}_{47}Ag$ **(b)** $^{10}_{5}B$ **11.48 (a)** $4\,{}^{1}_{0}n$
(b) $^{146}_{57}La$ **11.50** $^{198}_{80}Hg + {}^{1}_{0}n \rightarrow {}^{198}_{79}Au + {}^{1}_{1}H$; a proton **11.52** $^{228}_{90}Th$
11.54 Half of a sample decays in that time. **11.56** 0.006 g **11.58** 1 ng;
2×10^{-3} ng **11.60** The inside walls of a Geiger counter tube are negatively charged, and a wire in the center is positively charged. Radiation
ionizes argon gas inside the tube, which creates a conducting path for
current between the wall and the wire. **11.62** In a scintillation counter,
a phosphor emits a flash of light when struck by radiation, and the
flashes are counted. **11.64** more than 25 rems **11.66** 1.9 mL
11.68 1.9 rem **11.70** *in vivo* procedures, therapeutic procedures, boron
neutron capture **11.72** Irradiation kills harmful microorganisms by
destroying their DNA. **11.74** They yield more data, including three-
dimensional images. **11.76** Only living organisms incorporate C-14.
After death, the ratio of C-14/C-12 decreases, and the ratio can be measured to determine age. **11.78** Nuclear decay is an intrinsic property of a
nucleus and is not affected by external conditions. **11.80 (a)** β emission
(b) Mo-98 **11.82 (a)** $^{238}_{94}Pu \rightarrow {}^{4}_{2}He + {}^{234}_{92}U$ **(b)** for radiation shielding
11.84 Their cells divide rapidly. **11.86** advantages: few harmful
byproducts, fuel is inexpensive; disadvantage: needs a high temperature
11.88 (a) $^{253}_{99}Es + {}^{4}_{2}He \rightarrow {}^{256}_{101}Md + {}^{1}_{0}n$ **(b)** $^{250}_{98}Cf + {}^{11}_{5}B \rightarrow {}^{257}_{103}Lr + 4\,{}^{1}_{0}n$
11.90 $^{10}_{5}B + {}^{1}_{0}n \rightarrow {}^{7}_{3}Li + {}^{4}_{2}He$ **11.92** $^{238}_{92}U + 3\,{}^{4}_{2}He \rightarrow {}^{246}_{98}Cf + 4\,{}^{1}_{0}n$

Chapter 12
12.1 (a) alcohol, carboxylic acid **(b)** double bond, ester **(c)** aromatic ring,
amine, carboxylic acid **12.2 (a)** CH_3CHO **(b)** $CH_3CH_2CO_2H$
12.3 $CH_3CH_2CH_2CH_2CH_2CH_2CH_3$

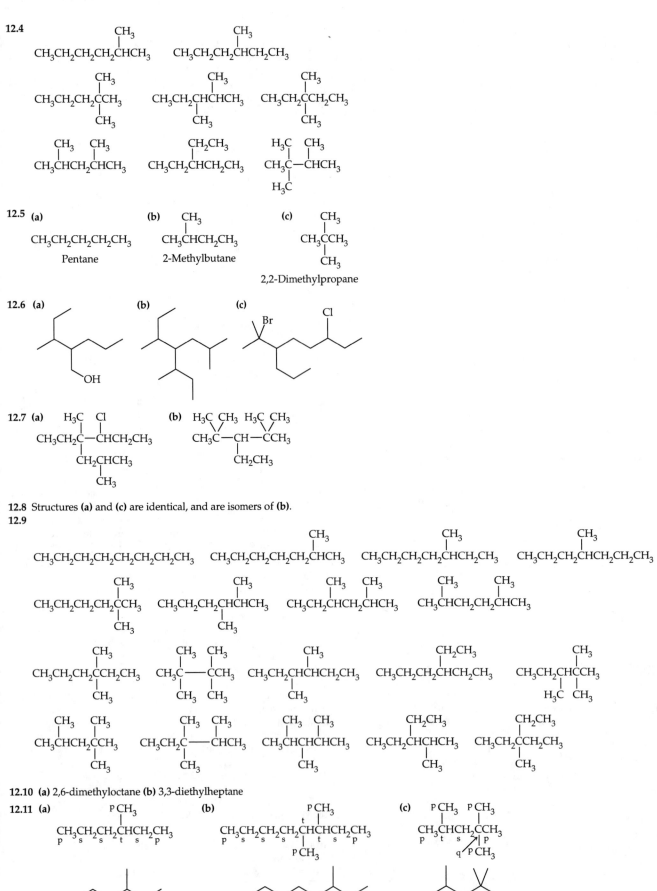

12.4

$CH_3CH_2CH_2CH_2CHCH_3$ with CH₃ branch

$CH_3CH_2CH_2CHCH_2CH_3$ with CH₃ branch

$CH_3CH_2CH_2CCH_3$ with CH₃, CH₃ branches

$CH_3CH_2CHCHCH_3$ with CH₃, CH₃ branches

$CH_3CH_2CCH_2CH_3$ with CH₃, CH₃ branches

$CH_3CHCH_2CHCH_3$ with CH₃, CH₃ branches

$CH_3CH_2CHCH_2CH_3$ with CH₂CH₃ branch

$CH_3C-CHCH_3$ with H₃C, CH₃, H₃C branches

12.5 **(a)**

$CH_3CH_2CH_2CH_2CH_3$

Pentane

(b) $CH_3CHCH_2CH_3$ with CH₃

2-Methylbutane

(c) CH_3CCH_3 with CH₃, CH₃

2,2-Dimethylpropane

12.6 **(a)** **(b)** **(c)**

12.7 **(a)** $CH_3CH_2C-CHCH_2CH_3$ with H₃C, Cl, CH₂CHCH₃, CH₃

(b) $CH_3C-CH-CCH_3$ with H₃C CH₃, H₃C CH₃, CH₂CH₃

12.8 Structures **(a)** and **(c)** are identical, and are isomers of **(b)**.

12.9

$CH_3CH_2CH_2CH_2CH_2CH_2CH_2CH_3$

$CH_3CH_2CH_2CH_2CH_2CHCH_3$ with CH₃

$CH_3CH_2CH_2CH_2CHCH_2CH_3$ with CH₃

$CH_3CH_2CH_2CHCH_2CH_2CH_3$ with CH₃

$CH_3CH_2CH_2CH_2CCH_3$ with CH₃, CH₃

$CH_3CH_2CH_2CHCHCH_3$ with CH₃, CH₃

$CH_3CH_2CHCH_2CHCH_3$ with CH₃, CH₃

$CH_3CHCH_2CH_2CHCH_3$ with CH₃, CH₃

$CH_3CH_2CH_2CCH_2CH_3$ with CH₃, CH₃

CH_3C-CCH_3 with CH₃, CH₃, CH₃, CH₃

$CH_3CH_2CHCHCH_2CH_3$ with CH₃, CH₃

$CH_3CH_2CH_2CHCH_2CH_3$ with CH₂CH₃

$CH_3CH_2CHCCH_3$ with CH₃, H₃C CH₃

$CH_3CHCH_2CCH_3$ with CH₃, CH₃, CH₃

$CH_3CH_2C-CHCH_3$ with CH₃, CH₃, CH₃

$CH_3CHCHCHCH_3$ with CH₃, CH₃, CH₃

$CH_3CH_2CHCHCH_3$ with CH₂CH₃, CH₃

$CH_3CH_2CCH_2CH_3$ with CH₂CH₃, CH₃

12.10 **(a)** 2,6-dimethyloctane **(b)** 3,3-diethylheptane

12.11 **(a)** $\underset{p}{CH_3}\underset{s}{CH_2}\underset{s}{CH_2}\underset{t}{CH}\underset{s}{CH}\underset{s}{CH_2}\underset{p}{CH_3}$ with P CH₃

(b) $CH_3CH_2CH_2CH_2CHCHCH_2CH_3$ with P CH₃ (t), P CH₃

(c) $CH_3CHCH_2CCH_3$ with P CH₃, P CH₃, q P CH₃

12.12 There are many possible answers; for example:

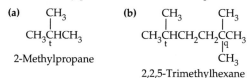

(a) CH₃CHCH₃ with CH₃ above — 2-Methylpropane

(b) CH₃CHCH₂CH₂CCH₃ with CH₃ groups — 2,2,5-Trimethylhexane

12.13 (a) 2,2-dimethylpentane **(b)** 2,3,3-trimethylpentane
12.14 $2\,C_2H_6 + 7\,O_2 \rightarrow 4\,CO_2 + 6\,H_2O$
12.15

$CH_3CH_2CH_2Cl$ + CH_3CHCH_3 (Cl) + CH_3CCH_3 (Cl, Cl) +

$CH_3CH_2CHCl_2$ + CH_3CHCH_2Cl (Cl) + $CH_2CH_2CH_2$ (Cl, Cl)

12.16 (a) 1-ethyl-4-methylcyclohexane **(b)** 1-ethyl-3-isopropylcyclopentane
12.17 (a) cyclohexane with CH₂CH₃, CH₂CH₃ **(b)** cycloheptane with CH₃, H₃C, CH₃

12.18 propylcyclohexane
12.19 (a) 12 hydrogens **(b)** 10 hydrogens **(c)** 8 hydrogens
12.20 (a) CH₃CCH₂CH₃ with CH₃ **(b)** CH₃CHCHCH₃ with CH₃, OH
12.21 (a) cyclopentanone **(b)** ring with CH₃, NH₂

12.22 (a) double bond, ketone, ether **(b)** double bond, amine, carboxylic acid   **12.23 (a)** 2,3-dimethylpentane **(b)** 2,5-dimethylhexane
12.24 (a) 1,1-dimethylcyclopentane **(b)** isopropylcyclobutane
12.25 The methyl groups are on the same side of the ring in one structure and on opposite sides in the other.   **12.26** Carbon can form four strong bonds to itself and to many other elements.   **12.28** Organic compounds are nonpolar.   **12.30** A polar covalent bond is a bond in which electrons are shared unequally.   **12.32 (a)** amine, aromatic ring, ether, amide, sulfonamide double bond **(b)** aromatic ring, carboxylic acid, ester
12.34 (a) CH₃CH₂CH₂CCH₃ (O) — Ketone **(b)** CH₃CH₂CH₂C—OCH₂CH₃ (O) — Ester

(c) H₂N—CH₂C—OH (O) — Amine carboxylic acid

12.36 They must have the same formula but different structures.
12.38 A primary carbon is bonded to one other carbon; a secondary carbon is bonded to two other carbons; a tertiary carbon is bonded to three other carbons; and a quaternary carbon is bonded to four other carbons.
12.40 (a) 2,3-dimethylbutane **(b)** cyclopentane
12.42

$CH_3CH_2CH_2OH$ CH_3CHCH_3 (OH) CH_3CH_2—O—CH_3

(skeletal: propanol, isopropanol, ethyl methyl ether)

12.44
(a) $CH_3CH_2CH_2CH_2OH$ $CH_3CH_2CHCH_3$ (OH) CH_3CHCH_2OH (CH₃)

CH_3CCH_3 (OH, CH₃)

(b) $CH_3CH_2CH_2NH_2$ CH_3CHCH_3 (NH₂) $CH_3CH_2NCH_3$ (H) CH_3NCH_3 (CH₃)

(c) $CH_3CH_2CH_2CCH_3$ (O) $CH_3CH_2CCH_2CH_3$ (O) CH_3CHCCH_3 (O, CH₃)

12.46 identical: **(a)**; isomers: **(b)**, **(d)**, **(e)**; unrelated: **(c)**   **12.48** All have a carbon with five bonds.   **12.50 (a)** 4-ethyl-3-methyloctane
(b) 5-isopropyl-3-methyloctane   **(c)** 2,2,6-trimethylheptane
(d) 4-isopropyl-4-methyloctane   **(e)** 2,2,4,4-tetramethylpentane
(f) 4,4-diethyl-2-methylhexane   **(g)** 2,2-dimethyldecane
12.52

(a) CH₃CH₂C—CHCHCH₂CH₃ with H₃C, C(CH₃)₃, CH₃, CH₃

(b) CH₃CHCH₂CHCH₃ with CH₃, CH₃

(c) CH₃CH₂CHCCH₂CH₂CH₂CH₃ with H₃C, CH₂CH₃, CH₂CH₃

(d) CH₃CHCCH₂CH₂CHCH₂CH₃ with CH₃CHCH₃, CH₃, H₃C CH₃, CH₃

(e) CH₃CH / H₃C (ring) ...CH₂CHCH₃ / CH₃, CH₃

(f) cyclopentane with CH₃, CH₃, H₃C

12.54 (a) 1-ethyl-3-methylcyclobutane **(b)** 1,1,3,3-tetramethylcyclopentane
(c) 1-ethyl-3-propylcyclohexane **(d)** 4-butyl-1,1,2,2-tetramethylcyclopentane
12.56 (a) 2,2-dimethylpentane **(b)** 2,4-dimethylpentane **(c)** isobutylcyclobutane   **12.58** heptane, 2-methylhexane, 3-methylhexane, 2,2-dimethylpentane, 2,3-dimethylpentane, 2,4-dimethylpentane, 3,3-dimethylpentane, 3-ethylpentane, 2,2,3-trimethylbutane
12.60 $C_3H_8 + 5\,O_2 \rightarrow 3\,CO_2 + 4\,H_2O$
12.62

$CH_3CH_2CCH_2Cl$ (CH₃, CH₃) + CH_3CHCCH_3 (Cl, CH₃, CH₃) + $ClCH_2CH_2CCH_3$ (CH₃, CH₃)

12.64 Minor differences in shape cause differences in behavior.
12.66 Branched-chain hydrocarbons   **12.68 (a)** ketone, alcohol, double bond **(b)** carboxylic acid, amine, amide, ester, aromatic ring
12.70 nonpolar solvents dissolve nonpolar substances   **12.72** pentane; more London forces

Chapter 13

13.1 (a) 2-methyl-3-heptene **(b)** 2-methyl-1,5-hexadiene
(c) 3-methyl-3-hexene

13.2
(a)

$$CH_3CH_2CH_2CH_2\overset{\overset{\displaystyle CH_3}{|}}{C}HCH=CH_2$$

(b)

$$H_3C-\overset{\overset{\displaystyle CH_3}{|}}{\underset{\underset{\displaystyle CH_3}{|}}{C}}-C\equiv C-CH_3$$

(c)

$$CH_3CH_2CH_2CH=\overset{\overset{\displaystyle CH_3}{|}}{C}HCHCH_3$$

(d)

$$CH_3CH_2CH=\overset{\overset{\displaystyle CH_3}{|}}{C}-\overset{\overset{\displaystyle CH_3}{|}}{\underset{\underset{\displaystyle CH_3}{|}}{C}}-CH_3$$

13.3 (a) 2,3-dimethyl-1-pentene **(b)** 2,3-dimethyl-2-hexene **13.4 (a), (c)**

13.5

$$\underset{cis\text{-}3,4\text{-Dimethyl-3-hexene}}{\overset{\overset{\displaystyle CH_3CH_2 \qquad CH_2CH_3}{\diagdown \qquad \diagup}}{\underset{\diagup \qquad \diagdown}{\underset{\displaystyle H_3C \qquad CH_3}{C=C}}}}$$

$$\underset{trans\text{-}3,4\text{-Dimethyl-3-hexene}}{\overset{\overset{\displaystyle CH_3CH_2 \qquad CH_3}{\diagdown \qquad \diagup}}{\underset{\diagup \qquad \diagdown}{\underset{\displaystyle H_3C \qquad CH_2CH_3}{C=C}}}}$$

13.6 (a) cis-4-methyl-2-hexene **(b)** trans-5,6-dimethyl-3-heptene
13.7 (a) substitution **(b)** addition **(c)** elimination   **13.8 (a), (b),**
(c) $CH_3CH_2CH_2CH_3$ **(d)** methylcyclohexane **13.9 (a)** 1,2-dibromo-
2-methylpropane **(b)** 1,2-dichloropentane **(c)** 4,5-dichloro-
2,4-dimethylheptane   **13.10 (a)** 1-chloro-1-methylcyclopentane
(b) 2-bromobutane **(c)** 2-chloro-2-methylbutane   **13.11 (a)** 3-ethyl-
2-pentene **(b)** 2,3-dimethyl-1-butene or 2,3-dimethyl-2-butene
13.12 2-bromo-2,4-dimethylhexane
13.13 (a), (b) Same product is obtained.

(c)

$$\underset{}{\overset{\overset{\displaystyle OH}{|}}{CH_3CHCH_2CH_2CH_3}} \quad + \quad \underset{}{\overset{\overset{\displaystyle OH}{|}}{CH_3CH_2CHCH_2CH_3}}$$

13.14 2-ethyl-1-butene or 3-methyl-2-pentene   **13.15** $(CH_3)_3C^+$
13.16

13.17 (a)

$$\underset{H_2C=\overset{}{C}Cl}{\overset{\overset{\displaystyle CN}{|}}{}}$$

(b)

$$\underset{H_2C=\overset{}{C}H}{\overset{\overset{\displaystyle CO_2CH_3}{|}}{}}$$

13.18 (a) m-ethylphenol **(b)** p-bromoaniline **(c)** 2-methyl-2-phenylbutane
13.19
(a)

(b)

(c)

(d)

13.20 (a) o-isopropylphenol **(b)** p-bromoaniline
13.21 (a)

(b)

(c)

13.22 o-, m-, and p-bromotoluene
13.23

(a) 2,5-Dimethyl-2-heptene

$$CH_3CH_2CHCH_2CH_2\overset{\overset{\displaystyle CH_3}{|}}{\underset{\underset{\displaystyle Br}{|}}{C}}CH_3$$

$$CH_3CH_2CHCH_2CH_2\overset{\overset{\displaystyle CH_3}{|}}{\underset{\underset{\displaystyle OH}{|}}{C}}CH_3$$

(b) 3,3-Dimethylcyclopentene

13.24 (a) 4,4-dimethyl-1-hexyne **(b)** 2,7-dimethyl-4-octyne
13.25 (a) m-isopropylphenol **(b)** o-bromobenzoic acid
13.26 (a)

(b)

13.27
(a)

$$CH_3CH_2CH_2\overset{\overset{\displaystyle CH_3}{|}}{\underset{\underset{\displaystyle CH_3}{|}}{C}}CH_2CH_3$$

3,3-Dimethylhexane

(b)

$$CH_3CHCH_2CH_2CH_2CH_2\overset{\overset{\displaystyle CH_3}{|}}{\underset{\underset{\displaystyle CH_3}{|}}{C}}HCH_3$$

2,7-Dimethyloctane

13.28

13.29 2-methyl-2-pentene, 2-methyl-1-pentene   **13.30** They have C—C
multiple bonds and can add hydrogen.   **13.32** alkene: –ene; alkyne: –yne;
aromatic: –benzene
13.34
(a)

$$CH_3CH_2CH_2CH_2CH_2CH=CH_2$$

(b)

$$CH_3CH_2CH_2C\equiv CH$$

(c)

13.36 (a) 1-pentene **(b)** 2,5-dimethyl-3-hexyne **(c)** 2,3-dimethyl-2-butene
(d) 2-ethyl-3-methyl-1,3-pentadiene **(e)** 2-ethyl-1.3-dimethylcyclohexene
(f) 3-ethylisopropylcyclobutene

13.38 (a)

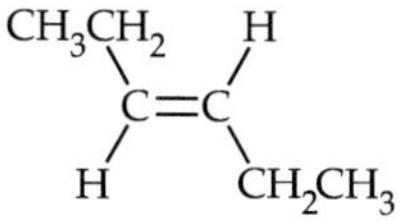

(b) 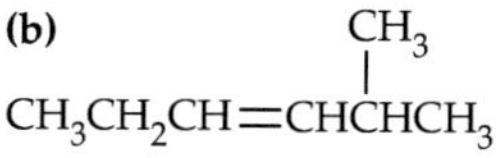 $CH_3CH_2CH=CHCHCH_3$ (with CH_3 branch)

(c)

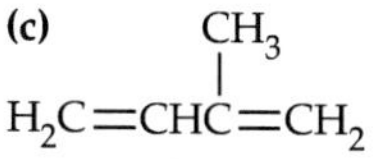

(d)

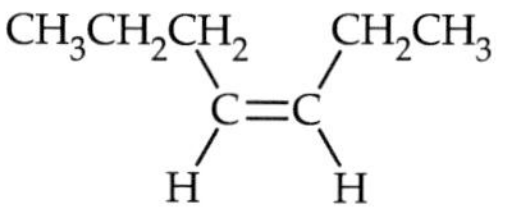

(e)

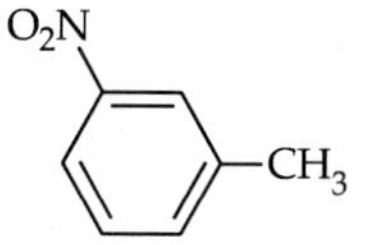

(f)

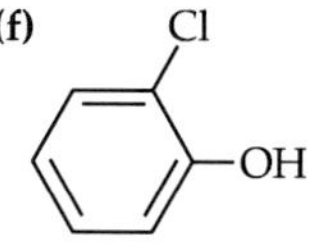

(g) 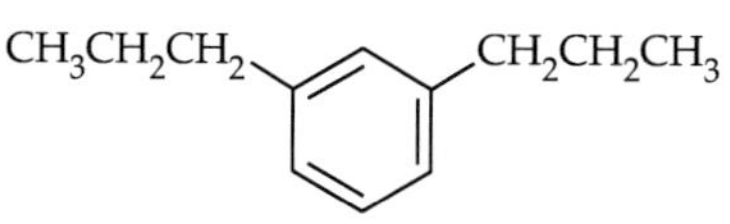 $CH_3CH_2CH_2$ $CH_2CH_2CH_3$

13.40 1-hexyne, 2-hexyne, 3-hexyne, 3-methyl-1-pentyne, 4-methyl-1-pentyne, 4-methyl-2-pentyne, 3,3-dimethyl-1-butyne   **13.42** 1-pentene, 2-pentene, 2-methyl-1-butene, 3-methyl-1-butene, 2-methyl-2-butene   **13.44** Each double bond carbon must be bonded to two different groups.   **13.46** 2-pentene

13.48

(a) 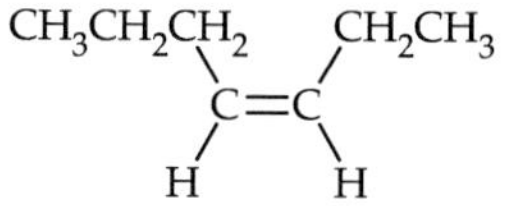   **(b)**

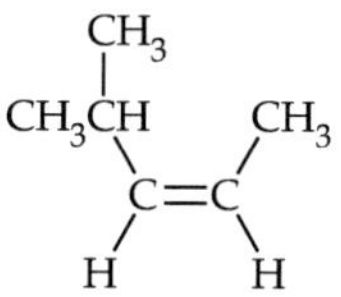

(c)

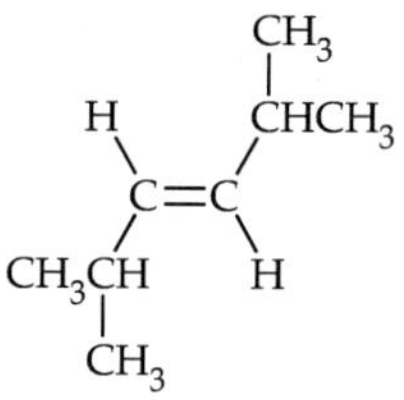

13.50 (a) identical **(b)** identical **13.52** substitution: two reactants exchange parts to give two products; addition: two reactants add to give one product   **13.54** rearrangement   **13.56 (a)** substitution **(b)** rearrangement

13.58

(a) 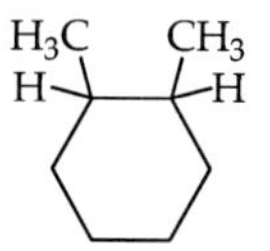   **(b)** 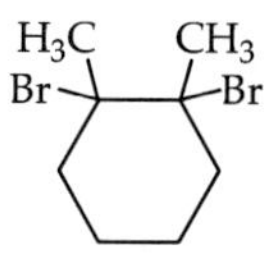   **(c)** 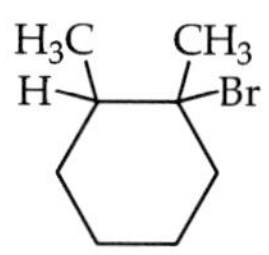   **(d)**

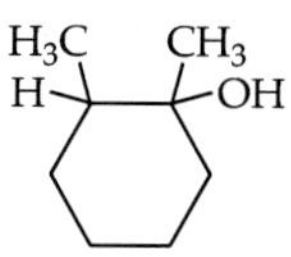

13.60

(a) 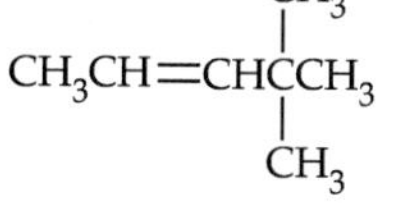 $CH_3CH=CHCCH_3$ (with CH_3 branches) $+ Cl_2$ **(b)** $CH_3CH=CH_2 + H_2$

(c) $CH_3CH=CHCH_3$ or $H_2C=CHCH_2CH_3 + HBr$

(d)  $+ HCl$ **(e)** 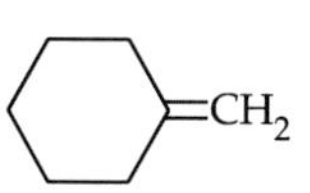 $=CH_2 + Cl_2$

13.62

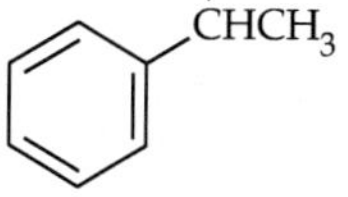

13.64

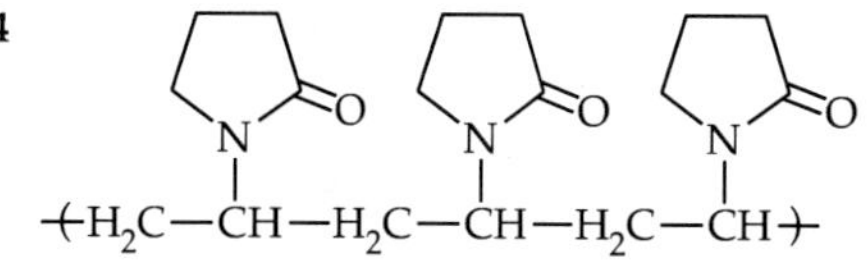

13.66 (b) benzene $+ Br_2 \rightarrow$ bromobenzene $+$ HBr   **13.68** methylcyclohexane   **13.70** Rod cells are responsible for vision in dim light; cone cells are responsible for color vision.

13.72

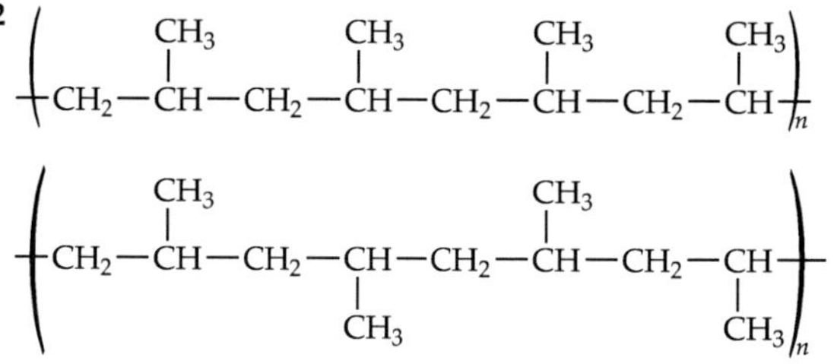

13.74 The body converts it to a water-soluble diol epoxide that can react with DNA and lead to cancer.   **13.76** yellow

13.78 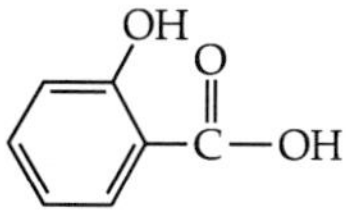   **Salicylic acid**

13.80 (a) 5-methyl-2-hexene **(b)** 4-methyl-2-heptyne **(c)** 2,3-dimethyl-1-butene **(d)** 1,2,4-trinitrobenzene **(e)** 3,4-dimethylcyclohexene **(f)** 3-methyl-1,3-pentadiene   **13.82** Cyclohexene reacts with Br_2; benzene doesn't.

13.84 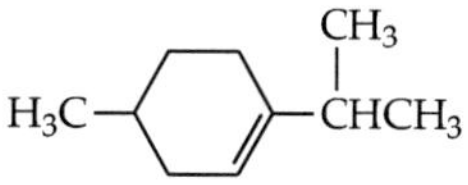   **Menthene**

13.86

(a) 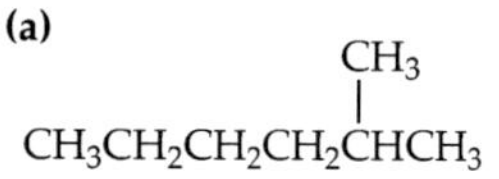 $CH_3CH_2CH_2CH_2CHCH_3$ (with CH_3 branch)   **(b)** 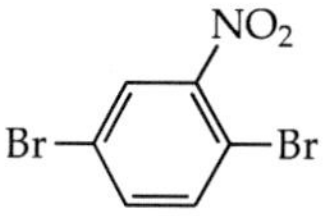   **(c)**

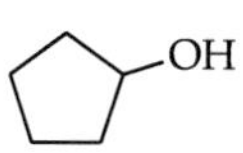

(d) 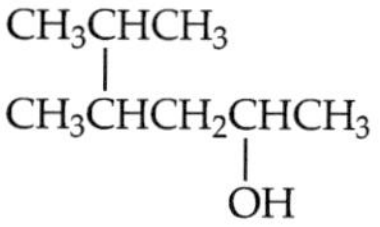   **(e)** $CH_3CH_2CH_2CH_2CH_3$ **(f)**

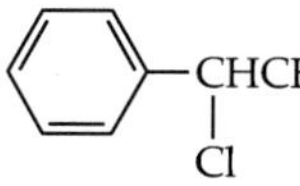

13.88 Naphthalene has a greater molar mass.

13.90

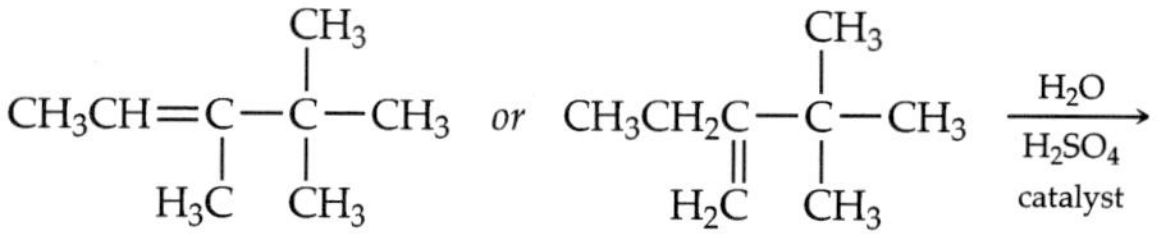

Chapter 14
14.1 (a) alcohol **(b)** alcohol **(c)** phenol **(d)** alcohol **(e)** ether **(f)** ether
14.2 A hydroxyl group is a part of a larger molecule.
14.3 (a) 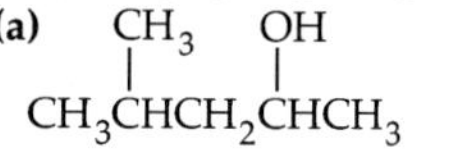   **(b)**

secondary alcohol   secondary alcohol

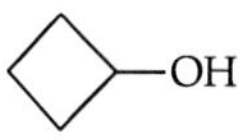

(c)

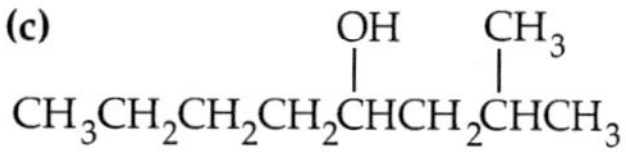

secondary alcohol

(d) 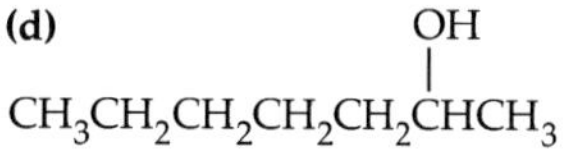   **(e)**

secondary alcohol   primary alcohol

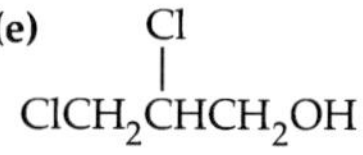

14.4 (a) 3-pentanol, secondary **(b)** 2-ethyl-1-pentanol, primary **(c)** 5,6-dichloro-2-ethyl-1-hexanol, primary **(d)** 2-isopropyl-4-methylcyclohexanol, secondary **14.5** See 14.3 and 14.4 **14.6 (a)** **14.7 (b)**
14.8 (a) propene **(b)** cyclohexene **(c)** 4-methyl-1-pentene (minor) and 4-methyl-2-pentene (major) **14.9 (a)** 2,3-dimethyl-2-butanol **(b)** 1-butanol or 2-butanol

14.10

$$\text{cyclohexene-CH}_2\text{CH}_3 \quad \text{and} \quad \text{cyclohexylidene}=\!\!\!\begin{array}{c}\text{CH}_3\\\text{C}\\\text{H}\end{array}$$

14.11 (a)

$$\underset{\text{O}}{\text{CH}_3\text{CH}_2\overset{\|}{\text{C}}-\text{H}} \quad \underset{\text{O}}{\text{CH}_3\text{CH}_2\overset{\|}{\text{C}}-\text{OH}} \qquad \textbf{(b)}\quad \underset{\text{O}}{\text{CH}_3\overset{\|}{\text{C}}\text{CH}_2\text{CH}_2\text{CH}_3}$$

(c)

$$\text{cyclopentyl}-\overset{\text{O}}{\overset{\|}{\text{C}}}\text{CH}_3$$

14.12 (a) 2-propanol **(b)** cycloheptanol **(c)** 3-methyl-1-butanol
14.13 (a)

$$\underset{H_3C}{\overset{H_2C}{>}}C-CH_2\underset{H_3C}{\overset{|}{C}}HCH_2OH \qquad \textbf{(b)}\quad Br-\text{(phenyl)}-CH_2CH_2OH$$

14.14 (a) O_2N—(phenyl)—OH **(b)** (phenyl with CH_2CH_3)—OH

14.15 (a) *p*-chlorophenol **(b)** 4-bromo-2-methylphenol **14.16 (a)** methyl propyl ether **(b)** diisopropyl ether **(c)** methyl phenyl ether
14.17 (a) $CH_3CH_2CH_2S-SCH_2CH_2CH_3$
(b) $(CH_3)_2CHCH_2CH_2S-SCH_2CH_2CH(CH_3)_2$
14.18 (a) 1-chloro-1-ethylcyclopentane **(b)** 3-bromo-5-methylheptane
14.19 (a) 5-methyl-3-hexanol **(b)** *m*-methoxytoluene
(c) 3-methylcyclohexanol
14.20

$$CH_3CH=\underset{\overset{|}{CH_3}}{C}\text{(phenyl)} \;+\; CH_3CH_2\underset{\overset{\|}{CH_2}}{C}\text{(phenyl)} \;+\; H_2O$$
$$\qquad\text{Major}\qquad\qquad\qquad\text{Minor}$$

14.21 $(CH_3)_2CHCH_2CH_2CHO$, $(CH_3)_2CHCH_2CH_2CO_2H$
14.22

$$\underset{\overset{|}{CH_3}}{CH_3CHCH_2}\underset{\overset{|}{CH_3}}{CHS-SCH}\underset{\overset{|}{CH_3}}{CH_2CHCH_3}$$
with CH_3 groups

14.23 (a)

cyclohexane with HO, H, CH$_3$

(b)

$$\underset{H}{\overset{H_3C}{>}}C=\underset{\overset{|}{CH_3}}{C}-CH_2OH$$

(c)

Br—(phenyl)—CH_2OH

14.24 Alcohols have an —OH group bonded to an alkane-like carbon atom; ethers have an oxygen atom bonded to two carbon atoms; and phenols have an —OH group bonded to a carbon of an aromatic ring.
14.26 Alcohols form hydrogen bonds. **14.28** ketone, carbon–carbon double bond, alcohol **14.30 (a)** 2-ethyl-1-pentanol **(b)** 3-methyl-1-butanol **(c)** 1,2,4-butanetriol **(d)** 2-methyl-2-phenyl-1-propanol **(e)** 2-ethyl-3-methylcyclohexanol **(f)** 3,3-dimethyl-2-hexanol

14.32 (a)

$$\underset{\overset{|}{OH}}{CH_3CH_2CH_2CHCH}\underset{}{\overset{CH_3\ \ CH_3}{CCH_3}}$$

(b)

cyclohexane with OH, CH$_3$, CH$_3$

(c)

$$\underset{\overset{|}{CH_3}}{CH_3CH_2\overset{\overset{CH_2CH_3}{|}}{C}CH_2CH_2CH_2CH_2OH}$$

(d)

$$\underset{\overset{|}{CH_2CH_3}}{CH_3CH_2CH_2\overset{\overset{OH}{|}}{CH}CHCH_3}$$

(e)

cyclooctane ring with H_3C, OH, CH$_3$, CH$_3$

(f)

$$\underset{\overset{|}{CH_2CH_3}}{HOCH_2CH_2CH_2\overset{\overset{CH_2CH_3}{|}}{C}CH_2CH_2OH}$$

14.34 (a) primary **(b)** primary **(c)** primary, secondary **(d)** primary **(e)** secondary **(f)** secondary **14.36 (a)** < **(c)** < **(b)** **14.38** a ketone **14.40** aldehyde or carboxylic acid **14.42** Phenols dissolve in aqueous NaOH; alcohols don't.
14.44

(a)

cyclopentane with CH$_2$CH$_3$ and OH; cyclopentane with OH and CH$_2$CH$_3$

(b)

$$\underset{}{CH_3CH_2\overset{\overset{CH_2CH_3}{|}}{CH}CH_2OH} \qquad \underset{\overset{|}{CH_3}}{CH_3CH_2\overset{\overset{OH}{|}}{C}CH_2CH_3}$$

(c)

$$CH_3CH_2CH_2\overset{\overset{OH}{|}}{CH}CH_2CH_3$$

(d)

(phenyl) with HO and isopropyl groups, OH

(e)

$$HOCH_2CH_2CH_2CH_2CH_2OH$$

(f)

$$\text{(phenyl)}\underset{\overset{|}{CH_3}}{\overset{\overset{OH}{|}}{C}CH_3} \qquad \text{(phenyl)}\underset{\overset{|}{CH_3}}{CHCH_2OH}$$

14.46

(a)

(phenyl)$\overset{\overset{O}{\|}}{C}CH_3$

(b) $CH_3\overset{\overset{H_3C\ \ O}{\ \ \|}}{CH}C-H$ $\quad$ $CH_3\overset{\overset{H_3C\ \ O}{\ \ \|}}{CH}C-OH$

(c) NR $\quad$ **(d)** cyclobutanone $\quad$ **(e)** NR $\quad$ **(f)** (phenyl)$\overset{\overset{O}{\|}}{C}CH_2CH_3$

14.48 odor
14.50

$$\underset{\overset{|}{NH_2}}{HO\overset{\overset{O}{\|}}{C}CHCH_2S-SCH_2}\underset{\overset{|}{NH_2}}{CH\overset{\overset{O}{\|}}{C}OH}$$

14.52 Alcohols can form hydrogen bonds; thiols and alkyl chlorides cannot. **14.54** depressant **14.56** The liver is the site of alcohol metabolism. **14.58** a reactive species that contains an unpaired electron **14.60** diethyl ether **14.62** The ozone layer shields the earth from intense solar radiation. **14.64** alcohols: 1-butanol, 2-butanol, 2-methyl-1-propanol, 2-methyl-2-propanol; ethers: diethyl ether, methyl propyl ether, isopropyl methyl ether **14.66** Alcohols become less soluble as their

nonpolar part becomes larger.   **14.68** An antiseptic kills microorganisms on living tissue.   **14.70** (a) *p*-dibromobenzene (b) 1,2-dibromo-1-butene (c) *m*-propylanisole (d) 1,1-dibromocyclopentane (e) 6-chloro-2,4-dimethyl-2,4-hexanediol (f) 4-methyl-2,4,5-heptanetriol (g) 4-bromo-6,6-dimethyl-2-heptyne (h) 1-bromo-2-iodoocyclobutane
14.72 3,7-Dimethyl-2,6-octadiene-1-ol

$$CH_3C=CHCH_2CH_2C=CHC-H$$
(with CH_3 groups and O)

14.74 $C_2H_6O + 3 O_2 \rightarrow 2 CO_2 + 3 H_2O$

Chapter 15
15.1 (a) primary (b) secondary (c) primary (d) secondary (e) tertiary
15.2 (a) Tetrabutylammonium hydroxide (b) Dimethylamine (c) *N*-Pentylaniline
15.3 (a) $CH_3CH_2CH_2CH_2CH_2CH_2NH_2$ (b) $CH_3CH_2CH_2CH_2NH$ with CH_3
(c) phenyl-N(CH_3)-NH (d) $CH_2CH_2CHCH_3$ with NH_2 and OH

15.4 The ion has one less electron than the neutral atoms.

$$H_3C-N^+-CH_3$$ (with CH_3 top and bottom)

15.5 $CH_3CH_2CH_2CH_2NHCH_2CH_3$ *N*-Ethylbutylamine
15.6 Compound (a) is lowest boiling; (b) is highest boiling (strongest hydrogen bonds).
15.7 (a) hydrogen bonding of amine with water (b) hydrogen bonding of trimethylamine with water

15.8 (a) Methylamine, Ethylamine, Dimethylamine, Trimethylamine (b) Pyridine (c) Aniline
15.9 (a) Piperidine: $C_5H_{11}N$ (b) Purine: $C_5H_4N_4$
15.10 (a) and (d)
15.11

aniline + H_2O ⇌ anilinium + OH⁻
base, acid / base, acid

15.12
(a) $CH_3CH_2CHNH_3^+ Br^-(aq)$ with CH_3 (b) phenyl-$NH_3^+Cl^-(aq)$
(c) $CH_3CH_2NH_3^+CH_3COO^-(aq)$ (d) $CH_3NH_2 + H_2O(l) + NaCl(aq)$

15.13 (a) *sec*-Butylammonium bromide (b) Anilinium chloride (c) Ethylammonium acetate (d) Methylamine   **15.14** (a) Ethylamine (b) Triethylamine

15.15
(a) HO-, HO- substituted benzene with $-CHCH_2NH_2CH_3$ and OH
(b) benzene with $-CH_2CHNH_3^+$ and CH_3

15.16–15.17 (a)
$$CH_3CH_2CH_2CH_2CH_2CH_2NH^+Cl^-$$ with CH_3 groups
Hexyldimethylammonium chloride
or N, N-Dimethylhexylammonium chloride
Salt of a tertiary amine

(b)
$$CH_3CHNH_3^+ Br^-$$ with CH_3
Isopropylammonium bromide
Salt of a primary amine

15.18 $CH_3CH_2CH_2CH_2NH_3^+ Cl^-(aq) + NaOH (aq) \rightarrow$
$CH_3CH_2CH_2NH_2 + H_2O(l) + NaCl(aq)$
15.19 Benadryl has the general structure. In Benadryl, R $= -CH_3$, and R' $=$ R" $= C_6H_5-$.
15.20
phenyl-$CH_2NH_3^+ Cl^-$ phenyl-$CH_2NH_2 \cdot HCl$
Benzylammonium chloride

15.21
pyrrolidine ring with CH_3, N⁺, $CH_2CH_2NHCH_2$-pyridine
provides and accepts a hydrogen bond; accepts a hydrogen bond

15.22 (a) All amine groups can participate in hydrogen bonding. (b) Histidine is water-soluble because it can form hydrogen bonds with water.
15.23
(a), (b), (c) hydrogen bonding diagrams

15.24

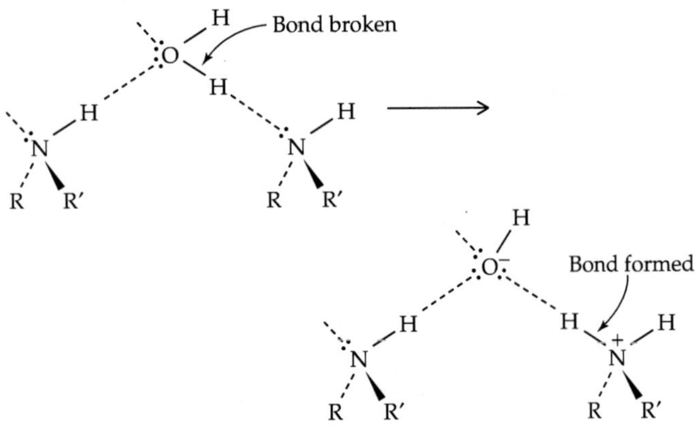

15.25   most basic: $(CH_3)_2NH$ least basic: $C_6H_5NH_2$

15.26

(a)

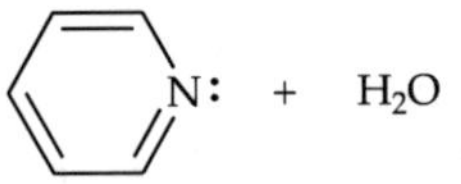

(b) $CH_3\overset{+}{N}H_2CH(CH_3)_2$ + OH^-

(c)   No reaction

(d) $(CH_3)_3CNH_3{}^+Cl^-$

15.28   **(a)**

$CH_3CH_2CH_2CH_2CH_2\overset{H}{\underset{|}{N}}CH_3$

(b)

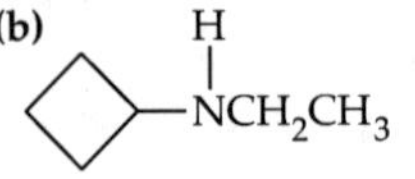

(c) $CH_3CH_2CH_2$—⬡—NH_2

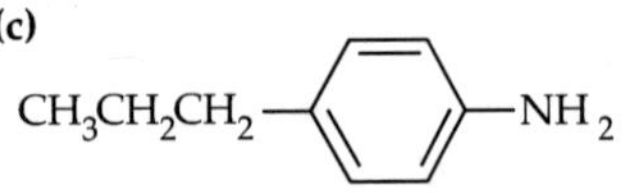

15.30   (a) Cyclobutylamine (primary) **(b)** Diphenylamine (secondary)
15.32 Diethylamine   **15.34   (a)** N-Methyl-2-butylammonium nitrate
(salt of a secondary amine).

(b)

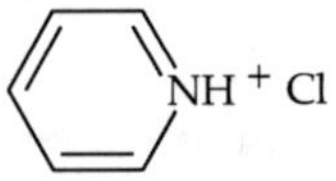

(salt of a tertiary amine)

(c)

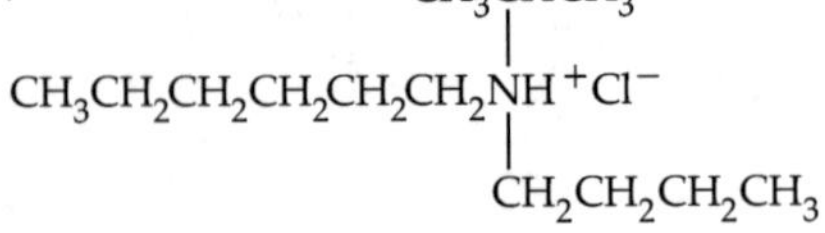

(salt of a tertiary amine)

15.36

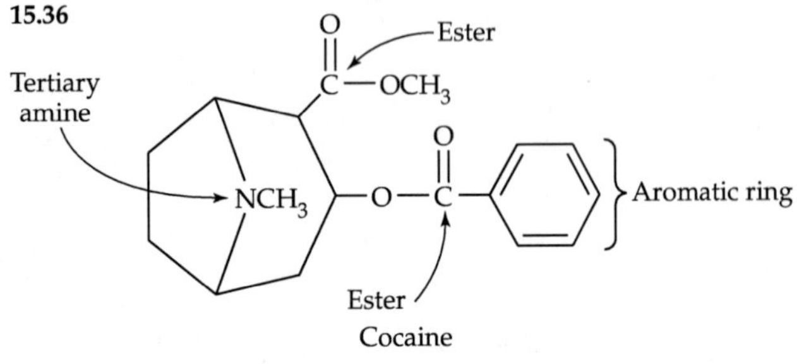

Cocaine

15.38

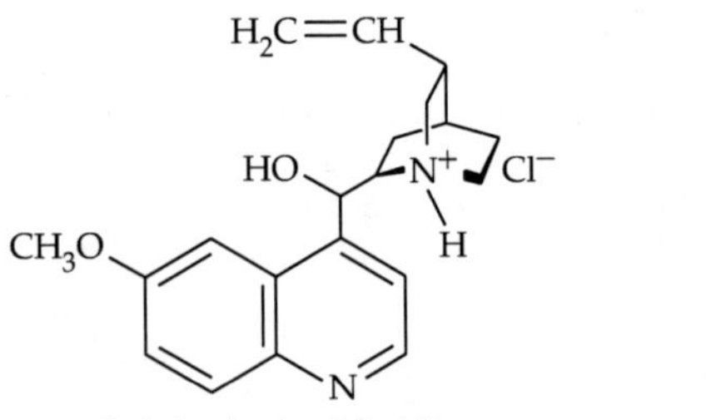

Quinine hydrochloride

15.40

(a)

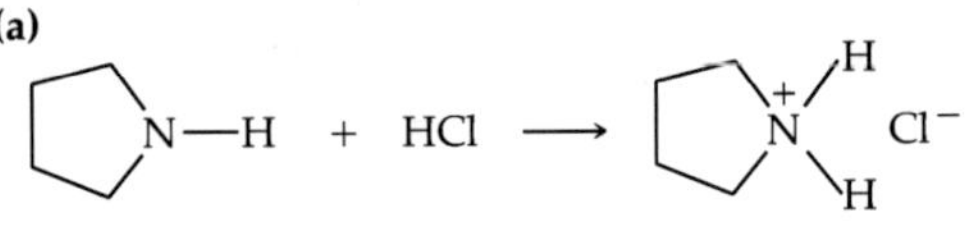

(b)

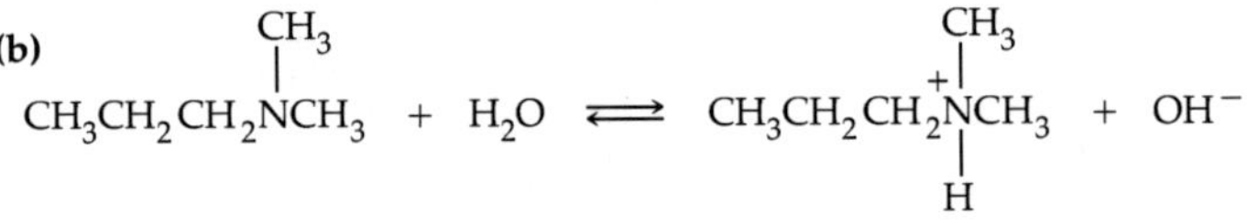

(c)

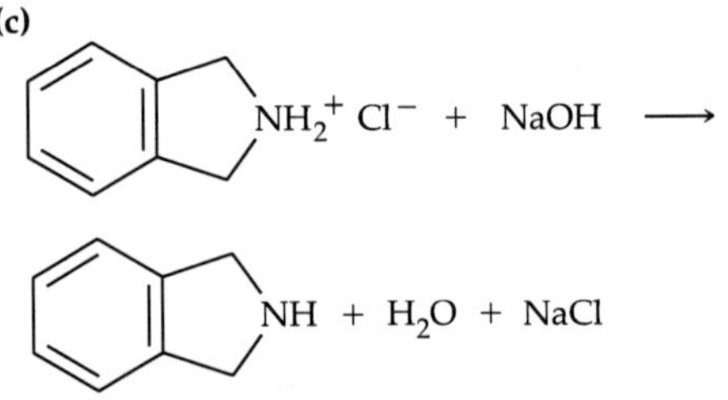

15.42 Choline doesn't react with HCl because its nitrogen isn't basic.
15.44 (1) lowering of blood pressure (2) memory enhancement (3) reduction of sickling in sickle-cell anemia (4) destruction of malaria parasites (5) destruction of the tuberculosis bacterium.
15.46

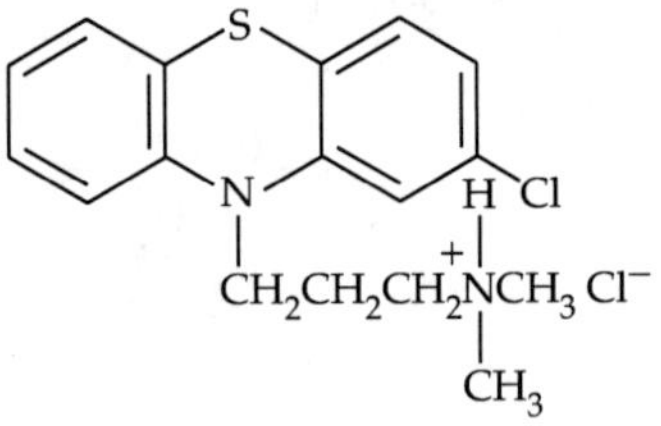

15.48 (a) A forensic toxicologist deals with criminal cases involving drug abuse and poisoning **(b)** the structure of the toxin, its mode of action, a mechanism to reverse its effects
15.50 Its large hydrocarbon region is water-insoluble.
15.52

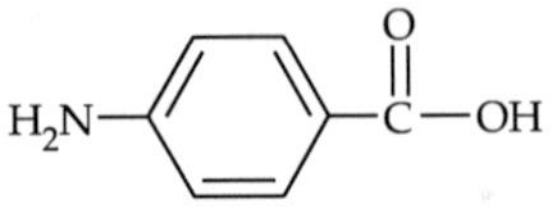

PABA

15.54

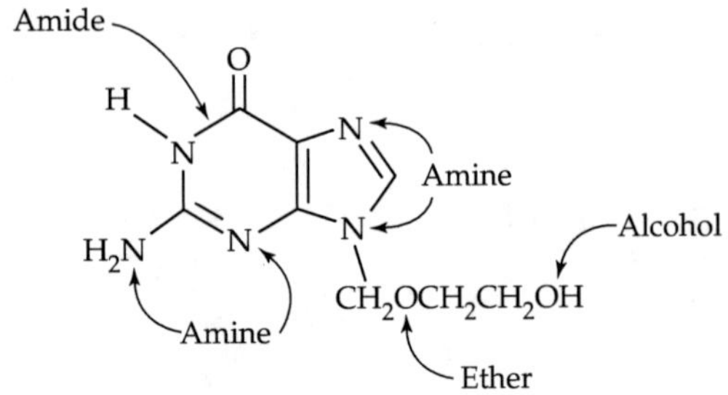

Acyclovir—related to purine

15.56 Amines: foul-smelling, somewhat basic, lower boiling (weaker hydrogen bonds); Alcohols: pleasant-smelling, not basic, higher boiling (stronger hydrogen bonds) **15.58 (a)** 6-Methyl-2-heptene **(b)** *p*-Isopropylphenol **(c)** Dibutylamine **15.60** Molecules of hexylamine can form hydrogen bonds to each other, but molecules of triethylamine can't. **15.62** Baeocystin is related to indole. **15.64** Pyridine forms H-bonds with water; benzene doesn't form H-bonds.

Chapter 16

16.1

(a)

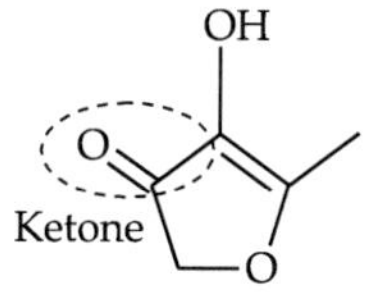

Ketone

(b)

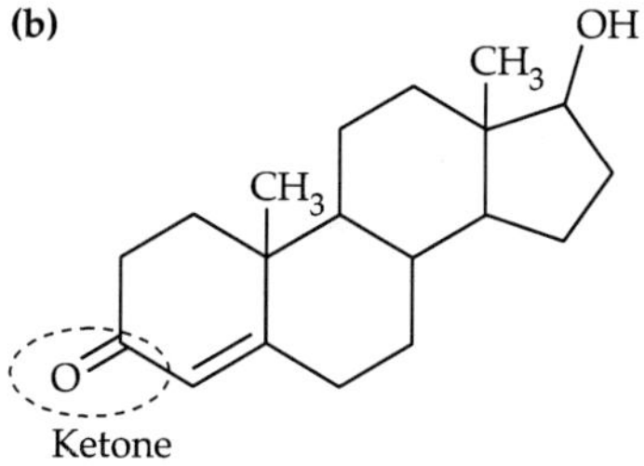

Testosterone

(c)

Aldehyde

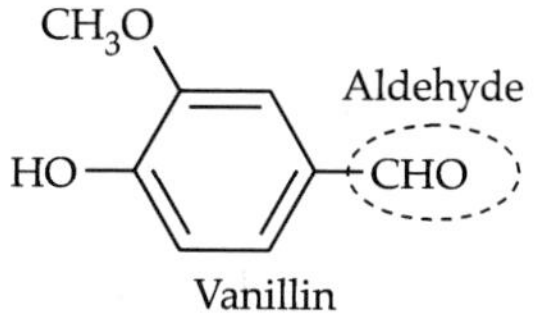

Vanillin

(d)

$C_4H_9COCH_3$

Ketone

(e)

C_4H_9CHO

Aldehyde

(f)

$C_4H_9COOCH_3$

Ester

16.2 (d)

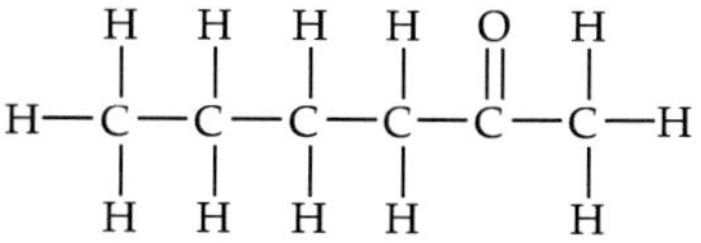

(e)

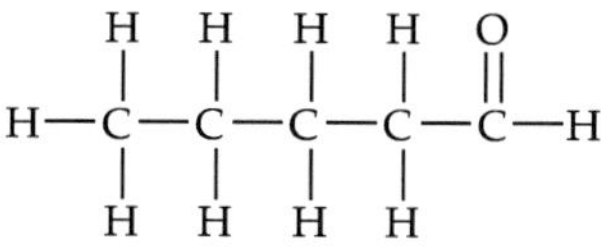

16.3 (a)

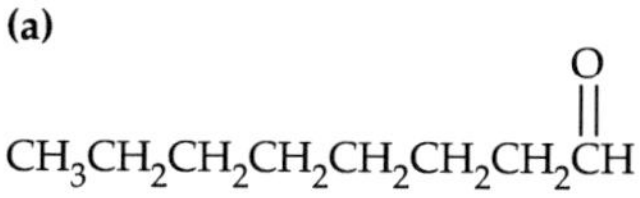

$CH_3CH_2CH_2CH_2CH_2CH_2CH_2CH$

(b)

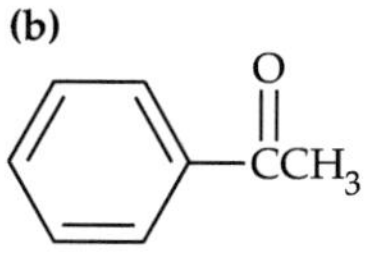

(c)

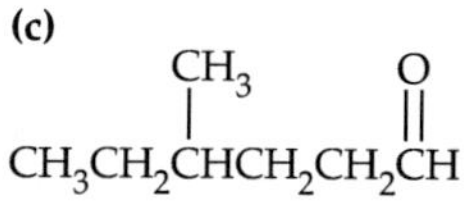

$CH_3CH_2CHCH_2CH_2CH$

(d)

CH_3C-CCH_3

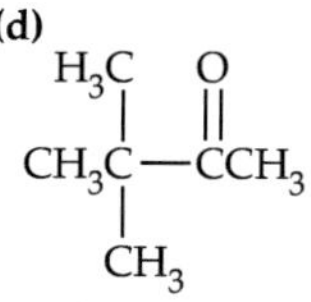

16.4 (a) Pentanal **(b)** 3-Pentanone **(c)** 4-Methylhexanal **(d)** 4-Heptanone

16.5 (a)

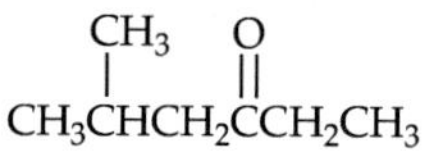

$CH_3CHCH_2CCH_2CH_3$

$C_7H_{14}O$

5-Methyl-3-hexanone
A ketone

(b)

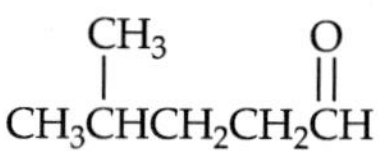

$CH_3CHCH_2CH_2CH$

$C_6H_{12}O$

4-Methylpentanal
An aldehyde

16.6 (a) polar **(b)** flammable **(c)** liquid **(d)** bp of 100 °C

16.7 Alcohols form hydrogen bonds, which raise their boiling points. Aldehydes and ketones have higher boiling points than alkanes because they are polar.

16.8 (a)

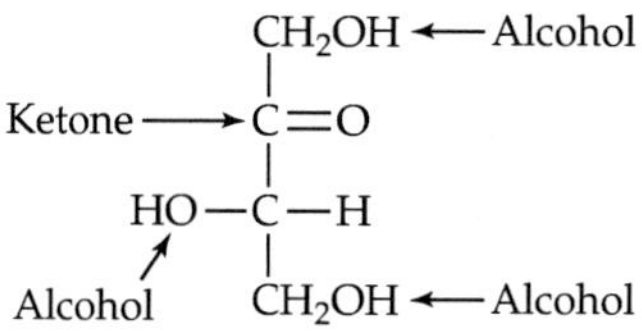

Ketone → C=O, Alcohol CH$_2$OH ← Alcohol, HO—C—H Alcohol, CH$_2$OH ← Alcohol

(b)

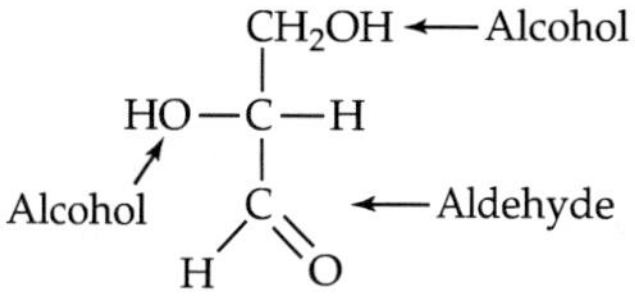

CH$_2$OH ← Alcohol, HO—C—H, Alcohol, C H O ← Aldehyde

(c)

CH_2CHO

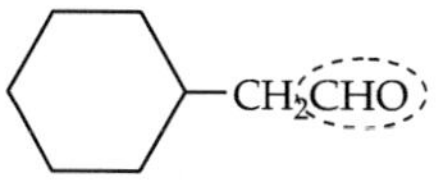

Aldehyde

(d)

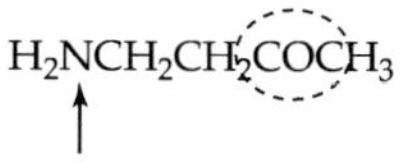

$H_2NCH_2CH_2COCH_3$

Amine   Ketone

16.9

(a)

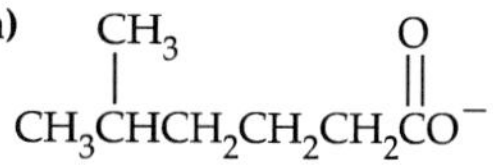

$CH_3CHCH_2CH_2CH_2CO^-$

(b)

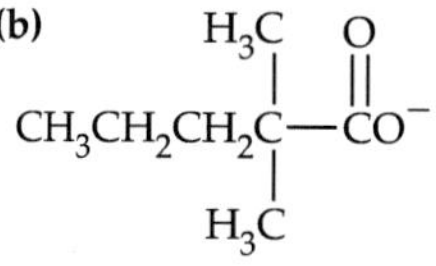

$CH_3CH_2CH_2C-CO^-$

(c) NR

16.10

(a)

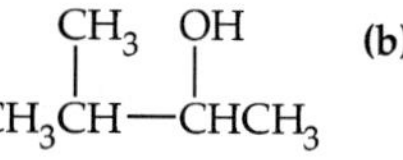

$CH_3CH-CHCH_3$

(b)

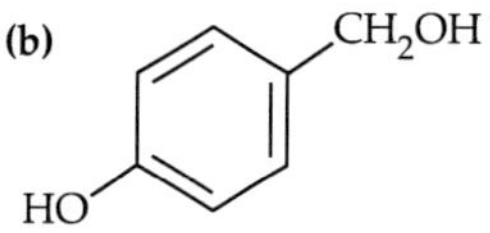

CH_2OH

(c)

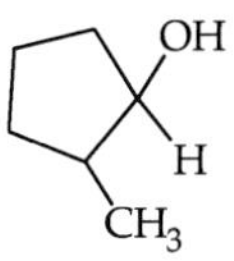

OH, H, CH$_3$

16.11 (a)

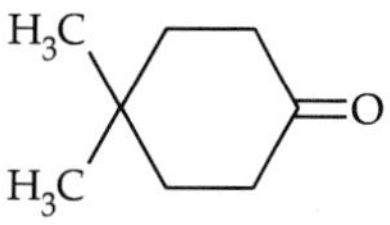

(b)

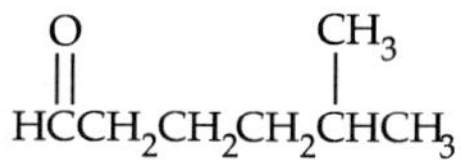

$HCCH_2CH_2CH_2CHCH_3$

(c)

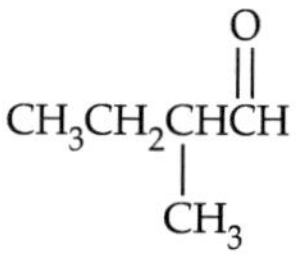

CH_3CH_2CHCH

CH_3

16.12 Compound **(a)**

16.13

(a)

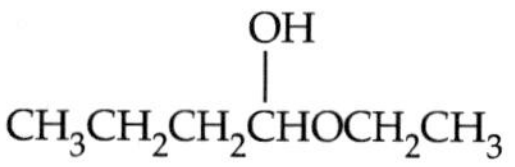

OH

$CH_3CH_2CH_2CHOCH_2CH_3$

(b)

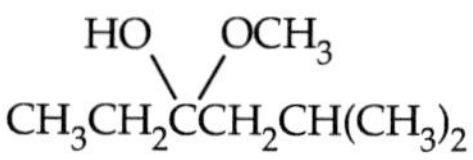

HO   OCH$_3$

$CH_3CH_2CCH_2CH(CH_3)_2$

16.14

(a)

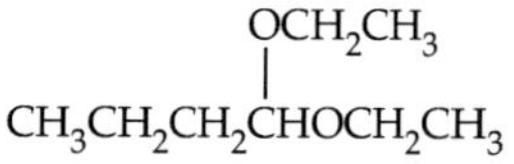

OCH$_2$CH$_3$

$CH_3CH_2CH_2CHOCH_2CH_3$

(b)

CH$_3$O   OCH$_3$

$CH_3CH_2CCH_2CH(CH_3)_2$

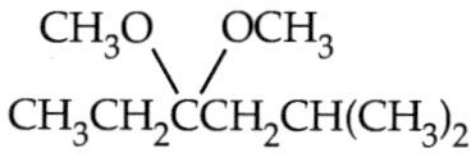

16.15 (a) neither **(b)** neither **(c)** acetal **(d)** hemiacetal **16.16** The acetal and the hemiacetal were both formed from ketones.

16.17 (a)

(benzene ring)—CH$_2$CCH$_2$CH$_3$ (with C=O) + 2 CH$_3$OH

(b)

CH$_3$CH$_2$CHO + 2 CH$_3$CH$_2$CH$_2$OH

(c)

HCH (with C=O) + 2 CH$_3$CH$_2$CH$_2$OH

16.18 (a) Hydride adds to the carbonyl carbon. **(b)** The arrow to the right represents reduction, and the arrow to the left represents oxidation.
16.19 Aldehydes can be oxidized to carboxylic acids. Tollens' reagent differentiates an aldehyde from a ketone.
16.20

16.21 (a) Under acidic conditions, an alcohol adds to the carbonyl group of an aldehyde to form a hemiacetal, which is unstable and further reacts to form an acetal.
(b)

··· Bonds broken
— Bonds formed

16.22 In solution, glucose exists as a cyclic hemiacetal because this structure is more stable.   **16.23** One equivalent of an alcohol adds to the carbonyl group of an aldehyde or ketone to form a hemiacetal. Two equivalents of alcohol add to the carbonyl group to yield an acetal.
16.24 (a) CH$_3$CCH$_2$CH$_3$ (C=O)   **(b)** CH$_3$CHCH$_2$CH (CH$_3$, C=O)   **(c)** CH$_3$CCH$_2$CH$_2$CH (C=O)

(d) HOCH$_2$CH$_2$CCH$_3$ (C=O)

16.26 Structure **(a)** is an aldehyde, and structure **(f)** is a ketone.
16.28

(a) CH$_3$CHCHCH (CH$_3$, C=O)   **(b)** CH$_3$CHCH$_2$CHCH (Cl, C=O, OH)   **(c)** O$_2$N—(benzene ring)—CH (C=O)

(d) CH$_3$CH$_2$CH$_2$CH$_2$CH$_2$CH$_2$CCH$_3$ (C=O)   **(e)** CH$_3$CHCHCCH$_3$H (CH$_3$, CH$_3$, C=O)   **(f)** (benzene ring)—CCH$_3$ (C=O)

16.30 (a) 2,3-Dimethylbutanal **(b)** 4-Hydroxy-2-methylpentanal **(c)** 2,2-Dimethylpropanal **(d)** 2-Butanone **(e)** 5-Methyl-2-hexanone   **16.32** For **(a)**, a ketone can't occur at the end of a carbon chain. For **(b)**, the methyl group receives the lowest possible number. For **(c)**, numbering must start at the end of the carbon chain closer to the carbonyl group.
16.34 A hemiacetal is produced.
16.36 (a) NR; cyclopentanol

(b)

CH$_3$CH$_2$CH$_2$CH$_2$CH$_2$COH (C=O) ;   CH$_3$CH$_2$CH$_2$CH$_2$CH$_2$CH$_2$OH

(c)

CH$_3$—C—C—C—OH (OH OH O, H H)   CH$_3$—C—C—C—H (OH OH OH, H H H)

16.38 (a)

H$_3$C—(benzene ring)—CHO   H$_3$C—(benzene ring)—CH$_2$OH

(b)

CHO
CH$_3$CH$_2$CHCH$_2$CHCH$_3$ (CH$_3$)

CH$_2$OH
CH$_3$CH$_2$CHCH$_2$CHCH$_3$ (CH$_3$)

(c) CH$_3$CH=CHCHO   CH$_3$CH=CHCH$_2$OH

16.40

(a)

OH
CH$_3$CH$_2$COCH$_2$CH$_2$CH$_3$ (CH$_3$)

(b)

OH
CH$_3$CH$_2$CH$_2$COCH(CH$_3$)$_2$ (H)

(c)

CH$_3$CH$_2$CH$_2$CH (C=O) + CH$_3$CH$_2$OH + CH$_3$OH

(d) H$_3$C
        C=O + HOCH$_2$CH$_2$OH
   H$_3$C

16.42

16.44 HOCH$_2$CH$_2$CH$_2$OH and CH$_2$O (formaldehyde).
16.46

Hemiacetal — OH
CH$_2$OH — Alcohol
C=O — Ketone
Ketone
C—C double bond
Aldosterone

16.48

HO—(benzene ring)—OH + H$_2$O$_2$ ⟶ O=(ring)=O

H$_2$O$_2$ is reduced   + 2 H$_2$O

16.50 Ethanol **16.52** **(a)** Advantages: inexpensive, no need to sacrifice animals. **(b)** Disadvantage: results of tests on cultured cells may not be reliable for more complex organisms. **16.54** *p*-Methoxybenzaldehyde **16.56** Aldehydes are easily oxidized.

16.58

$$Cl_3\overset{\overset{\displaystyle OH}{|}}{\underset{\underset{\displaystyle H}{|}}{C}}C-OH$$

16.60 **(a)** *o*-Isopropylmethoxybenzene **(b)** 5,5-Diethyl-3-heptyne **(c)** *N*-Ethylcyclopentylammonium bromide **(d)** *N,N*-Diethylhexylamine

16.62

(a)

$$CH_3CH_2\overset{\overset{\displaystyle I}{|}}{\underset{\underset{\displaystyle I}{|}}{C}}\overset{\overset{\displaystyle O}{||}}{C}HC\overset{\overset{\displaystyle }{|}}{\underset{\underset{\displaystyle I}{|}}{H}}$$

(b)

$$BrCH_2\overset{\overset{\displaystyle O}{||}}{C}CHBr_2$$

(c)

$$CH_3\overset{\overset{\displaystyle NH_2}{|}}{\underset{\underset{\displaystyle CH_3}{|}}{C}}CH_2CH_2\overset{\overset{\displaystyle O}{||}}{C}CH_3$$

16.64 **(a)**

$$\text{(benzene ring)}CH_2\overset{\overset{\displaystyle OCH_2CH_2CH_3}{|}}{CH}-OCH_2CH_2CH_3$$

(b)

$$CH_3CH_2\overset{\overset{\displaystyle CH_2CH_3}{|}}{\underset{\underset{\displaystyle Cl}{|}}{C}}CH_2CH_2CH_3$$

(c)

$$H_3C-\text{(benzene ring)}-CH=CH_2$$

16.66 Highest boiling = 1-butanol (strongest hydrogen bonds)

Chapter 17

17.1 carboxylic acid: **(c)**; amides: **(a) (f) (h)**; ester: **(d)**; none: **(b) (e) (g)**

17.2 **(a)**

$$CH_3\underset{6}{CH_2}\underset{5}{CH_2}\underset{4}{CH_2}\underset{3}{\overset{\overset{\displaystyle OH}{|}}{CH}}\underset{2}{\underset{\underset{\displaystyle CH_2CH_3}{|}}{CH}}\underset{1}{\overset{\overset{\displaystyle O}{||}}{C}}OH$$

(b)

$$O_2N-\text{(benzene ring)}-\overset{\overset{\displaystyle O}{||}}{C}OH$$

17.3

$$H-O-\overset{\overset{\displaystyle O}{||}}{C}-\overset{\overset{\displaystyle H}{|}}{\underset{\underset{\displaystyle H}{|}}{C}}-\overset{\overset{\displaystyle H}{|}}{\underset{\underset{\displaystyle H}{|}}{C}}-\overset{\overset{\displaystyle O}{||}}{C}-O-H$$

$$HO\overset{\overset{\displaystyle O}{||}}{C}CH_2CH_2\overset{\overset{\displaystyle O}{||}}{C}OH$$

17.4 2,3-Dibromopropanoic acid

17.5 **(a)**

$$\text{(benzene ring)}\overset{\overset{\displaystyle O}{||}}{C}OCH(CH_3)_2$$

(b)

$$CH_3CH_2CH_2CH_2\overset{\overset{\displaystyle O}{||}}{C}OCH_2CH_3$$

(c)

$$CH_3CH=CH\overset{\overset{\displaystyle O}{||}}{C}OCH(CH_3)_2$$

17.6 CH_3COOH is highest boiling (most H-bonding). $CH_3CH_2CH_3$ is lowest boiling (nonpolar). **17.7** **(a)** C_3H_7COOH is more soluble (smaller —R group). **(b)** $(CH_3)_2CHCOOH$ is more soluble (carboxylic acid).

17.8

$$CH_3CH_2\overset{\overset{\displaystyle O}{||}}{C}OH \qquad CH_3CH_2\overset{\overset{\displaystyle O}{||}}{C}OCH_3 \qquad CH_3CH_2\overset{\overset{\displaystyle O}{||}}{C}NH_2$$

Propanoic acid   Methyl propanoate   Propanamide

$$CH_3CH_2\overset{\overset{\displaystyle O}{||}}{C}NHCH_3 \qquad CH_3CH_2\overset{\overset{\displaystyle O}{||}}{C}\overset{}{\underset{\underset{\displaystyle CH_3}{|}}{N}}CH_3$$

N-Methylpropanamide   *N,N*-Dimethylpropanamide

17.9 **(a)** Propyl 3-hydroxypentanoate **(b)** *N*-Methyl-*p*-chlorobenzamide

17.10 **(a)**

$$CH_3\overset{\overset{\displaystyle CH_3}{|}}{CH}CH_2CH_2\overset{\overset{\displaystyle O}{||}}{C}NH_2$$

(b)

$$CH_3CH_2\overset{\overset{\displaystyle O}{||}}{C}\overset{}{\underset{\underset{\displaystyle CH_3}{|}}{N}}CH_2CH_3$$

17.11 **(a)** (ii) **(b)** (i) **(c)** (iv) **(d)** (iii)   **17.12** **(a)** (ii) **(b)** (i) **(c)** (iii) **(d)** (i) **(e)** (i) **(f)** (iii)

17.13 **(a)**

$$C_6H_5\overset{\overset{\displaystyle O}{||}}{C}NH_2$$

Amide (C_7H_7NO)

(b)

$$CH_3CH_2\overset{\overset{\displaystyle O}{||}}{C}OH$$

Carboxylic acid ($C_3H_6O_2$)

(c)

$$CH_3\overset{\overset{\displaystyle O}{||}}{C}OCH_2CH_3$$

Ester ($C_3H_6O_2$)

17.14 **(a)**

$$CH_3\overset{\overset{\displaystyle HO}{|}}{CH}\overset{\overset{\displaystyle O}{||}}{C}-O^-\,Na^+ \;+\; H_2O$$

(b)

$$\left[CH_3CH_2CH_2\overset{\overset{\displaystyle H_3C}{|}}{\underset{\underset{\displaystyle CH_3}{|}}{C}}-\overset{\overset{\displaystyle O}{||}}{C}-O^-\right]_2\,Ca^{2+}$$

17.15 **(a)**

$$\left[\text{(benzene ring with }COO^-\text{ and }OH)\right]_2\,Ca^{2+}$$

(b)

$$H_2C=CHCOO^-Ca^+$$

17.16 CH_3COO^- $^-OOCCH_2CH_2CH_2COO^-$ Na^+ K^+

17.17 $HCOOCH_2CH(CH_3)_{2,,}$

17.18 **(a)**

$$\text{(cyclohexane ring)}-OH \;+\; HO\overset{\overset{\displaystyle O}{||}}{C}CH_2CH_2CH(CH_3)_2$$

(b)

$$CH_3CH_2CH_2CH_2\overset{\overset{\displaystyle O}{||}}{C}OH \;+\; HOCH(CH_3)_2$$

17.19

(a)

$$CH_3\overset{\overset{\displaystyle O}{||}}{C}\overset{}{\underset{\underset{\displaystyle CH_3}{|}}{C}}H-NHCH_3$$

(b)

$$\text{(cyclopentane ring)}\overset{\overset{\displaystyle O}{||}}{C}-NH-\text{(benzene ring)}$$

17.20

$$CH_3CH_2O-\text{(benzene ring)}-NH_2 \;+\; HOOCCH_3$$

17.21

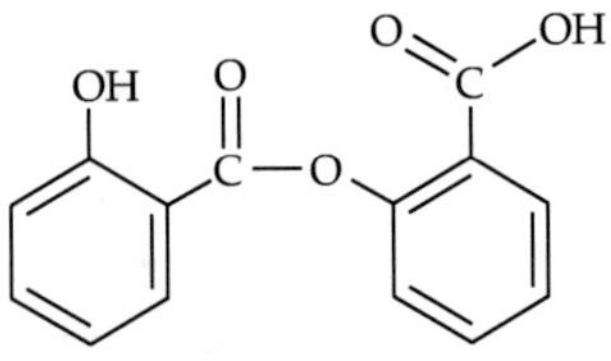

17.22 Aspirin is acidic (—COOH), lidocaine is basic (amine), benzocaine is weakly basic (aromatic amine), acetaminophen is weakly acidic (phenol).

17.23 Moisture in the air hydrolyzes the ester bond.

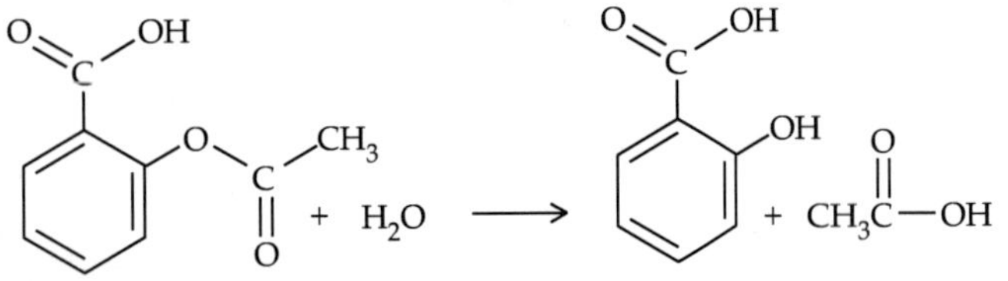

17.24 (a) p-Nitrobenzoic acid + 2-Propanol (b) Phenol + 2-Hydroxycyclopentanecarboxylic acid (c) Acrylic acid + Ethanol

17.25 (a) 2-Butenoic acid + Methylamine (b) p-Nitrobenzoic acid + Dimethylamine

17.26 (a)

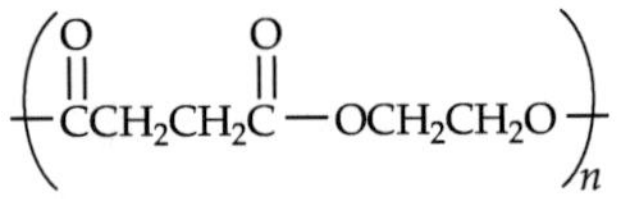

(b)

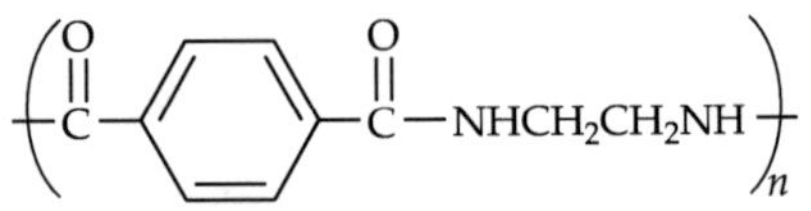

17.27

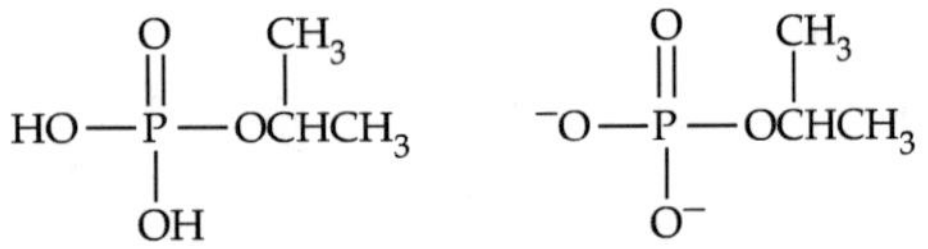

17.28 (a) amide + $H_2O \rightarrow CH_3COOH + NH_3$
(b) phosphate monoester + $H_2O \rightarrow CH_3CH_2OH + HOPO_3^{2-}$
(c) carboxylic acid ester + $H_2O \rightarrow CH_3CH_2COOH + HOCH_3$

17.29

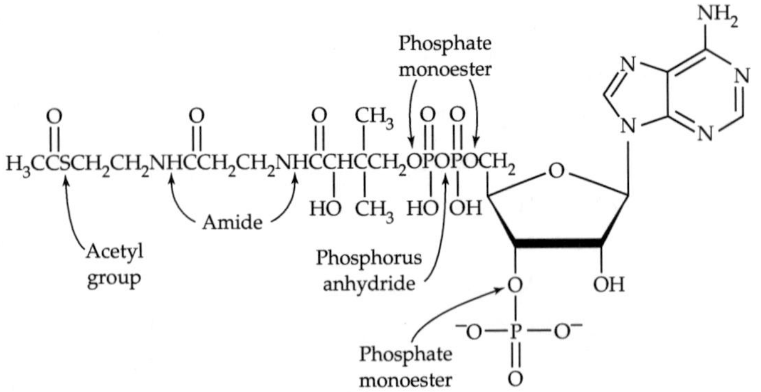

17.30 (a) At pH = 7.4, pyruvate and lactate are anions.

(b)

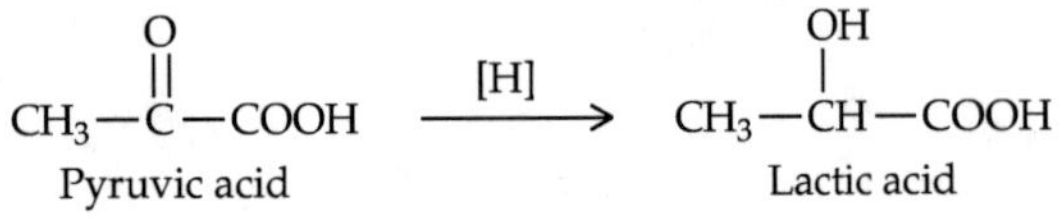

(c) Pyruvate and lactate have similar solubilities in water.

(d)

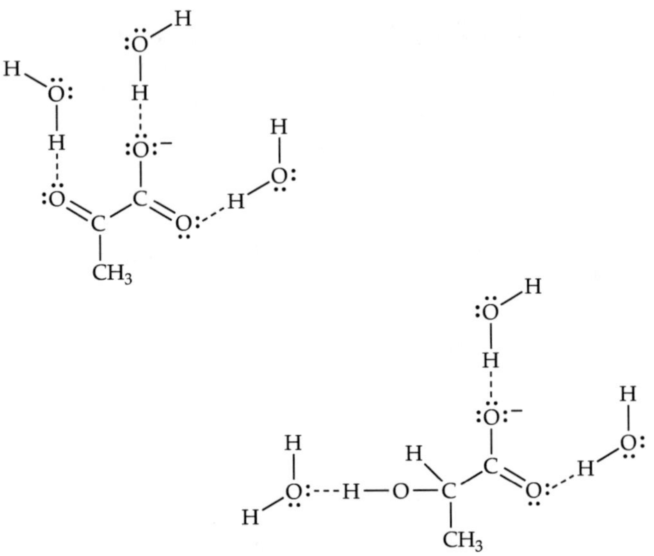

17.31 (a) H_2O + acid or base

(b)

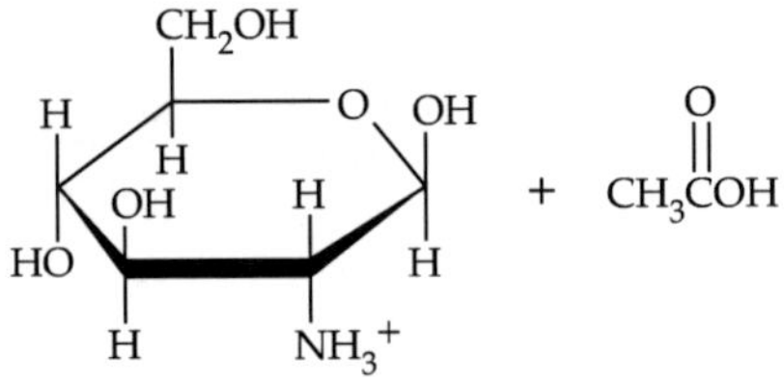

17.32 (a) a phosphate ester linkage

(b)

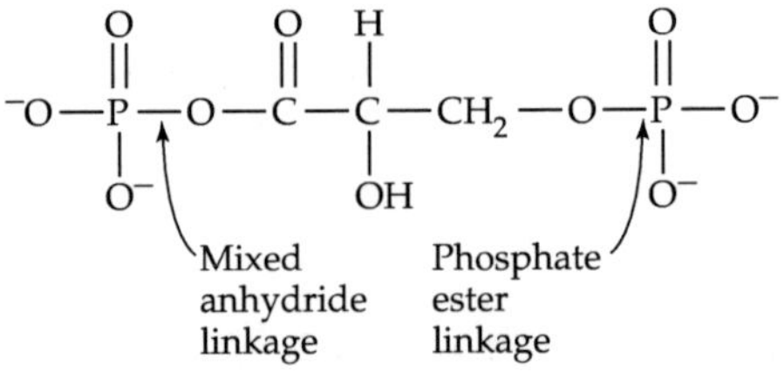

17.33

$^-OOCCOO^-$ $\qquad$ $^-OOCCH_2COO^-$
Oxalate $\qquad\qquad$ Malonate

$^-OOCCH_2CH_2COO^-$ $\qquad$ $^-OOCCH_2CH_2CH_2COO^-$
Succinate $\qquad\qquad$ Glutarate

17.34

(a)

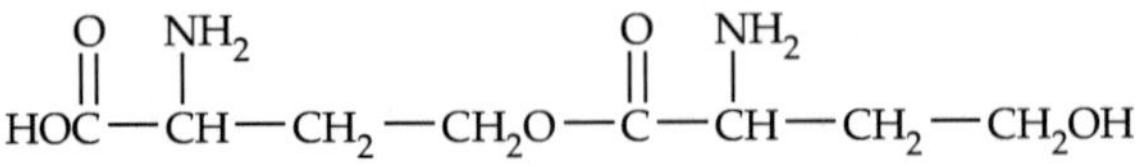

(b)

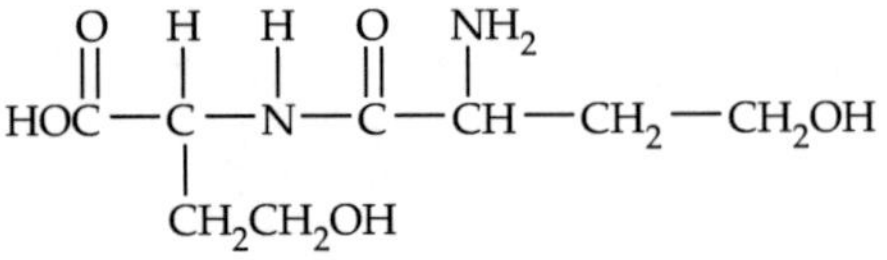

(c)

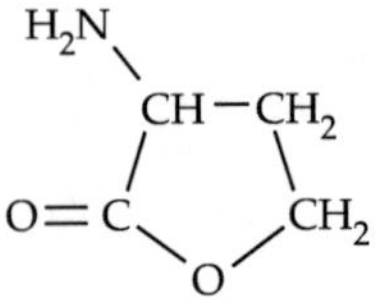

17.35

(a) (i)

Acetic acid

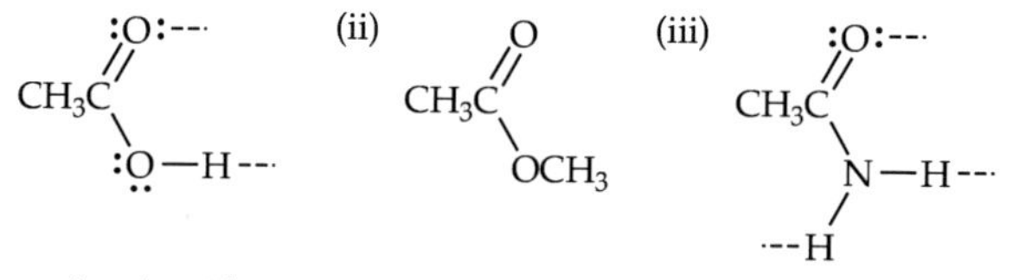

(ii)

Methyl acetate

(iii)

Acetamide

(b) Methyl acetate is lowest boiling (no hydrogen bonds); acetamide is highest boiling.

17.36

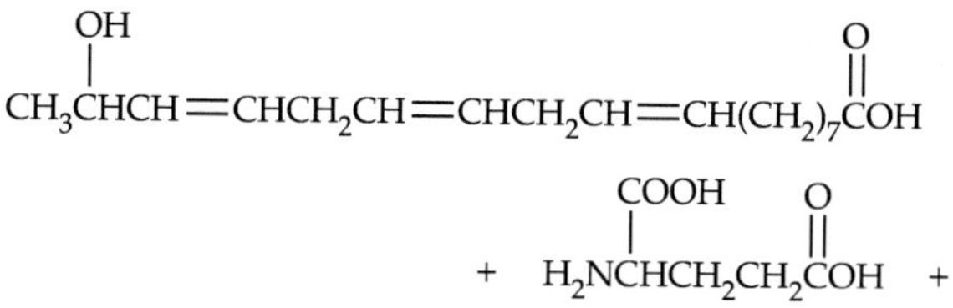

$$CH_3CHCH=CHCH_2CH=CHCH_2CH=CH(CH_2)_7COH$$

$$+ \quad H_2NCHCH_2CH_2COH \quad + \quad NH_3$$

17.37 **(a)** N-Ethyl benzamide **(b)** Ethyl pentanoate **(c)** Methyl isobutylmalonate **(d)** N,N-dimethylformamide. Compound **(c)** is acidic; all other compounds are neutral.

17.38

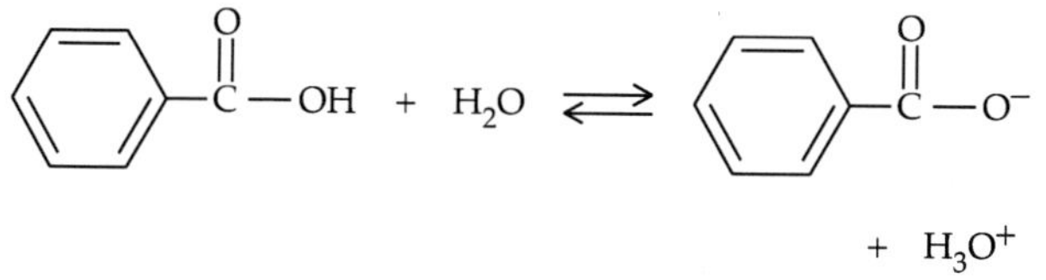

17.40

$$CH_3CH_2CH_2CH_2COOH$$
Pentanoic acid

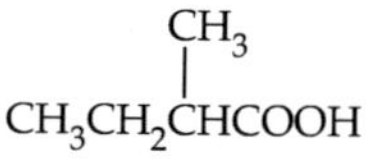

$$CH_3CH_2CHCOOH$$
2-Methylbutanoic acid

$$CH_3CHCH_2COOH$$
3-Methylbutanoic acid

$$(CH_3)_3CCOOH$$
2,2-Dimethylpropanoic acid

17.42 **(a)** 2-Ethyl-3-methylpentanoic acid **(b)** Nonanoic acid **(c)** Cyclohexanecarboxylic acid **(d)** p-Methylbenzoic acid

17.44 **(a)** Potassium 3-ethylpentanoate **(b)** Ammonium benzoate **(c)** Calcium propanoate

17.46

(a)

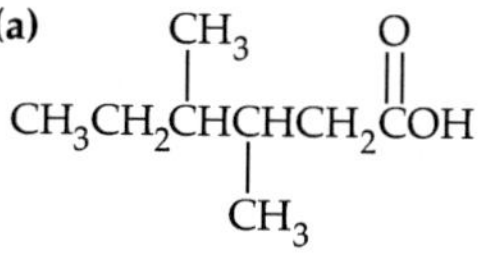

(b)

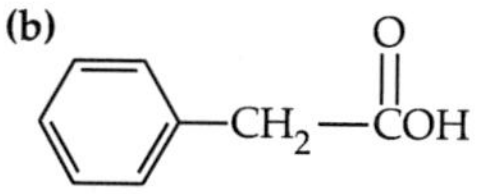

(c)

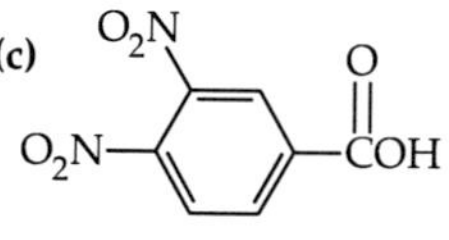

(d)

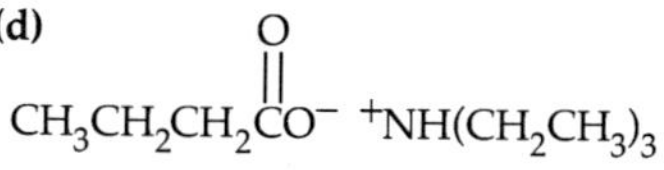

$$CH_3CH_2CH_2CO^- \ ^+NH(CH_2CH_3)_3$$

17.48

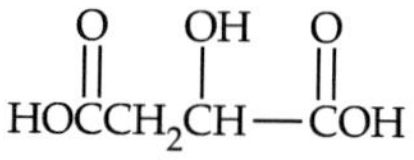

17.50

$$NH_4^+ \ ^-OCCH=CHCO^- \ NH_4^+$$

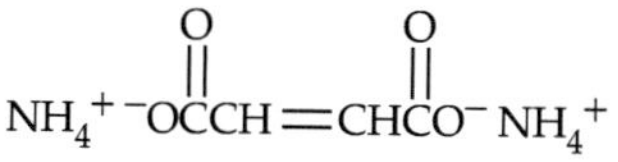

17.52 **(a)** $CH_3CH_2CH_2CH_2CONH_2$ $CH_3CH_2CONHCH_2CH_3$
Pentanamide   N-Ethylpropanamide

$$HCON(CH_2CH_3)_2$$
N,N-Diethylformamide

(b) $CH_3CH_2CH_2CH_2COOCH_3$ $CH_3CH_2COOCH_2CH_2CH_3$
Methyl pentanoate   Propyl propanoate

$$HCOOCH_2CH_2CH_2CH_3$$
Pentyl formate

17.54 **(a)** 3-Methylbutyl acetate **(b)** Methyl 4-methylpentanoate

(c)

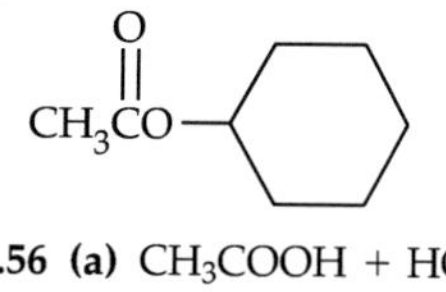

(d)

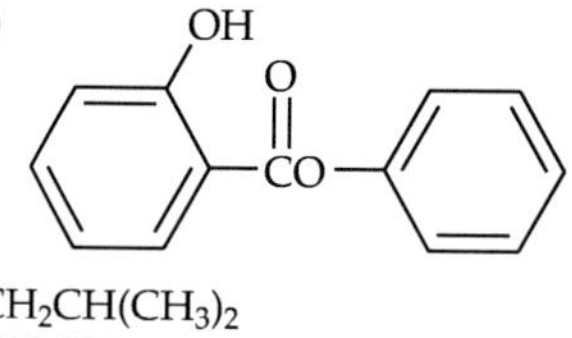

17.56 **(a)** $CH_3COOH + HOCH_2CH_2CH(CH_3)_2$
(b) $(CH_3)_2CHCH_2CH_2COOH + HOCH_3$

(c)

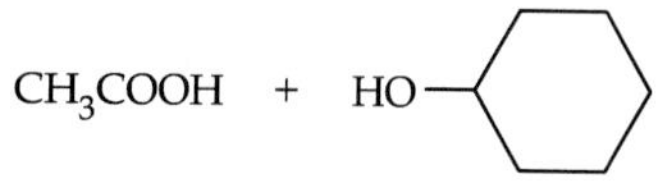

(d)

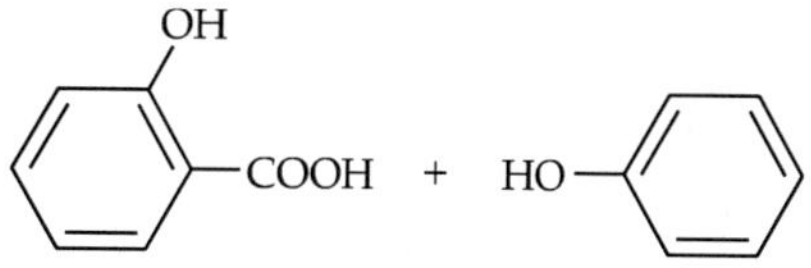

17.58 **(a)** 2-Ethylbutanamide **(b)** N-Phenylbenzamide

(c)

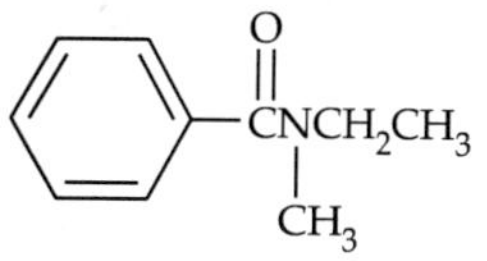

(d)

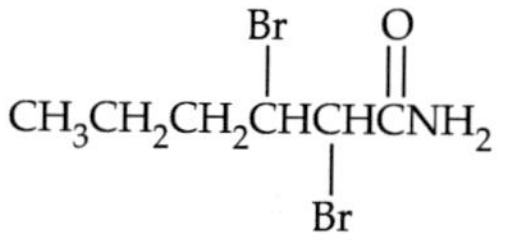

17.60 **(a)** 2-Ethylbutanoic acid + Ammonia **(b)** Benzoic acid + Aniline **(c)** Benzoic acid + N-Methylethylamine **(d)** 2,3-Dibromohexanoic acid + Ammonia

17.62

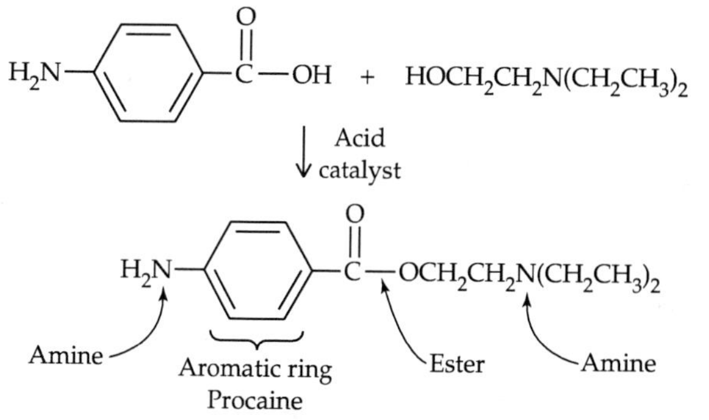

17.64 $HOCH_2CH_2CH_2COOH$

17.66

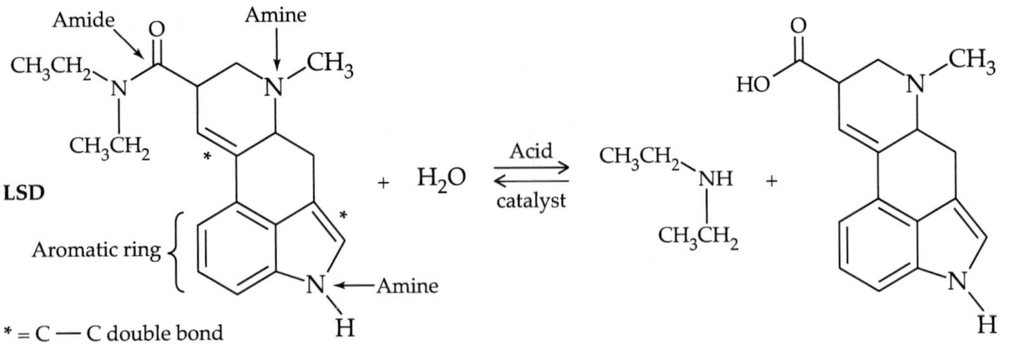

LSD, with labels: Amide, Amine, Amine, Aromatic ring, * = C—C double bond

$+ \ H_2O \ \underset{\text{catalyst}}{\overset{\text{Acid}}{\rightleftarrows}}$ diethylamine $+$ (carboxylic acid product)

17.68

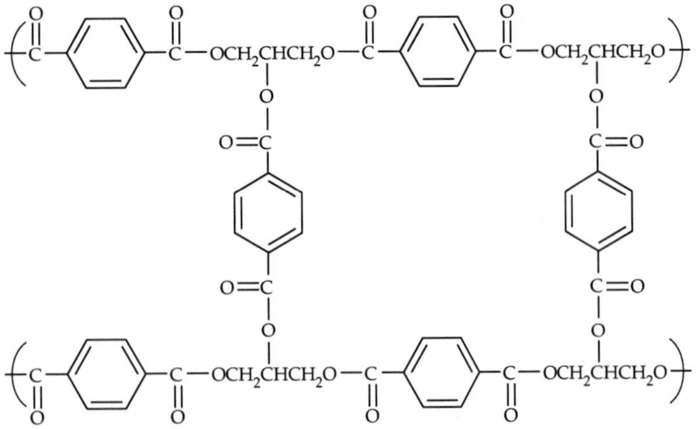

17.70 Dihydroxyacetone and hydrogen phosphate anion.

17.72

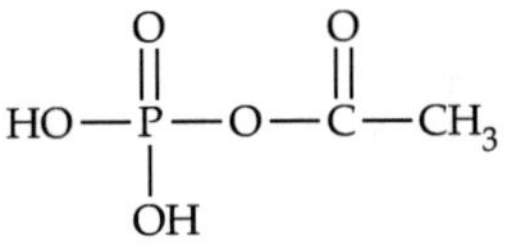

17.74 A cyclic phosphate diester is formed when a phosphate group forms an ester with two hydroxyl groups in the same molecule.

17.76 Trichloroacetic acid: used for chemical peeling of the skin. Lactic acid: used for wrinkle removal and moisturizing.

17.78

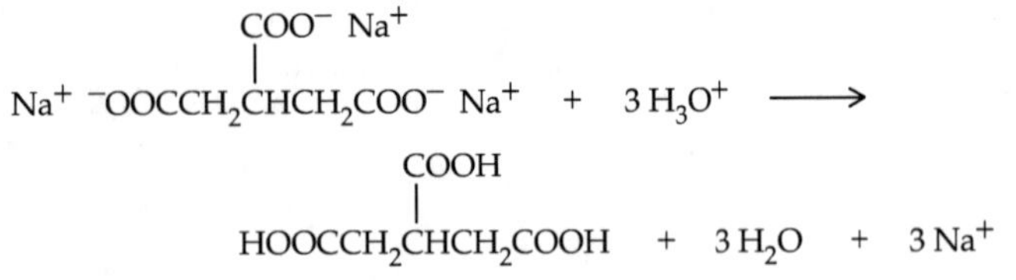

$$Na^+ \ {}^-OOCCH_2CHCH_2COO^- \ Na^+ \ + \ 3 \ H_3O^+ \ \longrightarrow$$

with $COO^- \ Na^+$ above

$$HOOCCH_2CHCH_2COOH \ + \ 3 \ H_2O \ + \ 3 \ Na^+$$

with COOH above

17.80 strong acids and bases.

17.82

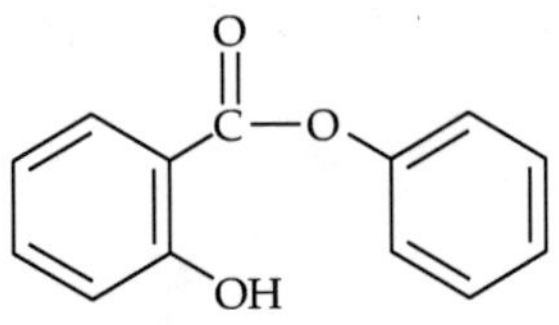

17.84 pH; Tollens' test **17.86** (a) 2-Chloro-3,4-dimethyl-3-hexene
(b) N-Methyl-N-phenylpropanamide (c) Phenyl 2,2-diethylbutanoate
(d) N-Ethyl-o-nitrobenzamide

Chapter 18
18.1 Aromatic ring: phenylalanine, tyrosine, tryptophan
Contain sulfur: cysteine, methionine
Alcohols: serine, threonine, tyrosine (phenol)
Alkyl side chain: alanine, valine, leucine, isoleucine

18.2

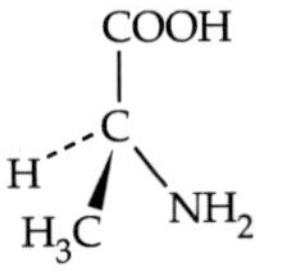

18.3

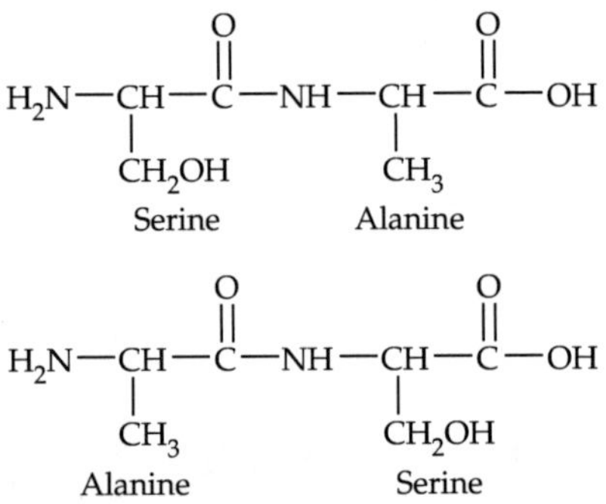

Serine — Alanine

Alanine — Serine

18.4 α–amino acids: (a), (d)
18.5 (b) Asn, Ser (c) Thr, Tyr

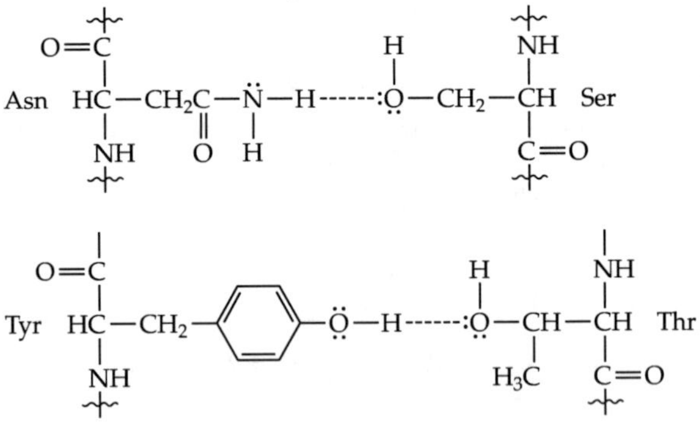

Asn ... Ser

Tyr ... Thr

18.6

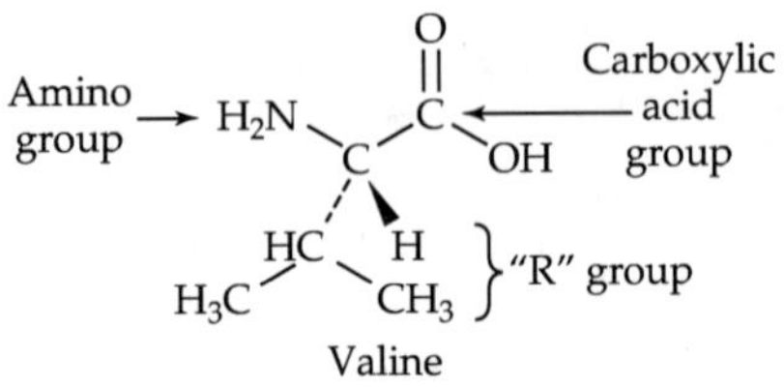

Valine, with labels: Amino group, Carboxylic acid group, "R" group

18.7

at low pH — at high pH

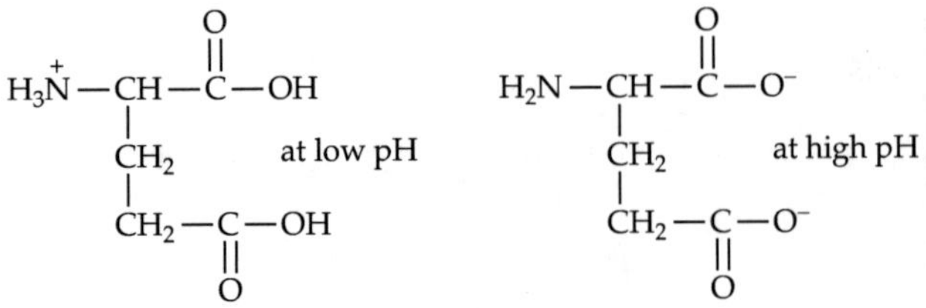

18.8 In the zwitterionic form of an amino acid, the $-NH_3^+$ group is an acid, and the $-COO^-$ group is a base. **18.9** Chiral: (a), (b), and (d)
18.10 Handed: wrench, corkscrew, jar lid
Not handed: thumbtack, pencil, straw

18.11 2-Aminobutane has a carbon with 4 different groups bonded to it.
18.12 chiral: **(b), (c)**

18.13

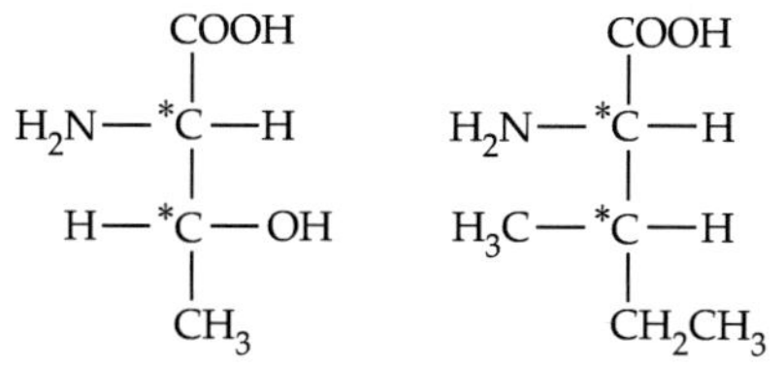

Threonine   Isoleucine

18.14

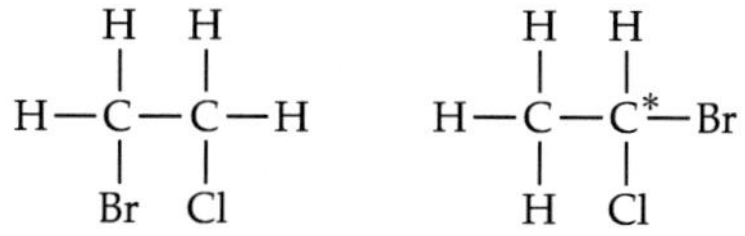

18.15 (a) Gly–Ser–Tyr   Tyr–Ser–Gly   Ser–Tyr–Gly
         Gly–Tyr–Ser   Tyr–Gly–Ser   Ser–Gly–Tyr

(b)

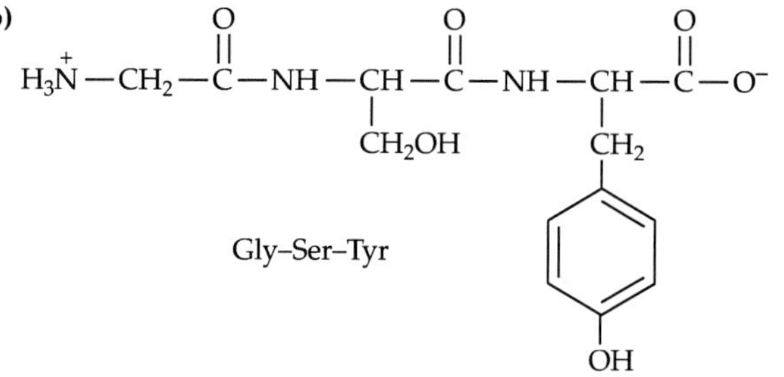

Gly–Ser–Tyr

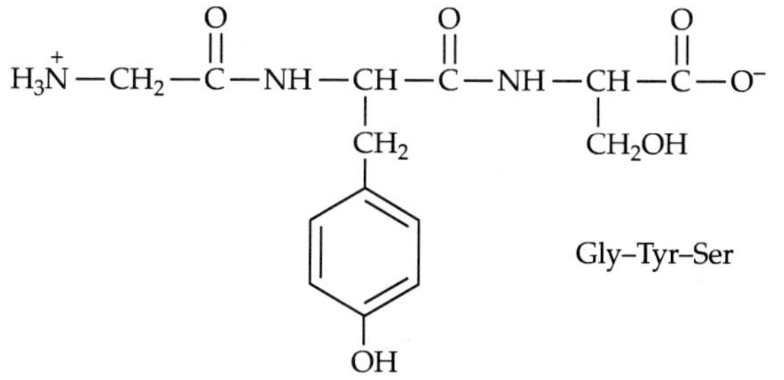

Gly–Tyr–Ser

18.16   Leu–Trp–Ser   Trp–Leu–Ser   Ser–Trp–Leu
            Leu–Ser–Trp   Trp–Ser–Leu   Ser–Leu–Trp
18.17 (a) Leu–Asp **(b)** Tyr–Ser–Lys
18.18

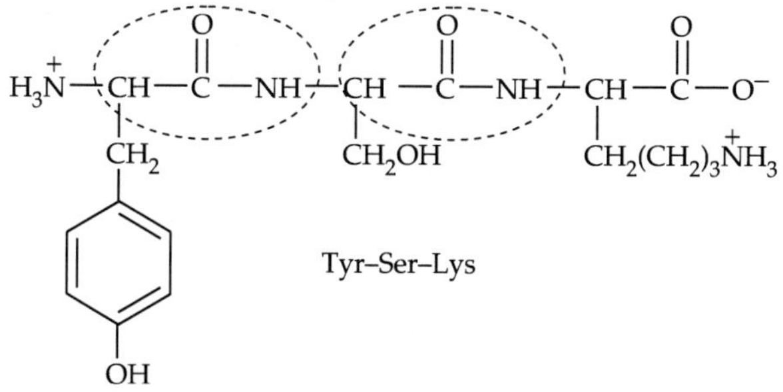

Tyr–Ser–Lys

18.19 Asp−Tyr + Phe + Glu−Asn−Cys−Pro−Lys−Gly
18.20 (a) hydrogen bond **(b)** hydrophobic interaction **(c)** salt bridge
(d) hydrophobic interaction   **18.21 (a)** Tyr, Asp, Ser **(b)** Ala, Ile, Val, Leu
18.22 eleven backbone atoms   **18.23** Secondary structure: stabilized by
hydrogen bonds between amide nitrogens and carbonyl oxygens of
polypeptide backbone. Tertiary structure: stabilized by hydrogen bonds
between amino acid side-chain groups.   **18.24 (a)** tertiary; **(b)** secondary; **(c)** quaternary   **18.25** At low pH, the groups at the end of the
polypeptide chain exist as $-NH_3{}^+$ and $-COOH$. At high pH, they exist
as $-NH_2$ and $-COO^-$. In addition, side chain functional groups may be
ionized as follows: **(a)** no change **(b)** Lys, His, Arg positively charged at
low pH; Lys, His neutral at high pH: **(c)** Tyr neutral at low pH, negatively charged at high pH: **(d)** Glu, Asp neutral at low pH, negatively
charged at high pH: **(e)** no change: **(f)** Cys neutral at low pH, negatively
charged at high pH.   **18.26 (a)** 1, 4 **(b)** 2, 4 **(c)** 2
18.27 *See below for answer.*
18.28 *Fibrous Proteins*: structural proteins, water-insoluble, contain many
Gly and Pro residues, contain large regions of α-helix or β-sheet, few
side-chain interactions. Examples: Collagen, α-Keratin, Fibroin.
Globular Proteins: enzymes and hormones, usually water-soluble, contain
most amino acids, contain smaller regions of α-helix and β-sheet, complex tertiary structure. Examples: Ribonuclease, hemoglobin, insulin.
18.29 (a) Leu, Phe, Ala or any other amino acid with a nonpolar side
chain. **(b)** and **(c)** Asp, Lys, Thr or any other amino acid with a polar side
chain.   **18.30** The prefix "α" means that $-NH_2$ and $-COOH$ are
bonded to the same carbon, the carbon atom in the alpha position (next
to) the carbonyl carbon atom in the carboxyl group.

18.32 (a)   **(b)**

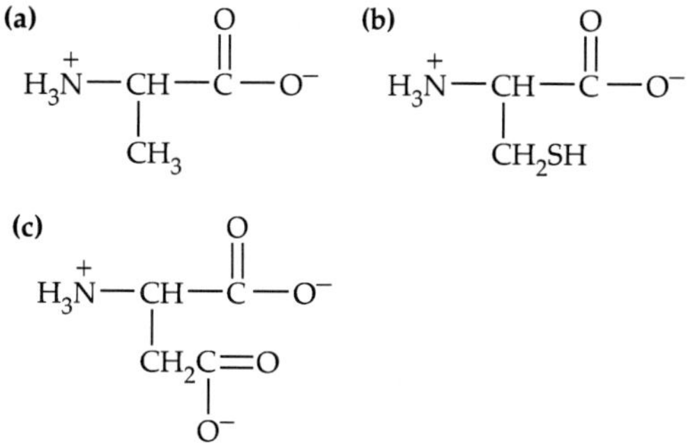

(c)

18.34 (a)   **(b)**

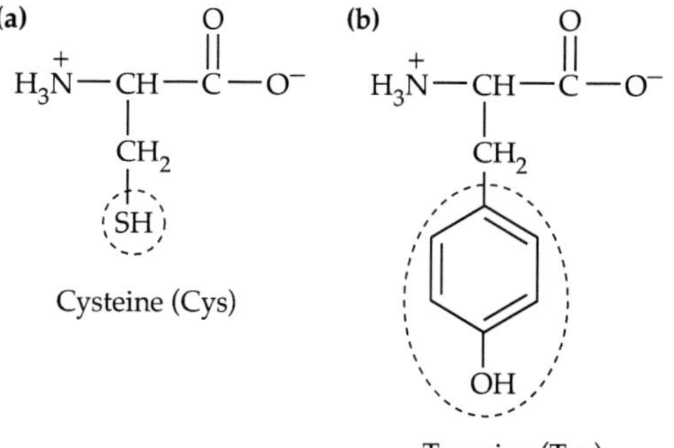

Cysteine (Cys)   Tyrosine (Tyr)

18.27

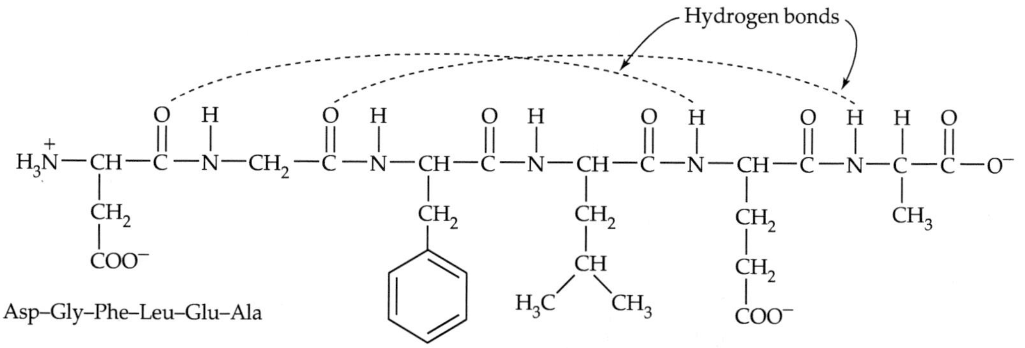

Asp–Gly–Phe–Leu–Glu–Ala

18.36 neutral: **(a) (c)** positive charge: **(b)** **18.38 (a)**, **(c)** low pH **(b)** high pH **18.40** A chiral object is handed. Examples: glove, car. **18.42 (a)**

18.44

(a)

CH$_3$CCH$_3$
Cl
Br
Achiral

(b)

CH$_3$CH$_2$*CCH$_3$
Cl
Br
Chiral

(c)

(CH$_3$)$_2$CH*CCH$_3$
Cl
Br
Chiral

18.46 Chiral ─── Achiral

CH$_3$CHCH$_2$CH$_3$
F
Achiral

18.48 A simple protein is composed only of amino acids. A conjugated protein consists of a protein associated with one or more nonprotein molecules.

18.50

TYPE OF PROTEIN	FUNCTION	EXAMPLE
Enzymes:	Catalyze biochemical reactions	Ribonuclease
Hormones:	Regulate body functions	Insulin
Storage proteins:	Store essential substances	Myoglobin
Transport proteins:	Transport substances through body fluids	Serum albumin
Structural proteins:	Provide shape and support	Collagen
Protective proteins:	Defend the body against foreign matter	Immunoglobulins
Contractile proteins:	Do mechanical work	Myosin and actin

18.52 Disulfide bonds stabilize tertiary structure. **18.54** In *hydrophobic interactions*, hydrocarbon side chains cluster in the center of proteins and make proteins spherical. Examples: Phe, Ile. *Salt bridges* bring together distant parts of a polypeptide chain. Examples: Lys, Asp. **18.56** When a protein is denatured, its nonprimary structure is disrupted, and it can no longer catalyze reactions. **18.58** Val–Met–Leu, Met–Val–Leu, Leu–Met–Val, Val–Leu–Met, Met–Leu–Val, Leu–Val–Met.
18.60 *Outside*: Asp, His (They can form H-bonds.) *Inside*: Val, Ala (They have hydrophobic interactions.) **18.62** Digestive enzymes would hydrolyze insulin if it were swallowed.

18.64 N-terminal   C-terminal

18.66 (a) H$_3$$^+NCH_2$COOH **(b)** H$_3$$^+NCH_2$COOCH$_3$
18.68 N-terminal: Val–Gly–Ser–Ala–Asp C-terminal
18.70 A peptide rich in Asp and Lys is more soluble, because its side chains are more polar and can form hydrogen bonds with water.
18.72

(a)

Tyrosine

Tyramine

Decarboxylation is the loss of CO$_2$. **(b)** Phenelzine resembles tyramine (it has a phenyl group and an amino group) and blocks the enzyme that catalyzes deamination of tyramine. **18.74** An incomplete protein lacks one or more essential amino acids. **18.76** They must provide complete nutrition to developing organisms. **18.78** Arg–Trp moves to negative electrode, Val–Met doesn't move, Asp–Thr moves to positive electrode. **18.80** Osteogenesis imperfecta is a dominant genetic defect in which collagen is synthesized incorrectly, resulting in weak bones. **18.82** It was hard to accept that a protein might duplicate itself, cause disease, be responsible for inherited disease, be transmitted, and might arise spontaneously. **18.84** A combination of grains, legumes, and nuts in each meal provides all of the essential amino acids. **18.86** Canned pineapple has been heated to inactivate enzymes

18.88 (a)

Arg ─── Pro ─── Pro ─── Gly ─── Phe ─── Ser ─── Pro ─── Phe ─── Arg

(b) Proline rings introduce kinks and bends and prevent hydrogen bonds from forming.
18.90 Carbon is no longer bonded to four different groups.
18.92

Asn—Cys—Pro—Leu—Gln

Oxytocin

Gln
Ile
Tyr—Cys

18.94 Arg, Asp, Asn, Glu, Gln, His, Lys, Ser, Thr, Tyr

18.96 On the outside of a globular protein: Glu, Ser. On the outside of a fibrous protein: Ala, Val. On the outside of neither: Leu, Phe.
18.98 Asp is similar in size and function to Glu.

Chapter 19
19.1 Kinases   **19.2** (1) The enzyme might catalyze reactions within the eye. (2) Saline is sterile and isotonic.   **19.3** iron, copper, manganese, molybdenum, vanadium, cobalt, nickel, chromium   **19.4 (a)** NAD^+, coenzyme A, FAD; **(b)** They are minerals.   **19.5 (a)** catalyzes the removal of two —H from glutamate. **(b)** catalyzes the transfer of an amino group from alanine to a second substrate. **(c)** catalyzes the formation of a bond between carbamoyl phosphate and another substrate. **(d)** catalyzes the isomerization of triose phosphate.   **19.6 (a)** arginase **(b)** maltase   **19.7** isomerase. It catalyzes the isomerization of glucose 6-phosphate.   **19.8** Water adds to fumarate (substrate) to give L-malate (product).   **19.9** Reaction **(a)**   **19.10** Acidic, basic, and polar side chains take part in catalytic activity. All types of side chains hold the enzyme in the active site.   **19.11** Substrate molecules are bound to all of the active sites. **(a)** no effect; **(b)** increases the rate.   **19.12** higher at 30°; somewhat higher at 40°.   **19.13** The rate is much greater at pH = 8.   **19.14** molecule **(b)**, because it resembles the substrate.   **19.15** a product that resembles the substrate.   **19.16 (a)** competitive inhibition **(b)** covalent modification or feedback control **(c)** covalent modification **(d)** genetic control   **19.17** Vitamin A—long hydrocarbon chain. Vitamin C—polar hydroxyl groups.   **19.18** Retinal—aldehyde. Retinoic acid—carboxylic acid. Retinol—alcohol. Same functional group modified in each molecule.   **19.19** enzyme cofactors; antioxidants; aid in absorption of calcium and phosphate ions; aid in synthesis of visual pigments and blood clotting factors.
19.20

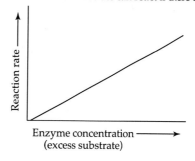

---- Hydrogen bonds
ıιιιιιı Salt bridges

19.21 (a) oxidoreductase **(b)** dehydrogenase **(c)** L-lactate **(d)** pyruvate **(e)** L-lactate dehydrogenase

19.22 No. An enzyme usually catalyzes the reaction of only one isomer. D-Lactate might be a competitive inhibitor.   **19.23** NAD^+ is an oxidizing agent and includes the vitamin niacin.   **19.24 (a)** Rate increases when [substrate] is low, but max. rate is soon reached; max. rate is always lower than max. rate of uninhibited reaction. **(b)** Rate increases.
19.25 (a) Addition or removal of a covalently bonded group changes the activity of an enzyme. **(b)** Hormones control the synthesis of enzymes. **(c)** Binding of the regulator at a site away from the catalytic site changes the shape of the enzyme. **(d)** Noncompetitive inhibition is a type of allosteric regulation (see part **(c)**). Competitive inhibition occurs when an inhibitor reversibly occupies an enzyme's active site. Irreversible inhibition results when an inhibitor covalently binds to an enzyme and destroys its ability to catalyze a reaction.   **19.26 (a)** feedback inhibition **(b)** irreversible inhibition **(c)** genetic control **(d)** noncompetitive inhibition   **19.27** From left to right: aspartate (acidic), serine, glutamine, arginine (basic), histidine (basic).   **19.28 (a)** oxidation or reduction of a substrate; **(b)** addition of a small molecule to a double bond, or removal of a small molecule to form a double bond; **(c)** transfer of a functional group from one substrate to another   **19.30 (a)** sucrase **(b)** fumarase **(c)** RNAse   **19.32** An enzyme is a large three-dimensional molecule with a catalytic site into which a substrate can fit. Enzymes are specific in their action because only one or a few molecules have the appropriate shape and functional groups to fit into the catalytic site.   **19.34 (a)** hydrolase **(b)** lyase **(c)** oxidoreductase   **19.36 (a)** loss of CO_2 from a substrate; **(b)** transfer of a methyl group between substrates; **(c)** removal of two —H to form a double bond   **19.38** hydrolase   **19.40 (a)** riboflavin (B_2) **(b)** pantothenic acid (B_5) **(c)** pyridoxine (B_6)   **19.42** Lock-and-key: An enzyme is rigid (lock) and only one specific substrate (key) can fit in the active site. Induced fit: An enzyme can change its shape to accommodate the substrate and to catalyze the reaction.   **19.44** No. Protein folding can bring the residues close to each other.   **19.46** In the stomach, an enzyme must be active at an acidic pH. In the intestine, an enzyme needs to be active at a higher pH and need not be active at pH = 1.5.
19.48

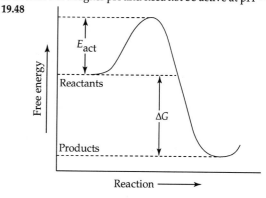

19.50 At a high substrate concentration relative to enzyme concentration, the rate of reaction increases as the enzyme concentration increases because more substrate can react if there are more active sites.

Reaction rate
Enzyme concentration
(excess substrate)

19.52 Increasing enzyme concentration increases the rate; increasing substrate concentration increases the rate until all active sites are filled, when the rate levels off.   **19.54 (a) (b)** lowers rate; **(c)** denatures the enzyme and stops reaction   **19.56** *Noncompetitive inhibition*: Inhibitor binds reversibly and noncovalently away from the active site and changes the shape of the site to make it difficult for the enzyme to

catalyze reactions. *Competitive inhibition*: Inhibitor binds reversibly and noncovalently at the active site and keeps the substrate from entering. *Irreversible inhibition*: Inhibitor irreversibly forms a covalent bond at the active site and destroys the catalytic ability of the enzyme. **19.58** diagram **(c)** **19.60** (1) displacing an essential metal from an active site; (2) bonding to a cysteine residue (irreversible) **19.62** Papain catalyzes the hydrolysis of peptide bonds and partially digests the proteins in meat. **19.64** One site is for catalysis, and one site is for regulation. **19.66** The end product of a reaction series is an inhibitor for an earlier step. **19.68** A zymogen is an enzyme synthesized in a form different from its active form because it might otherwise harm the organism. **19.70** Vitamins are small essential organic molecules that must be obtained from food. **19.72** Vitamin C is excreted, but vitamin A is stored in fatty tissue. **19.74** (1) Enzymes produce only one enantiomer of a product. (2) Enzymes allow difficult reactions to take place (3) Use of enzymes avoids reactions with hazardous byproducts. **19.76** Two strategies keep the enzyme active: (1) Use of chaperonins, enzymes that return a protein to its active form; (2) The protein itself is rigid and resists heat denaturation. **19.78** CPK, ALT, and LDH1 leak from damaged heart vessels. **19.80** A mild inhibitor allows closer control of blood pressure. A modification to pit viper protein might be to introduce a –SH residue near proline. **19.82** The body excretes excess water-soluble vitamins, but fat-soluble vitamins are stored in tissue. **19.84** They are the most important for maintaining good health.
19.86 *See below for answer.*
19.88 Blanching destroys enzymes that would cause deterioration in food quality. **19.90** Leu–Gly–Arg, Ile–Met–His, Tyr–Trp–Ala **19.92** Excess ethanol displaces methanol from the active site.

Chapter 20

20.1 (c) **20.2** The molecules resemble the heterocyclic part of cAMP, and they might act as inhibitors to the enzyme that inactivates cAMP. **20.3** Glu–His–Pro **20.4** The hydrophobic part of the structure is larger than the polar, hydrophilic part. **20.5** Testosterone has a —CH$_3$ group between the first two rings; nandrolone doesn't. Otherwise, their structures are identical. **20.6 (a)** 3 **(b)** 1 **(c)** 2 **20.7** Similarities: both structures have aromatic rings, secondary amine groups, alcohol groups. Differences: propranolol has an ether group and a naphthalene ring system; epinephrine has two phenol hydroxyl groups; the compounds have different side chain carbon skeletons. **20.8** Malathion: it's the least toxic. **20.9** An agonist (black widow spider venom) prolongs the biochemical response of a receptor. An antagonist (botulinus toxin) blocks or inhibits the normal response of a receptor. **20.10** phenol hydroxyl group, ether, carbon-carbon double bond, aromatic ring. THC is hydrophobic and is likely to accumulate in fatty tissue. **20.11 (a)** antihistamine **(b)** antidepressant **20.12 (a)** polypeptide hormone (produced in the anterior pituitary gland) **(b)** steroid hormone (produced in

ovaries) **(c)** Progesterone-producing cells have LH receptors. **(d)** Progesterone is lipid-soluble and can enter cells. **20.13** (1) Adenylate cyclase can produce a great many molecules of cAMP. (2) A large amount of glucose is released when glycogen phosphorylase is activated. **20.14 (a)** insulin (polypeptide hormone) **(b)** pancreas **(c)** in the bloodstream **(d)** Insulin doesn't enter cells directly because it can't pass through cell membranes. Instead, it binds with a cell surface receptor. **20.15** Neurotransmitters can act either by binding to receptors or by activating second messengers. **20.16** Enzymatic inactivation; reuptake of neurotransmitter molecules by presynaptic neuron. **20.17** These substances increase dopamine levels in the brain. The brain responds by decreasing the number and sensitivity of dopamine receptors. Thus more of the substance is needed to elevate dopamine levels, leading to addiction. **20.18** A hormone is a molecule that travels through the bloodstream to its target tissue, where it binds to a receptor and regulates biochemical reactions. **20.20** A hormone transmits a chemical message from an endocrine gland to a target tissue. A neurotransmitter carries an impulse between neighboring nerve cells. **20.22** Hormone binding is noncovalent and regulates a reaction, rather than catalyzing it. **20.24** The endocrine system manufactures and secretes hormones. **20.26** polypeptide hormones, steroid hormones, amino acid derivatives **20.28** Enzymes are proteins; hormones may be polypeptides, proteins, steroids, or amino acid derivatives. **20.30** Polypeptide hormones travel through the bloodstream and bind to cell receptors, which are on the outside of a cell. The receptors cause production within cells of "second messengers" that activate enzymes. **20.32** the adrenal medulla **20.34** through the bloodstream **20.36** In order of involvement; the hormone receptor, G protein, and adenylate cyclase. **20.38** It initiates reactions that release glucose from storage. Termination occurs when phosphodiesterase converts cAMP to AMP. **20.40** anaphylaxis **20.42** Insulin contains 51 amino acids, is released from the pancreas, and acts at cells, causing them to take up glucose. **20.44** mineralocorticoids (aldosterone), glucocorticoids (cortisone) sex hormones (testosterone, estrone). **20.46** estrone, estradiol, progesterone **20.48** epinephrine, norepinephrine, dopamine **20.50 (a)** amino acid derivative **(b)** polypeptide hormone **(c)** steroid hormone **20.52** A synapse is the gap between two nerve cells that neurotransmitters cross to transmit their message. **20.54** nerve cell, muscle cell, endocrine cell **20.56** A nerve impulse arrives at the presynaptic end of a neuron. The nerve impulse stimulates the movement of a vesicle, containing neurotransmitter molecules, to the cell membrane. The vesicle fuses with the cell membrane and releases the neurotransmitter, which crosses the synaptic cleft to a receptor site on the postsynaptic end of a second neuron. After reception, the cell transmits an electrical signal down its axon and passes on the impulse. Enzymes then deactivate the neurotransmitter so that the neuron can receive the next impulse. Alternatively, the neurotransmitter may be returned to the presynaptic neuron. **20.58** (1) Neurotransmitter

19.86

Vitamin E

molecules are released from a presynaptic neuron. (2) Neurotransmitter molecules bind to receptors on the target cell. (3) The neurotransmitter is deactivated **20.60** They are secreted in the central nervous system and have receptors in brain tissue. **20.62** Agonists prolong the response of a receptor. Antagonists block the response of a receptor. **20.64** Antihistamines such as doxylamine counteract allergic responses caused by histamine by blocking histamine receptors in mucous membranes. Antihistamines such as cimetidine block receptors for histamine that stimulate production of stomach acid. **20.66** Tricyclic antidepressant: Elavil MAO inhibitor: Nardil SSRI: Prozac **20.68** Cocaine increases dopamine levels by blocking reuptake. **20.70** Tetrahydrocannabinol (THC) increases dopamine levels in the same brain areas where dopamine levels increase after administration of heroin and cocaine. **20.72** Endorphins are polypeptides with morphine-like activity. They are produced by the pituitary gland and have receptors in the brain. **20.74** An ethnobotanist discovers what indigenous people have learned about the healing power of plants. **20.76** Scientists who know about the exact size and shape of enzymes and receptors can design drugs that interact with the active sites of these biomolecules. **20.78** Homeostasis is the maintenance of a constant internal environment. **20.80** Plants don't have endocrine systems or a circulatory fluid like blood. **20.82** Epibatidine acts as a painkiller at acetylcholine receptors in the central nervous system. **20.84** The *hormone receptor* recognizes the hormone, sets in motion the stimulation process, and interacts with *G-protein*. This protein binds GTP and activates *adenylate cyclase*, which catalyzes the formation of cAMP. **20.86** Signal amplification is the process by which a small signal induces a response much larger than the original signal. In the case of hormones, a small amount of hormone can bring about a very large response. **20.88** Testosterone has an —OH group in the 5-membered ring; progesterone has an acetyl group in that position. Otherwise, the two molecules are identical. **20.90** Chocolate acts at dopamine receptors and produces feelings of satisfaction. **20.92** Testosterone is converted to androsterone by reductions ($C=O$, $C=C$) in the first ring, and an oxidation of —OH in the five-membered ring.

Chapter 21

21.1 exergonic: **(a)**, **(c)**; endergonic: **(b)**; releases the most energy: **(a)**
21.2 Both pathways produce the same amount of energy.
21.3 **(a)** exergonic: oxidation of glucose; endergonic: photosynthesis **(b)** sunlight
21.4 **(a)**

Carbohydrates $\xrightarrow{\text{Digestion}}$ Glucose, sugars $\xrightarrow{\text{Glycolysis}}$

Pyruvate $\longrightarrow$ Acetyl-SCoA $\xrightarrow[\text{cycle}]{\text{Citric acid}}$

Reduced coenzymes $\xrightarrow[\text{transport}]{\text{Electron}}$ ATP

(b) pyruvate, acetyl-SCoA, citric acid cycle intermediates.
21.5

$$H_3C-\overset{\overset{O}{\|}}{C}-O-\overset{\overset{O}{\|}}{\underset{\underset{O^-}{|}}{P}}-O^- + H_2O \longrightarrow$$

$$H_3C-\overset{\overset{O}{\|}}{C}-O^- + {}^-O-\overset{\overset{O}{\|}}{\underset{\underset{OH}{|}}{P}}-O^- + H^+$$

21.6 Energy is produced only when it is needed.
21.7

$$HOCH_2CHCH_2OH \xrightarrow[\text{ATP}\quad\text{ADP}]{} HOCH_2CHCH_2O-\overset{\overset{O}{\|}}{\underset{\underset{O^-}{|}}{P}}-O^-$$
(with OH groups on the second carbon)

21.8 If a process is exergonic, its exact reverse is endergonic and can't occur unless it is coupled with an exergonic reaction in a different pathway. **21.9** favorable ($\Delta G = -3.0$ kcal/mol). **21.10** yes

21.11

$$\overset{(H\cdots O)}{\underset{(H)}{{}^-OOC-\underset{|}{C}-CH-CH_2COO^-}} \qquad {}^-OOC-\overset{(H)}{CH}-\overset{(H)}{CH}-COO^-$$

$${}^-OOC-CH_2-\overset{O(H)}{\underset{(H)}{C}}-COO^-$$

21.12 Citric acid, isocitric acid. **21.13** steps 3, 4, 6, 8. **21.14** Succinic dehydrogenase catalyzes the removal of two hydrogens from succinate to yield fumarate. **21.15** α-Ketoglutarate, oxaloacetate. **21.16** isocitrate **21.17** Steps 1–4 correspond to the first stage, and steps 5–8 correspond to the second stage. **21.18** Mitochondrial matrix **21.19** O_2. Movement of H^+ from a region of high $[H^+]$ to a region of low $[H^+]$ releases energy that is used in ATP synthesis.
21.20 **(a)** Succinyl phosphate + $H_2O \rightarrow$ Succinate + $HOPO_3{}^{2-}$ + H^+ **(b)** ADP + $HOPO_3{}^{2-}$ + $H^+ \rightarrow$ ATP + H_2O $\quad \Delta G = +7.3$ kcal/mol
21.21 **(a)** Stage 1 (digestion) **(b)** Stage 4 (ATP synthesis) **(c)** Stage 2 (glycolysis) **(d)** Stage 3 (citric acid cycle). **21.22** Endergonic; coupled reactions **21.23** NAD^+ accepts hydride ions; hydrogen ions are released to the mitochondrial matrix, and ultimately combine with reduced O_2 to form H_2O. **21.24** **(a)** Step A (NAD^+) **(b)** Step B **(c)** product of A (in brackets) **21.25** Step 1: lyase Step 2: isomerase Step 3: oxidoreductase Step 4: oxidoreductase, lyase Step 5: ligase Step 6: oxidoreductase Step 7: lyase Step 8: oxidoreductase **21.26** Metals are better oxidizing and reducing agents. Also, they can accept and donate electrons in one-electron increments. **21.28** An endergonic reaction requires energy, and an exergonic reaction releases energy. **21.30** Enzymes affect only the rate of a reaction, not the size or sign of ΔG. **21.32** Exergonic: **(a)**, **(b)**; endergonic: **(c)**. Reaction **(a)** proceeds farthest toward products.
21.34

PROKARYOTIC CELLS	EUKARYOTIC CELLS
Quite small	Relatively large
No nucleus	Nucleus
Dispersed DNA	DNA in nucleus
No organelles	Organelles
Occur in single-celled organisms	Occur in single-celled and higher organisms

21.36 The cytoplasm consists of everything between the cell membrane and the nuclear membrane. The cytosol is the medium that fills the interior of the cell and contains electrolytes, nutrients, and many enzymes, in aqueous solution. **21.38** A mitochondrion is egg-shaped and consists of a smooth, outer membrane and a folded inner membrane. The intermembrane space lies between the outer and inner membranes, and the space enclosed by the inner membrane is called the *mitochondrial matrix*. **21.40** 90% of the body's ATP is synthesized in mitochondria.
21.42 Metabolism refers to all reactions that take place inside cells. Digestion is a part of metabolism in which food is broken down into small organic molecules. **21.44** acetyl—ScoA **21.46** Energy is released when ATP transfers a phosphoryl group. **21.48** ATP has a triphosphate group bonded to C5 of ribose, and ADP has a diphosphate group in that position. **21.50** $\Delta G = -4.5$ kcal/mol.
21.52

1,3-Bisphosphoglycerate $\xrightarrow[\quad]{\text{ADP}\quad\text{ATP}}$ 3-Phosphoglycerate

21.54 **(a)** NAD^+ is reduced. **(b)** NAD^+ is an oxidizing agent. **(c)** NAD^+ oxidizes secondary alcohol to a ketone. **(d)** $NADH/H^+$
(e)

$$H-\overset{|}{\underset{|}{C}}-OH \xrightarrow[\quad]{\text{NAD}^+\quad\text{NADH/H}^+} \overset{|}{\underset{|}{C}}=O$$

21.56 cellular mitochondria **21.58** Both carbons are oxidized to CO_2. **21.60** 3 NADH, one $FADH_2$. **21.62** Step 3 (isocitrate $\rightarrow$ α-ketoglutarate),

Step 4 (α-ketoglutarate → succinyl-SCoA) and Step 8 (malate → oxaloacetate) store energy as NADH.   **21.64** One complete citric acid cycle produces four reduced coenzymes, which enter the electron transfer chain and ultimately generate ATP.   **21.66** H_2O, ATP, oxidized coenzymes   **21.68** **(a)** FAD = flavin adenine dinucleotide; **(b)** CoQ = coenzyme Q; **(c)** NADH/H$^+$ = reduced nicotinamide adenine dinucleotide, plus hydrogen ion; **(d)** Cyt c = Cytochrome c **21.70** NADH, coenzyme Q, cytochrome c   **21.72** The citric acid cycle would stop.   **21.74** formation of ATP from the reactions of reduced coenzymes in the electron transport system   **21.76** **(a)** ATP **(b)** H_2O, oxidized coenzymes   **20.78** Bacteria use H_2S because no light is available for the usual light-dependent reaction of H_2O that provides O_2 and electrons.   **21.80** Answer based on reader's own weight and activity level   **21.82** Daily activities such as walking use energy, and thus the body requires a larger caloric intake than that needed to maintain basal metabolism.   **21.84** Oxygen consumption increases because the proton gradient from ATP production dissipates.   **21.86** A seal has more brown fat because it needs to keep warm.   **21.88** The light reaction produces O_2, NADPH, and ATP. The dark reaction produces carbohydrates from water and CO_2.   **21.90** Refrigeration slows the breakdown of carbohydrates by decreasing the rate of respiration. Enzyme reactions are slower at low temperatures.

21.92

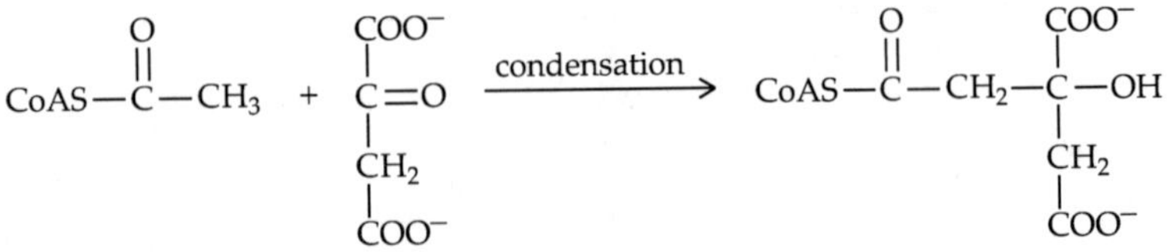

21.94 oxidoreductases   **21.96** FAD; oxidoreductases   **21.98** isocitrate; malate   **21.100** $O_2^- \cdot$, $OH^- \cdot$, and H_2O_2; superoxide dismutase, catalase, vitamins E, C, and A.   **21.102** adipose tissue, skin cells, skeletal muscle, heart muscle.

Chapter 22

22.1 **(a)** aldopentose **(b)** ketotriose **(c)** aldotetrose

22.2

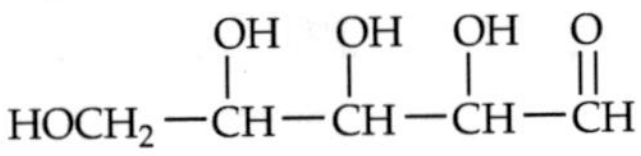

An aldopentose

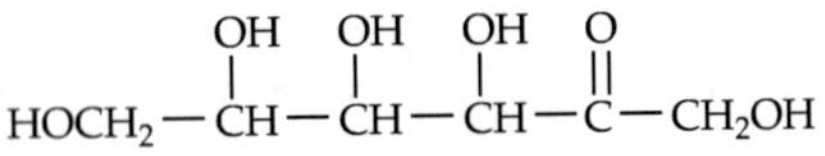

A ketohexose

22.3 eight stereoisomers   **22.4** **(d)**   **22.5** The bottom carbon is not chiral. The orientations of the hydroxyl groups bonded to the chiral carbons must be shown in order to indicate which stereoisomer is pictured.

22.6 **(a)**

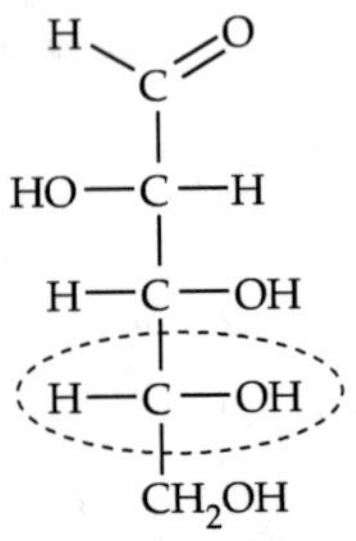

A D-aldopentose 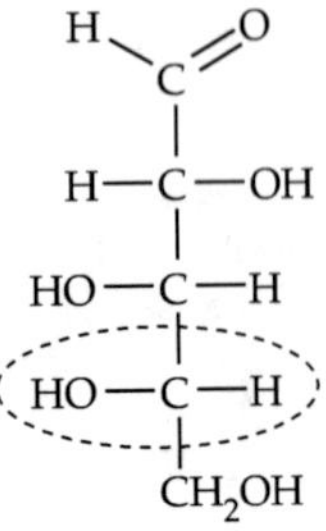   An L-aldopentose

(b)

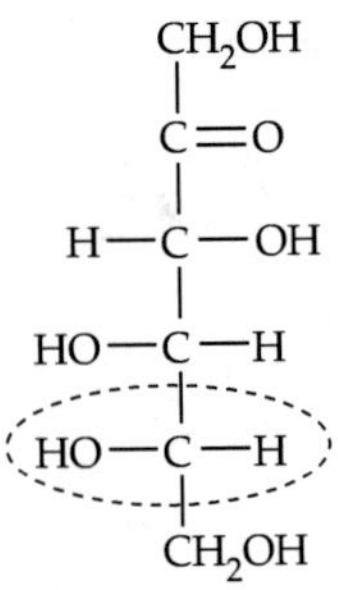

An L-ketohexose 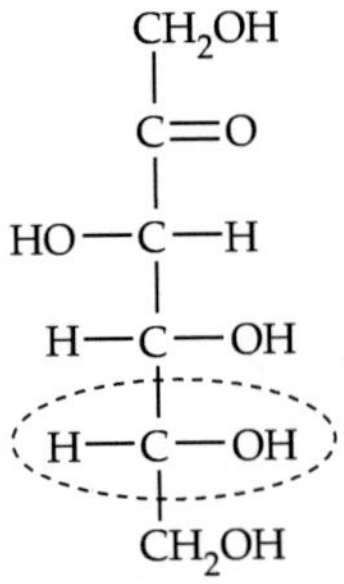   A D-ketohexose

22.7

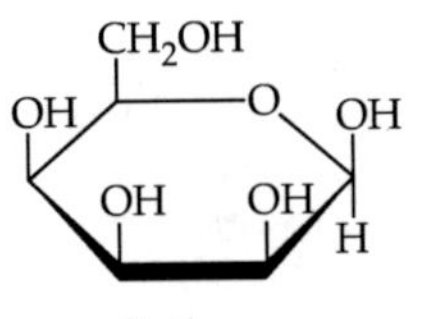

β-anomer α-anomer

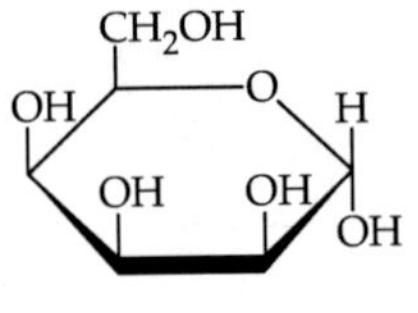

22.8

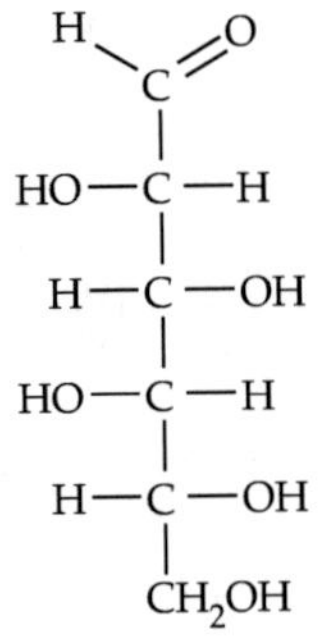

D-Idose

22.9 **(a)** an α-hexose **(b)** a steroid **(c)** an ester

22.10

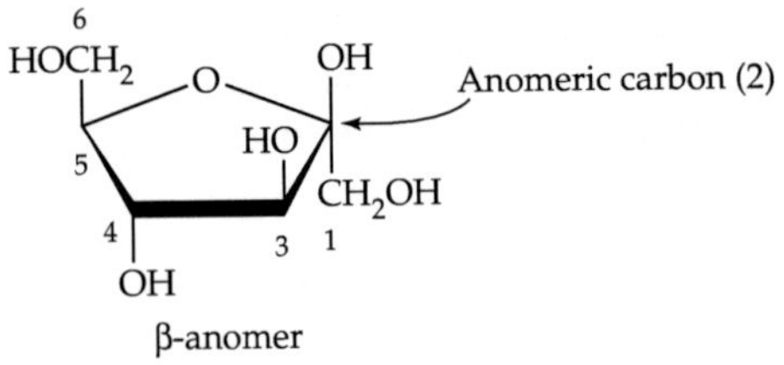

β-anomer

22.11

(a)

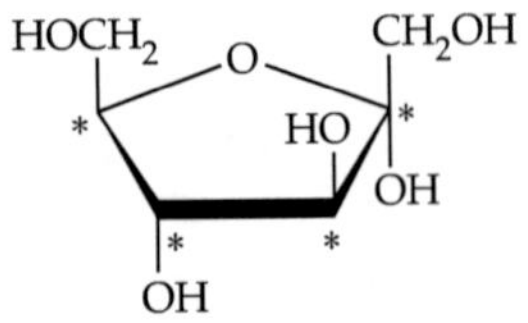

(b)

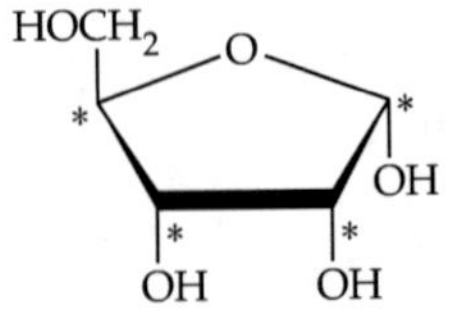

(c)

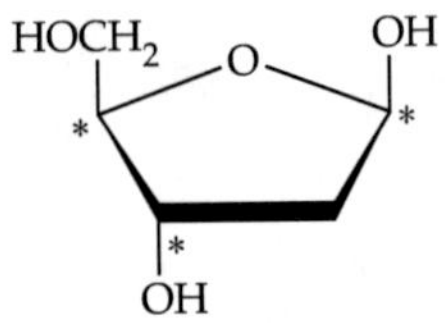

22.12

Cyclic AMP

ATP

22.13 **(a)** an α anomer **(b)** carbon 6 **(c)** Groups that are below the plane of the ring in D-galactose are above the plane of the ring in L-fucose. Groups that are above the plane of the ring in D-galactose are below the plane of the ring in L-fucose. **(d)** yes

22.14

Methyl α-D-riboside   Methyl β-D-riboside

22.15 a β-1,4 glycosidic link   **22.16** β-D-Glucose + β-D-Glucose
22.17 **(a)** maltose **(b)** sucrose **(c)** lactose   **22.18** glutamine, asparagine
22.19 an α-1,4 glycosidic link   **22.20** No. There are too few hemiacetal units to give a detectable result.

22.21   Starch $\xrightarrow{\text{Amylase}}$ Maltose $\xrightarrow{\text{Maltase}}$ Glucose
polysaccharide   disaccharide   monosaccharide

22.22 **(a)** diastereomers, anomers **(b)** enantiomers **(c)** diastereomers
22.23 **(a)** **(b)**

A   B   C
α-anomer β-anomer β-anomer

(c) α-1,4 linkage between C4 of B and C1 of A **(d)** β-1,4 linkage between C4 of C and C1 of B   **22.24** **(a)** **(b)** No monosaccharides are identical, and none are enantiomers.
(c) **(d)**

L-Fucose   D-Glucose   D-Galactose

22.25 Monosaccharide C is oxidized. Identification of the carboxylic acid also identifies the terminal monosaccharide.

22.26 No
22.27

POLYSACCHARIDE	LINKAGE	BRANCHING?
Cellulose	β-1,4	no
Amylose	α-1,4	no
Amylopectin	α-1,4	yes: α-1,6 branches occur ~ every 25 units
Glycogen	α-1,4	yes: even more α-1,6 branches than in amylopectin

22.28 Glucose is in equilibrium with its open-chain aldehyde form, which reacts with an oxidizing agent.   **22.30** -ose   **22.32** **(a)** aldotetrose **(b)** ketopentose **(c)** aldopentose **(d)** ketohexose
22.34 right part = 4 chiral carbons; left part = 5 chiral carbons; total = 9 chiral carbons
22.36

Oxygen missing here

A four-carbon deoxy sugar

22.38 glucose – food, all living organisms; galactose – brain tissue, milk; fructose – fruit; ribose – nucleic acids   **22.40** They are mirror images.
22.42 The reduction product of D-erythrose is achiral.   **22.44** A polarimeter measures the degree of rotation of plane-polarized light by a solution of an optically active compound.   **22.46** Equimolar solutions of enantiomers rotate light to the same degree but in opposite directions.
22.48 A reducing sugar contains an aldehyde or ketone group.
22.50 An anomer is one of a pair of hemiacetal stereoisomers formed when an open-chain sugar cyclizes. Anomers differ in the orientation of the hydroxyl group at the anomeric carbon.   **22.52** the α form

22.54

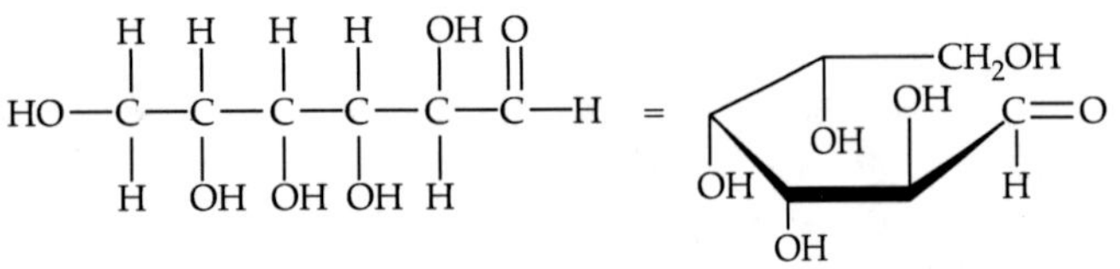

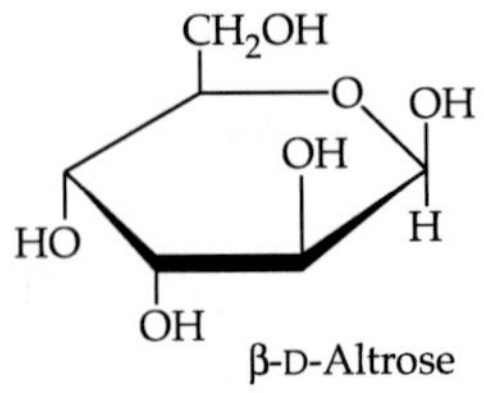

H H H H OH O
| | | | | ‖
HO—C—C—C—C—C—C—H =
| | | | |
H OH OH OH H

(ring structure with CH₂OH, OH, C=O, H)

β-D-Altrose

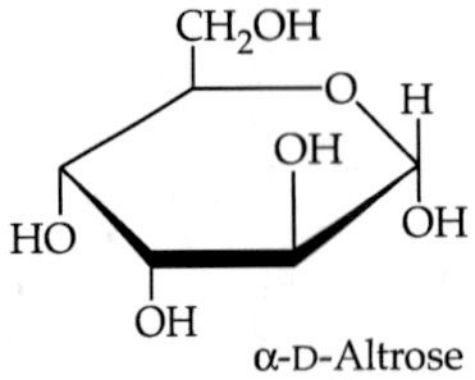

α-D-Altrose

22.56

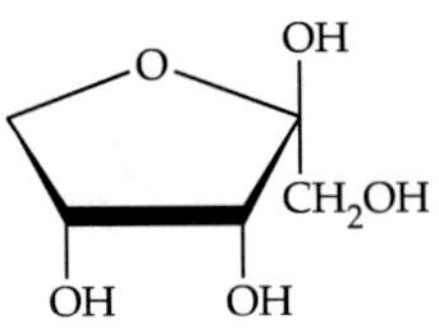

(furanose ring structure with OH, CH₂OH, OH, OH)

22.58

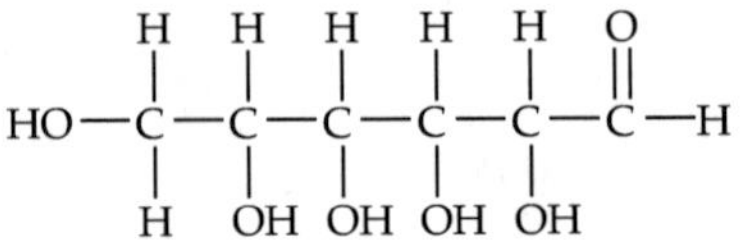

H H H H H O
| | | | | ‖
HO—C—C—C—C—C—C—H
| | | |
H OH OH OH OH

22.60

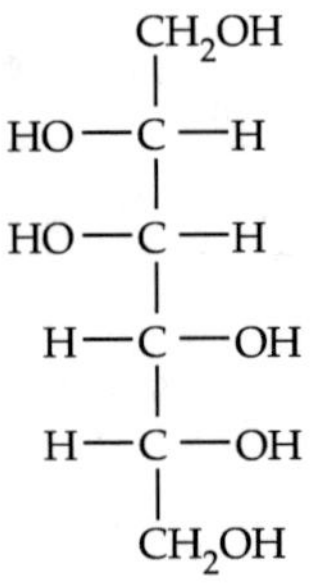

CH₂OH
|
HO—C—H
|
HO—C—H
|
H—C—OH
|
H—C—OH
|
CH₂OH

22.62

HO\
    C=O
|
H——OH
|
H——OH
|
H——OH
|
CH₂OH

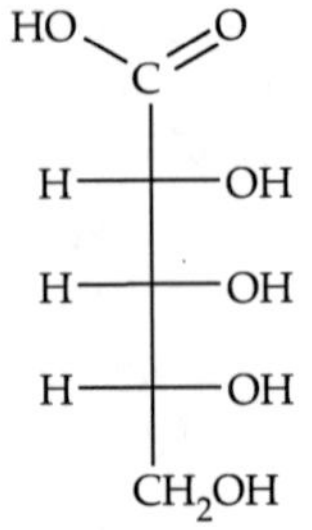

22.64 A glycoside is an acetal that is formed when the hemiacetal —OH group of a carbohydrate reacts with an alcohol.

22.66

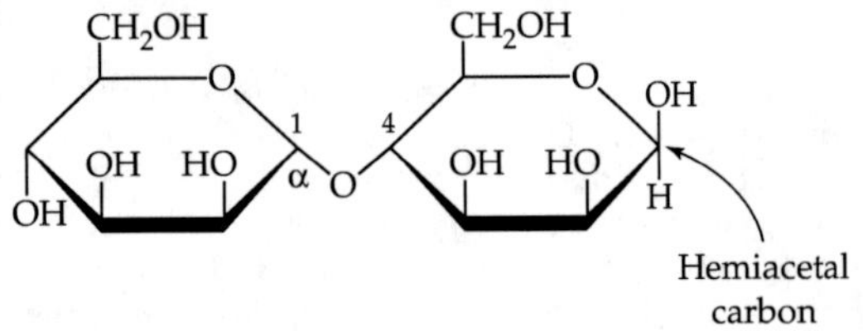

(disaccharide structure showing two CH₂OH rings linked through α O, with labels 1, 4, α, and arrow pointing to Hemiacetal carbon)

Hemiacetal carbon

The hemiacetal carbon in this problem is in equilibrium with an open-chain aldehyde that is a reducing sugar. **22.68** Sucrose has no hemiacetal group. **22.70** Amylose and amylopectin are both components of

starch and both consist of long polymers of α-D-glucose linked by α-1,4 glycosidic bonds. Amylopectin is much larger and has α-1,6 branches every 25 units or so along the chain. **22.72** Gentiobiose contains both an acetal grouping and a hemiacetal grouping. Gentiobiose is a reducing sugar. A β-1,6 linkage connects the two monosaccharides. **22.74** Trehalose is a nonreducing sugar because it contains no hemiacetal linkages. The two D–glucose monosaccharides are connected by an α-1,1 acetal link.

22.76

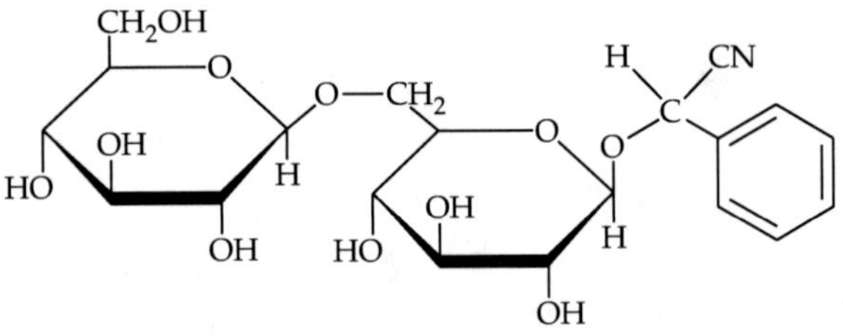

(disaccharide structure with CH₂OH, OH, HO, H, O—CH₂, OH, HO, OH, and a side group H, CN, C, phenyl ring, O)

22.78 Enzyme-catalyzed reactions usually produce only one enantiomer. **22.80** Starch is a complex carbohydrate. Glucose is a simple carbohydrate. Soluble and insoluble fiber are complex carbohydrates. **22.82** glucose, cellulose **22.84** Penicillin inhibits the enzyme that synthesizes bacterial cell walls. Mammals do not have this synthetic pathway. **22.86** People with type O blood can receive blood only from other donors that have type O blood. People with type AB blood can give blood only to other people with type AB blood. **22.88** pectin and vegetable gum: found in fruits, barley, oats, and beans. **22.90** D-Ribose and L-ribose are enantiomers that are identical in all properties (melting point, density, solubility, and chemical reactivity) except for the direction that they rotate plane-polarized light (b). **22.92** No, because they are not mirror images.

22.94

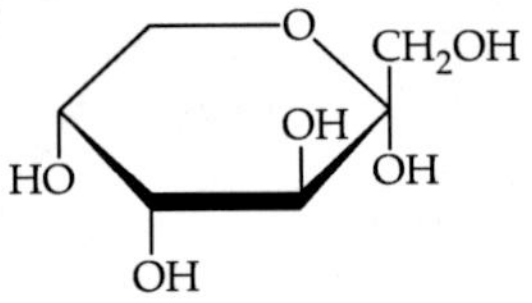

(pyranose ring structure with O, CH₂OH, OH, HO, OH, OH)

22.96 Raffinose is not a reducing sugar because it has no hemiacetal group. (It has acetal groups.)

22.98

O
‖
HOCH₂CCH₂OH

1,3-Dihydroxyacetone has no optical isomers because it has no chiral carbons. **22.100** Lactose intolerance is an inability to digest lactose. Symptoms include bloating, cramps, and diarrhea. **22.102** Symptoms of galactosemia: vomiting, liver failure, mental retardation, cataracts. **22.104** 4 chiral carbons.

Chapter 23

23.1 (a) glycogenesis **(b)** glycogenolysis **(c)** gluconeogenesis **23.2** glycogenesis, pentose phosphate pathway, glycolysis **23.3 (a)** steps 6 and 7 **(b)** steps 9 and 10 **23.4** Isomerizations: steps 2, 5, 8

23.5

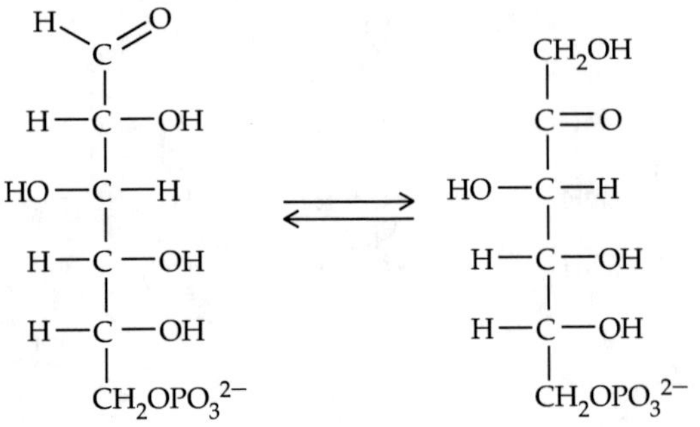

H\
   C=O
|
H—C—OH
|
HO—C—H
|
H—C—OH
|
H—C—OH
|
CH₂OPO₃²⁻

⇌

CH₂OH
|
C=O
|
HO—C—H
|
H—C—OH
|
H—C—OH
|
CH₂OPO₃²⁻

23.6 (a) pyruvate **(b)** Step 6: glyceraldehyde 3-phosphate is oxidized; NAD⁺ is the oxidizing agent

23.7 Fructose 6-phosphate enters glycolysis at step 3.

23.8 Glucose and galactose differ in configuration at C4. **23.9 (a)** The energy is lost as heat **(b)** The reverse of fermentation is very endothermic; loss of CO_2 drives the reaction to completion in the forward direction. **23.10** Insulin decreases; blood glucose decreases, the level of glucagon increases. Glucagon causes the breakdown of liver glycogen and the release of glucose. As glycogen is used up, the level of free fatty acids and ketone bodies increases.
23.11 Sorbitol can't form a cyclic acetal because it doesn't have a carbonyl group.

Sorbitol

23.12 (a) The increase in $[H^+]$ drives the equilibrium shown in Section 23.9 to the right, causing the production of CO_2. **(b)** Le Châtelier's Principle. **23.13** phosphorylation, oxidation **23.14** hydrolases **23.15 (a)** when the supply of glucose is adequate and the body needs energy. **(b)** when the body needs free glucose. **(c)** when ribose 5-phosphate or NADPH are needed. **(d)** when glucose supply is adequate, and the body does not need to use glucose for energy production. **23.16** Phosphorylations of glucose and fructose 6-phosphate produce important intermediates that repay the initial energy investment. Fructose 1,6-bisphosphate is cleaved into two three-carbon compounds, which are converted to pyruvate. **23.17 (a)** when the body needs energy, in mitochondria; **(b)** under anaerobic conditions, in yeast; **(c)** under anaerobic conditions, in muscle, red blood cells; **(d)** when the body needs free glucose, in the liver **23.18** Step 1: transferase Step 2: isomerase Step 3: transferase Step 4: lyase Step 5: isomerase Step 6: oxidoreductase, transferase Step 7: transferase Step 8: isomerase Step 9: lyase Step 10: transferase; transferases (because many reactions involve phosphate transfers). Ligases are associated with reactions that synthesize molecules, not with reactions that break down molecules. **23.19 (g)**, **(c)**, **(b)**, **(e)**, **(f)**, **(a)**, **(d)** **23.20** Sources of compounds for gluconeogenesis: pyruvate, lactate, citric acid cycle intermediates, many amino acids. **23.21** Germinating seeds need to synthesize carbohydrates from fats; humans obtain carbohydrates from food. **23.22 (a)** No **(b)** Molecular oxygen appears in the last step of the electron transport chain, where it combines with H^+ and electrons (from electron transport) to form H_2O. **23.24** glucose + galactose; in the lining of the small intestine

23.26

TYPE OF FOOD MOLECULES	PRODUCTS OF DIGESTION
Proteins	Amino acids
Triacylglycerols	Glycerol and fatty acids
Sucrose	Glucose and fructose
Lactose	Glucose and galactose
Starch	Glucose

23.28 acetyl-SCoA; lactate; ethanol + CO_2 **23.30** glycogenolysis: breakdown of glycogen to form glucose glycogenesis: synthesis of glycogen from glucose **23.32** glycolysis: catabolism of glucose to pyruvate glycogenolysis: breakdown of glycogen to form glucose **23.34** ribose 5-phosphate, glycolysis intermediates **23.36 (a)** all organs; **(b)** liver; **(c) (d)** muscle, liver **23.38 (a)** pyruvate $\rightarrow$ lactate; **(b)** pyruvate $\rightarrow$ ethanol + CO_2 **23.40 (a)** Steps 1, 3, 4, 7, 10; **(b)** Step 6; **(c)** Step 9 **23.42** Direct (substrate level) phosphorylation: **(a)** 2 mol ATP **(b)** 0 **(c)** 1 mol ATP Oxidative phosphorylation (ideal): **(a)** 6 ATP **(b)** 3 ATP **(c)** 11 ATP Most of the ATP in the citric acid cycle is produced from reduced coenzymes in the electron transport chain.
23.44

23.46 4 mol acetyl-SCoA **23.48** Hypoglycemia: low blood sugar; weakness, sweating, rapid heartbeat, confusion, coma, death; Hyperglycemia: high blood sugar; increased urine flow, low blood pressure, coma, death **23.50** ketone bodies **23.52** In Type 2 diabetes, insulin is in good supply, but cell membrane receptors fail to recognize insulin. Individuals are often overweight. **23.54** Excess glucose is converted to sorbitol, which can't be transported out of cells. This buildup changes osmolarity and causes cataracts and blindness. Excess glucose also causes neuropathy and poor circulation leading to limb amputation due to tissue death. **23.56** *Type 1 diabetes* is caused by insufficient production of insulin in the pancreas. *Type 2 diabetes* is caused by the failure of cell membrane receptors to recognize insulin. **23.58** muscle cells **23.60** The exact reverse of an energetically favorable pathway must occur by an alternate route in order to be favorable. **23.62** pyruvate, lactate **23.64** Several steps in the reverse of glycolysis are energetically unfavorable. **23.66** Steps 1, 3, 10 of glycolysis; all involve phosphate transfers and require energy. **23.68** when muscle glucose is depleted and oxygen is in short supply **23.70** glycoproteins, bacteria, dextran, polysaccharide storage granules **23.72** In an environment rich in sucrose, bacteria secrete an enzyme that transfers glucose units from digested sucrose to the dextran polymer. The residual fructose is metabolized to lactate, which lowers pH. The resulting acidic environment in the mouth dissolves minerals in teeth, leading to cavities. **23.74** beer, wine, cheese, yogurt, sour cream, and buttermilk **23.76** 140 g/dL (diabetic) vs 90 g/dL (normal) **23.78** between the curve for a diabetic and a nondiabetic **23.80** Creatine phosphate and glycogen are quickly used up. **23.82** Cotton fabric, paper, and rayon. Cotton fabric and paper are made from unmodified cellulose. In rayon, the hydroxyl groups of cellulose are converted to acetate groups. **23.84** Pyruvate is not phosphorylated. **23.86** Yes. Fructose 6-phosphate enters glycolysis as a glycolysis intermediate. **23.88** The body must avoid extreme fluctuations in glucose concentration.

Chapter 24

24.1 (a) eicosanoid (b) glycerophospholipid (c) wax

24.2

$$CH_3(CH_2)_{18}\overset{\displaystyle O}{\overset{\displaystyle \|}{C}}-OCH_2(CH_2)_{30}CH_3$$

24.3

$$CH_2O\overset{O}{\overset{\|}{C}}(CH_2)_7CH=CH(CH_2)_7CH_3$$
$$CHO\overset{O}{\overset{\|}{C}}(CH_2)_7CH=CH(CH_2)_7CH_3$$
$$CH_2O\overset{O}{\overset{\|}{C}}(CH_2)_7CH=CH(CH_2)_7CH_3$$

24.4 (a) butter (b) soybean oil (c) soybean oil **24.5** *See below for answer.*
24.6 When two different fatty acids are bonded to C1 and C3 of glycerol, C2 is chiral. **24.7** London forces; weak; hydrogen bonds between water molecules are stronger than London forces.
24.8 The acyl groups are from stearic acid.

$$CH_2O\overset{O}{\overset{\|}{C}}(CH_2)_7CH=CH(CH_2)_7CH_3$$
$$CHO\overset{O}{\overset{\|}{C}}(CH_2)_7CH=CH(CH_2)_7CH_3 \quad \xrightarrow{3\,H_2} \quad$$
$$CH_2O\overset{O}{\overset{\|}{C}}(CH_2)_7CH=CH(CH_2)_7CH_3$$

$$CH_2O\overset{O}{\overset{\|}{C}}(CH_2)_{16}CH_3$$
$$CHO\overset{O}{\overset{\|}{C}}(CH_2)_{16}CH_3$$
$$CH_2O\overset{O}{\overset{\|}{C}}(CH_2)_{16}CH_3$$

24.9

$$CH_2O\overset{O}{\overset{\|}{C}}(CH_2)_{16}CH_3$$
$$CHO\overset{O}{\overset{\|}{C}}(CH_2)_{16}CH_3 \quad \xrightarrow{NaOH,\ H_2O}$$
$$CH_2O\overset{O}{\overset{\|}{C}}(CH_2)_7CH=CH(CH_2)_7CH_3$$
or the isomer

$$\begin{array}{l} CH_2OH \\ | \\ CHOH \\ | \\ CH_2OH \end{array} \quad + \quad \begin{array}{l} 2\,CH_3(CH_2)_{16}COO^-\,Na^+ \\[6pt] CH_3(CH_2)_7CH=CH(CH_2)_7COO^-\,Na^+ \end{array}$$

24.10 (a) glycerol, phosphate ion, choline, RCOO⁻Na⁺, R'COO−Na⁺
(b) sphingosine, phosphate ion, choline, sodium palmitate

24.11

$$(CH_3)_3\overset{+}{N}CH_2CH_2O-\overset{\displaystyle O}{\overset{\displaystyle \|}{P}}-O-CH_2$$

Choline Phosphate

$$\begin{array}{l} CHNH-\overset{O}{\overset{\|}{C}}(CH_2)_{12}CH_3 \quad \text{Myristic acid} \\ CHOH \quad \text{Hydrophobic tail} \\ CH=CH(CH_2)_{12}CH_3 \end{array}$$

Hydrophilic head Hydrophobic tail

24.12

Stearic acid acyl group

$$CH_2-O-\overset{O}{\overset{\|}{C}}-(CH_2)_{16}CH_3$$

Oleic acid acyl group

$$CH-O-\overset{O}{\overset{\|}{C}}-(CH_2)_7CH=CH(CH_2)_7CH_3$$

$$CH_2-O-\overset{\displaystyle O}{\overset{\displaystyle \|}{P}}-OCH_2CH_2NH_3{}^+$$

Phosphate Ethanolamine

24.13 (a), (c), (e), (f) **24.14** They must be hydrophobic, contain many amino acids with nonpolar side chains, and must be folded so that the hydrophilic regions face outward. **24.15** yes; gasses diffuse through the cell membrane due to small size and no charge **24.16** Glucose 6-phosphate has a charged phosphate group and can't pass through the hydrophobic lipid bilayer. **24.17** The surfaces are in different environments and serve different functions. **24.18** carboxylic acid (most acidic), alcohol, C—C double bonds, ethers. The molecule has both polar and nonpolar regions. Form hydrogen bonds: —COOH, —OH.
24.19 A has the highest melting point. B and C are probably liquids at room temperature due to the high percentage of unsaturated fatty acids present. **24.20** B is 12.2% palmitic acid, 87.5% stearic acid after hydrogenation; C is 11.2% palmitic acid and 85.1% stearic acid after hydrogenation. These are very similar.
24.21

$$CH_2O\overset{O}{\overset{\|}{C}}(CH_2)_{14}CH_3$$
$$CHO\overset{O}{\overset{\|}{C}}(CH_2)_7CH=CH(CH_2)_7CH_3$$
$$CH_2O-\overset{\displaystyle O}{\overset{\displaystyle \|}{P}}-OCH_2CH_2$$
$$\overset{\ }{\underset{O^-}{|}} \qquad \overset{\ }{\underset{NH_3{}^+}{}}$$

A glycerophospholipid

24.22 Because the membrane is fluid, it can flow together after an injury.
24.23 C_{16} saturated fatty acids. The polar head lies in lung tissue, and

24.5

the hydrocarbon tails protrude into the alveoli. **24.24** a naturally-occurring molecule that dissolves in nonpolar solvents **24.26** $CH_3(CH_2)_{16}COOH$; straight chain **24.28** *Saturated fatty acids* are long-chain carboxylic acids that contain no carbon–carbon double bonds. *Monounsaturated fatty acids* contain one carbon–carbon double bond. *Polyunsaturated fatty acids* contain two or more carbon–carbon double bonds. **24.30** An essential fatty acid can't be synthesized by the human body and must be part of the diet. **24.32** The double bonds in unsaturated fatty acids make it harder for them to be arranged in a crystal. **24.34** a triester of glycerol and 3 fatty acids **24.36** Fats: composed of TAGs containing saturated and unsaturated fatty acids, solids; Oils: composed of TAGs containing mostly unsaturated fatty acids, liquids.

24.38

24.40 a protective coating

24.42

24.44

24.46 hydrogenation **24.48** Hydrogenate some of the double bonds. **24.50** a product with cis and trans double bonds; "trans fatty acids" **24.52** glycerol, K^+ stearate, K^+ oleate, K^+ linolenate **24.54** The products have one or more of the double bonds hydrogenated. There could be up to 12 different products. **24.56** Glycerophospholipids have polar heads (point outward) and nonpolar tails that cluster to form the membrane. Triacylglycerols don't have polar heads. **24.58** sphingomyelins, glycolipids **24.60** Glycerophospholipids are components of cell membranes. Stored fats in the body are triacylglycerols. **24.62** Both liposomes and micelles are spherical clusters of lipids. A liposome resembles a spherical lipid bilayer, in which polar heads cluster both inside and outside of the sphere. A micelle has a single layer of lipid molecules. **24.64** Concentrations of all substances would be the same on both sides of the membrane.

24.66

24.68 3 glycerols, $RCOO^-$ Na^+, $R'COO^-$ Na^+, $R'COO^-$ Na^+ $R'COO^-$ Na^+, 2 phosphates **24.70** Facilitated diffusion requires carrier proteins. **24.72** (a) facilitated diffusion (b) simple diffusion (c) active transport **24.74** A prostaglandin that stimulates uterine contractions.

24.76 an eicosanoid; Arachidonic acid is a precursor. **24.78** leukotrienes **24.80** prostaglandins **24.82** no more than 30% **24.84** fabric softeners, disinfecting soaps **24.86** cholesterol **24.88** glycolipids **24.90** (b) (c) (e) (f)

24.92

or

24.94 (a) beef fat (b) plant oil (c) pork fat **24.96** It is saponifiable. **24.98** sphingomyelins, cerebrosides, gangliosides **24.100** lower blood pressure, assist in blood clotting, stimulate uterine contractions, lower gastric secretions, cause swelling **24.102** 0.4g NaOH

Chapter 25

25.1 Cholate has 4 polar groups on its hydrophilic side that allow it to interact with an aqueous environment; its hydrophobic side interacts with TAGs. Cholate and cholesterol can't change roles. **25.2** Dihydroxyacetone phosphate is isomerized to glyceraldehyde 3-phosphate, which enters glycolysis. **25.3** (a), (b) *Step 1*; a $C=C$ double bond is introduced; FAD is the oxidizing agent. *Step 3*; an alcohol is oxidized to a ketone; NAD^+ is the oxidizing agent. (c) *Step 2*; water is added to a carbon-carbon double bond. (d) *Step 4*; HSCoA displaces acetyl-SCoA, producing a chain-shortened acyl-SCoA fatty acid **25.4** (a) 6 acetyl-SCoA, 5 β oxidations (b) 7 acetyl-SCoA, 6 β oxidations **25.5** Step 6, Step 7, Step 8 **25.6** (d) **25.7** (a) Acetyl-SCoA provides the acetyl groups used in synthesis of ketone bodies. (b) 3 (c) The body uses ketone bodies as an energy source during starvation. **25.8** Oxygen is needed to reoxidize reduced coenzymes, formed in β oxidation, that enter the electron transport chain. **25.9** (a) chylomicrons; because they have the greatest ratio of lipid to protein (b) chylomicrons (c) HDL (d) LDL (e) HDL (f) VLDL; used for storage or energy production (g) LDL **25.10** high blood glucose → high insulin/low glucagon → fatty acid and TAG synthesis: low blood glucose → low insulin/high glucagon → TAG hydrolysis; fatty acid oxidation **25.11** Formation of a fatty acyl-SCoA is coupled with conversion of ATP to AMP and pyrophosphate. This energy expenditure is recaptured in β oxidation. **25.12** Less acetyl-SCoA can be catabolized in the citric acid cycle, and acetyl-SCoA is diverted to ketogenesis. **25.13** Catabolism of fat provides more calories/gram than does catabolism of glycogen, and, thus, fats are a more efficient way to store calories. **25.14** Ketone bodies can be metabolized to form acetyl-SCoA, which provides energy. **25.15** No. Although both these processes add or remove two carbon units, one is not the reverse of the other. The two processes involve different enzymes, coenzymes, and activation steps. **25.16** They slow the rate of movement of food through the stomach. **25.18** Bile emulsifies lipid droplets. **25.20** mono- and diacylglycerols, stearic acid, oleic acid, linoleic acid, glycerol **25.22** Acylglycerols, fatty acids, and protein are combined to form *chylomicrons*, which are lipoproteins used to transport lipids from the diet into the bloodstream. **25.24** by albumins **25.26** Steps 6–10 of the glycolysis pathway. **25.28** 9 molecules ATP;

21 molecules ATP   **25.30** An adipocyte is a cell, almost entirely filled with fat globules, in which TAGs are stored and mobilized. **25.32** heart, liver, resting muscle cells   **25.34** A fatty acid is converted to its fatty acyl-SCoA in order to activate it for catabolism.   **25.36** The carbon β to the thioester group (two carbons away from the thioester group) is oxidized in the process.   **25.38** 17 ATP   **25.40** *Least* glucose, sucrose, capric acid, myristic acid *Most*

25.42

(a)

$$CH_3CH_2CH_2CH=CHCSCoA$$

(with C=O above CSCoA)

(b)

$$CH_3CH_2CH_2CHCH_2CSCoA$$

(with OH and C=O above)

(c)

$$CH_3CH_2CH_2CCH_2CSCoA$$

(with two C=O above)

(d)

$$CH_3CH_2CH_2CSCoA \; + \; CH_3CSCoA$$

(each with C=O above)

25.44 (a) 7 acetyl-SCoA, 6 cycles **(b)** 4 acetyl-SCoA, 3 cycles
25.46 lipogenesis **25.48** acetyl-SCoA **25.50** 7 cycles **25.52** Total cholesterol: 200 mg/dL or lower.   LDL: 160 mg/dL or lower. HDL: 60 mg/dL or higher.   **25.54** LDL carries cholesterol from the liver to tissues; HDL carries cholesterol from tissues to the liver, where it is converted to bile and excreted.   **25.56** Type II diabetes, colon cancer, heart attacks, stroke **25.58** calorie-dense food, lack of exercise **25.60** The liver synthesizes many important biomolecules, it catabolizes glucose, fatty acids and amino acids, it stores many substances, and it inactivates toxic substances.   **25.62** The excess acetyl-SCoA from catabolism of carbohydrates is stored as fat. The body can't resynthesize carbohydrate from acetyl-SCoA. **25.64** The alcohol intermediate is chiral. **25.66** Ketosis is a condition in which ketone bodies accumulate in the blood faster than they can be metabolized. Since two of the ketone bodies are carboxylic acids, they lower the pH of the blood, producing the condition known as ketoacidosis. Symptoms of ketoacidosis include dehydration, labored breathing, and depression; prolonged ketoacidosis may lead to coma and death.   **25.68** Ketones have little effect on pH, but the two other ketone bodies are acidic, and they lower the pH of urine. **25.70 (a)** endogenous **(b)** exogenous **25.72** $H_2C=CHC(CH_3)=CH_2$. Since cholesterol has 27 carbons, at least 6 2-methyl-1,3-butadiene molecules are needed.

Chapter 26
26.1

2'-Deoxythymidine

26.2 D-Ribose ($C_5H_{10}O_5$) has one more oxygen atom than 2-deoxy-D-ribose ($C_5H_{10}O_4$), and thus can form more hydrogen bonds.

26.3

2'-Deoxyadenosine 5'-monophosphate

26.4

Guanosine 5'-triphosphate (GTP)

26.5 dCMP—2'-Deoxycytidine 5'-monophosphate; CMP—Cytidine 5'-monophosphate; UDP—Uridine 5'-diphosphate; AMP—Adenosine 5'-monophosphate; ATP—Adenosine 5'-triphosphate **26.6** cytosine–guanine–adenine–uracil–adenine. The pentanucleotide comes from RNA because uracil is present.

26.7

26.8 (a) 3' C-G-G-A-T-C-A 5' **(b)** 3' T-T-A-C-C-G-A-G-T 5'
26.9

26.10 negatively charged (because of the phosphate groups)
26.11 (a) A longer strand has more hydrogen bonds. **(b)** A chain with a higher percent of G/C pairs has a higher melting point, because it has more hydrogen bonds. **26.12 (a)** 3' G-U-C-U-G-A-C-A-U-G-U-G 5' **(b)** 5' A-U-C-A-U-A-C-G-U-C-G-C 3' **26.13 (a)** GCU GCC GCA GCG **(b)** CCU CCC CCA CCG **(c)** UCU UCC UCA UCG AGU AGC **(d)** AAA AAG **(e)** UAU UAC **26.14** The sequence guanine-uracil-guanine codes for valine. **26.15 (a)** Ile **(b)** Ala **(c)** Arg **(d)** Lys **26.16** Six mRNA triplets can code for Leu: CUU, CUC, CUA, CUG, UUA, and UUG Among the many possible combinations for Leu-Leu-Leu are:

  5' UUAUUGCUU 3'   5' UUAUUGCUC 3'   5' UUAUUGCUA 3'
  5' UUAUUGCUG 3'   5' UUACUUCUC 3'   5' UUACUUCUA 3'

26.17–26.18

mRNA sequence:	5' CAG—AUG—CCU—UGG—CCC—UUA 3'
Amino-acid sequence:	Gln—Met—Pro—Trp—Pro—Leu
tRNA anticodons:	3' GUC—UAC—GGA—ACC—GGG—AAU 5'

26.19

Guanosine 5'-monophosphate

26.20

Sugar
Phosphate

Sequence of the left chain: 5' A-G-T-C 3'
Sequence of the right chain: 5' G-A-C-T 3'

26.21 ⬭ = DNA polymerase

Direction of synthesis of A

Direction of synthesis of B

Segments B and C are joined by the action of a DNA ligase.

26.22 The sugar-phosphate backbone is found on the outside of the DNA double helix. Histones are positively charged; they contain groups such as Lys, Arg, and His.

26.23

Initiation sequence

Direction of synthesis

Termination sequence

Template strand

RNA

Informational strand

⬭ = RNA polymerase

26.24 More than one codon can code for each amino acid. Only one possibility is shown.

(a) 5' | C | A | A | C | A | C | C | C | C | G | G | G | 3' mRNA

(b) 3' | G | T | T | G | T | G | G | G | G | C | C | C | 5' DNA template strand

(c) 5' | C | A | A | C | A | C | C | C | C | G | G | G | 3' DNA informational strand

(d) 64 possible sequences

26.26 2-deoxyribose (DNA); ribose (RNA). 2-Deoxyribose is missing an —OH group at C2. **26.28** The purine bases (two fused heterocyclic rings) are adenine and guanine. The pyrimidine bases (one heterocyclic ring) are cytosine, thymine (in DNA), and uracil (in RNA). **26.30** DNA is largest; tRNA is smallest. **26.32** *Similarities*: All are polymerizations; all use a nucleic acid as a template; all use hydrogen bonding to bring the subunits into position. *Differences*: In replication, DNA makes a copy of itself. In transcription, DNA is used as a template for the synthesis of mRNA. In translation, mRNA is used as a template for the synthesis of proteins. Replication and transcription take place in the nucleus of cells, and translation takes place in ribosomes. **26.34** DNA, protein **26.36** 46 chromosomes (23 pairs) **26.38** They always occur in pairs: they always H-bond with each other. **26.40** 19% G, 19% C, 31% A, 31% T. (%G = %C; %A = %T: %T + %A + %C + %G = 100%) **26.42** 5' to 3'

26.44

Deoxyribose

Bond between cytosine and C1 of deoxyribose. Water is removed in the formation of the bond.

26.46

5' end

Uridine

Cytidine

3' end

26.48 the template strand **26.50** Each new DNA has one newly synthesized strand and one old strand. **26.52** An anticodon is a 3 nucleotide tRNA sequence that is complementary to an mRNA codon for a specific amino acid. **26.54** tRNAs for each amino acid differ in their anticodon sequences. **26.56 (a)** GCU GCC GCA GCG **(b)** CAU CAC **(c)** CCU CCC CCA CCG **26.58** (3' →5') **(a)** GGA **(b)** CGU **(c)** UAA **26.60** (3' →5') TTGCCT **26.62** Asn-Gly **26.64** (5' →3') UAU–GGU–GGU–UUU–AUG–UAA Other sequences are possible. **26.66** Viruses consist of a strand of nucleic acid wrapped in a protein coat; viruses can't replicate or manufacture protein independent of a host cell. **26.68** To be effective, a drug must be powerful enough to act on viruses within cells without damaging the cells and their genetic material. Vaccines prime the body to recognize viruses as foreign and to destroy them. **26.70** Ribozyme activity is common among the simplest and most primitive life forms, such as viroids, leading scientists to speculate that ribozyme catalysis might have preceded enzyme catalysis. **26.72** Influenza A viruses are described by a code that describes the hemagglutinins (H) and the neuraminidases (N) in the virus. The H1N1 virus was responsible for the 1918 influenza pandemic, and the H5N1 virus is present in avian flu. Since these viruses can undergo antigenic drift in host animals, there is concern when infected birds and animals harbor influenza viruses. **26.74** 249 bases **26.76** Met is removed after synthesis is complete.

Chapter 27

27.1 "once upon a time" **27.2** As a result of the SNP, the base sequence codes for Trp, instead of Cys. This change would probably affect the functioning of the protein. **27.3** 3′–T–C–T–A–G–//–A–5′ **27.4** (a) sticky (b) (c) not sticky **27.5** (a) comparative genomics (b) genetic engineering (c) pharmacogenetics (d) bioinformatics **27.6** (1) A genetic map, which shows the location of markers one million nucleotides apart, is created. (2) Next comes a physical map, which refines the distance between markers to 100,000 base pairs. (3) The chromosome is cleaved into large segments of overlapping clones. (4) The clones are fragmented into 500 base pieces, which are sequenced. **27.7** The variations are only a small part of the genome; the rest is identical among humans. A diverse group of individuals contributed DNA to the project. **27.8** *telomeres* (protect the chromosome from damage, involved with aging), *centromeres* (involved with cell division), *promoter sequences* (determine which genes will be replicated), *introns* (function unknown) **27.9** Similarities: both are variations in base sequences. Differences: A mutation is an error that is transferred during replication and affects only a few people; a polymorphism is a variation in sequence that is common within a population. **27.10** Recombinant DNA contains two or more DNA segments that do not occur together in nature. The DNA that codes for a specific human protein can be incorporated into a bacterial plasmid using recombinant DNA technology. The plasmid is then reinserted into a bacterial cell, where its protein-synthesizing machinery makes the desired protein. **27.11** Major benefits of genomics: creation of disease-resistant and nutrient-rich crops, gene therapy, genetic screening. Major negative outcomes: misuse of an individual's genetic information, prediction of a genetic disease for which there is no cure. **27.12** Celera broke the genome into many unidentified fragments. The fragments were multiplied and cut into 500 base pieces, which were sequenced. A supercomputer was used to determine the order of the bases. **27.14** 50% **27.16** (a) Approx. 200 genes are shared between bacteria and humans. (b) A single gene may produce several proteins. **27.18** The clones used in DNA mapping are identical copies of DNA segments from a single individual. In mapping, it is essential to have a sample large enough for experimental manipulation. **27.20** The youngest cells have long telomeres, and the oldest cells have short telomeres. **27.22** It is the constriction that determines the shape of a chromosome during cell division. **27.24** A silent mutation is a single base change that specifies the same amino acid. **27.26** random and spontaneous events, exposure to a mutagen **27.28** A SNP can result in the change in identity of an amino acid inserted into a protein a particular location in a polypeptide chain. The effect of a SNP depends on the function of the protein and the nature of the SNP. **27.30** A physician could predict the age at which inherited diseases might become active, their severity, and the response to various types of treatment. **27.32** a change in the type of side chain **27.34** (a) Substitution of Ala for Val may have minor effects (b) Substitution of His for Pro is more serious because the amino acids have very different side chains. **27.36** Proteins can be produced in large quantities. **27.38** Sticky ends are unpaired bases at the end of a DNA fragment. Recombinant DNA is formed when the sticky ends of the DNA of interest and of the DNA of the plasmid have complementary base pairs and can be joined by a DNA ligase. **27.40** (a) (b) not sticky **27.42** Proteomics, the study of the complete set of proteins coded for by a genome or synthesized by a given type of cell, might provide information about the role of a protein in both healthy and diseased cells. **27.44** corn, soybeans **27.46** a DNA chip **27.48** a group of anonymous individuals **27.50** production of a large quantity of a specific segment of DNA **27.52** (1) digestion with a restriction endonuclease (2) separation of fragments by electrophoresis (3) fragments transferred to a nylon membrane (4) treatment of the blot with a radioactive DNA probe (5) identification of fragments by exposure to X-ray film. All samples must be analyzed under the same conditions in order to be compared. **27.54** A monogenic disease is caused by the variation in just one gene. **27.56** ATACTGA **27.58** A hereditary disease is caused by a mutation in the DNA of a germ cell and is passed from parent to offspring. The mutation affects the amino-acid sequence of an important protein and causes a change in the biological activity of the protein.

Chapter 28

28.1 (a) false (b) true (c) true (d) false (e) false **28.2** oxidoreductase; lyase

28.3

OH   O
| ||
$CH_3CHCH_2CCOO^-$

4-Hydroxy-α-ketopentanoate

28.4

O
||
$CH_3SCH_2CH_2CHCOO^-$

28.5 by the loss of two hydrogens to either NAD^+ or $NADP^+$

28.6 valine, leucine, isoleucine

H_3C $NH_3{}^+$
| |
$CH_3CHCHCOO^-$ + $^-OOCCH_2CH_2CCOO^-$

Valine   α-Ketoglutarate

H_3C O
| ||
$CH_3CHCCOO^-$ + $^-OOCCH_2CH_2CHCOO^-$

α-Keto-3-methylbutanoate   Glutamate

28.7 (a) 5 (b) 1 (c) 3

28.8

28.9 3-Phosphoglycerate → 3-Phosphohydroxypyruvate (oxidation)
3-Phosphohydroxypyruvate → 3-Phosphoserine (transamination)
3-Phosphoserine → Serine (hydrolysis)

28.10

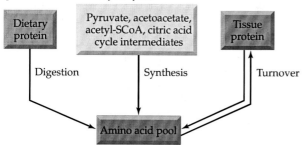

28.11 (1) Catabolism of an amino acid begins with a transamination reaction that removes the amino nitrogen (2) The resulting α-keto acid, which contains the carbon atoms, is converted to a common metabolic intermediate. (3) The amino group of glutamate (from the amino acid) is removed by oxidative deamination. (4) The amino nitrogen is transformed to urea in the urea cycle and is excreted. **28.12** glutamate dehydrogenase; alanine aminotransferase. Alanine is the product. **28.13** The carbon atoms from ketogenic amino acids can be converted to ketone bodies or to acetyl-SCoA. The carbon atoms from glucogenic amino acids can be converted to compounds that can enter gluconeogenesis and can form glucose, which can enter glycolysis and also yield acetyl-SCoA. **28.14** All amino acids are necessary for protein synthesis. The body can synthesize only some of them; the others must be provided by food and are thus essential in the diet. **28.15** to quickly remove ammonia from the body; buildup of urea and shortage of ornithine **28.16** throughout the body **28.18** pyruvate, 3-phosphoglycerate **28.20** In transamination, a keto group of an α-keto acid and an amino group of an amino acid change places.

28.22 (a)

N⁼⧸CH₂—C(=O)—COO⁻ (imidazole ring with N—H)

(b)

HSCH₂—C(=O)—COO⁻

28.24 An —NH₃⁺ group of an amino acid is replaced by a carbonyl group, and ammonium ion is eliminated.

28.26

(a)

(benzene ring)—CH₂—C(=O)—COO⁻

(b)

HO—(benzene ring)—CH₂—C(=O)—COO⁻

28.28 A ketogenic amino acid is catabolized to acetoacetyl-SCoA or acetyl-SCoA. Examples: leucine, isoleucine, lysine **28.30** Ammonia is toxic. **28.32** One nitrogen comes from carbamoyl phosphate, which is synthesized from ammonium ion by oxidative deamination. The other nitrogen comes from aspartate. **28.34** Nonessential amino acids are synthesized in humans in 1–3 steps. Essential amino acids are synthesized in microorganisms in 7–10 steps. **28.36** reductive amination; the reverse of oxidative deamination **28.38** phenylketonuria; mental retardation; restriction of phenylalanine in the diet **28.40 (b) (c) (d)** **28.42** Oxidized allopurinol inhibits the enzyme that converts xanthine to uric acid. The more soluble intermediates are excreted. The nitrogen at position 7 of hypoxanthine is at position 8 in allopurinol, where it blocks oxidation of xanthine. **28.44** tryptophan; emotional and behavioral problems **28.46** isoleucine + pyruvate → α-keto-3-methylpentanoate + alanine **28.48** Yes. Some amino acids yield two kinds of products—those that can enter the citric acid cycle and those that are intermediates of fatty acid metabolism. **28.50** Tissue is dynamic because its components are constantly being broken down and reformed.

28.52 (b) → (e) → (d) → (f) → (a) → (c) **28.54** An excess of one amino acid might overwhelm a transport system that other amino acids use, resulting in a deficiency of those amino acids. **28.56** The nitrogen may be converted to urea and excreted in the urine, or it may be used in the synthesis of a new nitrogen-containing compound.

Chapter 29

29.1 In the cell: the charged form. Outside the cell: the uncharged form. The uncharged form enters the cell more readily. **29.2 (a)** iii **(b)** ii **(c)** iv **(d)** v **(e)** i **29.3 (a)** pH goes down **(b)** [O₂], [CO₂], pH **29.4 (a)** respiratory acidosis **(b)** metabolic acidosis **(c)** metabolic alkalosis **(d)** respiratory alkalosis **(e)** respiratory acidosis **29.5 (a)** intracellular fluid **(b)** extracellular fluid **(c)** blood plasma, interstitial fluid **(d)** K^+, Mg^{2+}, HPO_4^{2-} **(e)** Na^+, Cl^-

29.6

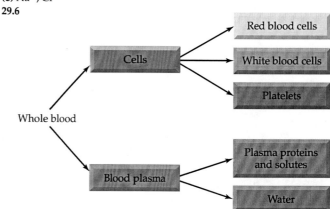

29.7 (a) O_2 **(b)** CO_2 **(c)** nutrients **(d)** waste products **(e)** hormones **(f)** white blood cells, platelets **29.8** swelling, redness, warmth, pain **29.9** enzymatic decarboxylation of histidine; Histamine dilates capillaries, increasing blood flow that reddens and warms the skin. Blood-clotting factors and defensive proteins cause pain and swelling. **29.10** *Cell-mediated immune response*: under control of T cells; arises when abnormal cells, bacteria, or viruses enter cells; invaders killed by T cells. *Antibody-mediated immune response*: under control of B cells, assisted by T cells; occurs when antigens enter cells; B cells divide to produce plasma cells, which form antibodies; an antibody-antigen complex inactivates the antigen. **29.11** Excess hydrogen ions are excreted by reaction with NH_3 or HPO_4^{2-}. H^+ ions also combine with bicarbonate, producing CO_2 that returns to the bloodstream. **29.12** intracellular fluid (64%), interstitial fluid (25%), plasma (8%) **29.14** Substances not soluble in blood, such as lipids, are transported by blood proteins. **29.16** Blood pressure in arterial capillaries is higher than interstitial fluid pressure, and blood pressure in venous capillaries is lower than interstitial fluid pressure. **29.18** the thoracic duct **29.20** it causes a decrease in the water content of the urine **29.22** seven percent **29.24** *Red blood cells* transport blood gases. *White blood cells* protect the body from foreign substances. *Platelets* assist in blood clotting. **29.26** *Inside cells*: K^+, Mg^{2+}, HPO_4^{2-}; *Outside cells*: Na^+, Cl^- **29.28** Antihistamines block attachment of the neurotransmitter histamine to its receptors. **29.30** immunoglobulins **29.32** Killer T cells destroy the invader; helper T cells enhance defenses; memory T cells can produce new killer T cells if needed. **29.34** Memory cells "remember" an antigen and are capable of producing antibodies to it for a long time. **29.36** Vitamin K, Ca^{2+} **29.38** They are released as zymogens in order to avoid undesirable clotting in noninjured tissues. **29.40** +2 **29.42** If pO_2 is below 10 mmHg, hemoglobin is unsaturated. If pO_2 is greater than 100 mmHg, hemoglobin is completely saturated. Between these pressures, hemoglobin is partially saturated. **29.44** a dissolved gas, bound to hemoglobin, bicarbonate ion

29.46

$$CO_2 + H_2O \underset{}{\overset{\text{Carbonic anhydrase}}{\rightleftharpoons}} HCO_3^- + H^+$$

29.48 7.35–7.45 below 7.35 = acidosis; above 7.35 = alkalosis
29.50 respiratory acidosis
29.52

$$H^+ + HCO_3^- \rightleftharpoons CO_2 + H_2O$$

$$H^+ + HPO_4^{2-} \rightleftharpoons H_2PO_4^-$$

29.54 Substances can either be transported into a cell or be transported out of a cell, but not both.   **29.56** The chemist might need to deliver a medication to brain cells of someone suffering from Parkinson's disease.

29.58 Automated analysis can reproducibly detect changes in enzyme levels that might indicate organ damage.   **29.60** It is a small, polar molecule.   **29.62** When $[Na^+]$ is high, secretion of ADH increases and causes the amount of water retained by the body to increase, causing swelling.   **29.64** Active transport is necessary when a cell needs a substance that has a higher concentration inside the cell than outside, or when a cell needs to secrete a substance that has a higher concentration outside the cell than inside.   **29.66** Hemostasis is the body's mechanism for preventing blood loss, and might be considered to be a part of homeostasis.

Photo Credits

Index

Note: Page numbers in **boldface** type indicate definitions of terms.

Functional Groups of Importance in Biochemical Molecules

Functional Group	Structure	Type of Biomolecule
Amino group	$-NH_3^+$, $-NH_2$	Alkaloids and neurotransmitters; amino acids and proteins (Sections 15.1, 15.3, 15.6, 18.3, 18.7, 20.6)
Hydroxyl group	$-OH$	Monosaccharides (carbohydrates) and glycerol: a component of triacylglycerols (lipids) (Sections 17.4, 22.4, 24.2)
Carbonyl group	$\overset{O}{\underset{\parallel}{-C-}}$	Monosaccharides (carbohydrates); in acetyl group (CH_3CO) used to transfer carbon atoms during catabolism (Sections 16.1, 17.4, 21.4, 21.8, 22.4)
Carboxyl group	$\overset{O}{\underset{\parallel}{-C-OH}}$, $\overset{O}{\underset{\parallel}{-C-O^-}}$	Amino acids, proteins, and fatty acids (lipids) (Sections 17.1, 18.3, 18.7, 24.2)
Amide group	$\overset{O}{\underset{\parallel}{-C-N-}}\ $	Links amino acids in proteins; formed by reaction of amino group and carboxyl group (Sections 17.1, 17.4, 18.7)
Carboxylic acid ester	$\overset{O}{\underset{\parallel}{-C-O-R}}$	Triacylglycerols (and other lipids); formed by reaction of carboxyl group and hydroxyl group (Sections 17.1, 17.4, 24.2)
Phosphates: mono-, di-, tri-	$-\overset{}{\underset{}{C}}-O-\overset{O}{\underset{O^-}{P}}-O^-$ $-\overset{}{\underset{}{C}}-O-\overset{O}{\underset{O^-}{P}}-O-\overset{O}{\underset{O^-}{P}}-O^-$ $-\overset{}{\underset{}{C}}-O-\overset{O}{\underset{O^-}{P}}-O-\overset{O}{\underset{O^-}{P}}-O-\overset{O}{\underset{O^-}{P}}-O^-$	ATP and many metabolism intermediates (Sections 17.8, 21.5, and throughout metabolism sections)
Hemiacetal group	$-\overset{}{\underset{OR}{C}}-OH$	Cyclic forms of monosaccharides; formed by a reaction of carbonyl group with hydroxyl group (Sections 16.7, 22.4)
Acetal group	$-\overset{}{\underset{OR}{C}}-OR$	Connects monosaccharides in disaccharides and larger carbohydrates; formed by reaction of carbonyl group with hydroxyl group (Sections 16.7, 22.7, 22.9)